TRIGONOMETRY
WITH TABLES

By A. M. WELCHONS

and W. R. KRICKENBERGER

GINN AND COMPANY

BOSTON   NEW YORK   CHICAGO   ATLANTA

DALLAS   PALO ALTO   TORONTO   LONDON

FOREWORD

Δ

This text in trigonometry is the outgrowth of the authors' many years of teaching mathematics in high school. Although it provides, in its entirety, a course that is fully as extensive and rigorous as that usually given in colleges, teachers will find that it was written to meet the needs of high-school students. In its preparation the following objectives have been paramount:

1. The text should create and maintain interest.
2. It should be based upon the students' background in mathematics and in other fields of learning.
3. It should develop concepts and principles in such a way that the student can easily understand and apply them.
4. It should offer all possible aid to the teacher.
5. By the sequence and inclusiveness of its subject matter, it should be adaptable to different courses of study.
6. It should provide for individual differences in the abilities of students.

The following paragraphs suggest some of the ways in which it is hoped that these aims have been realized:

Motivates the student

There are abundant applications of interest to the student and photographs which point up the need for mathematics in various trades and professions.

Links the new to the old

The development of new concepts is based upon the students' previous experience in mathematics. Since many students have been introduced to the trigonometry of the right triangle in earlier courses, the approach to the subject is through the acute angle rather than through the general angle.

Emphasizes understanding

The text is written to the student in language which he can easily understand. New terms are carefully explained, and there are numerous examples to illustrate definitions and principles. Care and thoroughness in presenting the theory lead to understanding rather than to memorization and thus to the ability to make applications.

Identities and equations are developed gradually and are fully treated; the distinction between them is stressed.

Helps the teacher

The simplicity of organization and presentation will be appreciated by the high-school teacher.

A proper balance between the analytical and numerical aspects of trigonometry has been maintained throughout the text.

Attention is called to the visual helps, including diagrams, boxed rules, and well-arranged illustrative examples.

There are reviews at the ends of chapters and a set of general exercises on plane trigonometry.

Both four-place and five-place tables are included.

Is adaptable to different courses of study

The organization and content permit of adaptations to meet the requirements of varying syllabi. At present, trigonometry is taught on two different levels in the secondary schools. In some schools it is offered in the junior year, after intermediate algebra; in others, it is taught in the last semester of the senior year, following solid geometry and advanced algebra. At the earlier level students cannot be expected to cover more than the first ten chapters of this book. At the senior level, because of the students' maturity and greater experience in mathematics, progress will usually be rapid enough to permit a study of all the topics.

A careful and adequate discussion of approximate numbers is given in Chapter II.

A full treatment of the theory and use of logarithms is provided for the sake of those students who are unfamiliar with this subject. For other students this chapter may be omitted or used for a rapid review.

A discussion of the use of the slide rule is included. It is suggested that students have a slide rule for use in checking solutions and occasionally in solving problems involving three significant figures.

The treatment of spherical trigonometry is brief and concise, but adequate for applications to navigation and geography.

Provides for individual differences

The text is well adapted to classes and students with varying aptitudes and different levels of preparation. The topics and exercises marked A are intended for all students, while those marked B are for those students who are able to do extra work. Some exceptional students will be able to complete the text in one semester. The following suggestions may be helpful in organizing the semester's work:

A minimum course. Chapters I, II, and IV–X, including only topics marked A and exercises selected from the A group.

A medium course. Chapters I–XII, including exercises selected from the A and B groups.

A maximum course. Chapters I–XV with selected exercises from the A and B groups.

CONTENTS

Δ

Plane Trigonometry

Spherical Trigonometry

PLANE TRIGONOMETRY

Railroad Surveyor Sighting around Curve

The construction of the curve shown required many measurements to assure the proper banking and a uniform grade of track, and to determine changes in its direction

INTRODUCTION

Δ

The Meaning of Trigonometry [A]

The word "trigonometry" is derived from three Greek words which mean "three-angle measurement," that is, "triangle measurement." By means of trigonometry we may determine the remaining sides and angles of a triangle when a sufficient number of them are known. In trigonometry we also study the theorems and formulas bearing upon the relations among the sides and angles of the triangle.

The Need of Measurement [A]

We are likely to underestimate the need and importance of measurement. Measurement is essential to our way of living. It is necessary not only in industry but in our everyday life.

To illustrate how measurement enters our daily life, suppose that we are making preparations for a vacation at some lake. When we purchase clothing and shoes for the trip, measurement is needed to obtain correct fitting. If we expect to fish, we need measurement in buying rods, line, and hooks. When we have our automobile serviced at a filling station, the attendant measures the air pressure of our tires and the oil and gasoline we purchase.

In industry, measurement is indispensable. Without it, boundaries of land could not be established, roads could not be made, houses and factories could not be constructed, and tools and machinery could not be manufactured.

Direct Measurement of Distances [A]

When we use a yardstick to measure the length of a line segment or the distance between two points, we are making a *direct* measurement. At home, for example, you may use the yardstick in finding the size of a room or of a piece of furniture. You have seen carpenters using the rule, steel square, and tape measure in making direct measurements.

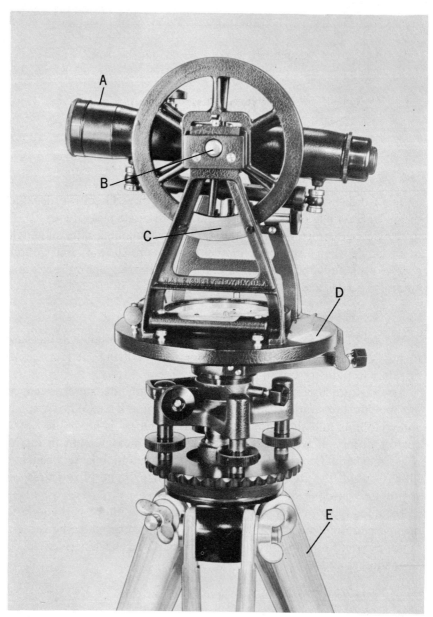

W. & L. E. Gurley

Engineer's Transit

The machinist uses the rule, micrometer caliper, vernier caliper, the thickness gauge, and precision blocks. Perhaps you have watched a surveyor making direct measurements of distances with the steel tape and leveling rod. In the past, land surveyors usually used the *chain* for measuring distances. Gunter's chain was 4 rods long and contained 100 links. On the following page are pictures of some of the instruments we have mentioned.

Direct Measurement of Angles [A]

Direct measurements of angles are made with the protractor, with which you are familiar. The protractor illustrated here is graduated from 0° to 180°. Some protractors used in aeronautics are graduated from 0° to 360°.

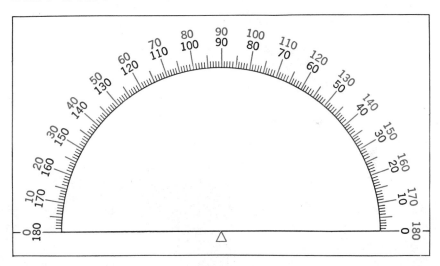

For measuring angles in the field the surveyor uses the *transit*. The transit, shown on the opposite page, consists of a telescope *A* which can be rotated on an axis *B*, two protractor scales *C* and *D*, and a tripod *E*. The scale *C* is used for measuring angles in the vertical plane, and the scale *D* is used for measuring angles in the horizontal plane.

In addition to the degree, other units used in measuring angles are the *mil* and the *radian*. The mil, which is used in military science, is an angle which is $\frac{1}{6400}$ of 360°. The radian, used in theoretical mathematics, is an angle which, when it is a central angle of a circle, has an arc equal to the radius.

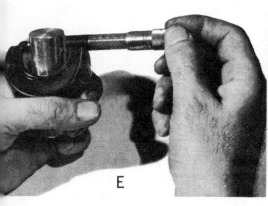
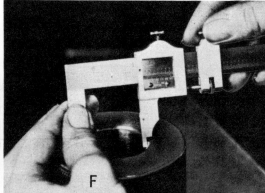

Brown & Sharpe Mfg. Co. (A, B, D); Central Scientific Co. (E); Keuffel & Esser Co. (C); West Tech (F)

Types of Measuring Instruments

A. Steel square   B. Trisquare   C. Engineer's steel tape
D. Thickness gauge   E. Micrometer caliper   F. Vernier caliper

Indirect Measurement [A]

Suppose that we wish to find the distance between two points, A and
B, which are on opposite sides of a build-
ing, and that we cannot find the distance
by direct measurement. If we can find
a point C such that it is visible from A
and B and such that $\angle ACB$ is a right
angle, then we can find the lengths of
CA and CB by direct measurement and
use the Pythagorean Theorem to find
AB. This measurement of AB is *indirect*.

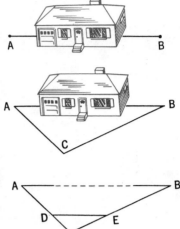

We can find AB by another method
of indirect measurement. Choose some
convenient point C visible from A and B.
On AC and BC locate the points D and
E such that $\dfrac{AC}{DC} = \dfrac{BC}{EC}$. Then why is
$\triangle CDE \sim \triangle CAB$? Measure DE. The measurements of AC, CD, BC,
EC, and DE are direct. Finally, find AB by the proportion $\dfrac{AB}{DE} = \dfrac{AC}{DC}$.

Again, suppose that we wish to find the distance between two points
C and D which are on opposite shores of a lake and that we are unable

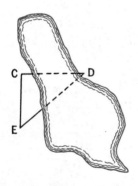

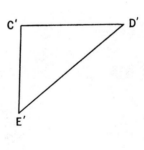

to find a point whose distance from both C and D can be measured directly. We choose a point E from which we can measure directly to C.
On paper we draw a convenient line segment $C'E'$. We measure $\angle C$
and $\angle E$ with the protractor. Then we draw $\triangle C'D'E'$ having $\angle C' = \angle C$
and $\angle E' = \angle E$. $\triangle C'D'E' \sim \triangle CDE$. Why? Then we find the lengths

Trigonometry Is a Prerequisite for the Study of Calculus

In the picture Professor Crull of Butler University is explaining the development
of a formula involving the use of trigonometric functions

of *CE*, *C'E'*, and *C'D'* by direct measurement. Then, using the proportion $\dfrac{CD}{C'D'} = \dfrac{CE}{C'E'}$, we find the length of *CD* by indirect measurement. This indirect measurement is made by means of a *scale drawing*. The method used in this example is called the *graphic method*.

EXERCISES [A]

1. Name three ways of proving triangles similar.

2. *Complete:* If two triangles are similar, their corresponding angles are _?_ and their corresponding sides are _?_.

3. Find the distance *BC* in the diagram, if *AB* = 168 feet, *AC* = 156 feet, and ∠*C* = 90°.

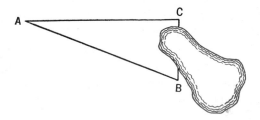

4. When a 6-foot pole casts a shadow of 13 feet, a telephone pole casts a shadow of 62 feet. How high is the telephone pole?

5. One side of a triangle is 200 feet and its adjacent angles are 30° and 54°, respectively. Use a scale drawing to find the other three parts of the triangle.

6. In △ *ABC*, *AC* = 90', *BC* = 70', and ∠*B* = 90°. Use a scale drawing to find ∠*A* and ∠*C*.

Why We Study Trigonometry [A]

In the exercises above scale drawings were used in making indirect measurements. Without doubt, the members of your class differed on the results obtained for distances found indirectly by scale drawings. This was to be expected since a small change in a scale drawing may cause a large change in the object to be measured. You probably remember that you were likewise not always able to obtain accurate results when you solved simultaneous equations graphically.

Solutions of problems by graphic methods illustrate the fact that scale drawings are not dependable where a high degree of accuracy is desired. However, they are useful in estimating results and in checking solutions for unreasonable answers.

A triangle consists of six parts, three sides and three angles. When any three of these parts (provided at least one is a side) are known, the remaining parts are determined. (In some cases two triangles are possible, as we shall discover later.) In special cases the remaining parts can be found by plane geometry. For example, we can find the third side of a right triangle when two of the sides are known; or we can find any two sides of a 30°–60° right triangle when the third side is known.

Trigonometry enables us to find the remaining parts of *any* triangle when any three parts are given, provided that one of the three given parts is a side. Since a polygon can be separated into triangles, trigonometry applies also to polygons.

Trigonometry is essential in many occupations. It is a necessary tool in surveying. It is used when large buildings are constructed. It is applied when a large dam is made, a railroad is built, and a large tunnel is constructed. The astronomer could do little without trigonometry. The armed forces have constant need of trigonometry in solving their problems.

Trigonometry is necessary for anyone who wishes to make an extensive study of mechanics, heat, light, sound, or electricity. It is necessary for the study of calculus, which may be said to be the groundwork of all higher mathematics.

The Growth of Trigonometry [A]

Trigonometry, like algebra and geometry, has had a slow growth. The earliest approach to trigonometry appeared in the *Rhind Papyrus*, which was written about 2000 B.C. In this treatise the word *seqt* was used in the sense that we use the word *cotangent*.

Centuries later, about 180 B.C., Hypsicles of Alexandria used chord functions of angles in making computations. Some think he learned this method of reckoning from the Babylonians. Most writers give Hipparchus (born about 160 B.C.) the credit of introducing trigonometry as a science. In order to solve problems in astronomy, he prepared a table of chords of circles and used this table in a manner similar to the way we use a table of sines.

In the first century B.C., Hero, the great mathematician, probably introduced the tangent function when making a study of the areas of polygons.

Ptolemy of Alexandria did much work in mathematics and was noted for his work in astronomy. His treatise on astronomy, the *Megiste Syntaxis*, was an authority on the subject for 1500 years. The Arabians translated his work and gave it the name of *Almagest*, which was considered as an authority on trigonometry.

We owe much to the Hindus and Arabs for their contributions to trigonometry. The Hindus replaced the table of chords by a table of half chords. (A table of half chords is a table of sines.) The Arabs accomplished more in mathematics than the Hindus. They introduced the other functions of angles and prepared tables for them.

The first book on trigonometry alone was *De Triangulis*. It was written in 1464 A.D. by Johann Mueller under the name of Regiomontanus. The book supplemented what was already known in trigonometry by accurate tables and by additions and discoveries of the author.

The first book bearing the name "Trigonometry" was written by Pitiscus in 1595. Additions and enrichments to the subject have since been made by the great mathematicians John Napier, Sir Isaac Newton, and Euler, and others as well.

Important Geometric Facts [A]

In your study of trigonometry, you should be able to apply the definitions, axioms, theorems, and corollaries of plane geometry. For your convenience the following summary is given.

Summary of Principal Methods of Proof of Plane Geometry

Line segments equal

a. If two angles of a triangle are equal, the sides opposite the equal angles are equal.

b. If one acute angle of a right triangle is 30°, the side opposite this angle is one half the hypotenuse.

c. If a line bisects one side of a triangle and is parallel to a second side, it bisects the third side.

d. The midpoint of the hypotenuse of a right triangle is equidistant from the vertices of the triangle.

e. The median of a trapezoid is equal to one half the sum of the bases.

f. The tangents to a circle from an external point are equal.

g. The locus of points within an angle equidistant from the sides is the bisector of the angle.

h. The locus of points equidistant from two given points is the perpendicular bisector of the line segment joining the two points.

Angles equal

a. All right angles are equal.

b. Complements of the same angle or of equal angles are equal.

c. Supplements of the same angle or of equal angles are equal.

d. If two parallels are cut by a transversal, the alternate interior angles are equal.

e. If two angles have their sides parallel, right side to right side, and left side to left side, the angles are equal.

f. If two angles have their sides perpendicular, right side to right side and left side to left side, the angles are equal.

Angles supplementary

a. Two angles are supplementary when their sum is a straight angle.

b. Any two consecutive angles of a parallelogram are supplementary.

c. If a quadrilateral is inscribed in a circle, the opposite angles are supplementary.

Angles complementary

a. Two angles are complementary when their sum is a right angle.

b. The acute angles of a right triangle are complementary.

Lines perpendicular; angle a right angle

a. Two lines are perpendicular to each other if one of them forms two equal adjacent angles with the other; or if the lines form a right angle.

b. The diagonals of a rhombus are perpendicular.

c. If a line is tangent to a circle, it is perpendicular to the radius drawn to the point of contact.

d. An angle inscribed in a semicircle is a right angle.

Angles and sums of angles

a. The sum of all the angles about a point in a plane is two straight angles, or 360°.

b. The sum of the angles of a triangle is a straight angle, or 180°.

c. An exterior angle of a triangle equals the sum of the two nonadjacent interior angles.

d. The sum of the exterior angles of a polygon is 360°.

e. The sum of the interior angles of a polygon of n sides is $(n-2)$ straight angles.

Arcs equal

a. In a circle or in equal circles equal central angles have equal arcs.

b. In a circle or in equal circles equal chords have equal arcs.

c. If a line through the center of a circle is perpendicular to a chord, it bisects its arc.

d. Parallel lines intercept equal arcs on a circle.

Comparison of angles and their arcs

a. A central angle is equal in degrees to its intercepted arc.

b. An inscribed angle is equal in degrees to one half its intercepted arc.

Line segments in proportion

a. A line parallel to one side of a triangle divides the other two sides proportionally.

b. A line parallel to one side of a triangle divides the other two sides so that either side is to one of its segments as the other side is to its corresponding segment.

c. The altitude on the hypotenuse of a right triangle is the mean proportional between the segments of the hypotenuse.

d. Either leg of a right triangle is the mean proportional between the hypotenuse and its projection on the hypotenuse.

e. If two chords intersect within a circle, the product of the segments of one chord is equal to the product of the segments of the other chord.

f. If a tangent and a secant are drawn to a circle from an external point, the tangent is the mean proportional between the secant and its external segment.

Similar polygons

a. Similar polygons are those whose corresponding angles are equal and whose corresponding sides are proportional.

b. If two triangles have two angles of one equal respectively to two angles of the other, the triangles are similar.

c. If two right triangles have an acute angle of one equal to an acute angle of the other, the triangles are similar.

d. If two triangles have an angle of one equal to an angle of the other and the including sides proportional, the triangles are similar.

e. If two triangles have their sides respectively proportional, they are similar.

f. The altitude on the hypotenuse of a right triangle forms two right triangles which are similar to the given triangle and to each other.

g. Two right triangles are similar if the hypotenuse and leg of one are proportional to the hypotenuse and leg of the other.

Areas

a. The area of a rectangle is equal to the product of its base and altitude.

b. The area of a square is equal to the square of one of its sides.

c. The area of a parallelogram is equal to the product of its base and altitude.

d. The area of a triangle is equal to one half the product of its base and altitude.

e. The area of a rhombus is equal to one half the product of its diagonals.

f. The area of a trapezoid is equal to one half the product of its altitude and the sum of its bases.

g. The area of an equilateral triangle of side s is given by the formula $A = \dfrac{s^2}{4}\sqrt{3}$.

h. The area of a triangle whose sides are a, b, and c is given by the formula $A = \sqrt{s(s-a)(s-b)(s-c)}$, where $s = \frac{1}{2}(a + b + c)$.

i. The area of a polygon circumscribed about a circle is given by the formula $A = rs$, where s is half the perimeter of the polygon and r the radius of the circle.

j. The area of a circle is given by the formula $A = \pi r^2$.

Miscellaneous Numerical Relations

a. The diagonal of a square is given by the formula $d = s\sqrt{2}$, where *s* is a side of the square.

b. Pythagorean Theorem. The square of the hypotenuse of a right triangle is equal to the sum of the squares of its legs.

c. The circumference of a circle is expressed by the formula $c = \pi d$.

d. $\pi = \dfrac{c}{d} = 3.1416$, approximately.

The Greek Alphabet

In higher mathematics letters of the Greek alphabet are often used to represent the magnitudes of angles. The Greek alphabet follows:

LETTERS	NAMES	LETTERS	NAMES	LETTERS	NAMES
A α	Alpha	I ι	Iota	P ρ	Rho
B β	Beta	K κ	Kappa	Σ σ s	Sigma
Γ γ	Gamma	Λ λ	Lambda	T τ	Tau
Δ δ	Delta	M μ	Mu	Υ υ	Upsilon
E ε	Epsilon	N ν	Nu	Φ φ	Phi
Z ζ	Zeta	Ξ ξ	Xi	X χ	Chi
H η	Eta	O o	Omicron	Ψ ψ	Psi
Θ θ	Theta	II π	Pi	Ω ω	Omega

Airport Construction, Litchfield Park, Arizona

The pipeline being laid will be used to drain storm water from the runways and landing field of the airport. Such a project requires skillful engineering, in which mathematics plays a major role

FUNCTIONS OF AN ACUTE ANGLE
SOLUTION OF RIGHT TRIANGLES

Δ

The methods used in making indirect measurements by geometry require much labor, apply only to special cases, or lack accuracy. Trigonometry was developed to make indirect measurements with a high degree of accuracy. In this chapter we shall learn how to make some of these measurements.

Notation in a Triangle [A]

It is convenient to denote certain points and lines associated with the triangle by definite letters. In $\triangle ABC$, the sides opposite $\measuredangle A$, B, and

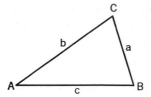 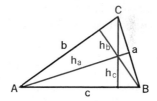

C are denoted by the lower-case letters a, b, and c respectively. The altitudes to sides a, b, and c are denoted by h_a, h_b, and h_c respectively, and the bisectors of the angles are denoted by t_a, t_b, and t_c. In this text R and r will denote the radii of the circumcircle and incircle respectively. Also, in a right $\triangle ABC$, $\angle C$ will denote the right angle.

Geometry of the Right Triangle [A]

In geometry you learned two important facts about the right triangle. With reference to right $\triangle ABC$, they are:

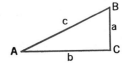

$$c^2 = a^2 + b^2 \qquad A + B = 90°$$

The relation $c^2 = a^2 + b^2$ enables us to find the third side of a right triangle when two sides are known, and the relation $A + B = 90°$ enables us to find one of the acute angles of the triangle when the other is known. The first equation is a relation among the sides of the triangle, and the second is a relation between the acute angles. Neither equation tells us how to find the angles when the sides are given or how to find the remaining parts when two angles and a side, or two sides and an angle, are given. Trigonometry offers the means of finding the remaining parts of any triangle when any three of its parts, one of which is a side, are known.

The Six Trigonometric Ratios of the Sides of a Right Triangle [A]

$\triangle ABC$ is a right triangle lettered as described on page 17. There are only six ratios of the sides a, b, and c. These ratios are:

$$\frac{a}{c}, \frac{b}{c}, \frac{a}{b}, \frac{c}{a}, \frac{c}{b}, \text{ and } \frac{b}{a}.$$

Notice that the last three of these ratios are the <u>reciprocals</u> of the first three. (The reciprocal of $\frac{a}{b} = 1 \div \frac{a}{b} = \frac{b}{a}$; the reciprocal of $\frac{2}{3}$ is $\frac{3}{2}$.) Each of these ratios has a name with reference to angle A and another with reference to angle B. The names and definitions of these ratios are:

For any right triangle

1. The *sine* (sīn) of an acute angle is the ratio of the opposite leg to the hypotenuse.
2. The *cosine* (kō'sīn) of an acute angle is the ratio of the adjacent leg to the hypotenuse.
3. The *tangent* (tăn'jĕnt) of an acute angle is the ratio of the opposite leg to the adjacent leg.
4. The *secant* (sē'kănt) of an acute angle is the ratio of the hypotenuse to the adjacent leg.
5. The *cosecant* (kō·sē'cănt) of an acute angle is the ratio of the hypotenuse to the opposite leg.
6. The *cotangent* of an acute angle is the ratio of the adjacent leg to the opposite leg.

The easiest way to remember these definitions is to visualize each ratio with reference to an angle, as indicated below. When naming the ratios of a given angle, abbreviations are customarily used,—*sin* for sine, *cos* for cosine, *tan* for tangent, *sec* for secant, *csc* for cosecant, and *ctn* or *cot* for cotangent.

With reference to right $\triangle ABC$, we have:

$$\sin A = \frac{\text{opposite leg}}{\text{hypotenuse}} = \frac{a}{c} \qquad \csc A = \frac{\text{hypotenuse}}{\text{opposite leg}} = \frac{c}{a}$$

$$\cos A = \frac{\text{adjacent leg}}{\text{hypotenuse}} = \frac{b}{c} \qquad \sec A = \frac{\text{hypotenuse}}{\text{adjacent leg}} = \frac{c}{b}$$

$$\tan A = \frac{\text{opposite leg}}{\text{adjacent leg}} = \frac{a}{b} \qquad \operatorname{ctn} A = \frac{\text{adjacent leg}}{\text{opposite leg}} = \frac{b}{a}$$

Notice that we do not write "sin $\angle A$," but "sin A." From this point on sin A will mean "sin $\angle A$," cos A will mean "cos $\angle A$," and so on. Note that csc A is the reciprocal of sin A, that sec A is the reciprocal of cos A, and that ctn A is the reciprocal of tan A.

For the acute angle B, we have:

$$\sin B = \frac{b}{c} \qquad\qquad \csc B = \frac{c}{b}$$

$$\cos B = \frac{a}{c} \qquad\qquad \sec B = \frac{c}{a}$$

$$\tan B = \frac{b}{a} \qquad\qquad \operatorname{ctn} B = \frac{a}{b}$$

These ratios are so important that you should learn them immediately. You must be able to name them for any position of the triangle. Perhaps the manufactured word "soh-cah-toa" will help you remember the first three ratios. "soh" suggests $sin = \dfrac{opposite\ side}{hypotenuse}$, "cah" suggests $cos = \dfrac{adjacent\ side}{hypotenuse}$, and "toa" suggests $tan = \dfrac{opposite\ side}{adjacent\ side}$.

The following exercises will help you to obtain a mental picture of these ratios.

EXERCISES [A]

*Using the first row of figures below, find the values of the ratios in
Exercises 1–6, expressing each value to the nearest tenth:*

1. sin A; sin B; sin E; sin F; sin H; sin K; sin N.

2. cos A; cos B; cos E; cos F; cos H; cos K; cos SPN.

3. tan A; tan B; tan E; tan F; tan H; tan K; tan M.

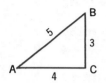 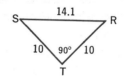 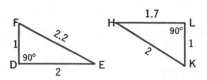

4. ctn A; ctn B; ctn E; ctn F; ctn H; ctn K; ctn MPS.

5. sec A; sec B; sec E; sec F; sec H; sec K; sec N.

6. csc A; csc B; csc E; csc F; csc H; csc K; csc MPS.

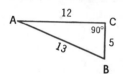 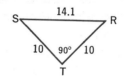

Using the figures above, find these values to the nearest tenth:

7. sin A; cos B; sin S; cos R; sin K; cos L.

8. tan A; ctn B; tan S; ctn R; tan K; ctn L.

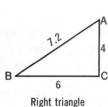 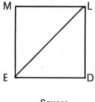 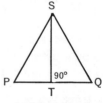

Right triangle Square Equilateral triangle

Using the figures above, find to the nearest tenth:

9. sin A; tan A; cos DEL; ctn P; tan Q; sin 30°; sin 60°.

10. tan B; cos A; sin DEL; cos P; tan 30°; tan 60°.

11. In the figure at the right $\angle ACB = 90°$ and $CD \perp AB$.

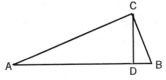

a. Express the six trigonometric ratios of $\angle A$, using the sides of $\triangle ADC$.

· **b.** Express these six ratios, using the sides of $\triangle ABC$.

c. Express the six trigonometric ratios of $\angle B$, using the sides of $\triangle DBC$.

Trigonometric Functions [A]

Suppose that each member of a trigonometry class were asked to compute the six trigonometric ratios of a given acute angle. Each member of the class would draw a right triangle having one of its acute angles equal to the given angle. Then he would measure the lengths of the sides of his triangle and compute the six ratios. Probably no two of the students' triangles would be congruent but all of them would be similar. If all the students could draw their triangles correctly, measure the sides correctly, and make no errors in their divisions, they would obtain the same results for their ratios. Let us see why.

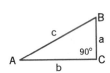 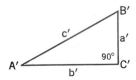

Let ABC and $A'B'C'$ be any two right triangles having $\angle A$ and $\angle A'$ each equal to any given acute angle.

Then $\angle B = \angle B'$ and $\triangle ACB \sim \triangle A'C'B'$. Why?

Then $\dfrac{a}{a'} = \dfrac{b}{b'} = \dfrac{c}{c'}$. Why?

Then $\dfrac{a}{c} = \dfrac{a'}{c'}$. Why? But $\dfrac{a}{c} = \sin A$ and $\dfrac{a'}{c'} = \sin A'$.

Therefore we conclude that the sine of any acute angle does not depend upon the size of the triangle containing the angle and that it can be obtained from any right triangle containing the angle. Similarly we can prove the same property for the other ratios. Thus for any angle there is only one value for each of the ratios.

Now suppose that we have two unequal acute angles A and A'. We shall prove that sin A does not equal sin A'.

Suppose that sin A = sin A'.

Then in rt. $\triangle ABC$ and $A'B'C'$, $\dfrac{a}{c} = \dfrac{a'}{c'}$, and so $\triangle ABC \sim \triangle A'B'C'$. Why? (See p. 14.)

Then $\angle A = \angle A'$, which is a contradiction of the hypothesis. Therefore two unequal acute angles have unequal sines.

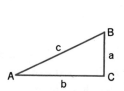
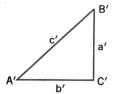

In the same manner, it can be proved that as the angle changes the other ratios change.

The converse is true for the six ratios.

Since the six ratios depend upon the size of the angle for their values, they are called *trigonometric functions*.

There are five other functions of angles which are used occasionally. These functions are not ratios, but functions of the sine and cosine ratios. We define these five functions as follows:

> versed sine A (vers A) = $1 - \cos A$.
> coversed sine A (cvs A) = $1 - \sin A$.
> haversine A (hav A) = $\frac{1}{2}(1 - \cos A)$.
> subversed sine A (suv A) = $1 + \cos A$.
> external secant A (exsec A) = $\sec A - 1$.

Finding the Functions of an Angle Graphically [A]

The following example illustrates the method of finding the approximate values of the six functions graphically.

EXAMPLE. Find the values of the six trigonometric functions of 23°.

SOLUTION. With the protractor draw right $\triangle ABC$ having $\angle A = 23°$. Then measure the lengths of the sides of the triangle and find their ratios. Doing this, we have the following values:

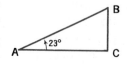

$$\sin 23° = .39 \qquad \cos 23° = .92 \qquad \tan 23° = .42$$
$$\csc 23° = 2.6 \qquad \sec 23° = 1.1 \qquad \text{ctn } 23° = 2.4$$

The same triangle can be used to compute all six functions, but the division can be made easier if the denominator of each ratio is 10. This would require three triangles.

How to Find an Angle Given One of its Functions [A]

Three examples will illustrate the graphic method of solving this problem.

EXAMPLE 1. Find the angle whose sine is $\frac{3}{4}$.

SOLUTION. The sine is the ratio of the opposite side to the hypotenuse.

Draw any line l and to it construct a perpendicular BC which is 3 units long. With B as center and a radius 4 units long draw an arc intersecting l in A. Draw AB. Then $\angle A$ is the angle whose sine is $\frac{3}{4}$. Use the protractor to measure $\angle A$. By measurement $\angle A$ is approximately 49°.

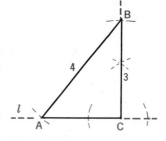

EXAMPLE 2. Find the angle whose co-tangent is $\frac{2}{3}$.

SOLUTION. The cotangent is the ratio of the adjacent side to the opposite side. Draw $AC = 4$ units. Construct $BC \perp AC$ and 6 units long. Draw AB. Measure $\angle A$ with a protractor. $\angle A$ is approximately 56°.

Why did we use the ratio $\frac{4}{6}$ instead of the ratio $\frac{2}{3}$?

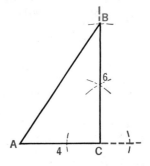

EXAMPLE 3. Find the angle whose co-sine is .81.

SOLUTION. .81 is equal approximately to $\frac{4}{5}$. We construct right $\triangle ACB$ having $AC = 4$ and $AB = 5$. We find by measuring that $\angle A$ equals approximately 35°.

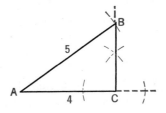

EXERCISES [A]

Using protractor and compasses, find the six functions of each of the following angles:

1. 30°   **2.** 45°   **3.** 60°   **4.** 75°   **5.** 20°   **6.** 25°   **7.** 50°   **8.** 68°

Construct and measure the angle whose

9. sine is $\frac{2}{3}$ **11.** cosine is .62   **13.** tangent is $\frac{5}{6}$

10. sine is $\frac{3}{5}$ **12.** cosine is .49   **14.** tangent is $\frac{1}{2}$

Finding the Remaining Functions When One is Given [A]

Page 23 enables us to determine the other functions when one of them is given.

EXAMPLE. If $\sin A = .65$, find the remaining functions.

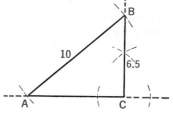

SOLUTION. $.65 = \dfrac{65}{100} = \dfrac{6.5}{10}$. We can construct right $\triangle ABC$, having $BC = 6.5$ and $AB = 10$, and then find AC by measurement. Or we may simply sketch $\triangle ABC$ and find AC by the Pythagorean Theorem. By either method $AC = 7.6$. Then

$$\cos A = \frac{7.6}{10} = .76, \quad \tan A = \frac{6.5}{7.6} = .86,$$
$$\sec A = 1.3, \ \csc A = 1.5, \text{ and } \operatorname{ctn} A = 1.2.$$

EXERCISES [A]

1. $\sin A = .5$; find the other functions of A.

2. $\tan B = 1$; find B and its other functions.

3. Construct an angle of 60° and find the functions of 60°.

4. Find the functions of 15° graphically.

5. Show that the sine of an acute angle is less than 1.

6. Show that the cosine of an acute angle is less than 1.

7. Two legs of a right triangle are 4 and 12. Construct the triangle, find the acute angles and their functions.

8. One side of a right triangle is 5 feet and the hypotenuse is 13 feet. Make a scale drawing of the triangle and find the functions of the smallest angle.

9. In a right triangle $\sin A = .8$ and side $c = 20$ inches. Compute sides a and b and find A and B.

10. In a right triangle $b = 16$ inches and $\tan A = .75$. Compute a and c and find A and B.

11. If $A > 45°$, show that $\tan A > 1$.

12. Show that:
    a. $\sin A < \tan A$ **b.** $\tan A < \sec A$

13. Show that:
    a. $\cos B < \sec B$ **b.** $\operatorname{ctn} A < \csc A$

14. In right $\triangle ABC$, show that:
    a. $a = c \sin A$ **c.** $a = b \tan A$ **e.** $c = b \sec A$
    b. $b = c \cos A$ **d.** $b = a \operatorname{ctn} A$ **f.** $c = a \csc A$

15. Draw right $\triangle ABC$ and show that:
    a. $\sin A = \cos B$ **c.** $\sec A = \csc B$
    b. $\tan A = \operatorname{ctn} B$ **d.** $\sin B = \cos A$

16. Draw right $\triangle ABC$ and show that:
    a. $\sin A \csc A = 1$ **b.** $\sec A \cos A = 1$

Reciprocal Functions [A]

The reciprocal of a number is unity (1) divided by the number. The reciprocals of 3, $\frac{2}{5}$, $\frac{1}{5}$, and $\frac{2x}{3}$ are $\frac{1}{3}$, $\frac{5}{2}$, 5, and $\frac{3}{2x}$ respectively. Note that the reciprocal of a fraction is obtained by inverting the fraction.

From the figure at the right, we have:

$$\sin A = \frac{a}{c} \qquad \csc A = \frac{c}{a}$$

$$\cos A = \frac{b}{c} \qquad \sec A = \frac{c}{b}$$

$$\tan A = \frac{a}{b} \qquad \operatorname{ctn} A = \frac{b}{a}$$

From this table, we see that the six functions consist of three pairs of *reciprocal functions,*—the sine and cosecant, the cosine and secant, and the tangent and cotangent.

From these relations, we have:

$$\sin A \csc A = 1, \quad \sin A = \frac{1}{\csc A}, \quad \text{and} \quad \csc A = \frac{1}{\sin A};$$

$$\cos A \sec A = 1, \quad \cos A = \frac{1}{\sec A}, \quad \text{and} \quad \sec A = \frac{1}{\cos A};$$

$$\tan A \operatorname{ctn} A = 1, \quad \tan A = \frac{1}{\operatorname{ctn} A}, \quad \text{and} \quad \operatorname{ctn} A = \frac{1}{\tan A}.$$

If you retain a mental picture of the right $\triangle ABC$ and the six functions of A, you should not find it difficult to remember the last nine relations.

Cofunctions [A]

Let us now compare the six functions of A with the six functions of B, when A and B are the acute angles of right $\triangle ABC$.

$$\sin A = \frac{a}{c} \qquad\qquad \cos B = \frac{a}{c}$$

$$\cos A = \frac{b}{c} \qquad\qquad \sin B = \frac{b}{c}$$

$$\tan A = \frac{a}{b} \qquad\qquad \operatorname{ctn} B = \frac{a}{b}$$

$$\operatorname{ctn} A = \frac{b}{a} \qquad\qquad \tan B = \frac{b}{a}$$

$$\sec A = \frac{c}{b} \qquad\qquad \csc B = \frac{c}{b}$$

$$\csc A = \frac{c}{a} \qquad\qquad \sec B = \frac{c}{a}$$

From the above relations we know that

$$\sin A = \cos B \qquad\qquad \operatorname{ctn} A = \tan B$$
$$\cos A = \sin B \qquad\qquad \sec A = \csc B$$
$$\tan A = \operatorname{ctn} B \qquad\qquad \csc A = \sec B$$

Since A and B are complementary angles, A is the complement of B and B is the complement of A. If we replace B by $90° - A$ in three of these formulas, we have

$$\cos A = \sin(90° - A), \quad \text{or } \cos A = \sin(\text{complement of } A)$$
$$\operatorname{ctn} A = \tan(90° - A), \quad \text{or } \operatorname{ctn} A = \tan(\text{complement of } A)$$
$$\csc A = \sec(90° - A), \quad \text{or } \csc A = \sec(\text{complement of } A)$$

These three relations may explain to you how the cosine, cotangent, and cosecant functions received their names.

If we replace B by $90° - A$ in the remaining functions, we have

$$\sin A = \cos(90° - A); \quad \tan A = \operatorname{ctn}(90° - A); \quad \sec A = \csc(90° - A).$$

Cofunctions are functions of complementary angles. The six functions consist of three pairs of cofunctions, the sine and cosine, the tangent and cotangent, and the secant and cosecant.

EXAMPLES.
$$\sin 40° = \cos 50°$$
$$\cos 18° = \sin 72°$$
$$\tan 30° = \operatorname{ctn} 60°$$

$$\operatorname{ctn} 15° = \tan 75°$$
$$\sec 10° = \csc 80°$$
$$\csc 35° = \sec 55°$$

EXERCISES [A]

Express the following as functions of the complementary angles:

1. $\sin 29°$ **4.** $\operatorname{ctn} 19°$ **7.** $\csc 35°$ **10.** $\sin 45°$

2. $\cos 22°$ **5.** $\sec 80°$ **8.** $\tan 31°$ **11.** $\tan 35°$

3. $\tan 74°$ **6.** $\sin 8°$ **9.** $\cos 45°$ **12.** $\operatorname{ctn} 71°$

Express as functions of angles less than 45°:

13. $\tan 88°$ **15.** $\cos 77°$ **17.** $\sec 48°$ **19.** $\sin 87° 6'$

14. $\operatorname{ctn} 76°$ **16.** $\sin 64°$ **18.** $\csc 57°$ **20.** $\cos 56° 32'$

21. $\sin(90° - A) = \frac{2}{5}$. Find $\cos A$.

22. $\tan(90° - A) = \frac{4}{7}$. Find $\operatorname{ctn} B$.

23. State which of the following are true:

     a. $\sin 20° \cos 70° = 1$ **e.** $\tan 19° \operatorname{ctn} 71° = 1$

     b. $\tan 31° \operatorname{ctn} 69° = 1$ **f.** $\cos 20° \sin 20° = 1$

     c. $\dfrac{\cos 19°}{\operatorname{ctn} 71°} = 1$ **g.** $\sec 25° \csc 65° = 1$

                        h. $\sec 44° \cos 46° = 1$

     d. $\dfrac{\sin 32°}{\csc 32°} = 1$

EXAMPLE. $\sin A = \cos 3A$. Find A.

SOLUTION.
$$\sin A = \cos 3A$$
$$\sin A = \sin(90° - 3A)$$
$$A = 90° - 3A$$
Solving, $\qquad A = 22° 30'$

Solve for A :

24. $\sin A = \cos A$ **26.** $\tan 3 A = \text{ctn } 3 A$ **28.** $\cos A = \sin 5 A$

25. $\sin A = \cos (4 A)$ **27.** $\sec A = \csc 4 A$ **29.** $\sin 2 A = \cos 3 A$

30. Find $\sec A$ when $\sin (90° - A) = \frac{2}{5}$.

31. Find $\text{ctn } B$ when $\tan (90° - B) = \frac{4}{7}$.

32. Find $\sin A$ when $\sin A = \csc A$.

Functions of 30° and 60° [A]

The functions of angles of 30°, 45°, and 60° occur so frequently that their exact values should be memorized.

To find the functions of 30° and 60°, draw equilateral triangle *ABD*, as below. Then draw $DC \perp AB$, forming two right triangles.

From geometry, $\angle A = 60°$, $\angle ADC = 30°$, and $AC = \frac{1}{2} AD$.

Let $AD = 2.$

Then $AC = 1. \quad DC = \sqrt{2^2 - 1^2} = \sqrt{3}.$

Then from the figure we have

$\sin 30° = \frac{1}{2}$ $\sin 60° = \frac{1}{2} \sqrt{3}$

$\cos 30° = \dfrac{\sqrt{3}}{2} = \frac{1}{2} \sqrt{3}$ $\cos 60° = \frac{1}{2}$

$\tan 30° = \dfrac{1}{\sqrt{3}} = \frac{1}{3} \sqrt{3}$ $\tan 60° = \sqrt{3}$

$\text{ctn } 30° = \sqrt{3}$ $\text{ctn } 60° = \frac{1}{3} \sqrt{3}$

$\sec 30° = \dfrac{2}{\sqrt{3}} = \dfrac{2\sqrt{3}}{3}$ $\sec 60° = 2$

$\csc 30° = 2$ $\csc 60° = \dfrac{2\sqrt{3}}{3}$

Functions of 45° [A]

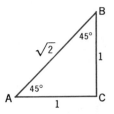

To find the functions of 45°, draw isosceles right triangle *ACB*. $\angle A = \angle B = 45°$. Why? Let each leg = 1. Then $AB = \sqrt{1^2 + 1^2} = \sqrt{2}$. Then from the figure we have the following values:

$$\sin 45° = \frac{1}{\sqrt{2}} = \tfrac{1}{2}\sqrt{2} \qquad\qquad \text{ctn } 45° = 1$$

$$\cos 45° = \frac{1}{\sqrt{2}} = \tfrac{1}{2}\sqrt{2} \qquad\qquad \sec 45° = \sqrt{2}$$

$$\tan 45° = \frac{1}{1} = 1 \qquad\qquad \csc 45° = \sqrt{2}$$

How to Remember the Values of the Functions of Certain Angles [A]

The table shown here will help you remember the results obtained in the two preceding sections. Although we have not studied the functions of 0° and 90°, their sines and cosines are included in the table.

To remember the values of the functions, notice which angles appear in the first column and their order. Then memorize the *sin* column, noticing how the values compare. Note how the *cos* column can be obtained from the *sin* column. Why are the values of the functions not written in their simplest forms?

To find the cosecant of any angle in the table, find the reciprocal of its sine; to find the

ANGLE	SIN	COS
0°	$\tfrac{1}{2}\sqrt{0}$	$\tfrac{1}{2}\sqrt{4}$
30°	$\tfrac{1}{2}\sqrt{1}$	$\tfrac{1}{2}\sqrt{3}$
45°	$\tfrac{1}{2}\sqrt{2}$	$\tfrac{1}{2}\sqrt{2}$
60°	$\tfrac{1}{2}\sqrt{3}$	$\tfrac{1}{2}\sqrt{1}$
90°	$\tfrac{1}{2}\sqrt{4}$	$\tfrac{1}{2}\sqrt{0}$

secant, find the reciprocal of its cosine; to find the tangent, divide its sine by its cosine; and to find its cotangent, divide its cosine by its sine.

Tables of Trigonometric Functions [A]

It is possible to prepare a table by the graphic method giving the values of the trigonometric functions for each degree from 0° to 90°, but even with extreme care the values would not be very accurate.

However, mathematicians have been able to prepare tables of these functions to any degree of accuracy desired. If you continue the study of mathematics, you will learn how these tables can be computed. Tables of trigonometric functions are called *tables of natural functions*.

How to Use a Table of Natural Functions [A]

Table X, page 69 at the end of the book, is a table of natural functions. This table gives the values of the trigonometric functions for each 10 minutes (10′) from 0° to 90°. Note that the sine, tangent, and secant are increasing functions and that the cosine, cotangent, and cosecant are decreasing functions. *Increasing functions* are those which increase when the angle increases and *decreasing functions* are those which decrease when the angle increases.

With this table we can find the value of any function for each minute from 0° to 90° and find the size of the angle when the value of any one of its functions is known.

The table is arranged so that the angles from 0° to 45° are in the first column and the angles from 45° to 90° are in the last column. The six columns in the middle give the values of the functions. For angles between 0° and 45°, we read the angles in the left-hand column and find their functions in the middle columns, using the column designations at the top. For angles between 45° and 90°, we read the angles in the column at the right and find their functions in the middle columns using the column designations at the bottom. Note that for angles less than 45°, we read from the top of the page downward and that for angles greater than 45°, we read from the bottom of the page upward.

Have you observed how condensed this table is? The condensation is possible because the function of an angle is equal to the cofunction of its complement. For example, the column of sines on page 70 of the Tables not only gives the values of the sines of angles from 9° to 18°, but it also gives the values of the cosines of angles from 72° to 81°.

EXAMPLE 1. Find sin 38° 20′.

SOLUTION. In Table X, find 38°|20′ in the first column, headed **Angle**. Then, in the column headed **Sin** at the top and in the same horizontal line with 38° 20′ find .6202. Then sin 38° 20′ = 0.6202.

EXAMPLE 2. Find cos 71° 40′.

SOLUTION. Since 71° 40′ is greater than 45°, we look in the *right-hand* column for 71° 40′. Remember we read from the bottom upward. Opposite 71° 40′ and in the column headed **Cos** at the bottom we find .3145. Then cos 71° 40′ = 0.3145.

EXAMPLE 3. Find ctn 46° 10′.

SOLUTION. Find 46° 10′ in the right-hand column. In the same horizontal line with 46° 10′ and in the column headed **Ctn** at the bottom find .9601. Then ctn 46° 10′ = 0.9601.

EXERCISES [A]

Using Table X, find:

1. tan 45°	**6.** sin 49°	**11.** sin 18° 20′	**16.** sin 70° 10′
2. cos 33°	**7.** cos 81°	**12.** cos 35° 20′	**17.** cos 19° 50′
3. sin 16°	**8.** tan 63°	**13.** tan 74° 40′	**18.** tan 48° 40′
4. sec 28°	**9.** csc 74°	**14.** sec 15° 50′	**19.** ctn 11° 20′
5. ctn 18°	**10.** ctn 78°	**15.** csc 32° 50′	**20.** sin 6° 50′

By reversing the procedure above find the size of each angle to the nearest 10′:

21. $\sin A = .5995$	**25.** $\text{ctn } X = .3217$	**29.** $\cos B = .0901$
22. $\cos A = .8223$	**26.** $\tan X = .9163$	**30.** $\tan B = 1.3351$
23. $\tan A = 1.8265$	**27.** $\tan X = 1.0380$	**31.** $\text{ctn } D = 1.2799$
24. $\sec A = 2.2411$	**28.** $\csc X = 1.9407$	**32.** $\sec D = 1.0889$

Interpolation [A]

In Table X any two consecutive angles differ by 10′. The method used to find the value of a function of an angle between any two of these consecutive angles is called *interpolation*. We shall now illustrate interpolation by three examples.

EXAMPLE 1. Find sin 29° 18′.

SOLUTION. Let $x = \sin 29° 18′$.

29° 18′ lies between 29° 10′ and 29° 20′.

$$\sin 29° 20′ = .4899 \;\;\rceil$$
$$\sin 29° 18′ = x \quad\;\; 0025$$
$$\sin 29° 10′ = .4874 \;\;\rfloor$$

29° 18′ is $\frac{8}{10}$ of the way from 29° 10′ to 29° 20′.
Then x is about $\frac{8}{10}$ of the way from .4874 to .4899; $\frac{8}{10}$ of .0025 = .0020.
Then $x = .4874 + \frac{8}{10}(.0025) = .4874 + .0020 = .4894$.
Then $\qquad\qquad\qquad \sin 29° 18′ = .4894$.

The difference between any two consecutive functions in the table is called the *tabular difference*. In Example 1, the tabular difference is .0025.

EXAMPLE 2. Find cos 36° 43'.

SOLUTION. 36° 43' lies between 36° 40' and 36° 50'. Since cos 36° 40' is larger than cos 36° 50', we write it above. Let x = cos 36° 43'.

$$\begin{array}{l} \cos 36° 40' = .8021 \\ \cos 36° 43' = x \qquad .0017 \\ \cos 36° 50' = .8004 \end{array}$$

36° 43' is $\frac{3}{10}$ of the way from 36° 40' to 36° 50'.

Then x is approximately $\frac{3}{10}$ of the way from .8021 to .8004. $\frac{3}{10}$ of .0017 = .0005. Since the cosine of the angle becomes smaller as the angle increases, the difference .0005 must be subtracted from .8021. x = .8021 − .0005 = .8016.

Then $\qquad\qquad\qquad$ cos 36° 43' = .8016.

EXAMPLE 3. Find ctn 74° 35'.

SOLUTION. The cotangent is also a decreasing function. 74° 35' lies between 74° 30' and 74° 40'. Let x = ctn 74° 35'.

$$\begin{array}{l} \text{ctn } 74° 30' = .2773 \\ \text{ctn } 74° 35' = x \qquad .0031 \\ \text{ctn } 74° 40' = .2742 \end{array}$$

74° 35' is $\frac{5}{10}$ of the way from 74° 30' to 74° 40'.
$\frac{5}{10}$ of .0031 = .00155.
x = .2773 − .00155 = .27575. We round off .27575 so that the last digit is even. x = .2758.

$$\text{ctn } 74° 35' = .2758.$$

EXERCISES [A]

Using Table X, find the values of

1. sin 18° 15'	**5.** cos 14° 15'	**9.** sin 73° 24'
2. tan 40° 28'	**6.** cos 25° 35'	**10.** sin 82° 47'
3. sin 37° 14'	**7.** ctn 18° 4'	**11.** cos 64° 8'
4. ctn 43° 48'	**8.** sec 30° 52'	**12.** csc 71° 13'

Inverse Use of the Table [A]

We shall now use interpolation to find the angle when one of its functions is given. Two examples will be given.

EXAMPLE 1. Find A if tan A = .0825.

SOLUTION. tan A lies between tan 4° 40′ and tan 4° 50′.

$$\begin{array}{ll} \text{tan } 4° \ 50′ = .0846 \\ \text{tan } A \qquad = .0825 \\ \qquad\qquad\qquad\ 9 \quad 30 \\ \text{tan } 4° \ 40′ = .0816 \end{array}$$

.0825 is $\frac{9}{30}$ of the way from .0816 to .0846. The *tabular difference* is 30*.
Then A is approximately $\frac{9}{30}$, or .3, of the way from 4° 40′ to 4° 50′. Then
the difference between A and 4° 40′ is about .3 of 10′, which is 3′.

Then A = 4° 40′ + 3′ = 4° 43′.

EXAMPLE 2. Find B when cos B = .4910.

SOLUTION. cos B lies between cos 60° 30′ and cos 60° 40′. We remember that
the cosine is a decreasing function.

$$\begin{array}{ll} \text{cos } 60° \ 30′ = .4924 \\ \text{cos } B \qquad = .4910 \\ \qquad\qquad\qquad\ 11 \quad 25 \\ \text{cos } 60° \ 40′ = .4899 \end{array}$$

.4910 is $\frac{11}{25}$ of the way from .4899 to .4924.
Then B is about $\frac{11}{25}$ of the way from 60° 40′ to 60° 30′. $\frac{11}{25}$ of 10′ = 4′.

$$B = 60° \ 40′ - 4′ = 60° \ 36′.$$

EXERCISES [A]

Find the size of each of the following angles:

1. sin A = .3432
2. sin A = .4630
3. tan A = 1.0925
4. tan A = 1.3840

5. cos B = .9220
6. cos B = .9018
7. csc B = 1.836
8. ctn B = .3510

9. ctn B = .1748
10. tan B = 3.8300
11. sec B = 1.3619
12. cos B = .4600

Lines and Planes [A]

A *vertical line* is a line that passes through the center of the earth.

A *plumb line* is a line that coincides with the vertical line. A plumb
line is made by suspending a weight on a cord.

A *vertical plane* is one that contains a vertical line. Two vertical lines
determine a vertical plane.

* This is an accepted way of writing .0030 in such work.

A *horizontal line* is one that is perpendicular to a vertical line.

A *horizontal plane* is one that is perpendicular to a vertical line. In the figure, AB is a vertical line at the place A on the earth. Here the line AC and the plane m are horizontal.

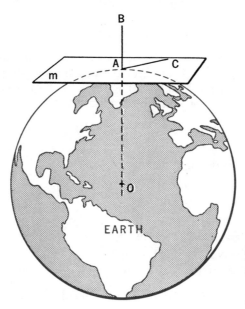

Angles of Elevation and Depression [A]

One of the many applications of trigonometry is that of finding heights of objects whose tops are inaccessible. For example, by indirect measurement we can compute the height of a tall broadcasting tower by making two direct measurements,—one of the distance of the tower from us and the other of the angle formed by the lines drawn from us to the top and bottom of the tower.

We shall now explain some of the phrases which are commonly used in stating problems of this type.

When an observer views an object from a distant point, the *line of sight* is the line drawn from the observer to the object.

If an observer at A, in the diagrams on the opposite page, sights an object at B, the angle which AB makes with the horizontal line AC in the vertical plane ABC is called the *angle of elevation* of B. Can you give a reason why it is so called?

The *inclination of the line AB* is the angle A.

The *slope of the line AB* is the tangent of ∠*A*.

If an observer at *B* sights an object at *A*, the angle which *BA* makes with the horizontal line *BD* in the vertical plane *ABD* is called the *angle of depression* of *A*.

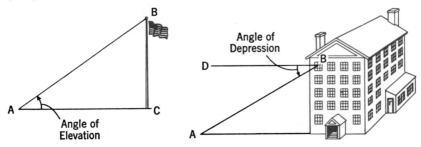

EXERCISES [A]

1. Explain why two vertical lines are not parallel.

2. A line is level at a point if it is horizontal at the point. Explain why a straight line that is level at one point will not be level at another point.

3. Why will the angle of depression of *A* from *B* equal the angle of elevation of *B* from *A*? (Neglect the curvature of the earth.)

4. What is the slope of a line that makes an angle of 42° with the horizontal?

5. Find the inclination of a line if its slope is $\frac{2}{3}$.

6. What is the slope of a roof if it rises 2 feet in a horizontal distance of 6 feet?

Finding Distances and Angles [A]

> For finding distances and angles by the use of trigonometric functions, the following directions are suggested:
>
> 1. *Draw a fairly accurate figure.*
> 2. *Write the known values on the figure.*
> 3. *Represent the quantity to be found by a letter and place the letter on the figure.*
> 4. *Write the proper equation.*
> 5. *Solve the equation and check your work.*

EXAMPLE. From an observation balloon the angle of depression of a farmhouse was 24°. The altimeter showed that the balloon was 4280 feet above the ground. Assuming that the earth's surface was flat in that location, find how far the house was from the point directly beneath the balloon.

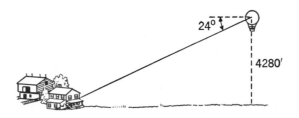

SOLUTION. For all practical problems of this type the angle of elevation of A from B is considered equal to the angle of depression of B from A, as indicated in the diagram below.

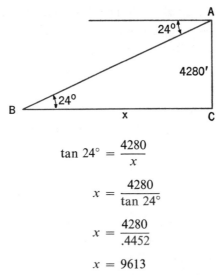

$$\tan 24° = \frac{4280}{x}$$

$$x = \frac{4280}{\tan 24°}$$

$$x = \frac{4280}{.4452}$$

$$x = 9613$$

The distance BC is 9613 feet.

In this problem 24 and 4280 are treated as exact numbers, and the result is rounded off to four places.

The solution can be checked by the formula

$$\text{ctn } 24° = \frac{x}{4280}$$

EXERCISES

A

Name two functions which can be used to find:

1. A when a and c are known.

2. b when A and c are known.

3. a when A and c are known.

4. c when b and B are known.

5. c when b and A are known.

6. B when a and c are known.

7. Given $A = 30° 15'$ and $b = 18$. Find c.

8. Given $A = 42° 34'$ and $b = 46$. Find c.

9. Given $B = 72° 42'$ and $b = 18.4$. Find a.

10. Find a when $b = 75.1$ and $B = 17° 25'$.

11. Find c when $A = 42° 36'$ and $a = 40$.

12. Find a when $A = 24° 12'$ and $c = 70$.

13. $a = 76, b = 45$. Find A.   **14.** $a = 30, c = 55$. Find B.

15. A man standing 152 feet from the foot of a flagpole, which is on his eye level, observes that the angle of elevation of its top is 48°. Find the height of the pole.

16. A rectangle is 14′ 2″ long and 9′ 4″ wide. Find the angles which a diagonal makes with the sides.

17. At a horizontal distance of 231.4 feet from the base of a tower the angle of elevation of its top is 62° 14′. Find the height of the tower.

18. From the top of a building 146 feet high the angle of depression of a road intersection is 15° 24′. How far from the building is the intersection?

B

19. The sides of a triangle are 15, 15, and 18. How large is the largest angle? HINT. Bisect the largest angle.

20. In this circle, diameter AB is 16 inches and chord AC is 14 inches. How large is $\angle A$?

21. Find the radius of a regular decagon each side of which is 8 inches.

22. The bases of an isosceles trapezoid are 16 inches and 28 inches. Find the size of each of its smallest angles if its area is 154 square inches.

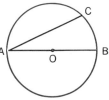

23. A man who had an oil well at *A* wished to drill another well higher up the mountain so that the wells would be 500 feet apart horizontally. He asked one of the authors how he could find the point. He could get a protractor but did not wish to use a transit. Tell how you would find the distance.

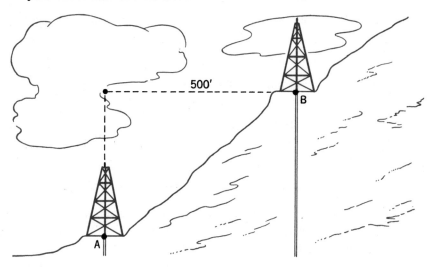

24. The sides of a trapezoid taken in order are 18″, 15″, 30″, and 15″. How large are its angles?

25. In Figure 1 below, *AD* = 100, ∠*A* = 12° 15′, and ∠*BDC* = 16°. Find *BC*.

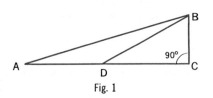 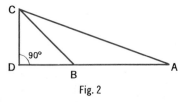

Fig. 1   Fig. 2

26. From *A* (Fig. 2) the angle of elevation of *C* is 24° and from *B*, which is 102 feet nearer the foot of the perpendicular from *C*, the angle of elevation of *C* is 45°. How high is *C*?

27. From an observation point the angles of depression of two boats in line with this point are found to be 18° 10′ and 27° 50′. Find the distance between the two boats if the point of observation is 4000 feet high.

28. Two automobiles are on the same side of and in the same horizontal line with the base of a tower 92 feet high. If the angles of depression of the cars from the top of the tower are 31° 45′ and 38° 25′, how far apart are they?

Solution of Right Triangles [A]

Solving a triangle means finding the remaining parts of the triangle when a sufficient number of known parts are given. When we solve a triangle, we should always be mindful of the fact that a triangle has six parts,—three sides and three angles.

To solve a triangle at least three parts (or their equivalents) are needed. To solve a right triangle, two parts besides the right angle are needed, and one of these two parts must be a side. (If the two given parts are angles, an infinite number of triangles is possible. What can you say of these triangles?) Since one of these two given parts must be a side, the other may be either a side or an angle. Then we have two cases of solving a right triangle.

Cases of Solution

        1. Given one side and one acute angle.

        2. Given two sides.

Show by the congruence theorems that the parts given in each of these cases determine the triangle.

Only four of the natural functions are usually used to solve right triangles. These are the sine, cosine, tangent, and cotangent. The following general outline will be helpful in solving a right triangle.

To Solve a Right Triangle

1. Draw a fairly accurate figure and write the known values on the figure.
2. To find each of the three unknown parts, use a formula that contains only the unknown part and the two known parts.
3. Make an outline of the solution.
4. Use the given parts and the table of natural functions to fill in the outline.
5. Solve the resulting equations for the unknown parts.
6. Check the results.

EXAMPLE 1. Solve the right triangle ABC, given $A = 52°\ 24'$ and $a = 31.45$.

SOLUTION

NOTE. The boldface parts of the solution indicate the outline you should write first. As each unknown part is found, its value is written in the proper space under *Required*.

GIVEN

$A = 52°\ 24'$
$a = 31.45$

1. To find B:

  $B = C - A$
  $B = 90° - 52°\ 24'$
  $\quad = 37°\ 36'$

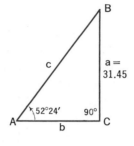

REQUIRED

$B = 37°\ 36'$
$c = 39.69$
$b = 24.22$

2. To find c:

  $\sin A = \dfrac{a}{c}$

  $\sin 52°\ 24' = \dfrac{31.45}{c}$

  $.7923 = \dfrac{31.45}{c}$

  $c = \dfrac{31.45}{.7923}$

  $c = 39.69$

3. To find b:

  $\tan A = \dfrac{a}{b}$

  $\tan 52°\ 24' = \dfrac{31.45}{b}$

  $1.2985 = \dfrac{31.45}{b}$

  $b = \dfrac{31.45}{1.2985}$

  $b = 24.22$

Check. $\dfrac{b}{c} = \sin 37°\ 36'$

$\dfrac{24.22}{39.69} = .6102$

$.6102 = .6102$

The solution can be checked for large errors by solving the triangle graphically. The check used above makes use of the three required parts. Do you see why a check such as this is preferred?

The formula $b^2 = (c - a)(c + a)$, which is a form of $b^2 = c^2 - a^2$, can also be used to check the solution.

EXAMPLE 2. Solve the right triangle ABC given $a = 124.8$ and $b = 150.2$.

SOLUTION

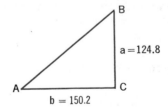

GIVEN

$a = 124.8$
$b = 150.2$

REQUIRED

$A = 39°\ 43'$
$B = 50°\ 17'$
$c = 195.3$

1. To find A: $\tan A = \dfrac{a}{b}$

$$\tan A = \frac{124.8}{150.2}$$

$$\tan A = .8309$$

$$A = 39° \, 43'$$

2. To find c: $\sin A = \dfrac{a}{c}$

$$\sin A = \frac{124.8}{c}$$

$$c = \frac{124.8}{\sin A}$$

$$c = \frac{124.8}{.6390}$$

$$c = 195.3$$

3. To find B:

$$B = C - A$$

$$B = 90° - 39° \, 43' = 50° \, 17'$$

Check. $\sin B = \dfrac{b}{c}$

$$.7692 = \frac{150.2}{195.3}$$

$$.7692 = .7692$$

EXERCISES

A

Solve right triangle ABC, *given*

1. $a = 14.7$, $B = 42° \, 10'$ **5.** $a = 762.9$, $b = 432.8$

2. $a = 350$, $c = 475.2$ **6.** $a = 64.7$, $b = 27.98$

3. $a = 84.31$, $A = 65° \, 15'$ **7.** $c = 431.4$, $a = 156.2$

4. $a = 32.45$, $B = 78° \, 16'$ **8.** $c = 7.281$, $b = 4.165$

9. Find the length of a chord of a 20-inch circle if its central angle is 47° 18′.

10. The length of a chord of a circle with a 12-inch radius is 16.4 inches. Find the central angle of the chord.

11. An airplane is flying a straight course at 160 m.p.h. If it maintains an altitude of 12,000 feet, what will be its angle of elevation 2 minutes after it passes directly above the observer?

12. From an airplane flying at a speed of 260 m.p.h. at an altitude of 21,000 feet the angle of depression of a disabled ship was 23° 15′. How many minutes were needed for the plane to reach a point directly over the ship?

13. Find the angle of elevation of the sun when a 20-foot pole casts a shadow 102 feet long on the level ground.

14. A railroad track rises 1 inch for each 36 feet measured along the track. Find the angle of elevation and the slope of the track.

15. The slope of a railroad track is 0.0892. Find the amount of rise in a mile of track.

16. The *pitch* of a gable roof is one half its slope. It equals the rise divided by the span. In the figure $\dfrac{CD}{AB}$ = the pitch, CD being the rise and AB the span. CE is the ridgepole.

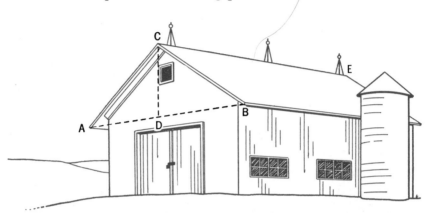

The span of a barn roof is 38 feet and the pitch of the roof is $\frac{1}{3}$. Find the lengths of the rafters (AC and CB).

17. A cattle barn is 30 feet by 50 feet. The ridgepole is 52 feet long and the slope of the roof is $\frac{1}{3}$. Find the cost of reroofing the barn at $6.80 per square, assuming that the roof does not extend beyond the sides of the barn. (1 square = 100 square feet)

18. In $\triangle ABC$, $AC = 8$, $BC = 10$, and $A = 42°$. Find AB.

19. In $\triangle RST$, $\angle R = 42°$, $RS = 18$ inches, and $RT = 44$ inches. Find ST.

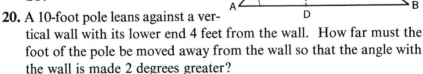

20. A 10-foot pole leans against a vertical wall with its lower end 4 feet from the wall. How far must the foot of the pole be moved away from the wall so that the angle with the wall is made 2 degrees greater?

21. Find the length of the belt passing around the two pulleys pictured, the belt to be perfectly tight.

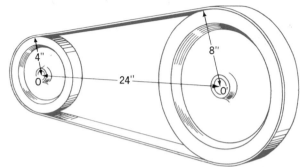

22. The latitude of New York City is 40° 45′. Find the velocity of New York in space due to the rotation of the earth on its axis. For this problem use 4000 miles for the earth's radius.

23. How high must one be above the earth's surface in order to see a point on the surface 40 miles away?

24. The peak of a mountain is observed from the base and from the top of a tower 180 feet high. Find the height of the mountain above the base of the tower if the angles of elevation of the peak are 21° 35′ and 24° 48′.

25. From a point in the street between two buildings the angles of elevation of the tops of the buildings are 45° each. When the observer moves 21 feet toward one of the buildings, the angles of elevation are 25° and 65° respectively. How high is each of the buildings?

26. Two straight railroad tracks which intersect at an angle of 71° are to be connected by the shorter circular track that is tangent to the intersecting tracks 320 feet from the intersection. Find the radius and length of the circular track.

27. Point A is directly in front of a corner of a building having 142.0 feet frontage. Find CD, the height of the building, if tan $BAC = 2.1463$ and tan $DAC = 1.4325$.

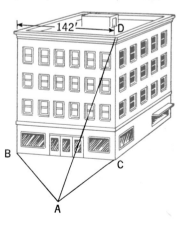

CHAPTER REVIEW [A]

State which of the following statements relating to △ABC are true and which are false:

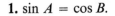

1. sin A = cos B.

2. tan A = ctn B.

3. sec A csc B = 1.

4. As A increases, cos B increases.

5. If tan A increases, sin A increases.

6. sin A, tan A, and sec A are increasing functions.

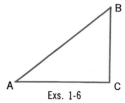

Exs. 1-6

Complete each of the statements 7–10.

7. sin 30° + cos 60° = _?_.

8. tan 45° + ctn 45° = _?_.

9. The angle of elevation of B from A is _?_.

10. The angle of depression of A from B is _?_.

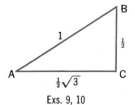

Exs. 9, 10

11. sin A = $\frac{5}{13}$. Construct $\angle A$ and without the use of a table find the other functions of A.

12. tan B = 1.5. Construct $\angle B$ and find the other functions of B.

13. sec A = 1.4376. Use Table X to find the other functions of A.

14. sin A = $\frac{2}{3}$. Is tan A greater or less than $\frac{2}{3}$?

15. Using the adjoining figure, complete:

    a. BC = _?_ tan A

    b. AB = _?_ sec A

    c. $b = a$ _?_ A

    d. $c = a$ _?_ A

    e. tan A = _?_ (90° − A)

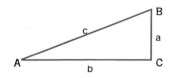

16. *Complete:* Any function of an acute angle is equal to the _?_ of its complementary angle.

17. The Alva B. Adams Tunnel is 13.07 miles long. The difference in elevation of its two portals is 107 feet. Find its slope. (See p. 182.)

Juneau, Alaska

Are you interested in air navigation or in the design and construction of airplanes?
If so, you will find a sound knowledge of mathematics essential to study in these fields

CHAPTER II

APPROXIMATE NUMBERS; LOGARITHMS

Δ

Approximate Numbers

Meaning of Approximate Numbers [A]

If you were asked to find the length of an iron bar, you might measure its length with a yardstick and say that its length is 23 inches, meaning that its length is nearer to 23 inches than to 22 inches or 24 inches. In this case, you would be measuring to the nearest inch, the figure 2 being exact and the figure 3 approximate. The measurement 23 is approximate because the figure 3 is approximate.

If you measure the same bar with a yardstick marked off in tenths of an inch, you may say that the length is 23.7 inches because the length is nearer to 23.7 inches than to 23.6 inches or 23.8 inches. The measurement in this case is made to the nearest tenth of an inch, the figures 2 and 3 being exact and the figure 7 approximate. Since the number 7 is approximate, the number 23.7 is approximate.

A mechanic might find the bar's length to be 23.78 inches, but the number 23.78 would be approximate because the number 8 would be approximate. Regardless of the instrument used in measuring the bar, no measurement of its length can be said to be exact. *Any measurement is subject to error and is therefore approximate.*

Tables of roots, of trigonometric functions, and of logarithms consist, in the main, of approximate numbers. For example, the square root of 3 is given on page 55 of the Tables by the approximate number 1.73205, and the square root of 4 is given on page 56 by the exact number 2.00000.

Rounding off Numbers [A]

Suppose that your speedometer shows the distance between two points to be 436.2 miles. If you have some doubt as to the accuracy of your speedometer, you may say that the distance is 436 miles. In this case you have *rounded off* the number to the nearest mile. If you say that the distance between the two points is 440 miles, meaning that the distance is nearer to 440 miles than to 430 miles or 450 miles, you have rounded off 436.2 to the nearest ten miles.

When the number 5.27 is expressed correct to the nearest tenth as 5.3, it has been rounded off to the nearest tenth. When rounded off to the nearest tenth, each of the numbers 5.20, 5.21, 5.22, 5.23, and 5.24 becomes 5.2; and each of the numbers 5.26, 5.27, 5.28, and 5.29 becomes 5.3. Since 5.25 is just as near 5.2 as it is to 5.3, either 5.2 or 5.3 could be the result when 5.25 is rounded off to the nearest tenth. However, it is a common practice of many mathematicians to use the following rule:

When the digit 5 (or the digit 5 followed by one or more zeros) is dropped in rounding off a number, the preceding digit is increased by one if it is odd but left unchanged if it is even.

By this plan approximately as many numbers will be increased as decreased:

EXAMPLES.   Rounded off to tenths,

4.35	becomes	4.4
17.55	becomes	17.6
1.45	becomes	1.4
3.250	becomes	3.2

ORAL EXERCISES [A]

1. Find the error involved when $\frac{1}{3}$ is expressed by the decimal .3; when it is expressed by the decimal .333.

2. Which of the two decimals .666 and .667 is nearer the value of $\frac{2}{3}$?

Round off each of the following numbers to the nearest tenth:

3. 4.83   **5.** 45.35   **7.** 18.96   **9.** 78.650

4. 191.18   **6.** 7.45   **8.** 143.27   **10.** 9.750

Round off each of the following numbers to the nearest hundredth:

11. 4.787   **13.** 23.147   **15.** 7.285   **17.** 4.1950

12. 2.162   **14.** 6.144   **16.** 6.175   **18.** 12.462

Units of Measure [A]

The unit of measure in any measurement is the smallest unit used in the measurement. Thus, the unit of measure in a recorded measurement of 3 feet is a foot; in 14.68 feet is .01 of a foot; in .006 inches is .001 inch; in $\frac{3}{8}$ inch is $\frac{1}{8}$ inch; and in 6 pounds 3 ounces is one ounce. Very precise measurements require extremely small units of measure.

Significant Figures [A]

A recorded distance of 24 feet means that the distance has been measured to the nearest foot and that the exact distance has a lower limit of 23.5 feet and an upper limit of 24.5 feet; a recorded distance of 24.7 feet means that the distance has been measured to the nearest tenth of a foot and that the exact distance has a lower limit of 24.65 feet and an upper limit of 24.75 feet; and a recorded distance of 24.78 feet means that the distance has been measured to the nearest hundredth of a foot and that the exact distance has a lower limit of 24.775 feet and an upper limit of 24.785 feet.

In each of these recorded measurements—24 feet, 24.7 feet, and 24.78 feet—all the digits are significant because they have a real meaning. In each of the numbers each digit except the last is an exact number and the last digit has no error greater than one half unit. For example, the digits 2, 4, and 7 in the number 24.78 are exact, and the digit 8 is not more than one half unit wrong. All the digits of a number are significant except zero, which may or may not be significant.

A zero *is not* significant

1. If it is used as a place-holder following a decimal point, as in .07, .0032, and .00017.

2. If it is used to fill places at the beginning of a number greater than unity. For example, the zeros in the number 0043 are not significant.

3. If it occurs at the end of a measured number unless it shows the unit of measurement used. For example, the zero in the measurement 240 feet is not significant if the measurement is made to the nearest 10 feet, but it is significant if the measurement is made to the nearest foot.

4. If it occurs at the end of a counted number which has been rounded. For example, 4555 typewriters may be rounded to 4600 typewriters.

A zero *is* significant when it occurs between two other digits, as in 709.

In general, the following rule can be used to determine the significant figures of a number:

1. *Disregard all initial zeros.*
2. *Disregard all final zeros unless they follow a decimal point.*
3. *The remaining digits are significant.*

ORAL EXERCISES [A]

Give the number of significant figures in each of the following numbers:

1. 7923	**4.** 8.026	**7.** 0630	**10.** 800
2. 478	**5.** 130.1	**8.** 700.0	**11.** 240,000
3. 16.41	**6.** 127.0	**9.** 10	**12.** 93,000,000

Round off each of the following numbers to three significant figures:

13. 8416	**15.** 47.65	**17.** .04171	**19.** .02415
14. 3.151	**16.** 1595	**18.** 87140	**20.** 0.7146

Round off each of the following numbers to four significant figures:

21. 71851	**23.** 3218.4	**25.** 480.75	**27.** 749132
22. 6210.8	**24.** 7622.5	**26.** 7.4315	**28.** 315968

Absolute Error [A]

The *absolute error* in any recorded measurement is the greatest possible error in the measurement. It can be found by subtracting the number used in recording the measurement from the largest number it may represent; or by subtracting the smallest number it may represent from the recorded measurement. Now study the following examples:

EXAMPLE 1. Find the absolute error in the measurement 473 feet.

SOLUTION. 473 feet may represent any number of feet ranging from 472.5 to 473.5. 473.5 − 473 = .5. Then .5 foot is the absolute error. The same result is obtained by subtracting 472.5 from 473.

EXAMPLE 2. Find the absolute error in the measurement 4.73 feet.

SOLUTION. 4.735 − 4.73 = .005. The absolute error is .005 foot.

In the first example the unit of measure is one foot and in the second example the unit of measure is .01 foot. The two examples illustrate the fact that the absolute error depends upon the unit of measure and therefore upon the decimal point. Thus the absolute error is a measure of the *precision* of the measurement.

Relative Error [A]

The *relative error* in a measurement is the ratio of the absolute error to the measurement. In Example 1, page 49, the measurement is 473 feet and the absolute error is .5 foot. Then the relative error is the ratio of .5 to 473, which is approximately .0011. In Example 2 the measurement is 4.73 feet and the absolute error is .005 foot. Then the relative error equals .005 ÷ 4.73, which is approximately .0011. Thus, the relative error in a measurement does not depend upon the unit of measure or on the position of the decimal point in the recorded measurement. It does not indicate the precision of the measurement.

The relative error in a measurement depends upon the significant figures in the measurement. If two measurements have the same number of significant figures, the measurement having the larger initial digit has the smaller relative error. For example, the relative error of 25 is .5 ÷ 25, or .02, and the relative error of 75 is .5 ÷ 75, or .0067.

If two measurements do not have the same number of significant figures, the measurement having the greater number of significant figures has the smaller relative error. For example, the relative error in the measurement 234.0 inches, which has four significant digits, is .05 ÷ 234.0, or .00021, while the relative error in the measurement 234 inches, which has three significant figures, is .5 ÷ 234, or .0021.

The *accuracy* of a measurement is shown by the relative error of the measurement; the smaller the relative error the greater the accuracy. Then the accuracy of a measurement is determined by the number of significant figures in the measurement. For example, the measurements 164 feet, 16.4 feet, and .164 feet are equally accurate; but they are less accurate than 2748 feet, 27.48 feet, and .2748 feet since they have fewer significant figures. Again, the measurement 6.2 inches is more accurate than the measurement 5.8 inches because it has a smaller relative error.

EXERCISES [A]

1. Give the absolute error in the following approximate numbers: 9.6 seconds; 13.01 inches; .0004 inch; 25,000 miles; 240,000 miles.

2. Give the relative error of each of the numbers in Ex.1.

3. Which measurement is the more precise, 18.13 inches or 181.3 inches? What can you say of the accuracies of the two measurements?

4. Which of the four measurements 4.124 feet, 16.3 feet, 2.61 feet, and 71.43 feet is the least accurate? the most accurate?

5. Why is the measurement having the larger number of significant figures the more accurate?

Computing with Approximate Numbers [A]

When approximate numbers are added, subtracted, multiplied, or divided, the results are approximate numbers.

Suppose that we wish to find the perimeter of a triangle whose sides are 13.62 inches, 17.5 inches, and 21.14 inches. If these dimensions are exact, the perimeter is exactly 52.26 inches; but if the numbers 13.62, 17.5, and 21.14 are found by measurement, they are approximate and the sum 52.26 is approximate.

13.62
17.5
21.14
52.26

If these dimensions are found by measurement, 13.62 represents some number whose lower limit is 13.615 and upper limit is 13.625; 17.5 represents a number ranging from 17.45 to 17.55; and 21.14 represents a number ranging from 21.135 to 21.145. Then the true perimeter is not less than 52.200 inches and not greater than 52.320 inches.

13.615	13.625
17.45	17.55
21.135	21.145
52.200	52.320

In this example, two of the sides are measured to the nearest hundredth of an inch and the third is measured only to the nearest tenth of an inch. Does it not seem useless to make any one of the three measurements more precise than the others? Quantities to be added should be measured by the same unit. The same is true for subtracting approximate numbers.

To add (or subtract) approximate numbers

1. *Round them off to the same unit of measurement and add (or subtract).*
2. *The sum (or difference) will have the same unit of measurement.*

EXAMPLE. Add: 47.16, 52.44, and 100.725.

SOLUTION. The smallest unit of measurement common to all three numbers is .01. 100.725 rounded off to hundredths is 100.72. Then

$$47.16 + 52.44 + 100.72 = 200.32.$$

Let us now consider a problem involving multiplication of approximate numbers. Suppose that we wish to find the area of a rectangle whose length is 4.2 inches and whose width is 2.7 inches. If 4.2 inches and 2.7 inches are the exact dimensions of the rectangle, its area is 11.34 square inches. If 4.2 and 2.7 are found by measurement, the true area may range from 10.9975 square inches to 11.6875 square inches, as shown at the right. It is common practice to round off the product 11.34 to two significant figures and say that the area is 11 square inches. This example illustrates the following rule:

4.2	4.15	4.25
2.7	2.65	2.75
294	2075	2125
84	2490	2975
11.34	830	850
	10.9975	11.6875

The product (or quotient) of two approximate numbers should not contain more significant figures than the given number containing the fewer significant figures.

REMEMBER. The sum and difference of approximate numbers are based upon the unit of measurement and the product and quotient of approximate numbers are based upon the number of significant figures in the numbers involved.

EXAMPLE 1. Add 3.47 and 1.3, both numbers being approximate.

SOLUTION. Round off 3.47 to tenths, obtaining 3.5.

$$3.5$$
$$\underline{1.3}$$
$$4.8, \text{ the approximate sum}$$

EXAMPLE 2. Multiply the approximate numbers 3.47 and 1.3.

SOLUTION. $3.47 \times 1.3 = 4.511$. 3.47 has three significant figures and 1.3 has only two. Then the product should have only two significant figures.

Then $\qquad 3.47 \times 1.3 = 4.5.$

EXAMPLE 3. Divide 76.95 by 0.03, both numbers being approximate.

SOLUTION. $76.95 \div 0.03 = 2565$. Since 0.03 has one significant figure, the quotient should not have more than one significant figure. When rounded off to one significant figure, 2565 becomes 3000.

Then $76.95 \div 0.03 = 3000.$

EXERCISES [A]

Perform the indicated operations, assuming that the numbers are approximate:

1. $4.6 + 2.35 + .042$ **4.** $320.19 + 21.4$ **7.** $43.75 \div 11.2$

2. $345.2 - 163.8$ **5.** 1.85×2.3 **8.** $87.4 \div 2.0$

3. $926.3 - 418.14$ **6.** 47.83×4.5 **9.** $8.16 - 1.3 + 4.2$

Computations Involving Exact and Approximate Numbers [A]

Since an exact number is correct to an infinite number of decimal places, the sum (or difference) of an exact number and an approximate number will have the same unit of measure as the approximate number.

Now suppose that we wish to multiply the approximate number 3.417 by the exact number 4. How shall we round off the product 13.668? Since 3.417×4 means $3.417 + 3.417 + 3.417 + 3.417$, the product is a sum and should have the same unit of measure as 3.417. Therefore the product should not be rounded off. This practice is followed when a logarithm is multiplied by an exact number. Likewise, the quotient obtained by dividing an approximate number by an exact number should have the same unit of measure as the approximate number.

When solving a problem involving approximate numbers, the results should not contain more significant figures than the approximate number having the least number of significant figures. If the data given in a problem contain approximate numbers, the result should be rounded off so as to contain no more significant figures than any item of the data. Since most of the numbers given in the tables are approximate, the results will be approximate and should be rounded off so as not to contain more significant figures than the numbers of the table. Thus no result should have any more significant figures than the table used or than any item of the given data.

Degree of Accuracy in Angle and Linear Measurement [A]

When using a three-place table of trigonometric functions in the solution of a problem, a linear result should be rounded off to three significant figures; when using a four-place table, the result should be rounded off to four significant figures; and when using a five-place table, the result should be rounded off to five significant figures.

In general, a two-place table will give angles correct to the nearest degree; a three-place table will give angles correct to the nearest 10 minutes; a four-place table will give angles correct to the nearest minute; and a five-place table will give angles correct to the nearest 5 seconds. The correspondence between angular and linear measurements is shown in the following table:

LINEAR MEASUREMENT HAVING ↓	CORRESPONDS TO	ANGULAR MEASUREMENT TO THE NEAREST ↓
2 significant figures		1°
3 significant figures		10′
4 significant figures		1′
5 significant figures		5″

NOTE TO THE TEACHER. To secure accuracy in the student's work, the following procedure is recommended:

The solution and check of each problem should be made on the assumption that the given data are exact, giving any result in angular measurement obtained from a five-place table to the nearest second. After checking, any result in angular measurement obtained from a five-place table should be rounded off to the nearest 5 seconds; and if the given data are approximate, the results should be rounded off to conform to the data.

REVIEW EXERCISES [A]

State the number of significant figures in the following:

1. 424 ft.   3. 0.02 in.   5. 17.0 yd.   7. 186,000 mi.

2. 17.61 in.   4. 1.25 in.   6. .108 ft.   8. 92,000,000 mi.

9. Which of the numbers 18.3 feet and 203 feet is the more accurate? Which is the more precise?

10. Which of the numbers .025 feet and 1.32 inches is the more accurate? Which is the more precise?

Standard or Scientific Notation [A]

Scientists often express large numbers like 186,000 and small numbers like .00015 as the product of two numbers, the first number having a value between 1 and 10 and the second number as a power of 10. This way of expressing numbers is called standard or scientific notation.

Thus, $186,000 = 1.86 \times 10^5$ and $0.00015 = 1.5 \times 10^{-4}$

EXAMPLE 1. Express 764,000 in standard notation.

SOLUTION. Place a caret to the right of the first significant figure, thus: 7ᵧ64000. Starting at the caret, count the number of places to the decimal point. Since we count 5 places to the *right* to the decimal point, 7.64000 must be multiplied by 10^5 to equal 764,000.

Then $764,000 = 7.64 \times 10^5$

EXAMPLE 2. Express .0347 as a scientific number.

SOLUTION. We place a caret to the right of the first significant figure, thus: .03ᵧ47. Starting at the caret we count two places to the *left* to the decimal point. Then 3.47 must be multiplied by 10^{-2} to equal .0347.

Then $.0347 = 3.47 \times 10^{-2}$.

EXAMPLE 3. $4,700,000 = 4.7 \times 10^6$.

EXAMPLE 4. $0.00123 = 1.23 \times 10^{-3}$.

EXERCISES [A]

Express as scientific numbers:

1. 1620	**4.** 75,000	**7.** .05	**10.** 0.0016
2. 800	**5.** .21300	**8.** .0072	**11.** 93,000,000
3. 46	**6.** 13.9	**9.** .065	**12.** 240,000

13. A wave of light is about 0.00005 centimeters long. Express its length in standard notation.

14. The half life of uranium is 4.5×10^{10} years. Express its half life using ordinary notation.

15. The maximum distance from Mars to the sun is 155,000,000 miles. Express this distance in standard notation.

16. The maximum distance from the earth to Pluto is 3,600,000,000 miles. Express this distance in standard notation.

17. The half-life interval of the radioactive element polonium 212 is 3×10^{-7} seconds. Express this number as a decimal.

18. The diameter, in centimeters, of the hydrogen atom is 1.35×10^{-8}. Express the diameter as a decimal.

19. Find the value of $\dfrac{7.24 \times 10^8}{1.81 \times 10^3}$.

20. Find the value of $\dfrac{12.5 \times 10^{-3}}{62.5 \times 10^4}$.

LOGARITHMS

Logarithms as a Time and Labor Saver [A]

Modern man has invented many machines to produce more work in less time. You have only to contrast the power loom with the hand loom, the tractor with the hand plow, the truck with the oxcart, to realize how important machines are in making production faster and less laborious.

In mathematics many inventions, including the abacus, adding machine, comptometer, slide rule, and the large-scale computing machine have been made to save time and labor.

One of the most useful devices for shortening arithmetic computations is the method of calculation by logarithms. By using logarithms, multiplication becomes a problem of addition, division becomes a problem of subtraction, raising a number to a power becomes a small multiplication problem, and a root of a number is found by a simple division.

Meaning of Logarithms [A]

In the statement $4^3 = 64$, the 4 is called the *base* and the 3 is called the *exponent*. We can express the relation $4^3 = 64$ in another form by using the word "logarithm." Instead of saying that 4 cubed equals 64, we say that the logarithm of 64 to the base 4 is 3, written $\log_4 64 = 3$. The abbreviation "log" is used for "logarithm."

Notice how the number which shows the base is written.

General Electric Company

Friden Calculating Machine Company

Abacus

A Fully Automatic Calculator

Mechanical Computers

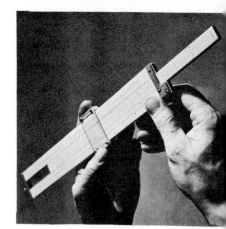

General Electric Company

Slide Rule

Electronic Calculator

This maze of tubes and electrical circuits is "Omibac," the digital computor developed by the General Electric Company to supply answers to complex mathematical problems at a speed 5000 times faster than with ordinary figuring

General Electric Company

Again, instead of saying that 2 cubed equals 8, we say that the logarithm of 8 to the base 2 is 3.

Other examples of the meaning of logarithms follow.

$\log_{10} 100 = 2$ means the same as $10^2 = 100$.
$\log_3 9 = 2$ means the same as $3^2 = 9$.
$\log_7 49 = 2$ means the same as $7^2 = 49$.
$\log_5 125 = 3$ means the same as $5^3 = 125$.

You should always remember that a <u>logarithm is an exponent.</u> We shall now define "logarithm."

The *logarithm* of a number to a given base is the exponent that indicates the power to which the base must be raised to equal this number.

The expression $2^5 = 32$ is written in *exponential notation* and the expression $\log_2 32 = 5$ is written in *logarithmic notation*.

EXAMPLE 1. Express $6^2 = 36$ in logarithmic notation.

SOLUTION. The base is 6 and the exponent is 2. Then $\log_6 36 = 2$.

EXAMPLE 2. Express $8^3 = 512$ in logarithmic notation.

SOLUTION. $\log_8 512 = 3$.

EXAMPLE 3. Express $\log_{10} 1000 = 3$ in exponential notation.

SOLUTION. $1000 = 10^3$.

EXAMPLE 4. Find $\log_3 27$.

SOLUTION. This means that you are to find what power of 3 equals 27. Since $3^3 = 27$, $\log_3 27 = 3$.

EXERCISES [A]

Change to logarithmic notation:

1. $4^2 = 16$	**8.** $4^0 = 1$	**15.** $4^{-2} = \frac{1}{16}$
2. $5^2 = 25$	**9.** $5^4 = 625$	**16.** $10^{-2} = .01$
3. $10^2 = 100$	**10.** $2^7 = 128$	**17.** $10^{-3} = .001$
4. $9^2 = 81$	**11.** $7^3 = 343$	**18.** $8^3 = 512$
5. $2^4 = 16$	**12.** $X^3 = 40$	**19.** $8^0 = 1$
6. $2^5 = 32$	**13.** $10^0 = 1$	**20.** $2^{-3} = .125$
7. $10^4 = 10000$	**14.** $10 = 10$	**21.** $5^{-2} = .04$

Change to exponential notation:

22. $\log_{10} 100 = 2$ **26.** $\log_4 64 = 3$ **30.** $\log_3 243 = 5$

23. $\log_4 4 = 1$ **27.** $\log_7 49 = 2$ **31.** $\log_4 256 = 4$

24. $\log_{10} 10 = 1$ **28.** $\log_4 X = 2$ **32.** $\log_{10} 8 = .903$

25. $\log_{10} 1 = 0$ **29.** $\log_{10} 4 = .602$ **33.** $\log_{10} 4.9 = .69$

Find the following logarithms:

34. $\log_2 16$ **38.** $\log_{12} 144$ **42.** $\log_6 1$

35. $\log_{100} 10000$ **39.** $\log_9 729$ **43.** $\log_{30} 30$

36. $\log_{16} 256$ **40.** $\log_{.5} .25$ **44.** $\log_{10} .01$

37. $\log_9 9$ **41.** $\log_{10} 1$ **45.** $\log_{.2} .04$

Common Logarithms [A]

Any positive integer except 1 may be used as the base of logarithms. Why can we not express numbers as powers of 1? However, only two bases are commonly used.

The *natural system* of logarithms has the base e, which has the approximate value 2.71828. This base is useful in theoretical mathematics because the rate of change in the function e^x for any value of x is always equal to the value of e^x. Natural logarithms are called *Napierian logarithms* because they were invented by John Napier. The expression $\log_e 45$ is abbreviated ln 45.

Logarithms having 10 as their base are called *common logarithms*. The base 10 is used in computation because we use the decimal system of notation in our thinking. Unless stated otherwise, "logarithms" means "common logarithms" and it is not necessary to write the base 10. Thus log 64 means $\log_{10} 64$.

Briggs (1560–1630), an English mathematician, by 1616 had computed a table of logarithms to the base 10 of all integers from 1 to 999. In other words, he had prepared a table by which all integers from 1 to 999 were expressed as powers of 10. Seven years later he extended the table of logarithms so as to include all integers from 1 to 20,000.

Decimal Powers of 10 [A]

The following table gives the integral powers of 10 from -2 to $+4$ inclusive. From this table we are led to the conclusions stated.

Any number (such as 1245) that is greater than 1000 but less than 10,000 is equal to 10 with an exponent whose value lies between 3 and 4.

$$10000 = 10^4$$
$$1000 = 10^3$$
$$100 = 10^2$$
$$10 = 10^1$$
$$1 = 10^0$$
$$.1 = 10^{-1}$$
$$.01 = 10^{-2}$$

Any number that lies between 100 and 1000 is equal to 10 with an exponent greater than 2 but less than 3.

Any number between 10 and 100 is equal to 10 with an exponent between 1 and 2.

Any number between 1 and 10 is equal to 10 with an exponent between 0 and 1.

Any number between .1 and 1 is equal to 10 with an exponent between −1 and 0.

Any number between .01 and .1 is equal to 10 with an exponent between −2 and −1.

From this table it is evident that only a small percentage of numbers can be expressed as integral powers of 10. All other positive numbers are decimal powers of 10. For example, $200 = 10^{2.30103}$, or log 200 = 2.30103; also log 961.7 = 2.98304.

Characteristic and Mantissa [A]

The integral part of a logarithm is called the *characteristic* and the fractional part the *mantissa*. Either the characteristic or the mantissa may be zero. In the expressions $45 = 10^{1.65321}$ and log 45 = 1.65321, the characteristic is 1 and the mantissa is .65321. In the expression $\log_{10}100 = 2$ the mantissa is zero; and in the expression log 4 = .60206, the characteristic is zero.

Finding the Logarithms of Numbers between 1 and 10 [A]

Since the logarithm of any number between 1 and 10 is greater than zero and less than 1, the characteristic of any such number is zero.

EXAMPLES. log 4.327 = 0 + (some mantissa)
log 3.160 = 0 + (some mantissa)
log 2.093 = 0 + (some mantissa)

Table I at the end of the book gives the mantissas of the logarithms of the numbers ranging from 1.000 to 10.000. Hence it gives the logarithms of these numbers. In the column headed **N** are the first three digits of the numbers whose mantissas are in the remaining columns. Now study the two examples which follow.

EXAMPLE 1. Find log 7.653.

SOLUTION. This problem means, "Find the power of 10 that equals 7.653."
In Table I look in the column headed **N** to find 765, consisting of the first
three digits of 7.653. Then follow the line 765 horizontally to the right
until you reach the column headed **3**, the fourth digit of 7.653. Here we
find 88383. The decimal points are omitted in this table; hence 88383
should be read as .88383.

Then $\qquad\qquad$ log 7.653 = 0.88383
In exponential form, $\qquad$ 7.653 = $10^{0.88383}$

EXAMPLE 2. Find log 5.8.

SOLUTION. We add two zeros to 5.8, making it 5.800. Then we look in the
column headed **N** in Table I to find the number 580, the first three digits
of 5.800. Then we follow the line 580 horizontally until we reach the
column headed **0**, the fourth digit of 5.800. Here we find the number
76343. Writing the decimal point before the number, we have .76343.

Then $\qquad\qquad$ log 5.8 = 0.76343.
In exponential form, $\qquad$ 5.8 = $10^{0.76343}$.

EXERCISES [A]

*Find the logarithm of each of the following numbers and express each
result in both exponential and logarithmic form:*

1. 7.476	**5.** 2.81	**9.** 8	**13.** 2.9
2. 4.163	**6.** 7.5	**10.** 6	**14.** 1.1
3. 5.214	**7.** 4.49	**11.** 1.428	**15.** 7.368
4. 4.325	**8.** 9.31	**12.** 8.462	**16.** 8.254

How to Find the Antilogarithm (Characteristic 0) [A]

To find the antilogarithm means to find the number when its logarithm is given. We find the antilogarithm when its logarithm is given
by reversing the method of finding the logarithm of a number.

EXAMPLE 1. Find the number that equals $10^{0.94748}$.

SOLUTION. The logarithm is 0.94748. We look among the mantissas in
Table I to find 94748. It is in row 886 in the column headed **1**. Since the
characteristic is zero, the number lies between 1 and 10. Then the antilogarithm of $10^{0.94748}$ is 8.861.

EXAMPLE 2. Find the antilog of 0.77341.

SOLUTION. Since the characteristic is zero, the number lies between 1 and 10. We look among the mantissas in the table for 77341. This number is not in the table but the number nearest to it in the table is 77342. The number 0.77342 is the logarithm of 5.935.

Then   antilog 0.77341 = 5.935, to the nearest thousandth

EXERCISES [A]

Find the numbers to the nearest thousandth which equal the following:

1. $10^{0.76380}$ **3.** $10^{0.06145}$ **5.** $10^{0.73918}$ **7.** $10^{0.25673}$

2. $10^{0.43169}$ **4.** $10^{0.27300}$ **6.** $10^{0.98864}$ **8.** $10^{0.00217}$

Find the antilogarithms of the following to the nearest thousandth:

9. 0.09377   **11.** 0.96591   **13.** 0.20548   **15.** 0.27345

10. 0.77880   **12.** 0.44011   **14.** 0.38828   **16.** 0.76870

How the Logarithm of a Number Changes When the Number is Multiplied by a Power of 10 [A]

So far we have used Table I to find the logarithms of numbers ranging from 1.000 to 10.000 and to find these numbers when their logarithms were given.

We shall now prove a theorem which will enable us to find the logarithms of numbers less than 1 and the logarithms of numbers greater than 10.

Theorem. *If a positive number N is multiplied by the nth power of* 10, *its logarithm is increased by* n.

PROOF: Let $\log_{10} N = x$

Then $N = 10^x$.

Multiplying both members of the equation by 10^n, we have

$$N \cdot 10^n = 10^{x+n}.$$

Or, $\log (N \cdot 10^n) = x + n.$

Substituting $\log_{10} N$ for x, $\log (N \cdot 10^n) = \log_{10} N + n.$

If the number is multiplied by a negative nth power of 10 (divided by 10^n), the logarithm is decreased by n.

EXAMPLE 1.   Given log 6.754 = 0.82956, find log 6754.

SOLUTION. The decimal point of 6.754 must be moved three places to the right to give 6754. 6754 = 6.754 × 10³. Then log 6754 is 3 more than log 6.754.

Then   log 6754 = .82956 + 3 = 3.82956.

EXAMPLE 2.   log 4.371 = 0.64058. Find log 437.1.

SOLUTION. 437.1 = 4.371 × 10². By the theorem on page 62,
$$\log 437.1 = \log 4.371 + 2$$
$$= .64058 + 2$$
$$= 2.64058.$$

EXAMPLE 3.   Given log 925.4 = 2.96633. Find log 92.54.

SOLUTION. 92.54 = 925.4 × 10⁻¹.
Then
$$\log 92.54 = \log 925.4 - 1$$
$$= 2.96633 - 1$$
$$= 1.96633.$$

EXERCISES [A]

1. Given log 1.811 = 0.25792
   a. Find log 1811
   b. Find log 18.11
   c. Find log 181.1
   d. Find log 18110

2. Given log 8.409 = 0.92474
   a. Find log 84.09
   b. Find log 840.9
   c. Find log 8409
   d. Find log 84090

3. Given log 7.522 = 0.87633
   a. Find log 7522
   b. Find log 75220
   c. Find log 75.22
   d. Find log 752.2

4. Given log 4 = 0.60206
   a. Find log 40
   b. Find log 400
   c. Find log 4000
   d. Find log 4 × 10⁵

5. Given log 583.2 = 2.76582
   a. Find log 5.832
   b. Find log 58.32
   c. Find log 5832
   d. Find log 58320

6. Given log 95.55 = 1.98023
   a. Find log 955.5
   b. Find log 9.555
   c. Find log 9555
   d. Find log 95550

7. What do the logarithms of the numbers 32.15, 3.215, 32150, and 0.3215 have in common?

8. $763.4 = 7.634 \times 10^2$. What is the logarithm of 10^2? How can you find the logarithm of 7.634? How then can you find log 763.4?

9. $0.2789 = 2.789 \times 10^{-1}$. What is the logarithm of 10^{-1}? How can you find log 2.789? How can you find log 0.2789?

How to Find the Logarithm of Any Four-Digit Number [A]

From the preceding work you have learned that logarithms of numbers which consist of the same sequence of digits and differ only in the position of the decimal point have the same mantissa but different characteristics. For example,

$$\log 8.241 = .91598$$
$$\log 82.41 = 1.91598$$
$$\log 8241 = 3.91598$$

You know how to use Table I to find the logarithm of a number between 1 and 10. The characteristic in such cases is always 0. When a number is written in standard notation you therefore know how to find the logarithm of its first factor. Then you can use the theorem on page 62 to find the logarithm of the number.

Study the following examples:

EXAMPLE 1. Find log 764.2.

SOLUTION. We can use Table I to find log 7.642. From the table,

$$\log 7.642 = 0.88321.$$
$$764.2 = 7.642 \times 10^2.$$

By the theorem on page 62,

$$\log 764.2 = 2 + \log 7.642.$$

Then $\log 764.2 = 2 + 0.88321 = 2.88321.$

EXAMPLE 2. Find log 850000.

SOLUTION. From Table I, log 8.5 = 0.92942.

$$850,000 = 8.5 \times 10^5.$$

Then $\log 850,000 = 5 + .92942 = 5.92942.$

A convenient method of finding the characteristic 5 in the solution of Example 2 is as follows:

Place a caret to the right of the first significant figure in the number, thus, 8ᴧ50000. Starting at the caret, count the number of decimal places to the decimal point. We count 5 places to the right. Then the characteristic is 5.

To Find the Logarithm of a Number

1. Place a caret to the right of the first significant figure of the number.
2. To find the characteristic (i.e. the integral part of the logarithm) start at the caret and count the number of decimal places to the decimal point. If you count to the right, the characteristic is positive; and if you count to the left, it is negative.
3. Find the mantissa in Table I.
4. Find the logarithm of the number by adding the characteristic and mantissa.

With practice you will find that Steps 1 and 2 can be done mentally.

EXAMPLE 3. Find log 4613.

SOLUTION. We place the caret thus, 4ᴧ613. Starting at the caret, we count 3 places to the right to the decimal point. The characteristic is 3. Considering the caret as a decimal point, we find in the table that log 4.613 = 0.66398. Then we add 3 to 0.66398 and have log 4613 = 3.66398.

EXERCISES [A]

Find the logarithms of the following numbers:

1. 8463	**4.** 951.6	**7.** 4.81	**10.** 1000	**13.** 9314
2. 27.93	**5.** 518	**8.** 545	**11.** 218.9	**14.** 7562
3. 4.632	**6.** 7.5	**9.** 8	**12.** 34.76	**15.** 7006

The characteristics in the examples and exercises above are positive. We shall now consider negative characteristics, following the steps in the rule above.

Suppose that we wish to find log 0.078. We place the caret thus, 0.07˄8. Starting at the caret, we count to the left 2 places to the decimal point. Then $0.078 = 7.8 \times 10^{-2}$; that is, 7.8 must be multiplied by 10^{-2} to equal 0.078. Then the logarithm of 0.078 is 2 less than the logarithm of 7.8. Hence the characteristic is -2.

From the table we find that log 7.80 = 0.89209. We cannot write the logarithm of 0.078 in the form -2.89209 because the mantissa .89209 is positive. We always avoid negative mantissas. How shall we write the logarithm then?

Shall we write it in the form $-2 + .89209$?

or in the form $\overline{2}.89209$?

or in the form -1.10791, which equals $-2 + .89209$?

or in the form $8.89209 - 10$?

The last form is the one we shall use because it simplifies computation.

Thus, if the characteristic is -4 and the mantissa is .53849, we write the characteristic in the form $6 - 10$ and write the logarithm in the form $6.53849 - 10$; and if the characteristic is -3 and the mantissa is .21347, we write the characteristic in the form $7 - 10$ and write the logarithm in the form $7.21347 - 10$.

EXERCISES [A]

Write the following numbers with exponents in the last form shown above, that is, with -10.

1. $10^{.92941-1}$ **3.** $10^{.23070-4}$ **5.** $10^{-5+.4284}$

2. $10^{-2+.04139}$ **4.** $10^{-4+.69504}$ **6.** $10^{\overline{5}.34998}$

Write the following logarithms in the -10 form:

7. $.64171 - 3$ **9.** $-1 + .2173$ **11.** $.4632 - 5$

8. $\overline{4}.6218$ **10.** $.2164 - 7$ **12.** $-4 + .2178$

EXAMPLE 4. Find log 0.0014.

SOLUTION. We place the caret thus: 0.001˄4. From the caret we count 3 places to the left to the decimal point. Then the characteristic is -3, or $7 - 10$.

In Table I, we find   log 1.4 = 0.14613.

Then   log 0.0014 = 7.14613 − 10.

EXERCISES [A]

Find the logarithms of:

1. 0.4758	**5.** 0.3214	**9.** 0.1125	**13.** 0.04632
2. 0.6891	**6.** 0.0159	**10.** 0.0063	**14.** 0.2799
3. 0.0078	**7.** 0.5323	**11.** 0.0047	**15.** 0.0008
4. 0.0005	**8.** 0.9146	**12.** 0.325	**16.** 0.081

Finding the Antilogarithm When the Characteristic Is Not Zero [A]

On page 61 you learned how to find a number when its given logarithm had a zero characteristic. The following rule can be used in finding the antilogarithm in all cases, whatever the characteristic:

To Find a Number When Its Logarithm Is Given

1. Use Table I to find the number whose logarithm is the mantissa of the given logarithm. Use a caret to the right of the first significant figure of the number as the decimal point.
2. Starting at the caret count (to the right if the characteristic is positive and to the left if it is negative) the number of places equal to the absolute value of the characteristic to find the position of the decimal point in the number.

EXAMPLE 1. Find the number whose logarithm is 3.86723.

SOLUTION. We look in Table I to find the mantissa .86723. We find that .86723 is the logarithm of 7ᴧ366 (we use the caret for the temporary decimal point). From the caret we count 3 places to the right to find the position of the decimal point, and have 7366. as the result.

Then   antilog 3.86723 = 7366.

EXAMPLE 2. Find antilog 8.47562 − 10.

SOLUTION. We search in Table I for the mantissa .47562. There is no such mantissa. The nearest mantissa to it is .47567. The number .47567 = log 2.990. We use the caret as the temporary decimal point, thus, 2ᴧ990. Since the characteristic is −2, that is, 8 − 10, we count 2 places to the left from the caret to find the position of the decimal point. We have 0.0299 as the result.

Then   antilog 8.47562 − 10 = 0.0299, to the nearest ten thousandth.

EXERCISES [A]

Find the antilogarithms of:

1. 3.84516	**4.** 2.89515	**7.** 2.59506	**10.** 8.90090 − 10
2. 4.71475*	**5.** 8.51693 − 10	**8.** 1.37493	**11.** 7.34753 − 10
3. 1.76388	**6.** 7.87128 − 10	**9.** 2.46404	**12.** 9.58377 − 10

The Logarithmic Curve [A]

The logarithmic curve, shown below, should help you to remember some of the important facts concerning logarithms. The graph does not give a true picture of the function because the *y* unit is 5 times as long as the *x* unit. If you have squared paper available, you may find it helpful to construct the graph using the same scale on each axis.

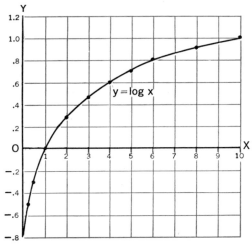

EXERCISES [A]

1. What is the value of log 1? of log 10? Use the graph.

2. What is the characteristic of any number between 1 and 10?

3. When a number becomes larger, how does its logarithm change?

4. Complete: The logarithm of any positive number greater than _?_ is positive and the logarithm of any positive number between _?_ and _?_ is negative.

* An underline under a 5 (5) in the table means that the figure in this decimal place was actually 4 and that the next figure in a larger table was 5 or more.

Facts to Be Remembered

I. *The mantissas of two numbers are the same when the numbers differ only in the position of their decimal points.*

II. *The characteristic of a number depends upon the position of the decimal point. For each place the decimal point of a number is moved to the right, the characteristic (and logarithm) is increased by 1; and for each place the decimal point is moved to the left, the characteristic (and logarithm) is decreased by 1.*

III. *The characteristic of a number between 1 and 10 is zero.*

IV. *To find the logarithm of a number:*
   1. Place a caret to the right of the first significant figure.
   2. To find the characteristic, start at the caret and count the number of decimal places to the decimal point of the number. If you count to the right, the characteristic is positive; and if you count to the left, it is negative.
   3. Considering the caret as a decimal point, find the mantissa in Table I.

V. *To find the antilogarithm:*
   1. Use the table to find the antilogarithm of the mantissa of the number. Use a caret as the temporary decimal point of the antilogarithm.
   2. Starting at the caret, count (to the right if the characteristic is positive and to the left if it is negative) the number of places equal to the absolute value of the characteristic to find the position of the decimal point.

Properties of Logarithms [A]

Before we begin to compute with logarithms, we shall consider some of their properties. Since logarithms are exponents, they have all the properties of exponents.

The four laws of exponents which are most needed in logarithmic computations are:

1. $x^m \times x^n = x^{m+n}$

2. $x^m \div x^n = x^{m-n}$

3. $(x^m)^n = x^{mn}$

4. $\sqrt[n]{x^m} = x^{m/n}$

We shall now express these laws in logarithmic form.

1. *The logarithm of a product is equal to the sum of the logarithms of the factors.*

PROOF: Let $\qquad\log_a M = m$ and $\log_a N = n.$

Then $\qquad\qquad M = a^m$ and $N = a^n.$

$$MN = a^{m+n}.$$

In logarithmic form, $\log_a(MN) = m + n.$

By substitution, $\qquad\log_a(MN) = \log_a M + \log_a N.$

2. *The logarithm of a quotient is equal to the logarithm of the dividend minus the logarithm of the divisor.*

PROOF: Let $\qquad\log_a M = m$ and $\log_a N = n.$

Then $\qquad\qquad M = a^m$ and $N = a^n.$

$$M/N = a^{m-n}.$$

In logarithmic form, $\log_a(M/N) = m - n.$

By substitution, $\qquad\log_a(M/N) = \log_a M - \log_a N.$

3. *The logarithm of a power of a number is equal to the exponent times the logarithm of the number.*

PROOF: Let $\qquad\log_a M = m.$

Then $\qquad\qquad M = a^m.$

Then $\qquad\qquad M^n = a^{mn}.$

In logarithmic form, $\quad\log_a(M^n) = mn.$

By substitution, $\qquad\log_a(M^n) = (\log_a M)\, n = n\log_a M.$

4. *The logarithm of a root of a number is equal to the logarithm of the number divided by the index of the root.*

PROOF: Let $\qquad\log_a M = m.$

Then $\qquad\qquad M = a^m.$

$$\sqrt[n]{M} = a^{m/n}.$$

In logarithmic form, $\quad\log_a \sqrt[n]{M} = \dfrac{m}{n}.$

By substitution, $\qquad\log_a \sqrt[n]{M} = \dfrac{\log_a M}{n} = \dfrac{1}{n}\log_a M.$

Computing with Logarithms [A]

When working with logarithms, you should always remember that logarithms are exponents, and that the properties of logarithms are the laws of exponents expressed in different form.

Now use pencil and paper to follow the solutions to Examples 1–4, working each step yourself.

EXAMPLE 1. Multiply 38.71 by .0181.

SOLUTION. Let $x =$ the product.
$$x = 38.71 \times .0181$$
Then
$$\log x = \log 38.71 + \log .0181$$

$$\log 38.71 = 1.58782$$
$$\log .0181 = 8.25768 - 10$$
$$\overline{\log x = 9.84550 - 10}$$
$$x = .7006$$
Then
$$38.71 \times .0181 = .7006.$$

The mantissa .84550 is halfway between the mantissas .84547 and .84553. At this time we choose .84547 because its antilog is an even number. The product is given to four significant figures.

EXAMPLE 2. Divide 118.6 by 94.

SOLUTION. Let
$$x = 118.6 \div 94.$$
Then
$$\log x = \log 118.6 - \log 94$$

$$\log 118.6 = 2.07408$$
$$\log 94 = 1.97313$$
$$\overline{\log x = \quad .10095}$$
$$x = 1.262$$
Then
$$118.6 \div 94 = 1.262, \text{ to four significant figures.}$$

EXAMPLE 3. Find the value of $(47.52)^4$.

SOLUTION. Let
$$x = (47.52)^4.$$
Then
$$\log x = 4 \log 47.52$$
$$\log 47.52 = 1.67688$$
$$\log x = 6.70752$$
$$x = 5099000$$
Then
$$47.52^4 = 5,099,000, \text{ to four significant figures.}$$

EXAMPLE 4. Find the value of $\sqrt[5]{786.3}$.

SOLUTION. Let $\qquad\qquad x = \sqrt[5]{786.3}$

Then $\qquad\qquad\quad \log x = \frac{1}{5} \log 786.3$

$$\log 786.3 = 2.89559$$
$$\log x = .57912$$
$$x = 3.794.$$

Then $\qquad\qquad \sqrt[5]{786.3} = 3.794$, correct to four significant figures.

EXERCISES [A]

Compute by logarithms:

1. 2478 × 465	**7.** 931.4³	**13.** 1.07⁸
2. 9.230 × 3.5	**8.** 84.13⁵	**14.** $\sqrt[3]{3.216}$
3. 4728 ÷ 431	**9.** 541.7 × 863.4	**15.** $\sqrt[7]{.4127}$
4. 916.3 ÷ 12.5	**10.** 1000 ÷ 0.525	**16.** .132 × .074
5. $\sqrt{436}$	**11.** .125 ÷ 47.19	**17.** .041 ÷ 20.5
6. $\sqrt[4]{721.6}$	**12.** 3.6 × 4.28	**18.** 640 ÷ 200

Cologarithms [B]

The *cologarithm* (abbreviated colog) of a number is the logarithm of the reciprocal of the number. From the definition,

$$\text{colog } N = \log \frac{1}{N}.$$

Then $\qquad\qquad\qquad \text{colog } N = \log 1 - \log N.$

Since $\quad \log 1 = 0, \qquad \text{colog } N = -\log N.$

Thus, the cologarithm of a number is the negative of the logarithm of the number; and adding the cologarithm of a number is the same as subtracting the logarithm of the number.

To find the cologarithm of a number, we subtract the logarithm of the number from 10.00000 − 10, which is zero.

EXAMPLES.

log 457.7 = 2.66058	log .08903 = 8.94954 − 10
10.00000 − 10	10.00000 − 10
2.66058	8.94954 − 10
colog 457.7 = 7.33942 − 10	colog .08903 = 1.05046

In practice we do the subtractions mentally without writing the 10.00000 − 10. Note that the last digit of the cologarithm can be found by subtracting the last digit of the logarithm from 10 and the others can be found by subtracting the remaining digits of the logarithm from 9.

The advantage of cologarithms can be seen by comparing the two solutions of the following example.

EXAMPLE. Find by logarithms the value of $\dfrac{47.36}{72.89 \times .032}$.

SOLUTION 1

Let $x = \dfrac{47.36}{72.89 \times .032}$.

$$\begin{array}{rl} \log 72.89 = & 1.86267 \\ \log .032 = & 8.50515 - 10 \\ \hline \log \text{product} = & 10.36782 - 10 \end{array}$$

$$\begin{array}{rl} \log 47.36 = & 1.67541 \\ \log \text{product} = & .36782 \\ \hline \log x = & 1.30759 \\ x = & 20.30 \end{array}$$

SOLUTION 2

Let $x = \dfrac{47.36}{72.89 \times .032}$.

$$\begin{array}{rl} \log 47.36 = & 1.67541 \\ \text{colog } 72.89 = & 8.13733 - 10 \\ \text{colog } .032 = & 1.49485 \\ \hline \log x = & 11.30759 - 10 \\ x = & 20.30 \end{array}$$

EXERCISES [B]

1. What is the sign of the cologarithm of a number when the sign of the logarithm of the number is positive? when it is negative?

Find the cologarithms of:

2. 78.19	**4.** .416	**6.** 32841	**8.** .00064
3. 163.4	**5.** .0728	**7.** 12917	**9.** 0.01593

How to Find Logarithms by Interpolation [A]

The logarithms of all numbers having no more than four significant figures can be found directly by Table I. The logarithms of numbers having more than four significant figures can be approximated by interpolation. Study the following examples:

EXAMPLE 1. Find log 52.1639.

SOLUTION. We round off the number so that it has one more digit than is listed in the table. When we use Table I, we round off the number so that it has 5 significant figures. Then 52.1639 becomes 5ₓ2.164. The characteristic is 1.

We shall now approximate the mantissa of 52.164. Since 52164 lies between 52160 and 52170, the mantissa of 52164 lies between the mantissa of 52160 and the mantissa of 52170. When interpolating, we usually omit the decimal points of the numbers.

$$
\begin{array}{ll}
\text{NUMBERS} & \text{MANTISSAS} \\
52170\ldots\ldots & .71742 \\
52164\ldots\ldots & x \qquad 8 \\
52160\ldots\ldots & .71734
\end{array}
$$

Since 52164 is $\frac{4}{10}$ of the way from 52160 to 52170, then x, the mantissa of 52164, is approximately $\frac{4}{10}$ of the way from .71734 to .71742. The tabular difference = .71742 − .71734 = .00008. When writing the tabular difference, we usually omit the decimal point and the zeros following it. In this case, we say that the tabular difference is 8, meaning that it is .00008. Then $x = .71734 + \frac{4}{10}(.00008) = .71734 + .00003 = .71737$. Note that $\frac{4}{10}$ of .00008 is .000032 and that the product is rounded off to 5 decimal places. Then log 52.1639 = 1.71737.

If you understand the discussion above, you are prepared for the following rule:

To Find the Mantissa by Interpolation

1. Round off the number to five significant figures.*
2. Find the mantissa of the number consisting of the first four digits.
3. Multiply $\frac{1}{10}$ of the tabular difference by the fifth digit.
4. Add the results of steps 2 and 3.

EXAMPLE 2. Find log 4.31472.

SOLUTION. 4.31472 rounded off to five significant figures becomes 4.3147. The characteristic is zero.

$$
\begin{array}{ll}
43150\ldots\ldots & .63498 \\
43147\ldots\ldots & x \qquad 10 \\
43140\ldots\ldots & .63488
\end{array}
$$

$$x = .63488 + \tfrac{7}{10}(0.00010) = .63495$$

Then　　　　　　　　log 4.31472 = 0.63495

* When using a four-place table, round off the number to four significant figures.

EXAMPLE 3. Find log .0154765.

SOLUTION. We round off .0154765 and get .015476. The characteristic is
8 − 10.

$$15480\ldots\ldots .18977 \rbrack$$
$$15476\ldots\ldots x \qquad 28$$
$$15470\ldots\ldots .18949 \rbrack$$

$$x = .18949 + \tfrac{6}{10}\,(.00028)$$
$$= .18966$$

Then   log .0154765 = 8.18966 − 10.

EXAMPLE 4. Find log 87.563.

SOLUTION. The characteristic is 1.

$$87570\ldots\ldots .94236 \rbrack$$
$$87563\ldots\ldots x \qquad 5$$
$$87560\ldots\ldots .94231 \rbrack$$

$$x = .94231 + \tfrac{3}{10}\,(.00005)$$
$$= .94232$$

$$\log 87.563 = 1.94232.$$

Since $\tfrac{3}{10}(.00005) = .000015$, you might think that the even number .00002
would be added to .94231. We do not round off the correction to make
it even in such cases but we round off the correction so as to make the
mantissa an even number.

EXERCISES [A]

Find the logarithms of:

1. 42.1463	**5.** 71,864,700	**9.** .461485
2. 7800.4	**6.** 0.043126	**10.** 4.3218
3. 5247.6	**7.** 1914.162	**11.** 9.21045
4. 721.68	**8.** .0841935	**12.** 341.819

How to Find the Antilogarithm by Interpolation [A]

By reversing the procedure of finding the logarithm of a number by
interpolation, we can find the antilogarithm of a number to five significant figures. Study the examples on the following page so that you may
understand the process.

EXAMPLE 1. Find the number whose logarithm is 4.13468.

SOLUTION. The table does not contain the mantissa .13468. The mantissa
.13468 lies between the mantissas .13450 and .13481. The antilogarithm
of .13450 is 1.363 and the antilogarithm of .13481 is 1.364. We ignore
the decimal points of the antilogarithms and add a zero to each one.
Then we prepare the table:

$$\begin{array}{ll} \text{NUMBERS} & \text{MANTISSAS} \\ 13640\ldots\ldots & .13481 \\ x\ldots\ldots & .13468 \quad 31 \\ 13630\ldots\ldots & .13450 \end{array}$$

The tabular difference is 31. The mantissa .13468 is $\frac{18}{31}$ of the way from
.13450 to .13481. Then x, the antilogarithm of .13468, is approximately
$\frac{18}{31}$ of the way from 13630 to 13640.

Then
$$x = 13630 + \tfrac{18}{31}(10)$$
$$x = 13630 + 6$$
$$x = 13636$$

We place the caret, 1ˏ3636.
Since the characteristic is $+4$, we have
$$\text{antilog } 4.13468 = 13636.$$

EXAMPLE 2. Find the antilog 7.27356 − 10.

SOLUTION.
$$\begin{array}{ll} 18780\ldots\ldots & .27370 \\ x\ldots\ldots & .27356 \quad 24 \\ 18770\ldots\ldots & .27346 \end{array}$$
$$x = 18770 + \tfrac{10}{24}(10)$$
$$x = 18774.$$
$$\text{antilog } .27356 = 1.8774.$$

We find the decimal point thus, .001ˏ8774.
Then   antilog 7.27356 − 10 = .0018774.

EXERCISES [A]

Find the antilogarithms of:

1. 1.76608	**5.** 1.30240	**9.** 3.79637
2. 4.02345	**6.** 4.40000	**10.** 2.62965 − 10
3. 7.96876 − 10	**7.** 6.5000 − 10	**11.** 2.06155
4. 4.50238	**8.** 7.99806 − 10	**12.** 3.24680

Computations Involving Interpolation [A]

Without interpolation computations with a five-place table can be made correct to four significant figures. By using interpolation, these computations can be performed correct to five significant figures.

EXAMPLE 1. Multiply 486.73 by .0432.

SOLUTION. Let x = 486.73 × .0432

$$\begin{aligned} \log 486.73 &= 2.68779 \\ \log .0432 &= 8.63548 - 10 \\ \hline \log x &= 1.32277 \\ x &= 21.027 \end{aligned}$$

In this solution, some of the paper work is omitted.

When logarithms are used in computations involving negative numbers, we calculate the results as if all the numbers were positive, and then give the proper signs to the results.

EXAMPLE 2. Divide −81.4 by 765.32.

SOLUTION. Let x = 81.4 ÷ 765.32

$$\begin{aligned} \log 81.4 &= 11.91062 - 10 \\ \log 765.32 &= 2.88384 \\ \hline \log x &= 9.02678 - 10 \\ x &= .10636 \end{aligned}$$

The sign of the quotient is negative. Then
$$(-81.4) \div 765.32 = -.10636.$$
Note that the characteristic of log 81.4 is written 11 − 10 instead of 1 to avoid a negative mantissa in log x.

EXAMPLE 3. Find the positive fourth root of .9463.

SOLUTION. Let $x = \sqrt[4]{.9463}$, or $x^4 = .9463$.
$$\begin{aligned} \log .9463 &= 39.97603 - 40 \\ \log x &= 9.99401 - 10 \\ x &= .9863 \end{aligned}$$
The characteristic of log .9463 is written in the form 39 − 40 instead of 9 − 10 so that its negative part divided by 4 equals −10.

EXERCISES [A]

Compute with logarithms:

1. 476.3 × 814.5
2. 304.7 × 516.2
3. 47.814 ÷ .093
4. −19.36 ÷ 547

5. 276.83 ÷ 5.19265
6. 1971.0 × 3468.2
7. $(-2.138)^3$
8. $(-741.62)^3$

9. $\sqrt[3]{217946}$
10. $(132.4)^5$
11. $\sqrt[5]{4.71862}$
12. $\sqrt[7]{928}$

EXAMPLE 4. Find the value of $\sqrt{\dfrac{819.7 \times 3.26}{481.5}}$.

SOLUTION. It is advisable to estimate the result in any problem. In this example, we estimate the numerator of the fraction to be about 2500 and the value of the fraction to be between 5 and 6. Then the value of the positive root lies between 2 and 3.

Let
$$x = \sqrt{\frac{819.7 \times 3.26}{481.5}}.$$

Then
$$x^2 = \frac{819.7 \times 3.26}{481.5} \text{ and}$$

$$\log x^2 = \log 819.7 + \log 3.26 - \log 481.5$$

$$\begin{aligned}
\log 819.7 &= 2.91365 \\
\log 3.26 &= 0.51322 \\
\hline
&3.42687 \\
\log 481.5 &= 2.68260 \\
\hline
\log x^2 &= .74427 \\
\log x &= .37214 \\
x &= 2.3558
\end{aligned}$$

EXERCISES[A]

Compute with logarithms:

1. $\dfrac{46.3 \times 172.5}{163.4}$

2. $\dfrac{217.6 \times 189.3}{2146.5}$

3. $\sqrt{\dfrac{43.62 \times 97.1}{.0348}}$

4. $\sqrt{\dfrac{761.5 \times 191.3}{7.954}}$

5. $\sqrt[3]{\dfrac{21.489}{48.3}}$

6. $\sqrt[5]{\dfrac{4217.8 \times 0.15}{71.89}}$

7. $\dfrac{1462.3}{\sqrt{8149}}$

8. $\dfrac{\sqrt{721.84}}{\sqrt[3]{49.95}}$

9. $48.3\sqrt{84.73}$

10. $\sqrt{972} \sqrt[3]{51.87}$

11. $\dfrac{\sqrt[3]{.896} \sqrt[5]{5.042}}{\sqrt{75}}$

12. $89.6^{\frac{1}{2}} \times 35.18^{\frac{3}{2}}$

MISCELLANEOUS EXERCISES [A]

1. Given $\log 6 = .77815$, find without using the table: $\log 36$; $\log 216$; $\log 600$; $\log \sqrt{6}$.

2. Given log 8 = .90309, find without using the table: log 2; log 4; log 32; log 16; log 125.

3. Given log 9 = .9542, find: log 300; log 11.11.

4. Given log 2 = .3010, find log 5.

5. Given log 700 = 2.8451, find: log($\frac{1}{7}$); log 343.

6. Given log 12 = 1.0792 and log 4 = .6020, find log 6.

7. The base of a triangle is 11.4 inches and the altitude is 7.6 inches. Find the area if the dimensions are found by measurement. Find the area if the dimensions are exact numbers.

8. Find the area of an equilateral triangle having a side of 18.42 inches.
$$\left(A = \frac{s^2}{4}\sqrt{3}\right)$$

9. Find the side of an equilateral triangle whose area is 225 square inches.

10. Find the area of a triangle whose sides are 51.6, 18.1, and 49.3.
$$A = \sqrt{s(s-a)(s-b)(s-c)} \text{ and } s = \tfrac{1}{2}(a+b+c).$$

11. $t = \pi\sqrt{\dfrac{l}{g}}$. Find t when $\pi = 3.1416$, $g = 32.16$, and $l = 36$.

12. $s = \frac{1}{2}gt^2$ is a formula for falling bodies. Find s when $g = 32.16$ and $t = 9$.

13. H.P. $= \dfrac{TV}{550}$ is a formula giving the horsepower exerted by the propeller of an airplane. In the formula, T is the thrust in pounds and V is the velocity in miles an hour. Find the horsepower exerted by a propeller that has a thrust of 1214 pounds at 180 miles an hour.

14. H.P. $= \dfrac{1.28apv^2}{1100}$ is a formula used in aeronautics. Find H.P. when $p = .002$, $a = 4.5$, and $v = 243.8$.

15. $F = \dfrac{mv^2}{r}$ is a formula for centripetal force. Find F when $m = 186$, $v = 180$, and $r = 145$.

16. Using $F = \dfrac{mv^2}{r}$, find v when $F = 19845$, $m = 1640$, and $r = 80$.

17. Find the capacity in bushels of a granary 12 feet long, 9 feet high, and 5 feet wide. (1 bu. = 2150.42 cu. in.)

18. Find the area of a sphere whose diameter is 21.3 inches. ($A = 4\pi r^2$)

19. Find the cost of painting a spherical water tank 30 feet in diameter at 30 cents a square yard if 8% of the surface is used as the base and is not to be painted.

Exponential Equations [A]

An *exponential equation* is one in which the unknown appears in an exponent. Thus, $3^x = 9$ and $4^{x+2} = 64$ are exponential equations. If x is a rational number, it can often be found by inspection; but if x is an irrational number, we solve for it by logarithms.

EXAMPLE 1. Solve $4^x = 64$.

SOLUTION. We express 64 as a power of 4. Then $4^x = 4^3$ and $x = 3$.

EXAMPLE 2. Solve $5^{-x} = 125$.

SOLUTION. $5^{-x} = 5^3$. Then $-x = 3$ and $x = -3$.

EXAMPLE 3. Solve $6^x = 20$.

SOLUTION. 20 cannot be written as a rational power of 6. So we take the logarithms of both members of the equation $6^x = 20$.

$$x \log 6 = \log 20$$
$$x = \frac{\log 20}{\log 6} = \frac{1.30103}{.77815}$$
$$\log 1.30103 = 10.11428 - 10$$
$$\log .77815 = 9.89106 - 10$$
$$\overline{\log x = 0.22322}$$
$$x = 1.6719$$

EXERCISES [A]

Solve for x:

1. $2^x = 8$
2. $8^x = 64$
3. $5^x = 625$
4. $12^x = 1728$
5. $7^x = 343$

6. $7^{x+1} = 49$
7. $3^{x-1} = 81$
8. $4^{-x} = 16$
9. $6^{-x} = 216$
10. $2^{x-5} = 4$

11. $4^x = 100$
12. $6^x = 575$
13. $\log 2x = 2.18436$
14. $\log x^2 = 3.47913$
15. $2.13^x = 452$

16. $A = p(1 + r)^n$ is the compound-interest formula. In this formula, A = the amount, p = the principal, r = the rate of interest per period, and n = the number of periods.

In how many years will $100 amount to $200 at 4% compounded semiannually? ($A = 200, p = 100$, and $r = .02$. Remember that n is the number of half years.)

17. A $100 E bond cost $75 and matured in 10 years. Find the rate of interest of the bond assuming that interest is compounded every 6 months.

18. How many dollars must be invested in a building and loan association which pays 3% compounded semiannually, to produce a scholarship of $4000 in 10 years?

Change of Base [A]

We sometimes need to find the logarithm of a number to a different base. For example, suppose that we wish to find the logarithm of 60 to the base 2.

Let $$x = \log_2 60$$

Then $$2^x = 60$$

Taking logarithms of both members of the equation to base 10,

$$x \log_{10} 2 = \log_{10} 60.$$

$$x = \frac{\log_{10} 60}{\log_{10} 2} = \frac{1.77815}{.30103}$$

$$x = 5.9070$$

Theorem. *The logarithm of a number* N *to the base* b *is equal to the logarithm of* N *to the base* a *divided by the logarithm of* b *to the base* a.

PROOF: Let $$x = \log_b N$$

Then $$b^x = N$$

$$x \log_a b = \log_a N$$

$$x = \frac{\log_a N}{\log_a b}$$

EXERCISES [A]

Find the logarithms of the following:

1. 10 to the base 4

2. 20 to the base 3

3. 80 to the base 4

4. 100 to the base 5

5. 1000 to the base 100

6. 400 to the base 25

7. 750 to the base 5

8. 10 to the base 2

9. Find the logarithm of 2.71828 to the base 2.71828.

How to Find Logarithms of Trigonometric Functions [A]

Table III starting on page 21 at the end of the book is a five-place table of the logarithms of the sines, cosines, tangents, and cotangents of acute angles. Pages 27 to 48 inclusive give the logarithms of these functions for every minute from 1° to 89°. Because some of the functions change so rapidly when the angles are very small or near 90°, the first six pages of the table give the logarithms for every 10 seconds from 0° to 2° and from 88° to 90°.

Since the sines and cosines of all positive angles less than 90°, the tangents of all positive angles less than 45°, and the cotangents of all angles greater than 45°, up to and including 90°, are less than unity (1), the characteristics of the logarithms of their functions are negative. In order to make the table more compact and save space, the characteristics of the logarithms are printed 10 too large. Therefore −10 must be added to each printed logarithm. For example, the table gives the logarithm of the sine of 24° as 9.60931, whereas the logarithm of the sine of 24° is actually 9.60931 − 10. Excepting on the first six pages of the table, the positive part of the characteristic is printed at the top of the column for reading downward and at the bottom of the column for reading upward. When the characteristics at the top and bottom of a column differ, a bar is used to mark the place of division.

For angles less than 45° we read the number of degrees at the top of the page and the number of minutes in the left-hand column and use the column designations log sin, log cos, log tan, and log ctn. For angles between 45° and 90°, we read the number of degrees at the bottom of the page and the number of minutes in the right-hand column and use the column designations at the bottom.

The following examples should be studied carefully in connection with the table.

EXAMPLE 1. Find log tan 36° 27'.

SOLUTION. We find 36° at the top of page 44. In the first column headed
minute (') of the right half of the page, we find 27. In the column headed
log tan and in the horizontal line with 27 we find 86842. The decimal
point is omitted in the table. We remember that all mantissas are positive
numbers. Then the mantissa is .86842.

We shall now find the characteristic. At the top of the column we find the
positive part of the characteristic, which is 9. We remember that the -10
of the characteristic is not printed.

Then   log tan 36° 27' = 9.86842 $-$ 10.

EXAMPLE 2. Find log sin 52° 18' 20''.

SOLUTION. Table III does not give the logarithms of the functions of angles
measured in seconds, so we must use interpolation to find the approximate
logarithm.

52° 18' 20'' lies between 52° 18' and 52° 19'. Then log sin 52° 18' 20'' lies between log sin 52° 18' and log sin 52° 19'.

We shall first find log sin 52° 19'. We find 52° at the bottom of the left half of
page 45. In the column headed log sin at the bottom and in the horizontal
line with 19 in the minute (') column reading upward, we find 89840. At
the bottom of the log sin column reading upward, we find 9, the positive
part of the characteristic. We remember the negative part, -10. Then
log sin 52° 19' = 9.89840 $-$ 10.

In like manner, we find log sin 52° 18' = 9.89830 $-$ 10.

We shall now approximate the value of log sin 52° 18' 20''. We arrange the
work as follows:

$$
\left.
\begin{array}{r}
\log \sin 52° 19' = 9.89840 \\
60'' \quad \log \sin 52° 18' 20'' = x \\
\log \sin 52° 18' = 9.89830
\end{array}
\right] \quad 10, \text{ tabular difference}
$$

52° 18' 20'' is $\frac{20}{60}$ or $\frac{1}{3}$ the way from 52° 18' to 52° 19'. Then x will be
about $\frac{1}{3}$ the way from 9.89830 $-$ 10 to 9.89840 $-$ 10.

Then $x = 9.89830 + \frac{1}{3}(.00010)$
                        $x = 9.89833$
        log 52° 18' 20'' = 9.89833 $-$ 10.

EXAMPLE 3. Find log cos 13° 33′ 10″.

SOLUTION. log cos 13° 33′ 10″ lies between log cos 13° 33′ and log cos 13° 34′. Since the cofunctions are decreasing functions, the logarithms of the cofunctions decrease as the angles increase. Then log cos 13° 33′ is larger than log cos 13° 34′.

We arrange the work as follows:

$$\left[\begin{array}{c} \quad\quad \log\cos 13°\ 33' = 9.98774 \\ 60'' \quad \log\cos 13°\ 33'\ 10'' = x \\ \quad\quad \log\cos 13°\ 34' = 9.98771 \end{array}\right] 3$$

13° 33′ 10″ is $\frac{1}{6}$ the way from 13° 33′ to 13° 34′. Then x is about $\frac{1}{6}$ the way from 9.98774 to 9.98771.

Then $x = 9.98774 - \frac{1}{6}(.00003) = 9.987735.$

We round off to make the mantissa even, getting 9.98774. We have omitted the −10.

Then   log cos 13° 33′ 10″ = 9.98774 − 10.

EXERCISES

A

Find the value of:

1. log sin 10° 30′	**6.** log cos 41° 10′	**11.** log tan 45°
2. log tan 23° 50′	**7.** log cos 81° 50′	**12.** log ctn 45°
3. log sin 48° 40′	**8.** log cos 10° 32′	**13.** log ctn 12° 40′ 45″
4. log tan 72° 35′	**9.** log sin 35° 17′ 10″	**14.** log cos 24° 18′ 36″
5. log ctn 36° 45′	**10.** log cos 72° 41′ 30″	**15.** log sin 56° 38′ 24″

EXAMPLE 4. [B] Find log sec 18° 34′ 15″.

SOLUTION. The logarithms of the secants and cosecants are not given in Table III, but their values can be found from the logarithms of their reciprocal functions.

Since $\sec 18°\ 34'\ 15'' = \dfrac{1}{\cos 18°\ 34'\ 15''},$

$$\log \sec 18°\ 34'\ 15'' = \log 1 - \log \cos 18°\ 34'\ 15''$$

$$\begin{array}{r} \log 1 = 10.00000 - 10 \\ \underline{\log \cos 18°\ 34'\ 15'' = 9.97678 - 10} \\ \log \sec 18°\ 34'\ 15'' = .02322 \end{array}$$

B

Find the value of:

16. log sec 20° 13'

17. log sec 40° 24'

18. log csc 34° 34' 34"

19. log csc 72° 23' 10"

20. log sec 81° 50' 30"

21. log csc 15° 22' 45"

Using the part of Table III for small angles, find:

22. log sin 41' 10"

23. log sin 20' 8"

24. log cos 53' 15"

25. log cos 1° 4' 10"

26. log ctn 88° 30'

27. log ctn 89° 9' 50"

28. log tan 1° 18' 15"

29. log tan 27' 30"

30. log sin 8' 45"

31. log cos 1° 59' 15"

32. log tan 50' 35"

33. log ctn 88° 56' 35"

How to Find the Angles When the Logarithms of Their Functions Are Known [A]

When the logarithm of a function of an angle is given, we can find the angle by Table III.

EXAMPLE 1. Find A if log sin $A = 9.37237 - 10$.

SOLUTION. We find 9.37237 in the log sin column of Table III. The number 37237 is in the same horizontal line as 13° 38' in the minute column.

Then $A = 13° 38'$.

When the logarithm of a function of an angle is not given in the table, the angle can be found by interpolation.

EXAMPLE 2. Find A if log cos $A = 9.46590 - 10$.

SOLUTION.
$$\begin{bmatrix} & \log \cos 73° 0' = 9.46594 & \\ 60'' & \log \cos A = 9.46590 & 42 \\ & \log \cos 73° 1' = 9.46552 & \end{bmatrix}$$

9.46590 is $\frac{38}{42}$ of the way from 9.46552 to 9.46594.

Then $\frac{38}{42}$ of 60" = 54" and 73° 1' − 54" = 73° 0' 6".

Then $A = 73° 0' 6"$.

EXERCISES [A]

Find the value of A *when:*

1. $\log \sin A = 9.65356 - 10$
2. $\log \tan A = 9.26403 - 10$
3. $\log \cos A = 9.85815 - 10$
4. $\log \operatorname{ctn} A = 9.95901 - 10$
5. $\log \sin A = 9.45340 - 10$
6. $\log \tan A = 9.40488 - 10$

7. $\log \cos A = 9.99275 - 10$
8. $\log \operatorname{ctn} A = 9.35250 - 10$
9. $\log \sin A = 9.94350 - 10$
10. $\log \tan A = 9.30220 - 10$
11. $\log \cos A = 9.94405 - 10$
12. $\log \operatorname{ctn} A = 9.71940 - 10$

CHAPTER REVIEW

Express in scientific notation:

1. 72600
2. 47.12
3. 0.0016
4. 0.00049
5. 240,000
6. 193,000,000

7. Round off to three significant figures:

    a. 1764
    b. 8145
    c. 84.650
    d. 7.9314
    e. 42.58
    f. 183.5

Exercises 8–13 deal with approximate numbers. Perform the indicated operations:

8. $1.4 + 3.25 + 0.31$
9. $196.4 \div 71.35$
10. 1.42×1.8
11. $28.4 \div .25$
12. $18.0 \div 2.5$
13. $3.62 + 8.1$

Give the characteristics of the logarithms of the following numbers:

14. 425
15. 6.381
16. .0042
17. 200
18. 563.9
19. 22
20. 0.005
21. 0.716
22. 320
23. 93000
24. .7298
25. 100

Perform the indicated operations, using logarithms:

26. 27.8×1.36
27. $456.7 \div 1.839$
28. $(1.1472)^5$
29. 193.2×84.61
30. $\sqrt[6]{3429.8}$
31. $(4.712)^7$
32. $34.7 \div 9.28$
33. $\sqrt[5]{789.63}$
34. 1.09^{20}

35. $\dfrac{147.6 \times 2.38}{421}$

36. $\dfrac{91.2 \times 36.4}{189 \times .092}$

37. $\dfrac{-34.7 \times 6.42}{-93.8}$

38. $\dfrac{27.9^3 \times \sqrt[3]{35.27}}{420}$

39. $\dfrac{.652 \times 18.4}{-\sqrt[3]{349}}$

40. $\dfrac{0.043\sqrt{7926}}{\sqrt[4]{7900}}$

41. Given log 4 = .60206, find: log 2; log 16; log ($\frac{1}{4}$).

42. Given log 9 = .9542, find: log 3; log 27; log (1.1111).

43. Given log x = .2574, find: log x^2; log $\sqrt{x}$.

44. Given log 2 = .3010, find: log 5; log 500.

Solve:

45. $2^x = 16$

46. $3^{x-1} = 81$

47. $x^{1.7} = .346$

48. $8^x = 12^{x-1}$

49. $3^{2x+1} = 2187$

50. $4^x = .3649$

51. What is the name of the fractional part of a logarithm? of the integral part of the logarithm?

52. What is the cologarithm of 2 to the base 10?

53. If log x = a and log y = b, find in terms of a and b the following:

log(xy); log $\dfrac{x}{y}$; log $\dfrac{x^2}{y}$; log $\dfrac{x}{y^2}$.

54. $s = \frac{1}{2}gt^2$. Express log t in terms of s and g.

Find the values of the following:

55. log sin 18° 27′ 5″

56. log cos 27° 13′ 10″

57. log tan 10° 40′ 40″

58. log ctn 17° 4′ 45″

A. Devane

**Architecture in New York City, with the Empire State
Building in the Background**

Before work can begin on the construction of a large building,
scores of architects and draftsmen must prepare designs, drawings, and
specifications for all parts of the building. This work could not be done
without the help of mathematics

CHAPTER III

THE SLIDE RULE (*Optional*)

Δ

The Parts of the Slide Rule

The *slide rule* is an instrument used to solve problems involving multiplication, division, squares, cubes, square roots, and cube roots of numbers. It performs multiplication of numbers by mechanically adding their logarithms, and division by mechanically subtracting the logarithm of the divisor from the logarithm of the dividend. It squares numbers by doubling their logarithms, and finds the square roots of numbers by halving their logarithms.

A slide rule consists of three parts,—the fixed part or *rule* proper, the *slide*, and the *runner*. The rule of the slide rule shown here contains three logarithmic scales, A, D, and K. The slide contains three logarithmic scales, B, C, and CI, on its face and two logarithmic scales, S and T, on its back.

Scales C and D, which are identical, are used in multiplication and division; scales A and D are used in squaring numbers and in finding their square roots. The K scale is used with the D scale in cubing numbers and in finding their cube roots. The CI scale gives the reciprocals of numbers on the C scale. Scale S on the back of the slide is used to find the sines of angles, and scale T on the back of the slide is used to find the tangents of angles. The simplest slide rule (the Mannheim slide rule) has only six logarithmic scales,—A, B, C, D, S, and T. It may have the scale L, which is the scale of equal parts.

Polyphase Slide Rule (Mannheim Type)

Keuffel & Esser Co.

The runner is often made of glass and metal with a hairline on the surface of the glass. The hairline is used to align the scales.

Observe that each of the scales A and B, which are identical, consists of two identical parts and that each part is half of the scale C or scale D.

The Logarithmic Scale

Before we learn how to read a logarithmic scale, let us see how one is made. Below is a table of logarithms (correct to two decimal places) of the integers 1 to 10 inclusive.

Numbers	1	2	3	4	5	6	7	8	9	10
Logarithms	0	.30	.48	.60	.70	.78	.85	.90	.95	1

On a strip of paper draw any convenient line segment AL. We chose the segment below, which is 10 centimeters long.

Since log 1 = 0 and log 10 = 1, we label A with 1 and L with 10. Remember that AL is one unit long. Next we plot the logarithms of the other numbers of the table. For example, the logarithm of 2 is represented by AB, which is .30 of AL, that is, 3 centimeters. Then AB represents log 2, AC represents log 3, etc.

AL is called a *logarithmic scale*. Do you see that a logarithmic scale is similar to Table I in that it gives the logarithms of numbers from 1 to 10?

Suppose that we wish to find log 40 on our logarithmic scale. We know that log 40 = log 10 + log 4. Now log 10 = AL and log 4 = AD. Then log 40 = $AL + AD$. Since AL = 1 and AD is a fraction less than 1, we know that AL is the characteristic of the logarithm of 40 and AD is the mantissa. We use the logarithmic scale, just as we use Table I, to find the mantissas of the logarithms of numbers. Then AD on the scale represents any number of the form 4×10^n, n being an integer.

To simplify operations on a slide rule the number 10 is replaced by the number 1. Then the scale starts with 1 and ends with 1. Each of the two 1's which are at the ends of the scale is called an *index* (plural *indices*). We denote the left index by 1 L and the right index by 1 R. Can you explain why 1 R always represents 10 times the number represented by 1 L?

How to Read a Logarithmic Scale

Let us learn how to read scale D, which is identical to scale C. After you have learned how to read one of the scales, the reading of the other scales will not be difficult.

Using the picture of the slide rule on page 89, you can see that scale D is divided into 9 unequal parts, or units. Unit *one* extends from large 1 to large 2, unit *two* from large 2 to large 3, and so on. Let us see how each of these units is divided.

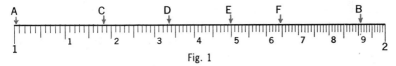

Fig. 1

Unit *one* (Fig. 1) starts at large 1 and ends at large 2. It is divided into 10 unequal parts, the division points being numbered by the smaller digits 1, 2, 3, etc. Each of these parts represents 0.1 of a unit. Each of these parts (0.1 units) is divided into 10 unequal parts, each of which represents 0.01 of a unit. In Fig. 1, the A reading is 1, the B reading is 19, the C reading is 118, the D reading is 133, the E reading is 1494, and the F reading is 164.

Unit *two* extends from large 2 to large 3. It is the same as unit *one* except that each of the smallest parts represents 0.02 of a unit instead of 0.01 of a unit and the subdivisions are not numbered.

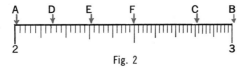

Fig. 2

In unit *two* (Fig. 2) the A reading is 2, the B reading is 3, the C reading is 28, the D reading is 214, the E reading is 23, and the F reading is 249.

Unit *three* is like *two* except that the divisions are smaller.

Each of the units *four, five, six, seven, eight,* and *nine* is divided into ten parts, each of which is divided into two parts. Each of the smallest parts of these units represents 0.05 of a unit.

How to Add and Subtract Numbers with Two Rulers

Multiplication is performed with the slide rule by adding the logarithms of the numbers and division is performed by subtracting the logarithm of the divisor from the logarithm of the dividend.

To understand better how we add and subtract logarithms with the slide rule, let us see how we can use two rulers to add and subtract numbers.

At this point you should make two rulers marked off in centimeters as suggested below. Heavy paper or cardboard can be used. When the rulers are completed we are ready to continue.

| C 0 | 1 | 2 | 3 | 4 | 5 | 6 | 7 | 8 | 9 | 10 |

| 0 D | 1 | 2 | 3 | 4 | 5 | 6 | 7 | 8 | 9 | 10 |

Now suppose that we wish to add the number 5 to the number 4. We place the two rulers C and D together (as shown below) so that the zero mark of C is opposite the 4 mark on ruler D. Then opposite 5 on scale C read 9 on scale D. Then the sum of 4 and 5 is 9. Without moving

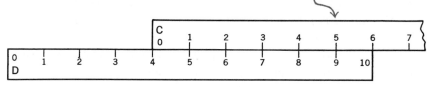

the scales we can add other numbers to 4. For example, to add 3 to 4, find the sum on scale D opposite 3 on scale C.

If the scales were marked off in millimeters, we could add decimal numbers; for example, we could add the numbers 3.4 and 5.2 and read 8.6.

The next setting of the rulers shows the addition of 7 and 3, with 10 as the sum.

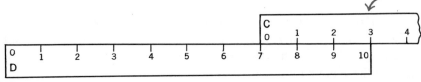

Now suppose that we wish to add 8 to 4. The number 8 on the C scale extends beyond the D scale. We can use two D scales as shown in the diagram below. The 8 on the C scale is opposite 2 on the right-hand D scale. From the figure $4 + 8 = 10 + 2$.

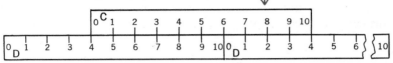

Now suppose that the left D scale were removed and that we wished to add 8 to 4 by using only one of the D scales, say the right one. We place the 10 of the C scale opposite the 4 of the D scale and read 2 of the D scale opposite the 8 of the C scale. Then we remember to add 10 to the 2 to get 12.

Thus, when the number on scale C to be added extends beyond the D scale, place the right end (1 R) of the C scale opposite the addend on the D scale. Then opposite the number on the C scale to be added find the last digit of the sum on the D scale.

To subtract one number from another by the use of rulers, we reverse the process of addition.

For example, to subtract 3 from 7, we set 3 of the C scale opposite the 7 of the D scale. Then opposite the zero of the C scale, we read 4 on the D scale. Then $7 - 3 = 4$. Without changing the positions of the scales, we see that $5 - 1 = 4, 8 - 4 = 4, 9 - 5 = 4$, and $10 - 6 = 4$.

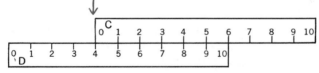

How to Multiply with a Slide Rule

As you know, two numbers are multiplied by adding their logarithms. You should use your slide rule to follow the solutions of Examples 1, 2, and 3.

EXAMPLE 1. Multiply 3 by 2.

SOLUTION. Place 1 L (left index) of scale C above 3 of scale D. Use the hairline of the runner to find the number of scale D that is below 2 of scale C. The number is 6. Then $3 \times 2 = 6$.

EXAMPLE 2. $24 \times 18 = ?$

SOLUTION. Place 1 L of scale C above 24 of scale D. Use the hairline to find the number on scale D that is below 18 on scale C. It is 432. The digit 2 is estimated. Since 18 is more than 10 and less than 20, the product is more than 240 and less than 480; that is, the product has three digits to the left of the decimal point. Then $24 \times 18 = 432$.

EXAMPLE 3. $74.51 \times 4.60 = ?$

SOLUTION. We round off 74.51 to three significant figures, thus, 74.5. If we place 1 L of scale C over 745 of scale D, the 460 of scale C extends beyond scale D. In such a case we place 1 R (right index) of scale C over 745 of scale D. As before, we find the number of scale D that is below 460 of scale C. The number is 343. By inspection, the product has three digits to the left of the decimal point. Then $74.51 \times 4.60 = 343$. In general, the results are only accurate to three significant figures.

EXERCISES

Multiply, using the slide rule:

1. 7×2	**4.** 65×25	**7.** 36×27	**10.** 2.38×6.47
2. 5×6	**5.** 16×46	**8.** 72×84	**11.** 84.3×79.24
3. 5×40	**6.** 75×63	**9.** 324×647	**12.** 641×2137

How to Divide with a Slide Rule

Division is performed by subtracting the logarithm of the divisor from the logarithm of the dividend. Study the next three examples by following each step with your slide rule.

EXAMPLE 1. $60 \div 4 = ?$

SOLUTION. Place the 4 of scale C above 60 of scale D. Then find the number on scale D that is opposite 1 L of scale C. The number is 15. We find the position of the decimal point by inspection.

EXAMPLE 2. Divide 85 by 20.

SOLUTION. Place 20 of scale C above 85 of scale D. Then find the number of scale D that is opposite 1 L of scale C. It is 425. By inspection, $85 \div 20 = 4.25$.

EXAMPLE 3. Divide 364 by 4.748.

SOLUTION. We round off 4.748 to three significant figures and get 4.75. When 4.75 of scale C is placed over 364 of scale D, the 1L of scale C extends beyond scale D. So we find the number of scale D that is opposite 1R of scale C. The number is 766. By inspection, the quotient has two integral digits. Then $364 \div 4.748 = 76.6$.

EXERCISES

Divide, using the slide rule:

1. $96 \div 6$	**4.** $775 \div 25$	**7.** $24.7 \div 45$	**10.** $914.3 \div 54$
2. $48 \div 8$	**5.** $780 \div 20$	**8.** $790 \div 4.15$	**11.** $8392 \div 51.2$
3. $64 \div 16$	**6.** $324 \div 18$	**9.** $7.25 \div 32.6$	**12.** $124.8 \div 9.2$

How to Square a Number with the Slide Rule

Scales A and D are used to square a number.

EXAMPLE 1. Square 75.

SOLUTION. Find 75 on scale D. Opposite it on scale A read 5620. By inspection 75^2 has four integral digits. Then $75^2 = 5620$.

EXAMPLE 2. Square 26.1.

SOLUTION. Find 261 on scale D. Opposite it on scale A read 681. By inspection, the square has three integral digits. Then $26.1^2 = 681$.

How to Find the Square Root with the Slide Rule

We use scales A and D. Study the two examples.

EXAMPLE 1. Find the value of $\sqrt{784}$.

SOLUTION. Point off the number as you do when finding the square root arithmetically, thus: $\overline{7}\,\overline{84}$. The first group, 7, has one digit. When the first group has one digit, use the left half of scale A. Find 784 on the left half of scale A. Opposite it on scale D we find 28. Then $\sqrt{784} = 28$.

EXAMPLE 2. $\sqrt{56.7} = ?$

SOLUTION. We point off the number thus: $\overline{56}.\overline{70}$. The first group, 56, has two digits. When the first group has two digits, we use the right half of scale A. Then we find 567 on the right half of scale A. Opposite it on scale D is 753. The root has one integral digit. Then $\sqrt{56.7} = 7.53$.

EXERCISES

Square the following:

1. 9	**3.** 7	**5.** 64	**7.** 29.3
2. 8	**4.** 12	**6.** 53	**8.** 71.6

Find the positive square roots of the following:

9. 625	**12.** 1225	**15.** 10	**18.** 4.84
10. 784	**13.** 2025	**16.** 8	**19.** 4.50
11. 169	**14.** 1296	**17.** 125	**20.** 514

How to Solve Proportions with the Slide Rule

The solution of a simple proportion involves one multiplication and one division. Thus, the solution of $\dfrac{x}{a} = \dfrac{b}{c}$, which is $x = \dfrac{ab}{c}$, can be obtained by multiplying a by b and dividing the product by c; or it can be obtained by dividing a by c, and multiplying the quotient by b; or it can be found by dividing b by c and multiplying the quotient by a.

EXAMPLE 1 Solve $\dfrac{x}{6} = \dfrac{16}{64}$ with the slide rule.

SOLUTION 1. $x = \dfrac{6 \times 16}{64}$. Align 1 R on C with 1 R on D. Opposite 6 on D set 1 L on C. Move the hairline to 16 on C. Move 64 on C to the hairline. Opposite 1 L on C read 15 on D. We estimate the decimal point. Then $x = 1.5$.

SOLUTION 2. $x = \dfrac{6}{64} \times 16$. Opposite 6 on D place 64 on C. Opposite 16 on C read 15 on D. Then $x = 1.5$.
Is this solution shorter than Solution 1? A similar solution is $x = \frac{16}{64} \times 6$.

SOLUTION 3. We leave the proportion $\dfrac{x}{6} = \dfrac{16}{64}$ as it is. We use scale C for the numerators and scale D for the denominators. We start with the fraction $\frac{16}{64}$, which does not contain x. Opposite 64 on D set 16 on C. Then opposite 6 on D read 15 on C. Then $x = 1.5$.

Do you agree that Solution 3 is the one we should use? The following directions are for this method.

To Solve a Proportion for x with the Slide Rule:

1. Use scale C for the numerators and scale D for the denominators.
2. Using the fraction not containing x, align the reading on scale C for the numerator with the reading on scale D for the denominator.
3. a. If x is in the numerator, read its value on scale C* opposite the reading of its denominator in scale D.
   b. If x is in the denominator, read its value on scale D* opposite the reading of its numerator on scale C.

EXAMPLE 2. Solve $\dfrac{x}{45} = \dfrac{35}{83}$.

SOLUTION. Set 35 on C opposite 83 on D. Opposite 45 on D read 19 on C. By inspection, the decimal point follows the 9. Then $x = 19.0$.

EXAMPLE 3. Solve $\dfrac{3}{10} = \dfrac{14}{x}$.

SOLUTION. Opposite 10 (1 R) on D set 3 on C. Opposite 14 on C read 467 on D. We estimate x to be about 50. Then $x = 46.7$.

EXAMPLE 4. Solve $\dfrac{7}{x} = \dfrac{18}{46}$.

SOLUTION. Place 18 on C opposite 46 on D. Since 7 on C extends beyond the D scale we interchange 1 L and 1 R of C by placing the hairline on 1 L of C and then moving 1 R of C to the hairline. Now opposite 7 on C we read 179 on D. We place the decimal point by inspection. $x = 17.9$.

EXERCISES

Solve for x, *using the slide rule:*

1. $\dfrac{x}{8} = \dfrac{3}{5}$

2. $\dfrac{x}{7} = \dfrac{2}{3}$

3. $\dfrac{x}{74} = \dfrac{63}{18}$

4. $\dfrac{18}{x} = \dfrac{19}{32}$

5. $\dfrac{27}{x} = \dfrac{43}{64}$

6. $\dfrac{x}{18.1} = \dfrac{13.6}{48.2}$

7. $\dfrac{4.63}{18.9} = \dfrac{4.28}{x}$

8. $\dfrac{134}{49} = \dfrac{x}{152}$

9. $\dfrac{15}{x} = \dfrac{36}{45}$

* If necessary, interchange 1 L and 1 R. See Example 4.

How to Use the Slide Rule in a Series of Operations

The method of using the slide rule in a series of multiplications and divisions will be illustrated by an example.

EXAMPLE. Find the value of $\dfrac{7.62 \times 68.2 \times 1.84}{4.14 \times 25.6}$.

SOLUTION. We approximate the answer to be about 9. We move the runner to 762 on scale D. We move scale C until 414 is opposite 762 on scale D. We move the runner to 1L on scale C.

We now multiply by 682. Since 682 on scale C is to the right of 1R on scale D, we interchange 1L and 1R of scale C. We move the runner to 682 on scale C. The runner gives the product on scale D.

Now we divide by 256. Move 256 of scale C to the runner. Move the runner to 1R on scale C. It gives the last quotient on scale D.

Finally we multiply by 184. Move 1L of scale C to the runner. Then opposite 184 on scale C we read 902 on scale D.

Then $\dfrac{7.62 \times 68.2 \times 1.84}{4.14 \times 25.6} = 9.02.$

EXERCISES

Using the slide rule, find the value of x *in the following:*

1. $x = \dfrac{63.7 \times 18.9}{7.4 \times 14.1}$

2. $x = \dfrac{29.5 \times 8.6}{32.5}$

3. $x = \dfrac{28.3 \times 34.8 \times 97.1}{4.22 \times 17.5}$

4. $x = \dfrac{1.95 \times 1.47 \times 19.1}{84.1 \times 75.9}$

5. $x = \dfrac{18.6 \times 18.1^2}{36.2}$

6. $x = \dfrac{1.9^2 \times 4.32}{5.4}$

7. $x = \sqrt{\dfrac{4.3 \times 7.8}{1.6}}$

8. $x = \sqrt{\dfrac{32.4 \times 19.3}{0.06}}$

9. $x = \sqrt{\dfrac{17.1 \times 3.2 \times 1.9}{2.7}}$

10. $x = 189.6 \sqrt{74.3 \times 16.3}$

How to Find the Sine and Cosine on the Slide Rule

When we remove the slide from the rule and turn it over, we find that the under side of the slide has a scale marked S and one marked T. Scale S is a scale of sines and scale T is a scale of tangents. Now turn the rule over and observe that each end of it has two notches and that each notch has a line across it. Each of these lines corresponds to terminal index 1 of the A and D scales.

There are two methods of finding the sine on the slide rule. You should learn each of them.

First Method. (Scales A and S.) If necessary, remove the slide, turn it over, and insert it in the rule so that scales A, S, T, and D face upwards. Align the terminal indices. This method requires no movement of the slide. The sines are found on scale A opposite the angles on scale S.

EXAMPLE 1. Find sin 36°.

SOLUTION. Opposite 36 on scale S, we find 588 on scale A. Since 588 is on the right half of scale A, no zero is inserted between the decimal point and the 5. Then sin 36° = .588.

EXAMPLE 2. Find sin 4°.

SOLUTION. Opposite 4 on scale S, we read 698 on scale A. Since 698 is on the left half of scale A, we insert a zero between the decimal point and the first significant figure. Then sin 4° = .0698. If the angle is 34' or less, we insert two zeros between the decimal point and the first significant figure.

Second Method. (Scales B and S.) When using this method scale S is on the back of the rule, and scales A, B, C, and D face up. Now turn the slide rule over so that scale S is uppermost.

Pull out the slide to the right until the angle on scale S is opposite the line in the notch. Then turn the rule over so that it is face upwards. Opposite 1 R on scale A read the sine on scale B. If the reading is taken from the right half of scale B, the decimal point precedes the first significant figure of the reading; and if the reading is taken from the left half of scale B, a zero is inserted between the decimal point and the first significant figure of the reading. If the angle is 34' or less, insert two zeros.

EXAMPLE 3. Find sin 50°.

SOLUTION. Pull the slide to the right until 50 on scale S is opposite the line in the notch. Opposite 1 R on scale A, we read 766 on scale B. Since 766 is on the right half of scale B, no zero is inserted between the decimal point and the 7. Then sin 50° = .766.

EXAMPLE 4. Find sin 5° 30′.

SOLUTION. Pull out the slide until 5° 30′ is opposite the line in the notch. (If the sine scale is graduated in tenths of degrees, pull out the slide until 5.5° is opposite the line in the notch.) Turn the rule face upwards. Opposite 1 R on scale A read 958 on scale B. Since 958 is on the left half of scale B, a zero is inserted between the decimal point and the 9. Then sin 5° 30′ = .0958.

To find the cosine of an angle on the slide rule, find the sine of the complement of the angle. Thus cos 63° = sin (90° − 63°) = sin 27° = .454

EXERCISES

Using the slide rule, find the sine of each of the following angles:

1. 72°	**3.** 15° 30′	**5.** 15° 20′	**7.** 40° 10′
2. 13°	**4.** 1°	**6.** 50° 20′	**8.** 87° 40′

Using the slide rule, find the cosine of each of the following angles:

9. 70°	**11.** 18°	**13.** 77° 20′	**15.** 44° 50′
10. 55°	**12.** 24°	**14.** 80° 10′	**16.** 19° 40′

EXAMPLE 5. Find the value of 40 × sin 25° 30′.

SOLUTION. Place scale S on back of rule. Pull out the slide so that 25° 30′ on scale S aligns with the line in the notch in the right end of the rule. Turn the rule over so that scales A, B, C, and D are uppermost. We shall now add logarithms on scale B. Opposite 40 on scale A, find 172 on scale B. Then 40 × sin 25° 30′ = 17.2.

EXERCISES

Find the following products:

1. 10 × sin 18°	**3.** 18 cos 35°	**5.** 75 sin 10° 30′
2. 25 × sin 20° 10′	**4.** 60 cos 22° 45′	**6.** 44 cos 63° 45′

How to Find the Tangent and Cotangent on the Slide Rule

To find the tangent of an angle on the slide rule, scale T on the back of the slide is used. It can be used with either scale C or scale D. The method of finding the tangent is similar to that used in finding the sine. Scales C and D give the tangents of angles on scale T. In each reading of a tangent on scale C or D a decimal point precedes the first significant figure. For angles less than about 6° the sines and tangents are almost identical. They are identical to three decimal places. Since the sine is more accurate for small angles, it should be used for angles less than 6 degrees. Note that tan 6° and sin 6° are about .105. The two methods for finding the tangent on the slide rule will now be shown.

First Method. Pull out the slide, if necessary, and insert it in the rule so that scales S and T are on the face of the rule. Align the terminal indices of A, S, T, and D. Then opposite the angle on scale T read the tangent on scale D.

EXAMPLE 1. Find tan 12° 20′ on the slide rule.

SOLUTION. Insert the slide in the rule so that the indices of scale T align with the indices of scale D. Then opposite 12° 20′ on scale T read 219 on scale D. Then tan 12° 20′ = .219.

EXAMPLE 2. Find tan 5°.

SOLUTION. Find sin 5°. Then tan 5° = sin 5° = .0872.

Second Method. In this method the scales S and T are on the back of the rule. The rule is placed face down with scales S and T uppermost. The slide is drawn to the right until the angle on scale T is opposite the line in the notch. Then the rule is placed face upwards. Opposite 1R on scale D we read the tangent on scale C.

EXAMPLE 3. Find tan 34° on the slide rule.

SOLUTION. For this method scale T is on the back of the rule. Place the rule so that its face is down. Pull out the slide to the right until 34 on scale T aligns with the mark in the notch. Now turn the rule to have its face upward. Opposite 1 R scale D read 675 on scale C. Then tan 34° = .675.

EXERCISES

Using the slide rule find the tangents of the following angles:

1. 24°	**3.** 15° 10′	**5.** 7° 40′	**7.** 45°
2. 40°	**4.** 20° 20′	**6.** 38° 10′	**8.** 42° 40′

Using the sine scale find the tangents of:

9. 4°	**10.** 2° 20′	**11.** 5° 20′	**12.** 1°

Scale T contains the tangents of angles only as far as 45°. Note that tan 45° = 1 and that log tan 45° = 0.

Since $\tan x = \operatorname{ctn}(90° - x) = \dfrac{1}{\tan(90° - x)}$, we can find the tangent of an angle greater than 45° by finding the reciprocal of the tangent of its complement. The decimal point is found by inspection.

To find the cotangent of an angle, we find the tangent of its complement.

EXAMPLE 4. Find tan 70°.

SOLUTION. $\tan 70° = \operatorname{ctn} 20° = \dfrac{1}{\tan 20°}$. Using the slide rule, we find that $\tan 20° = .364$. Then $\tan 70° = \dfrac{1}{.364} = 2.75$. (We estimate the position of the decimal point as follows: tan 45° = 1 and tan 30° is about $\frac{1}{2}$. Therefore tan 20° is about $\frac{1}{3}$. Therefore $\dfrac{1}{\tan 20°}$ is about 3.)

EXERCISES

Find the tangents of the following angles:

1. 85°	**3.** 50°	**5.** 80° 20′	**7.** 48°
2. 75°	**4.** 65°	**6.** 64° 30′	**8.** 67°

EXAMPLE 5. Find the value of 180 × tan 26°.

SOLUTION. We use the second method to find tan 26° and then we add logarithms on scale C. To do this, we align 26° on scale T with the mark in the notch. Then we move the slide to interchange 1 L and 1 R. Then opposite 180 on scale D we read 879 on scale C. We estimate the position of the decimal point to be between the 7 and the 9. Then we have the value 180 × tan 26° = 87.9.

EXERCISES

Find the value of:

1. 45 tan 34°	**3.** 15 tan 15°	**5.** 20 ctn 75°
2. 250 tan 40°	**4.** 45 tan 52°	**6.** 30 ctn 41°

7. 80 ÷ tan 55°. *Hint.* 80 ÷ tan 55° = 80 tan 35°.

CHAPTER REVIEW

1. Is the sine scale a logarithmic scale?

2. Which scale is identical to the A scale?

3. Which scale is identical to the C scale?

4. Which scales are used for finding squares and square roots?

5. Which part of a logarithm is measured on the slide rule?

6. Why does the T scale contain only angles from 0° to 45°?

Use the slide rule to find:

7. sin 28°   **9.** tan 15°   **11.** sin 65°

8. cos 34°   **10.** ctn 80°   **12.** cos 81°

Simplify the following, using the slide rule:

13. $79.6 \div 13.4$ **15.** 8.4×9.7 **17.** 49^2 **19.** $\sqrt{473}$

14. $296.3 \div 4.7$ **16.** 93.1×25 **18.** 53^2 **20.** $\sqrt{84.02}$

Solve for x:

21. $\dfrac{x}{7} = \dfrac{23}{4}$ **22.** $\dfrac{x}{18} = \dfrac{13}{25}$ **23.** $\dfrac{27}{45} = \dfrac{10}{x}$

A Skilled Machinist
Trigonometry is useful to men in this occupation

CHAPTER IV

SOLUTION OF RIGHT TRIANGLES BY LOGARITHMS

Δ

In Chapter I we used Table X, which contains a four-place table of natural functions, to solve right triangles.

For example, the side a of $\triangle ABC$ is found by the use of Table X as follows:

$$\sin A = \frac{a}{c} \text{ and } a = c \sin A.$$

From Table X,

$$\sin 27° 20' = .4592.$$
$$a = 146 \times .4592 = 67.04.$$

In Chapter II, we learned that computation work can be decreased by using logarithms. Now let us solve for the side a by logarithms.

$$\sin A = \frac{a}{c}$$

and
$$a = c \sin A$$
$$a = 146 \times .4592$$
$$\log a = \log 146 + \log .4592$$

$$\log 146 = 2.1644$$
$$\log .4592 = 9.6620 - 10$$
$$\overline{\log a = 1.8264}$$
$$a = 67.05$$

In the last solution for side a two tables were used to find the value of log sin 27° 20'. Table X was used to find sin 27° 20' and Table I was used to find log .4592. Now let us use Table I and Table III to find the side a.

The third solution for side *a* follows:

$$a = c \sin A$$
$$a = 146 \sin 27° 20'$$
$$\log a = \log 146 + \log \sin 27° 20'$$

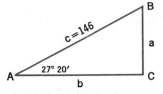

From Table I, $\log 146 = 2.16435$
From Table III, $\underline{\log \sin 27° 20' = 9.66197 - 10}$
$$\log a = 1.82632$$
$$a = 67.038$$

This solution is more accurate than the second one because a five-place table is more accurate than a four-place table. In this example, the numbers 146 and 27° 20′ were considered as exact. Then the result should have five significant figures to agree with the number of significant figures in Table III. Now if the numbers 146 and 27° 20′ are found by measurement, they are approximate. The number 146 has three significant figures and 27° 20′ corresponds to a linear measurement having four significant figures. Then the answer should be rounded off to 67.0 to agree with 146 in significant figures.

It is hoped that you discovered that Table III enables us to eliminate one step in the solution of the example above.

Solving Right Triangles by Logarithms [A]

When we use logarithms to solve right triangles, we use the same formulas that we used when we solved them with the use of the table of natural functions. But, instead of using Table X, we shall use Table I and Table III. Assuming that the data given in the problems are exact, the results will be accurate to five significant figures. Then the results should be rounded off so that they will have the same number of significant figures as used in the least accurate of the data.

You should remember that we have two cases in the solution of right triangles.

1. Case I, given a side and an acute angle.

2. Case II, given two sides.

In each of these cases three parts of the triangle are given. What is the third given part? A side and an acute angle determine a right triangle because two right triangles are congruent if a side and an acute angle of one are equal respectively to a side and an acute angle of the other. (h.a. = h.a. and a.s.a. = a.s.a.)

Two sides determine a right triangle because two right triangles are congruent if two sides of one are equal respectively to two sides of the other.

You should now review the outline for solving right triangles on page 39. Study the two examples which follow:

EXAMPLE 1. Solve the right triangle ABC given

$$a = 4.325 \text{ and } \angle B = 27° \, 42'.$$

SOLUTION

GIVEN
$a = 4.325$
$B = 27° \, 42'$

1. To find A:

$A = 90° - 27° \, 42'$
$A = 62° \, 18'$

2. To find b:

$\dfrac{b}{a} = \tan B$

$b = a \tan B$

$b = 4.325 \times \tan 27° \, 42'$

$\log 4.325 = 0.63599$
$\underline{\log \tan 27° \, 42' = 9.72017 - 10}$
$\log b = \quad .35616$
$b = 2.2707$

REQUIRED
$A = 62° \, 18'$
$b = 2.2707$, or 2.271
$c = 4.8849$, or 4.885

3. To find c:

$$\cos B = \frac{a}{c}$$

$$c = \frac{a}{\cos B}$$

$$c = \frac{4.325}{\cos 27° \, 42'}$$

$\log 4.325 = 10.63599 - 10$
$\underline{\log \cos 27° \, 42' = 9.94714 - 10}$
$\log c = \quad .68885$
$c = \quad 4.8849$

Check. $a^2 = c^2 - b^2 = (c - b)(c + b)$

$c = 4.8849$	$\log(c + b) = 0.85465$
$b = 2.2707$	$\log(c - b) = 0.41734$
$c + b = 7.1556$	$\log a^2 = 1.27199$
$c - b = 2.6142$	$\log a = .63600$

Since this value of log a is practically the same as log a in the solution, the solution checks.

EXAMPLE 2. Solve the right triangle ABC given
$$a = 424.1 \text{ and } b = 653.7.$$

SOLUTION

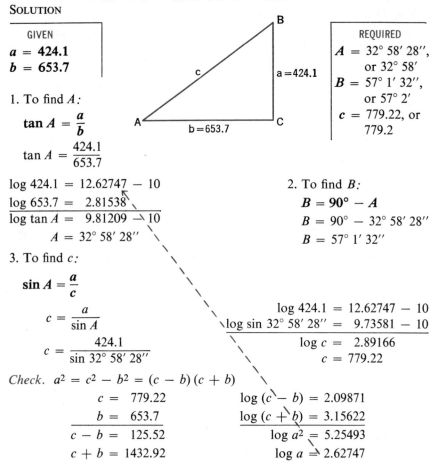

GIVEN
$a = 424.1$
$b = 653.7$

REQUIRED
$A = 32° 58' 28''$,
or $32° 58'$
$B = 57° 1' 32''$,
or $57° 2'$
$c = 779.22$, or
779.2

1. To find A:

$$\tan A = \frac{a}{b}$$

$$\tan A = \frac{424.1}{653.7}$$

$\log 424.1 = 12.62747 - 10$
$\log 653.7 = 2.81538$
$\overline{\log \tan A = 9.81209 - 10}$
$ A = 32° 58' 28''$

3. To find c:

$$\sin A = \frac{a}{c}$$

$$c = \frac{a}{\sin A}$$

$$c = \frac{424.1}{\sin 32° 58' 28''}$$

Check. $a^2 = c^2 - b^2 = (c - b)(c + b)$

$$\begin{aligned}
c &= 779.22 \\
b &= 653.7 \\
\hline
c - b &= 125.52 \\
c + b &= 1432.92
\end{aligned}$$

2. To find B:

$$B = 90° - A$$
$$B = 90° - 32° 58' 28''$$
$$B = 57° 1' 32''$$

$\log 424.1 = 12.62747 - 10$
$\log \sin 32° 58' 28'' = 9.73581 - 10$
$\overline{\log c = 2.89166}$
$c = 779.22$

$\log (c - b) = 2.09871$
$\log (c + b) = 3.15622$
$\overline{ \log a^2 = 5.25493}$
$\log a = 2.62747$

This value of log a checks in the fifth decimal place with log a in the problem.

Note that the results in Examples 1 and 2 above were rounded off to four significant figures so as to contain no more significant figures than any number in the data.

Before attempting the following exercises, review again the directions for solving right triangles on page 39. The results should be correct to five significant figures when you use a five-place table. These results should be used in the checks. Finally, round off the results to agree with the data given in the problem.

EXERCISES [A]

Solve right triangle ABC *given the following parts:*

1. $a = 423$
   $B = 34°\ 10'$

2. $b = 176$
   $B = 27°\ 30'$

3. $B = 58°\ 32'$
   $c = 1964$

4. $A = 62°\ 23'$
   $c = 427.0$

5. $a = 31.24$
   $b = 44.29$

6. $a = 17.4$
   $b = 12.6$

7. $a = 17.29$
   $c = 34.58$

8. $b = 42.6$
   $c = 85.2$

9. $c = 943.81$
   $A = 20°\ 32'\ 45''$

10. $c = 795.36$
    $B = 73°\ 18'\ 38''$

11. $c = 1.9367$
    $A = 25°\ 13'\ 18''$

12. $a = 2.1449$
    $B = 81°\ 17'\ 45''$

13. Two tangents to a circle meet at an angle of 47′ 13′ 42″. Find the radius of the circle if one of the tangents is 26.4 inches.

14. The diameter of a circle is 14.03 inches. Two tangents to the circle meet at an angle of 45° 16′. How long are the tangents?

15. A triangle is inscribed in a circle having a radius of 4.28 inches. Find the shortest side of the triangle if its smallest angle is 25° 52′.

16. Find the radius of a circle in which an arc of 52° 45′ 40″ is 20.000 inches long.

17. A chord of a circle with radius 14.176 inches is 8.724 inches. Find the central angle of the chord.

18. A regular pentagon is inscribed in a circle with radius of 12.00 inches. Find the perimeter of the pentagon.

19. The perimeter of a regular pentagon is 18.24 inches. Find the radius of its circumscribed circle.

20. A rectangle is 92′ by 164′. Find the angle made by one of the shorter sides and a diagonal.

21. Two vertical poles, one 32.4 feet high and the other 48.1 feet high, are 97.1 feet apart. What is the length of a taut wire connecting their tops?

22. A steel plate is to be ground so as to have the shape of a figure bounded by an arc of a circle and two tangents to the circle from an external point. Find the lengths of the tangent portions of the plate if the vertex of the angle formed by the tangents is 2.78″ from the circle and 3.52″ from the center of the circle.

23. The *pitch* of a roof is equal to its height divided by its whole width. The pitch of this roof is $\frac{4}{12}$, or $\frac{1}{3}$. The tangent of $\angle CAB$ is $\frac{2}{3}$. Then the pitch of a roof is one half of its slope. Find $\angle CAB$ in this roof. Find $\angle CAB$ when the pitch is $\frac{1}{2}$; when it is $\frac{3}{4}$.

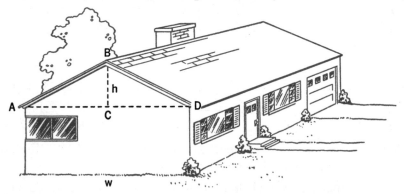

24. What is the angle of elevation of a stairway if the steps have a 10-inch tread and a 7-inch rise?

25. Find the equal sides of an isosceles triangle if the base is 18.476 inches and each of the equal angles is 48° 13′ 27″.

Area of a Right Triangle [A]

Let K denote the area of the right triangle ABC. Then $K = \dfrac{ab}{2}$, or $2K = ab$. In finding the area of the triangle it is easier to find $2K$ by logarithms and take half of the result than to use the form $K = \dfrac{ab}{2}$. Why? The formula $K = \dfrac{ab}{2}$ gives the area of a right triangle when the two legs a and b are given. If the hypotenuse and a leg of a right triangle are given, the other leg can be found by using the Pythagorean theorem and then the area can be found by this formula.

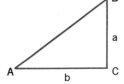

Area of Any Triangle [A]

Let us now develop a formula for finding the area of any triangle when two sides and the included angle are given.

Let ABC be any triangle and let K denote its area. From C draw the altitude h to side c, as shown in the diagram at the top of the next page.

Since $\dfrac{h}{b}$ = sin A, $h = b$ sin A.

$K = \frac{1}{2} ch$.

Then substituting b sin A for h, we have

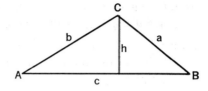

$$K = \tfrac{1}{2} cb \sin A,$$

or

$$K = \tfrac{1}{2} bc \sin A.$$

Other forms of the formula are $K = \frac{1}{2} ab$ sin C and $K = \frac{1}{2} ac$ sin B.

EXAMPLE. Find the area of the right triangle ABC given $a = 32.16$ and $A = 25°\ 30'$.

SOLUTION. We can solve for b and use the formula $K = \dfrac{ab}{2}$ or we can solve for c and B and then use the formula $K = \frac{1}{2} ac$ sin B. We shall solve for b.

$$\frac{a}{b} = \tan A.$$

Then $\qquad b = \dfrac{a}{\tan A}$

$\log b = \log a - \log \tan A$
$\log 32.16 = 11.50732 - 10$
$\log \tan 25°\ 30' = \ \ 9.67850 - 10$
$\overline{ \log b = \ \ 1.82882}$

$2K = ab$
$\log (2K) = \log a + \log b$
$\log 32.16 = 1.50732$
$\log b = 1.82882$
$\overline{\log (2K) = 3.33614}$
$2K = 2168.4$
$K = 1084.2$, or 1084

The solution can be checked by the formula $K = \frac{1}{2} ac$ sin B.

EXERCISES

A

Find the area of right triangle ABC, *given:*

1. $a = 41.23$
$b = 62.74$

2. $a = .0476$
$b = .1325$

3. $a = 21.461$
$c = 49.273$

4. $b = 88.7$
$c = 100.3$

5. $a = 942.8$
$A = 48°\ 27'$

6. $b = 293.4$
$B = 54°\ 13'$

7. $A = 62°\ 42'$
$b = 52.82$

8. $B = 27°\ 13'\ 10''$
$a = 142.31$

9. $A = 10°\ 24'\ 12''$
$c = 13.641$

10. One leg of a right triangle is 24 inches. Find its adjacent acute angle if the area of the triangle is 100 square inches.

11. Find the area in square feet of a city lot whose map is shown at the right.

12. Find the area of a parallelogram if one of its angles is 64° 20′ and two of its sides are 19.14 inches and 8.34 inches.

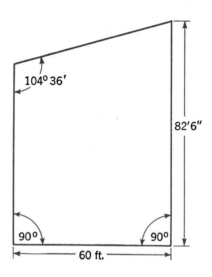

13. Show that the area of a parallelogram is one half the product of its diagonals and the sine of their included angle.

14. Show that the area of a parallelogram is given by the formula $K = bc \sin A$ when b and c are two adjacent sides and A is their included angle.

In a right triangle ABC,

15. Prove that $K = \frac{1}{2} b^2 \tan A$ or $K = \frac{1}{2} a^2 \tan B$.

16. Prove that $K = \frac{1}{2} b^2 \operatorname{ctn} B$ or $K = \frac{1}{2} a^2 \operatorname{ctn} A$.

17. Prove that $K = \frac{1}{2} c^2 \sin A \cos A$ or $K = \frac{1}{2} c^2 \sin B \cos B$.

Solving Isosceles Triangles [A]

The altitude to the base of an isosceles triangle divides the triangle into two congruent triangles. When any two of the parts which determine one of these two right triangles are known, the remaining parts, including the altitude, of the isosceles triangle can be determined; and conversely.

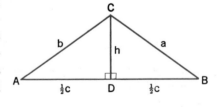

For example, if A and b are known parts of the triangle, the formulas

$B = A$, $C = 180° - 2A$, $a = b$, $h = b \sin A$, and $\cos A = \dfrac{\frac{1}{2} c}{b}$ can be used to find the remaining parts.

EXERCISES [A]

Write formulas expressing each of the parts A, B, C, a, b, c, *and* h *remaining when two of the parts of the isosceles triangle* ABC *with base* AB *are given as follows:*

1. *A, c*	**3.** *B, a*	**5.** *C, c*	**7.** *A, b*
2. *A, h*	**4.** *B, h*	**6.** *C, h*	**8.** *h, c*

Using logarithms, solve the following isosceles triangles, ABC, *with* a *and* b *the equal sides:*

9. $A = 38° 42'$
$a = 11.80$

11. $A = 54° 32'$
$h = 176.1$

13. $c = 7216$
$C = 54° 47'$

10. $a = 146.3$
$c = 82.4$

12. $b = 23.144$
$c = 11.403$

14. $B = 28° 33'$
$a = 19.46$

15. Find the area of a triangle whose sides are 24 feet, 30 feet, and 24 feet.

16. Find the area of a triangle whose sides are 42 inches, 53 inches, and 53 inches.

17. Find the area of a rhombus whose perimeter is 280 inches and which has an angle of 62°.

18. Find the lengths of the diagonals of the rhombus in Ex. 17.

Solving Regular Polygons [A]

A regular polygon is one which has equal sides and equal angles. In the regular polygon *ABCDEF*, the *apothem OH* bisects the central angle *AOB*, is perpendicular to a side *AB*, and forms two right triangles *AHO* and *BHO*. *OA* is the radius of the polygon and of the circumcircle. *OH*, the apothem of the polygon, is the radius of the incircle. If a regular polygon has *n* sides, each of its angles contains $\dfrac{n-2}{n} \cdot 180°$ and its central angle contains $\dfrac{360°}{n}$.

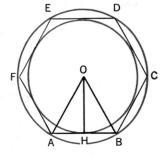

The solution of a regular polygon having a given number of sides consists in finding the remaining parts when a side, the radius of the incircle, or the radius of the circumcircle is known.

EXAMPLE 1. Solve the regular polygon of 10 sides each of which is 10.

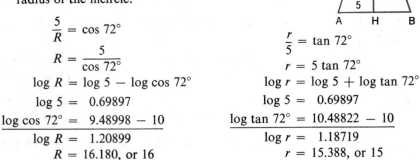

SOLUTION. Each angle of the polygon $= \dfrac{n-2}{n} \cdot 180°$
$= 144°.$

Then $\angle OAH = \frac{1}{2} \cdot 144° = 72°.$ $AH = 5.$

Let $R =$ the radius of the circumcircle and let $r =$ the radius of the incircle.

$$\frac{5}{R} = \cos 72°$$

$$R = \frac{5}{\cos 72°}$$

$$\log R = \log 5 - \log \cos 72°$$

$$\log 5 = \ \ 0.69897$$

$$\underline{\log \cos 72° = \ \ 9.48998 - 10}$$

$$\log R = \ \ 1.20899$$

$$R = 16.180, \text{ or } 16$$

$$\frac{r}{5} = \tan 72°$$

$$r = 5 \tan 72°$$

$$\log r = \log 5 + \log \tan 72°$$

$$\log 5 = \ \ 0.69897$$

$$\underline{\log \tan 72° = \ \ 10.48822 - 10}$$

$$\log r = \ \ 1.18719$$

$$r = 15.388, \text{ or } 15$$

EXAMPLE 2. Find the area of a regular pentagon having a side of 12 inches.

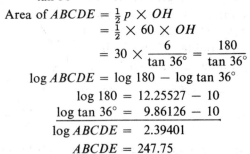

SOLUTION. Draw the apothem OH and the radius $OA.$

$AH = 6$ inches, and $\angle AOH = 36°.$

$$\frac{AH}{OH} = \tan 36°$$

Then $\qquad OH = \dfrac{AH}{\tan 36°}$

and $\qquad OH = \dfrac{6}{\tan 36°}$

$$\text{Area of } ABCDE = \tfrac{1}{2} p \times OH$$

$$= \tfrac{1}{2} \times 60 \times OH$$

$$= 30 \times \frac{6}{\tan 36°} = \frac{180}{\tan 36°}$$

$$\log ABCDE = \log 180 - \log \tan 36°$$

$$\log 180 = 12.25527 - 10$$

$$\underline{\log \tan 36° = \ \ 9.86126 - 10}$$

$$\log ABCDE = \ \ 2.39401$$

$$ABCDE = 247.75$$

Then the area of the polygon is 247.75 square inches. If 12 inches is approximate, the area is about 250 square inches.

EXERCISES [A]

1. Find the perimeter of a regular pentagon inscribed in a circle having a radius of 20 inches.

2. Find the perimeter of a regular octagon inscribed in a circle with radius 10 inches.

3. Find the radius of the incircle of an equilateral triangle whose perimeter is 96 feet.

4. Find the radius of a circle inscribed in a regular dodecagon (12 sides) whose perimeter is 164.4 inches.

5. Solve the regular polygon of 20 sides if the radius of its circumcircle is 20 inches.

6. Find the diameter of the smallest iron rod from which the hexagonal nut shown in the diagram can be cut.

7. Find the area of a regular octagon inscribed in a circle with radius 14 inches.

8. How many square inches are there in the area of a regular decagon inscribed in a 10-inch circle?

Projections of Lines and Planes [A]

The projection of a line segment upon a line is the part of the line cut off by the perpendiculars to that line from the ends of the line segment. The foot of each perpendicular is an end point of the projection.

In the accompanying figures, $A'B'$ is the projection of AB on l.

Since

$$\frac{A'B'}{AB} = \cos \theta,$$

$$A'B' = AB \cos \theta.$$

That is,

The projection of a line segment upon a line is equal to the line segment times the cosine of the angle between the lines.

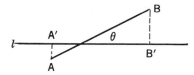

The projection of a line segment on a plane is equal to the line segment times the cosine of the angle between the line and its projection on

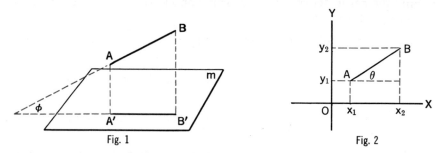

Fig. 1   Fig. 2

the plane. In Fig. 1, the projection $A'B'$ of AB on the plane m is found by drawing perpendiculars from A and B to m. Then $A'B' = AB \cos \phi$.

If the co-ordinates of A in Fig. 2 are (x_1, y_1) and of B are (x_2, y_2), and AB forms $\angle \theta$ with the x-axis, then the projections of the line segment AB on the x-axis and the y-axis are given by the following equations:

On the x-axis, $x_1 x_2 = AB \cos \theta.$
On the y-axis, $y_1 y_2 = AB \sin \theta.$

The projection of a plane figure on a plane equals the plane figure times the cosine of the angle between the planes.

Meaning of Subtend [A]

The word "subtend" in mathematics means "opposite to." In Fig. 3, $\angle O$ subtends the chord AB and the arc AB subtends the chord AB.

Fig. 3   Fig. 4

Bearing [A]

The *bearing* of a line is the direction of the line. Every line has two opposite directions. When a line is named by two letters, its direction is indicated by the order of the letters naming it. Thus AB and SR in Fig. 4 give the directions to the two lines shown.

The bearing of one point from another is the direction of the first from the second. Thus the *bearing of a point A* from a point *B* is the direction of *A* from *B* (Fig. 1). There are two common methods used in expressing the bearing of a line and a point.

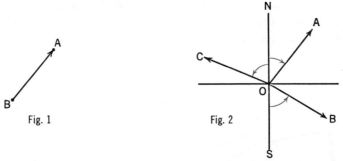

Fig. 1   Fig. 2

First Method. The bearing of a line *OA* is the acute angle that the line makes with the north-south line (meridian) through *O*. In Fig. 2 the bearing of *OA* is 40° east of north, designated by N 40° E; the bearing of *OB* is 60° east of south, designated by S 60° E; and the bearing of *OC* is 68° west of north, designated by N 68° W.

The bearing of a ship at sea can be found by a mariner's compass. The reading is taken from a compass card, which is shown below. The

compass card has two scales, one giving the thirty-two points of the compass and the other the bearing with reference to the north-south line.

Second Method. The word "bearing" as used in the Air Force indicates the clockwise angle measured from the north. The bearing of the line *OA*, or of the point *A* from *O*, is the angle that the line makes with the north line through *O* (Fig. 1). Thus the bearing of *OA* is 60°. Likewise, the bearing of *OB* is 120°, and the bearing of *OC* is 280°.

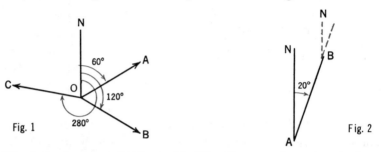

Fig. 1   Fig. 2

In Fig. 2, the bearing of *B* from *A* is 20°. Can you show that the bearing of *A* from *B* is 200°?

The pilot or navigator (or avigator) of a plane may wish to find on his chart the bearing of one point from another. On each sectional or regional chart at least one compass rose is printed. The compass rose gives the true north line. To find the bearing on the chart of a

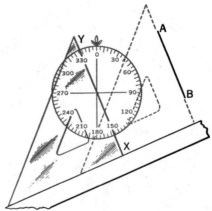

point *A* from a point *B* not too far away, the line *AB* is drawn. Then through the center of the compass rose a line *XY* is drawn parallel to the line *AB*. Then the bearing of *A* from *B* and of *B* from *A* can be read from the intersections of *XY* and the compass rose.

Course, Latitude, and Departure [A]

The word "course" when used in surveying means a horizontal line segment having direction. Thus, course AB means line segment AB with A being the initial point of the course and B the terminal point.

The *latitude of a course* is the distance north or south one goes when traveling the length of the course.

The *departure of a course* is the distance east or west one goes when traveling the length of the course. In traveling on the course OB, one goes north the distance OA and east the distance OC. Then the latitude of the course is OA and the departure of it is OC. Since OA is the projection of OB on ON and OC is the projection of OB on OE, we have from the figure:

latitude $= OB \cos \theta.$

departure $= OB \sin \theta.$

$$OB = \sqrt{OA^2 + OC^2} = \sqrt{\text{lat}^2 + \text{dep}^2}.$$

$$\tan \theta = \frac{OC}{OA} = \frac{\text{dep}}{\text{lat}}.$$

In aeronautics the course is usually spoken of as the *track*. The course in aeronautics then means only the direction and position of the track, not its length.

EXERCISES [A]

1. What angle does line AB make with line l when the projection of AB on l equals
   - **a.** AB?
   - **b.** Zero?
   - **c.** $\frac{1}{2} AB$?
   - **d.** $\dfrac{AB}{2}\sqrt{3}$?

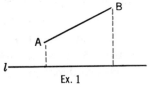

Ex. 1

2. Line segment AB is 8 inches long. Find its projections on OX and OY.

3. Line segment CD is 8 inches long. Find its projections on OX and OY.

4. The projection of line segment EF on the x-axis is 4.728 inches and the projection on the y-axis, 3.694 inches. Find the length of EF and the acute angle it makes with the x-axis.

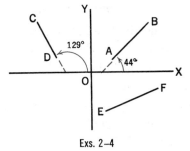

Exs. 2–4

5. The boathouse shown here has outside dimensions 20′ × 24′. Find the area of the roof if its pitch is $\frac{1}{4}$. Add 10% for the overhang.

6. An invisible target is 4.73 miles north and 3.24 miles east of a battery. What is the target's bearing from the battery?

7. A ship is sailing S 47° E at 12.8 knots. How fast is it going south and how fast is it going east?

8. A ship is sailing N 25° W at 14.3 knots. Find its rate going north and its rate going west.

9. The departure of a course is positive when it is eastward and negative when it is westward. What is the sum of the eastward and westward departures of the sides of △*ABC*?

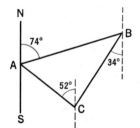

10. What is the bearing of a road which leads to a point 6 miles east and 7 miles north?

11. Find the latitude and departure of a course N 24° E and 1847 feet long.

12. Find the latitude and departure of a course S 13° 40′ W and 14,250 feet long.

13. The bearing of side *AB* of △*ABC* which is lettered counterclockwise is N 26° E. ∠*A* = 80° and ∠*B* = 60°. Find the bearings of *BC* and *AC*.

14. The bearing of side AB of $\triangle ABC$ which is lettered clockwise is S 18° 00′ E. $\angle A = 47°\ 18'$ and $\angle B = 70°\ 42'$. Find the bearings of BC and AC.

15. If an airplane can climb 600 feet a minute when flying 120 miles an hour, what is its climbing angle?

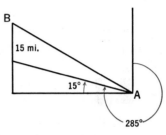

16. An airplane took off from airport A at 390 m.p.h. In 45 minutes it landed at airport B. During the flight the plane was headed in direction 285°, but due to a wind from 180°, the plane was carried north 15 miles. What direction is airport B from airport A?

17. A balloon at B is directly over point A on level ground. From a point due south of A the elevation of the balloon was found to be 64° 30′. From a point 150 feet due west of this point the angle of elevation of the balloon was 61° 20′. Find the height of the balloon.

SUGGESTION. First express AC and AD in terms of x and then use the Pythagorean Theorem.

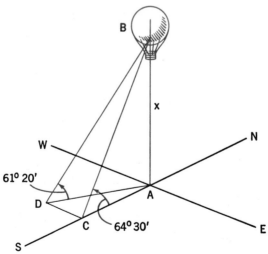

18. If a ship sails on course N 35° 20′ E for 120 miles, what are its latitude and departure?

19. Two airplanes, A and B, leave the same airfield at the same time. A flies on course 100° at a speed of 250 knots and B flies on course 160° at 400 knots. What is the bearing of B from A when they have been flying 30 minutes?

20. From a point P a vertical flagstaff subtends an angle of 16° 24′. If the flagstaff is 440 feet from P, how high is it?

21. A vessel sailing NNW is observed at 10:30 A.M. from a lighthouse 6.2 miles away to be ENE. At 11:10 A.M. the vessel is due north. Find the speed of the vessel in miles an hour.

22. From a ship sailing due north two lighthouses are observed due east. After sailing 9.4 miles one lighthouse is SE and the other is ESE. How far from the ship were the lighthouses at the first observation?

23. Find the latitude and departure of a course whose bearing is S 42° 20′ E and whose length is 947 feet.

Using the Slide Rule in Checking the Solution of a Right Triangle (Optional)

In the right triangle ABC,

$$\sin A = \frac{a}{c} \quad \text{and} \quad \sin B = \frac{b}{c}.$$

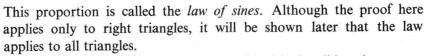

Then $\quad \dfrac{\sin A}{a} = \dfrac{1}{c} \quad$ and $\quad \dfrac{\sin B}{b} = \dfrac{1}{c}.$

Since $\sin C = 1,$ $\dfrac{\sin C}{c} = \dfrac{1}{c}.$

Then $\qquad\qquad \dfrac{\sin A}{a} = \dfrac{\sin B}{b} = \dfrac{\sin C}{c}.$

This proportion is called the *law of sines*. Although the proof here applies only to right triangles, it will be shown later that the law applies to all triangles.

Since a proportion can be easily solved with the slide rule, we can use the slide rule and the law of sines to check the solution of a right triangle.

The slide rule and the law of sines can be used to solve a right triangle when a side and an acute angle are given.

EXAMPLE 1. Check the solution of Example 1 on page 107.

SOLUTION. Given. $a = 4.325$ *Values found.* $A = 62° 18'$
                                   $B = 27° 42'$ $b = 2.2707$
                                                                                                        $c = 4.8849$

Check:

By the law of sines, $\dfrac{\sin A}{a} = \dfrac{\sin B}{b} = \dfrac{\sin 90°}{c}$

Then $\dfrac{\sin 62° 18'}{4.325} = \dfrac{\sin 27° 42'}{2.2707} = \dfrac{\sin 90°}{4.8849}.$

To make the work easier, we invert the ratios,

$$\frac{4.325}{\sin 62° 18'} = \frac{2.2707}{\sin 27° 42'} = \frac{4.8849}{\sin 90°}.$$

Using the slide rule, set 62° 18′ of scale S under 4.325 of scale A. The right half of scale A is used because the angle is more than 5° 44′. Then below 2.2707 on scale A we find 27° 42′ on scale S, and below 4.8849 on scale A we find 90° on scale S. If your slide rule is very accurate and your vision is good this method of checking is often desirable.

EXAMPLE 2. Using the slide rule, solve the right triangle ABC given
                          $A = 51° 25'$, $c = 40$.

SOLUTION.

GIVEN
$A = 51° 25'$
$c = 40$

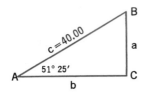

REQUIRED
$B = 38° 35'$, or $38° 40'$
$a = 31.3$
$b = 24.9$

$B = 90° - 51° 25' = 38° 35'$

$$\frac{a}{\sin A} = \frac{b}{\sin B} = \frac{c}{\sin C}.$$

Then $\dfrac{a}{\sin 51° 25'} = \dfrac{b}{\sin 38° 35'} = \dfrac{40}{\sin 90°}.$

We start with the ratio $\dfrac{40}{\sin 90°}$. Why? We set 90° of scale S under 40 of scale A, right half. Above 38° 35′ on scale S we read 249 on scale A. By inspection the decimal point is between the 4 and the 9. Then $b = 24.9$. Above 51° 25′ on the S scale we read 313. The decimal point is between the last two digits. Then $a = 31.3$.

EXERCISES

Solve the following right triangles, using the slide rule:

1. $A = 34° 30'$
$c = 42.67$

2. $B = 48° 50'$
$b = 34.76$

3. $A = 75° 30'$
$a = 42.8$

4. $A = 62° 45'$
$c = 34.2$

5. $B = 20° 28'$
$c = 345$

6. $B = 37° 35'$
$a = 194$

CHAPTER REVIEW

A

The following statements apply to the right triangle ABC. *Tell which are true and which are false.*

1. $a = b \tan A$

2. $b = c \cos A$

3. $c = a \cos A$

4. $\sec A = \dfrac{1}{\cos A}$

5. $\tan B = \operatorname{ctn} A$

6. $\sec B = \csc A$

7. $\sin A = \cos B$

8. $\tan A = \dfrac{1}{\operatorname{ctn} B}$

9. $\sin C = 1$

10. $b \sec B = c$

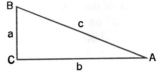

Complete the following statements:

11. As an angle increases from 0° to 90°, the _?_, _?_, and _?_ functions decrease.

12. The tangent of an angle of _?_ degrees is 1.

13. Why is the formula $a^2 = (c - b)(c + b)$ preferable to $a^2 = c^2 - b^2$ when solving right triangles?

Use Table III for exercises 14–17 to find:

14. $\log \sin 32° 13' 30''$

15. $\log \tan 77° 13' 40''$

16. A, if $\log \tan A = 10.51694 - 10$

17. B, if $\log \cos B = 8.68200 - 10$

Which of the following right triangles can be solved?

18. $\triangle ABC$, given $A = 32°$, $C = 90°$

19. $\triangle DEF$, given $E = 90°$, $e = 142$, and $f = 126$.

20. $\triangle TPW$, given $T = 90°$, $t = 135$, and $p = 125$.

21. From a point midway between two towers upon the same horizontal plane the angles of elevation of their tops are 42° 18' and 57° 36'. Find the ratio of the heights of the towers.

22. Solve the rt.$\triangle ABC$, given $a = 461$ and $b = 235$.

23. Solve the rt.$\triangle ABC$, given $A = 36° 18'$ and $a = 134.7$.

24. Solve the rt.$\triangle ABC$, given $B = 71° 24'$ and $a = 167.8$.

25. Solve the rt.$\triangle ABC$, given $a \overset{\bullet}{=} 4.236$ and $c = 7.914$.

26. Find the area of rt.$\triangle ABC$, given $\angle B = 40° 22' 18''$ and $c = 421.46$.

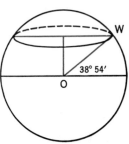

27. Solve the isosceles triangle ABC having the base $b = 24.68$ and $\angle A = 71° 48'$.

28. Find the area of a regular octagon if its apothem is 21.16 inches.

29. Find the length of one degree of longitude in the latitude of Washington, D. C., $38° 54'$, assuming the earth to be a sphere with a radius of 3960 miles.

B

30. Each side of a regular polygon of 18 sides is 18 inches. Find the radius of its circumcircle.

Use the slide rule to solve the following right triangles:

31. $A = 36° 20'$, $a = 247$.

32. $B = 31° 50'$, $b = 45.2$.

33. $A = 27°$, $c = 131.4$.

34. $i = \dfrac{rh \tan \theta}{2 \pi n}$ is a formula for finding the amount of current passing through a galvanometer, an instrument for measuring a small electric current.

In the formula,

  i = current in amperes.
  r = numbers of centimeters in the radius of the coil.
  h = the horizontal component of earth's magnetism, expressed in dynes.
  θ = the deflection of the needle.
  n = the number of turns of coil.

Find the amount of current passing through a galvanometer when $r = 28$ centimeters, $n = 6$, $h = .1580$ dynes, and $\theta = 42° 18'$.

FORM B. D. 2
9-50—12M

STRUCTURE NO. *31-HH-3533*

PAGE *1*

STATE HIGHWAY COMMISSION OF INDIANA
BRIDGE DESIGN COMPUTATIONS

N.E. Wing Length

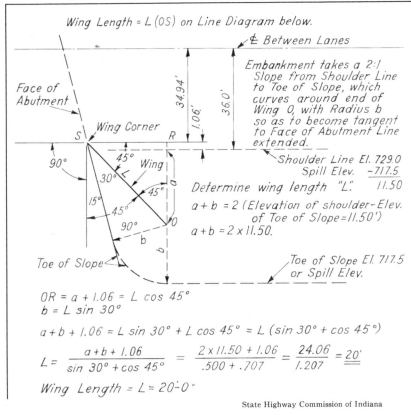

Wing Length = L (0S) on Line Diagram below.

⅃ Between Lanes

Face of Abutment

34.94'

1.06'

36.0'

Wing Corner

S

R

90°

45°

30°

15°

45°

45°

90°

Wing

L

a

b

b

0

Toe of Slope

Embankment takes a 2:1 Slope from Shoulder Line to Toe of Slope, which curves around end of Wing 0, with Radius b so as to become tangent to Face of Abutment Line extended.

Shoulder Line El. 729.0
Spill Elev. −717.5
11.50

Determine wing length "L".

$a + b = 2$ *(Elevation of shoulder—Elev. of Toe of Slope=11.50')*

$a + b = 2 \times 11.50.$

Toe of Slope El. 717.5 or Spill Elev.

$OR = a + 1.06 = L \cos 45°$
$b = L \sin 30°$

$a + b + 1.06 = L \sin 30° + L \cos 45° = L (\sin 30° + \cos 45°)$

$$L = \frac{a + b + 1.06}{\sin 30° + \cos 45°} = \frac{2 \times 11.50 + 1.06}{.500 + .707} = \frac{24.06}{1.207} = \underline{\underline{20'}}$$

Wing Length = L = 20'-0"

A Bridge, and Some of the Mathematics Used in Designing It

TRIGONOMETRIC FUNCTIONS

OF ANY ANGLE

Δ

We have thus far considered the trigonometric functions of acute angles only. These functions are sufficient for the solution of right triangles. However, in many applications of trigonometry we need to know the functions of angles greater than 90°. In the solution of oblique triangles, the functions of obtuse angles are used. Angles up to 360° are employed in navigation and surveying. In the study of wave motion, angles of any magnitude are necessary.

In defining the trigonometric functions for angles of any size we make use of the rectangular co-ordinate system. You are already familiar with the system from your study of algebra. The next paragraphs will enable you to recall the terms used.

Rectangular Co-ordinates [A]

In the figure, XX' is the horizontal axis and YY' is the vertical axis. Together they are referred to as the co-ordinate axes. Their intersection is the origin (O). They divide the plane of the co-ordinate system into four quadrants, the first, second, third, and fourth, as shown by the Roman numerals in the figure.

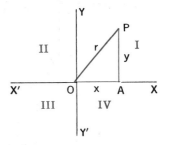

The distance of any point, such as P, from the Y-axis is called its *abscissa* (x), its distance from the X-axis is its *ordinate* (y), and its distance from the origin is the *radius vector* (r). The abscissa and ordinate are written in parentheses in the form (x, y) and are referred to as the co-ordinates of P. x is positive in the first and fourth quadrants and negative in the second and third; y is positive in the first and second quadrants and negative in the third and fourth. The radius vector, r, will always be considered positive. The angle AOP may be thought of as generated by the rotation of line OP from coincidence with OX. OA is the *initial side* of the angle and OP is its *terminal side*.

Positive and Negative Angles [A]

An angle is in *standard position* when the vertex is at the origin and the initial side coincides with the positive part of the x-axis. An angle is *positive* if the generating line is rotated counterclockwise and *negative* if the rotation is clockwise. An angle may be of any magnitude since the generating line may rotate any number of times in either direction. An angle is said to be in the quadrant in which its terminal side lies. Thus angles of 100°, 150°, 480°, and −225° are second-quadrant angles, while angles of −100°, −160°, and 200° are third-quadrant angles. *Quadrantal angles* are angles whose terminal sides coincide with one of the axes. Angles of 90°, 180°, etc., are quadrantal angles.

Trigonometric Functions of Any Angle [A]

Let θ be any angle in standard position, P any point not at the origin, on the terminal side of θ, and $PA \perp X'X$. Then the functions are defined as follows:

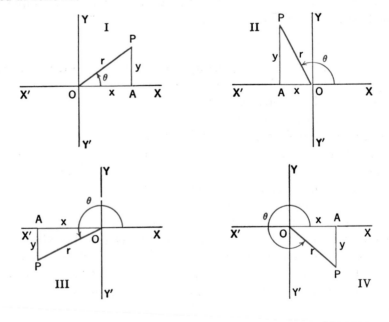

$$\sin \theta = \frac{\text{ordinate}}{\text{radius vector}} = \frac{y}{r} \qquad \text{ctn } \theta = \frac{\text{abscissa}}{\text{ordinate}} = \frac{x}{y}$$

$$\cos \theta = \frac{\text{abscissa}}{\text{radius vector}} = \frac{x}{r} \qquad \sec \theta = \frac{\text{radius vector}}{\text{abscissa}} = \frac{r}{x}$$

$$\tan \theta = \frac{\text{ordinate}}{\text{abscissa}} = \frac{y}{x} \qquad \csc \theta = \frac{\text{radius vector}}{\text{ordinate}} = \frac{r}{y}$$

These ratios are called functions of θ since they depend solely on the value of θ, and are independent of the position of P on the terminal side of the angle.

Signs of Functions [A]

The signs of the functions of an angle depend upon the signs of the abscissa and ordinate, the radius vector being positive. Each function is positive in two quadrants and negative in the other two. The sign of a function in any quadrant can be easily remembered by visualizing the diagram at the right. The diagram indicates in which quadrants certain functions are positive, all other functions being negative.

	Y	
II		I
$\sin \theta$ + $\csc \theta$ +		all +
X' $\tan \theta$ + $\text{ctn } \theta$ +	O	$\sec \theta$ + $\cos \theta$ + X
III	Y'	IV

To Find All Functions When One is Known [A]

EXAMPLE 1. Given $\sin \theta = -\frac{3}{5}$, find the other functions.

SOLUTION. Since the radius vector is always positive and the ordinate is negative in the third and fourth quadrants, θ may be either a third or fourth quadrant angle. The two positions of θ are shown in the figure. From the Pythagorean theorem, $x^2 + y^2 = r^2$, or

$$x = \pm \sqrt{r^2 - y^2}$$

$$= \pm \sqrt{5^2 - (-3)^2}$$

$$= \pm \sqrt{25 - 9} = \pm 4$$

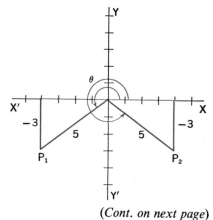

(Cont. on next page)

Then by definition the values of the other functions are:

QUADRANT III	QUADRANT IV
$\cos \theta = -\dfrac{4}{5}$	$\cos \theta = \dfrac{4}{5}$
$\tan \theta = \dfrac{-3}{-4} = \dfrac{3}{4}$	$\tan \theta = -\dfrac{3}{4}$
$\text{ctn } \theta = \dfrac{-4}{-3} = \dfrac{4}{3}$	$\text{ctn } \theta = -\dfrac{4}{3}$
$\sec \theta = -\dfrac{5}{4}$	$\sec \theta = \dfrac{5}{4}$
$\csc \theta = -\dfrac{5}{3}$	$\csc \theta = -\dfrac{5}{3}$

EXAMPLE 2. Given that $\tan \theta = -\dfrac{5}{12}$ and that $\cos \theta$ is negative, find all the functions of θ.

SOLUTION. The tangent is negative in the second and fourth quadrants, and the cosine is negative in the second and third quadrants. Therefore θ is a second-quadrant angle. The angle is shown in the figure.

$$r = \sqrt{x^2 + y^2}$$
$$= \sqrt{(-12)^2 + 5^2}$$
$$= \sqrt{169} = 13.$$

$\sin \theta = \dfrac{5}{13} \qquad \csc \theta = \dfrac{13}{5}$

$\cos \theta = -\dfrac{12}{13} \qquad \sec \theta = -\dfrac{13}{12}$

$\tan \theta = -\dfrac{5}{12} \qquad \text{ctn } \theta = -\dfrac{12}{5}$

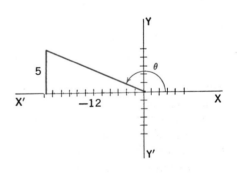

EXERCISES [A]

1. For what quadrants are:

a. $\sin \theta$ and $\csc \theta$ positive? negative?
b. $\cos \theta$ and $\sec \theta$ positive? negative?
c. $\tan \theta$ and $\text{ctn } \theta$ positive? negative?

2. In what quadrant does θ terminate when:

a. sin θ is positive and tan θ is negative?
b. sin θ is negative and tan θ is positive?
c. cos θ is positive and ctn θ is negative?
d. sec θ is positive and tan θ is positive?

3. Given the following functions, sketch the two possible angles less than 360° and find the other functions. (Give answers in simplest radical form.)

a. $\sin \theta = -\frac{2}{3}$ **d.** $\operatorname{ctn} \theta = -\frac{3}{4}$ **g.** $\csc \theta = \frac{3}{2}$

b. $\cos \theta = \frac{1}{2}$ **e.** $\sec \theta = \frac{13}{12}$ **h.** $\cos \theta = -\frac{2}{3}$

c. $\tan \theta = \frac{4}{5}$ **f.** $\tan \theta = -\frac{3}{7}$ **i.** $\sec \theta = -\frac{5}{3}$

4. Locate θ in standard position and find the other functions if:

a. $\cos \theta = \frac{4}{7}$ and sin θ is negative.
b. $\cos \theta = -\frac{8}{17}$ and ctn θ is positive.
c. $\sec \theta = -\frac{13}{5}$ and tan θ is negative.
d. $\sin \theta = -\frac{7}{10}$ and ctn θ is positive.
e. $\tan \theta = x$ and sin θ is negative.
f. $\sin \theta = y$ and cos θ is positive.

5. Find the value of $\cos^2 \theta - \sin^2 \theta$ when $\tan \theta = -\frac{3}{4}$ and cos θ is negative.

6. Find the value of $\dfrac{2 \tan \theta}{1 - \tan^2 \theta}$ when $\cos \theta = -\frac{3}{7}$ and tan θ is positive.

To Find the Functions When the Angle Is Given [A]

For any given angle there exists one and only one value for each function. As you know, tables give the values of these functions for positive angles in the range 0° to 90°. In order to find the function of any angle not in this range, we must first express the functions of the given angle in terms of functions of a positive acute angle.

Reference Angle [A]

Let $\angle AOB = \theta$ be any first-quadrant angle in standard position. $\angle AOD$, AOE, and AOC are positive angles equal to $180° - \theta$, $180° + \theta$, and $360° - \theta$ respectively. The angles $180° - \theta$, $180° + \theta$, and $360° - \theta$ are said to be referred to the x-axis and θ is the *reference angle*. Take

OB, OD, OE, and *OC* each equal to *r*. Then rt. △*AOB, DOF, EOF*, and *AOC* are congruent. The abscissas of points *B, D, E*, and *C* have the same absolute values. Also, the ordinates of *B, D, E*, and *C* have the same absolute values. Writing the functions of θ, $180° - \theta$, $180° + \theta$, and $360° - \theta$ in their respective quadrants, we have:

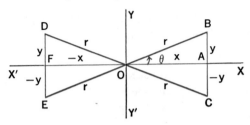

QUADRANT I

$$\sin \theta = \frac{y}{r}$$

$$\cos \theta = \frac{x}{r}$$

$$\tan \theta = \frac{y}{x}$$

$$\operatorname{ctn} \theta = \frac{x}{y}$$

$$\sec \theta = \frac{r}{x}$$

$$\csc \theta = \frac{r}{y}$$

QUADRANT II

$$\sin (180° - \theta) = \frac{y}{r} = \sin \theta$$

$$\cos (180° - \theta) = \frac{-x}{r} = -\frac{x}{r} = -\cos \theta$$

$$\tan (180° - \theta) = -\frac{y}{x} = -\tan \theta$$

$$\operatorname{ctn} (180° - \theta) = \frac{-x}{y} = -\operatorname{ctn} \theta$$

$$\sec (180° - \theta) = -\frac{r}{x} = -\sec \theta$$

$$\csc (180° - \theta) = \frac{r}{y} = \csc \theta$$

QUADRANT III

$$\sin (180° + \theta) = -\frac{y}{r} = -\sin \theta$$

$$\cos (180° + \theta) = -\frac{x}{r} = -\cos \theta$$

$$\tan (180° + \theta) = \frac{-y}{-x} = \tan \theta$$

$$\operatorname{ctn} (180° + \theta) = \frac{-x}{-y} = \operatorname{ctn} \theta$$

$$\sec (180° + \theta) = -\frac{r}{x} = -\sec \theta$$

$$\csc (180° + \theta) = -\frac{r}{y} = -\csc \theta$$

QUADRANT IV

$$\sin (360° - \theta) = -\frac{y}{r} = -\sin \theta$$

$$\cos (360° - \theta) = \frac{x}{r} = \cos \theta$$

$$\tan (360° - \theta) = -\frac{y}{x} = -\tan \theta$$

$$\operatorname{ctn} (360° - \theta) = -\frac{x}{y} = -\operatorname{ctn} \theta$$

$$\sec (360° - \theta) = \frac{r}{x} = \sec \theta$$

$$\csc (360° - \theta) = -\frac{r}{y} = -\csc \theta$$

In deriving these formulas θ was taken as a positive acute angle but the formulas are valid when $\theta \gtreqless 90°$ or when θ is a negative angle of any magnitude.

Since all angles can be written in one of the forms θ, $180° - \theta$, $180° + \theta$, or $360° - \theta$, the preceding formulas enable us to write the functions of any angle greater than $90°$ in terms of functions of an acute angle. If an angle is greater than $360°$, first subtract some multiple of $360°$ from the angle so that it is less than $360°$.

EXAMPLE 1. Find the functions of $130°$ in terms of the functions of an acute angle.

SOLUTION.
$$\sin 130° = \sin (180° - 50°) = \sin 50°$$
$$\cos 130° = \cos (180° - 50°) = -\cos 50°$$
$$\tan 130° = \tan (180° - 50°) = -\tan 50°$$
$$\text{ctn } 130° = \text{ctn } (180° - 50°) = -\text{ctn } 50°$$
$$\sec 130° = \sec (180° - 50°) = -\sec 50°$$
$$\csc 130° = \csc (180° - 50°) = \csc 50°$$

EXAMPLE 2. Reduce $\tan 220°$ to the same function of an acute angle.

SOLUTION. $\tan 220° = \tan (180° + 40°) = \tan 40°$

EXAMPLE 3. Find the cosine and cotangent of $312°$.

SOLUTION.
$$\cos 312° = \cos (360° - 48°) = \cos 48° = .6691$$
$$\text{ctn } 312° = \text{ctn } (360° - 48°) = -\text{ctn } 48° = -.9004$$

EXAMPLE 4. Express
$$\sin (180° - \theta) \cos (180° + \theta) + \cos (360° - \theta) \sin (180° + \theta)$$
in terms of the functions of θ.

SOLUTION. From the formulas, page 132,

$\sin (180° - \theta) \cos (180° + \theta) + \cos (360° - \theta) \sin (180° + \theta)$
$= \sin \theta [-\cos \theta] + \cos \theta [-\sin \theta] = -\sin \theta \cos \theta - \cos \theta \sin \theta$
$= -2 \sin \theta \cos \theta.$

The method of applying the formulas of page 132 to known angles is best remembered if stated in the words which follow.

To find the function of any angle between 90° and 360° (except 180° or 270°) express the angle as (180° ± θ) or (360° − θ); then take the same function of the reference angle θ and give it the sign determined by the function of the given angle in the quadrant to which it belongs.

EXERCISES [A]

1. Express the following as functions of positive acute angles:

a. sin 165°	**g.** tan 190°	**m.** sin 340° 6′
b. csc 125°	**h.** cos 212°	**n.** cos 281° 10′
c. ctn 170°	**i.** ctn 250°	**o.** sec 300° 20′
d. cos 115°	**j.** sin 200°	**p.** tan 350° 50′
e. tan 145°	**k.** csc 235°	**q.** ctn 323° 49′
f. sec 100°	**l.** sec 185°	**r.** csc 295° 56′

2. Find the numerical value of each of the following:

a. sin 105°	**e.** sec 97° 30′	**i.** cos 333° 11′
b. cos 215°	**f.** csc 193° 10′	**j.** sec 288° 18′
c. tan 332°	**g.** tan 247° 50′	**k.** ctn 110° 45′
d. ctn 186°	**h.** sin 311° 20′	**l.** csc 98° 33′

3. Express as functions of θ:

a. $\tan(180° + \theta) \sin(180° - \theta) + \tan(360° - \theta) \sin(180° + \theta)$.
b. $\sin(360° - \theta) \cos(360° - \theta) - \sin(180° + \theta) \cos(180° - \theta)$.
c. $\sec(180° - \theta) \csc(180° - \theta) + \sec(360° - \theta) \csc(180° + \theta)$.

4. Evaluate the following, using the tables:

a. cos 800° − sin 105°
b. sec 107° + csc 163°
c. tan 208° + ctn 342° − sin 112° 10′

Functions of Special Angles [A]

Angles of 150°, 210°, and 330° have 30° as the reference angle. In like manner 45° is the reference angle for angles of 135°, 225°, and 315°. 60° is the reference angle for angles 120°, 240°, and 300°. Since the exact values of the functions of 30°, 45°, and 60° are known, we can give the exact values of these special angles.

EXAMPLE 1. Find tan 135°.

SOLUTION. Since the tangent is negative in the second quadrant and the reference angle is 45°, tan 135° = −1.

EXAMPLE 2. Find cos 300°.

SOLUTION. Since the cosine is positive in the fourth quadrant and the reference angle is 60°, cos 300° = $\frac{1}{2}$.

EXERCISES [A]

1. Write the exact value for each of the following:

a. sin 150°	**f.** sec 300°	**k.** ctn 210°
b. csc 210°	**g.** sin 135°	**l.** sin 300°
c. cos 330°	**h.** cos 225°	**m.** cos 135°
d. tan 120°	**i.** csc 315°	**n.** tan 225°
e. ctn 240°	**j.** tan 150°	**o.** ctn 120°

2. Evaluate the following:

    a. sin 150° tan 210° − cos 135° ctn 240°
    b. sin² 120° cos² 300° + sin² 300° cos² 240°
    c. tan² 135° sin² 225° − ctn² 225° cos² 315°

Functions of Quadrantal Angles [A]

Each of the angles 0°, 90°, 180°, and 270° has its terminal side on an axis.

In the figure, let P_1, P_2, P_3, P_4, be points on the axes representing points on the terminal sides of angles of 0°, 90°, 180°, 270° respectively, and equidistant from the origin. At each point the values of x, y, and r are given in parentheses. Then from the definitions of the trigonometric functions, we have:

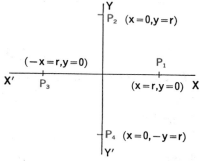

$$\sin 0° = \frac{y}{r} = \frac{0}{r} = 0 \qquad\qquad \sin 90° = \frac{y}{r} = 1$$

$$\cos 0° = \frac{x}{r} = 1 \qquad\qquad \cos 90° = \frac{x}{r} = \frac{0}{r} = 0$$

$$\tan 0° = \frac{y}{x} = \frac{0}{x} = 0 \qquad\qquad \tan 90° = \frac{y}{x} = \frac{y}{0}, \text{ undefined}$$

$$\text{ctn } 0° = \frac{x}{y} = \frac{x}{0}, \text{ undefined} \qquad\qquad \text{ctn } 90° = \frac{x}{y} = \frac{0}{y} = 0$$

$$\sec 0° = \frac{r}{x} = 1 \qquad\qquad \sec 90° = \frac{r}{x} = \frac{r}{0}, \text{ undefined}$$

$$\csc 0° = \frac{r}{0}, \text{ undefined} \qquad\qquad \csc 90° = \frac{r}{y} = 1$$

Since division by zero is excluded in mathematics, ctn 0° and csc 0° do not exist. However, as an angle approaches zero, ctn θ and csc θ become numerically larger and larger and are said to approach infinity. This may be expressed symbolically as "lim ctn $\theta = \infty$" and read "the limit, as θ approaches 0, of ctn θ is infinity." The symbol ∞ is not a number, but it will be used to indicate that, as an angle approaches a specified value, the corresponding function increases in numerical value without bound.

The following table gives the values of the quadrantal angles:

ANGLE	SIN	COS	TAN	CTN	SEC	CSC
0°	0	1	0	∞	1	∞
90°	1	0	∞	0	∞	1
180°	0	−1	0	∞	−1	∞
270°	−1	0	∞	0	∞	−1

EXERCISES [A]

Find the values of the following functions:

1. sin 90°   **5.** sin 270°   **9.** cos 270°

2. csc 180°   **6.** cos 180°   **10.** tan 90°

3. tan 270°   **7.** sec 270°   **11.** ctn 180°

4. ctn 90°   **8.** csc 90°   **12.** sec 180°

Evaluate the following:

13. 2 sin 90° cos 180° + tan 180° sec 180°

14. sin 180° ctn 270° − sec 180°   **15.** sin² 270° + cos² 180°

Functions of Negative Angles [A]

The values of the trigonometric functions of negative angles can be found by the use of reference angles. However, it is more desirable to express a function of a negative angle in terms of the same function of a positive angle of the same magnitude.

Let us consider the functions of θ and $-\theta$ where θ is an angle of any magnitude. In the figure, θ and $-\theta$ are in standard position and P and P' are points on the terminal sides of the angles, respectively, having the same distance r from the origin. The co-ordinates of P are (x, y) and of P' are (x', y'). The right triangles AOP and AOP' are congruent; hence $x = x'$ and $-y = y'$.

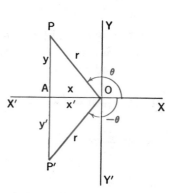

Then $\sin(-\theta) = \dfrac{y'}{r} = \dfrac{-y}{r} = -\sin\theta$

$\cos(-\theta) = \dfrac{x'}{r} = \dfrac{x}{r} = \cos\theta$

$\tan(-\theta) = \dfrac{y'}{x'} = \dfrac{-y}{x} = -\tan\theta$

$\operatorname{ctn}(-\theta) = \dfrac{x'}{y'} = \dfrac{x}{-y} = -\operatorname{ctn}\theta$

$\sec(-\theta) = \dfrac{r}{x'} = \dfrac{r}{x} = \sec\theta$

$\csc(-\theta) = \dfrac{r}{y'} = \dfrac{r}{-y} = -\csc\theta$

From the above proof we see that changing the sign of an angle does not change the value of the cosine or secant but does change the sign of the other four trigonometric functions.

EXERCISES [A]

Express in terms of the same function of a positive acute angle:

1. sin (−25°)   **6.** csc (−95°)   **11.** csc (−282°)
2. cos (−36°)   **7.** cos (−170°)   **12.** ctn (−80°)
3. tan (−20°)   **8.** sec (−112°)   **13.** sin (−295°)
4. ctn (−125°)   **9.** sin (−303°)   **14.** cos (−163°)
5. sec (−151°)   **10.** tan (−111°)   **15.** sec (−12°)

Evaluate:

16. $\sin(-30°)\cos 45° + \tan(-135°)\operatorname{ctn} 225°$.

17. $\sec(-45°)\csc(-135°) - \tan(-315°)\cos(-240°)$.

18. $\sec^2(-60°)\sin^2(-135°) - \cos^2(-30°)\tan^2(-210°)$.

19. $\sin^2(-120°) + \cos^2(-120°) + \tan^2(-45°)$.

20. $\sin 240° \sec(-45°) - \tan(-30°)\csc(-315°)$.

Functions of (90° ± θ) and (270° ± θ) [A]

In more advanced mathematics it is frequently necessary to express functions of (90° ± θ) and (270° ± θ) in terms of θ. The functions of 90° − θ were given on pages 26–27.

Functions of (90° + θ).

In the figure, $\angle XOP = \theta$ and $XOP' = 90° + \theta$. OP' is drawn equal to OP. Since $\triangle OP'Q'$ and OPQ are congruent, we have $x' = -y$, $y' = x$, and $r' = r$. Then

$$\sin(90° + \theta) = \frac{y'}{r'} = \frac{x}{r} = \cos\theta$$

$$\cos(90° + \theta) = \frac{x'}{r'} = \frac{-y}{r} = -\sin\theta$$

$$\tan(90° + \theta) = \frac{y'}{x'} = \frac{x}{-y} = -\operatorname{ctn}\theta$$

$$\operatorname{ctn}(90° + \theta) = \frac{x'}{y'} = \frac{-y}{x} = -\tan\theta$$

$$\sec(90° + \theta) = \frac{r'}{x'} = \frac{r}{-y} = -\csc\theta$$

$$\csc(90° + \theta) = \frac{r'}{y'} = \frac{r}{x} = \sec\theta$$

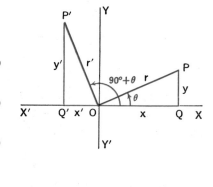

EXAMPLES. $\sin 110° = \sin(90° + 20°) = \cos 20°$

                 $\cos 130° = \cos(90° + 40°) = -\sin 40°$

                 $\operatorname{ctn} 170° = \operatorname{ctn}(90° + 80°) = -\tan 80°$

Functions of $(270° \pm \theta)$.

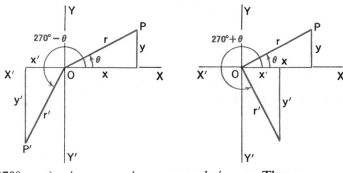

For $(270° - \theta)$, $x' = -y$, $y' = -x$, and $r' = r$. Then:

$$\sin (270° - \theta) = \frac{y'}{r'} = \frac{-x}{r} = -\cos \theta$$

$$\cos (270° - \theta) = \frac{x'}{r'} = \frac{-y}{r} = -\sin \theta$$

$$\tan (270° - \theta) = \frac{y'}{x'} = \frac{-x}{-y} = \text{ctn } \theta$$

$$\text{ctn } (270° - \theta) = \frac{x'}{y'} = \frac{-y}{-x} = \tan \theta$$

$$\sec (270° - \theta) = \frac{r'}{x'} = \frac{r}{-y} = -\csc \theta$$

$$\csc (270° - \theta) = \frac{r'}{y'} = \frac{r}{-x} = -\sec \theta$$

For $(270° + \theta)$, $x' = y$, $y' = -x$, and $r' = r$. Then:

$$\sin (270° + \theta) = \frac{y'}{r'} = \frac{-x}{r} = -\cos \theta$$

$$\cos (270° + \theta) = \frac{x'}{r'} = \frac{y}{r} = \sin \theta$$

$$\tan (270° + \theta) = \frac{y'}{x'} = \frac{-x}{y} = -\text{ctn } \theta$$

$$\text{ctn } (270° + \theta) = \frac{x'}{y'} = \frac{y}{-x} = -\tan \theta$$

$$\sec (270° + \theta) = \frac{r'}{x'} = \frac{r}{y} = \csc \theta$$

$$\csc (270° + \theta) = \frac{r'}{y'} = \frac{r}{-x} = -\sec \theta$$

EXAMPLES. sin 200° = sin (270° − 70°) = −cos 70°
$\qquad$ cos 212° = cos (270° − 58°) = −sin 58°
$\qquad$ tan 300° = tan (270° + 30°) = −ctn 30°
$\qquad$ sec 310° = sec (270° + 40°) = csc 40°

In the figures for (90° + θ) and (270° ± θ), θ is the reference angle and (90° + θ), (270° − θ), and (270° + θ) are said to be referred to the y-axis.

The method of applying the formulas of pages 138–139 may be stated as follows:

> *To find the function of any angle between 90° and 360° (except 180° or 270°) express the angle as (90° + θ) or (270° ± θ); then take the co-function of the reference angle θ and give it the sign determined by the function of the given angle in the quadrant to which it belongs.*

EXERCISES

A

1. Express the following as co-functions of positive acute angles:

a. sin 18° $\qquad$ **i.** tan 12° $\qquad$ **q.** sec 22°
b. sin 95° $\qquad$ **j.** tan 160° $\qquad$ **r.** sec (−160°)
c. sin 212° $\qquad$ **k.** tan 190° $\qquad$ **s.** sec 202°
d. sin 320° $\qquad$ **l.** tan 330° $\qquad$ **t.** sec 344°
e. cos 70° $\qquad$ **m.** ctn 3° $\qquad$ **u.** csc (−7°)
f. cos 130° $\qquad$ **n.** ctn 300° $\qquad$ **v.** csc 250°
g. cos 295° $\qquad$ **o.** ctn 250° $\qquad$ **w.** csc 98°
h. cos 350° $\qquad$ **p.** ctn 115° $\qquad$ **x.** csc 300°

2. Express as functions of θ:

a. sin (90° + θ) cos (270° − θ) − sin (270° − θ) cos (270° + θ)
b. sin (270° − θ) cos (270° + θ) + sin (90° + θ) cos (180° − θ)
c. sec (90° + θ) csc θ + csc (270° − θ) sec θ
d. tan (90° + θ) ctn θ − tan θ ctn (90° + θ)

B

3. Express as functions of θ:

a. sin (900° − θ) $\qquad$ **c.** sec (−180° − θ) $\qquad$ **e.** ctn (θ − 360°)
b. tan (800° + θ) $\qquad$ **d.** cos (θ − 90°) $\qquad$ **f.** csc (400° + θ)

Prove the formulas for $(90° + \theta)$ when:

4. θ is a second-quadrant angle.
5. θ is a third-quadrant angle.
6. θ is a fourth-quadrant angle.

CHAPTER REVIEW [A]

1. Given the following functions, sketch the two possible angles less than 360° and give their functions.

a. $\sin A = \frac{2}{3}$ **d.** $\operatorname{ctn} A = -\frac{1}{3}$ **g.** $\csc A = -\sqrt{2}$
b. $\cos A = -\frac{1}{2}\sqrt{2}$ **e.** $\sec A = \frac{13}{5}$ **h.** $\sin A = -\frac{1}{5}$
c. $\tan A = \frac{3}{4}$ **f.** $\tan A = -\frac{4}{7}$ **i.** $\cos A = \frac{2}{7}$

2. Express each as the same function of a positive acute angle.

a. $\sin 155°$ **e.** $\operatorname{ctn} 340°$ **i.** $\sin 112°$
b. $\cos 200°$ **f.** $\sec 200°$ **j.** $\operatorname{ctn} 213°$
c. $\cos (-160°)$ **g.** $\sin (-50°)$ **k.** $\operatorname{ctn} (-180°)$
d. $\tan (-222°)$ **h.** $\sec 195°$ **l.** $\csc 630°$

3. Express as functions of θ:

a. $\sin (180° - \theta) \sin (90° + \theta) + \sin (-\theta) \cos (\theta + 90°)$.
b. $\tan (90° + \theta) + \cos (270° + \theta) \sin (90° - \theta) - \sin (180° - \theta)$.
c. $\sin (-\theta) \sin (90° - \theta) \sin (90° + \theta)$.
d. $\sin (90° - \theta) \cos (270° + \theta) + \tan (90° + \theta) + \sin (180° - \theta)$.
e. $\cos (-30°) \operatorname{ctn} (90° + \theta) + 2 \sin (90° + \theta)$.

4. Find the value of

a. $\cos 90° - \csc 300° + \tan 225° - \sec 150°$

b. $\dfrac{\tan 210° + \operatorname{ctn} 240°}{1 + \tan 310° \operatorname{ctn} (-60°)}$

c. $\sin 270° + \tan 180° \cos 90°$

5. In $\triangle ABC$, if $A = 40°$ and $B = 30°$, find the functions of C.

Two soldiers sit at rangefinder; all the guns in the battery are directed by its calculations

Diverse Occupations Require Mathematics

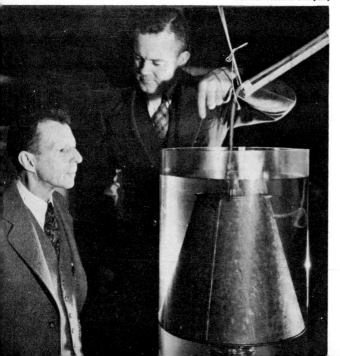

Two eminent scientists, Dr. W. D. Coolidge and Dr. E. E. Charlton, inspecting high-voltage apparatus in the X-ray section of a research laboratory

CHAPTER VI

RADIAN MEASURE; MIL MEASURE

Δ

Systems of Angle Measurement [A]

When studying arithmetic, algebra, and geometry, you used the degree or right angle as the unit for measuring the size of angles. When we use the degree or right angle as the unit in measuring angles, we are using the *sexagesimal system* of measurement. In this system there are six 60° angles about a point, each degree contains 60 minutes, and each minute contains 60 seconds. Do you see why this system is so named? The sexagesimal system of measurement is usually used in practical problems involving numerical computations.

In the study of higher mathematics and in the physical sciences the *circular system of measurement* is often more useful. The unit for circular measurement is the *radian*, which will be discussed in the next article.

The armed forces use a unit for measuring angles called the *mil*, which will be studied later on in this chapter.

The Radian [A]

Now let us see what a radian is. In a circle with center O and radius r, let $\overset{\frown}{AB} = r$. Draw AO and BO. Then $\angle O$ is called a radian. If the chord AB were equal to r, then $\angle O$ would equal 60°. But since chord AB is less than r, $\angle O$ is less than 60°.

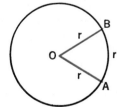

A *radian* is an angle which, when it is a central angle of a circle, intercepts an arc of the circle equal to the radius.

143

Now let us consider two radians and see if the radian is independent of the size of the circle. Let $\angle O$ and $\angle O'$ be two radians and circles O and O' unequal.

From geometry,

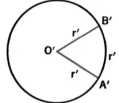

$$\frac{\angle O}{360} = \frac{r}{2\pi r}$$

and
$$\frac{\angle O'}{360} = \frac{r'}{2\pi r'}$$

Simplifying, $\dfrac{\angle O}{360} = \dfrac{1}{2\pi}$ and $\dfrac{\angle O'}{360} = \dfrac{1}{2\pi}$.

Then $\angle O = \angle O'$.

Thus the radian is independent of the size of the circle and of the unit used in measuring the radius.

Relations between the Radian and the Degree [A]

From geometry, $C = 2\pi r$. Since $AB = r$, we know that the arc AB is contained 2π times in the circle. Therefore $\angle O$ is contained 2π times in $360°$. In other words,

$$2\pi \text{ radians} = 360°.$$

Then π **radians** $= 180°.$

Then 1 radian $= \dfrac{180°}{\pi} = 57.2958° = 57°\ 17'\ 45''.$

Also, since $180° = \pi$ radians,

$$1° = \frac{\pi}{180} \text{ radian} = 0.01745 \text{ radian.}$$

You should remember that the equation π radians $= 180°$ is used for changing from one unit of measurement to the other.

In future work you should be careful to give the correct meaning to such expressions as $\sin \dfrac{\pi}{2}$, $\tan \dfrac{3\pi}{4}$, and $\dfrac{\pi}{4} = 45°$, because the word "radian" is usually omitted. For example, $\sin \dfrac{\pi}{2}$ means $\sin \left(\dfrac{\pi}{2} \text{ radians} \right)$.

EXAMPLE 1. Using π in the answer, express 24° 15′ in radians.

SOLUTION.
$$\pi \text{ radians } = 180°$$

$$1° = \frac{\pi}{180} \text{ radian}$$

$$24° 15′ = 24.25° = \frac{24.25}{180} \pi \text{ radian}$$

$$= .13472 \pi \text{ radian}$$

EXAMPLE 2. Express $\frac{4\pi}{5}$ in degrees.

SOLUTION.
$$\pi \text{ radians } = 180°$$
$$\tfrac{4}{5}\pi \text{ radians } = \tfrac{4}{5} \times 180° = 144°$$

EXAMPLE 3. Using Table IV, page 49, express 24° 15′ in radians correct to 5 decimal places.

SOLUTION. From Table IV, 20° = .34907 radian
4° = .06981 radian
10′ = .00291 radian
5′ = .00145 radian
24° 15′ = .42324 radian

EXAMPLE 4. Use Table IV to express 4.2 radians in degrees, minutes, and seconds.

SOLUTION. From Table IV,
$$4 \text{ radians } = 229° 10′ 59''$$
$$.2 \text{ radian } = 11° 27′ 33''$$
$$4.2 \text{ radians } = 240° 38′ 32''$$

EXERCISES

A

Express the following angles in radians, using π in each answer:

1. 18°	**5.** 30°	**9.** 120°	**13.** 22½°
2. 90°	**6.** 360°	**10.** 135°	**14.** 200°
3. 180°	**7.** 15°	**11.** 270°	**15.** 300°
4. 45°	**8.** 60°	**12.** 67½°	**16.** 720°

Express the following angles in degrees:

17. π **19.** $\dfrac{\pi}{2}$ **21.** $\dfrac{\pi}{4}$ **23.** $\dfrac{2\pi}{3}$ **25.** $\dfrac{\pi}{20}$ **27.** $\frac{5}{4}\pi$

18. 2π **20.** $\dfrac{\pi}{3}$ **22.** $\dfrac{\pi}{5}$ **24.** $\dfrac{3\pi}{4}$ **26.** $\frac{3}{2}\pi$ **28.** $\dfrac{\pi}{15}$

Use Table IV to express the following angles in radians correct to 5 decimal places:

29. 50°	**31.** 5°	**33.** 8° 6′ 20″	**35.** 45° 25′ 25″
30. 8°	**32.** 15°	**34.** 30° 8′ 40″	**36.** 41° 37′ 55″

Use Table IV to express the following radians in degrees, minutes, and seconds:

37. 2.31	**39.** .58	**41.** 2.19	**43.** .006
38. 1.67	**40.** .72	**42.** .74	**44.** .007

B

45. Find the radius of a circle in which an arc of 23 inches has a central angle of 2.6 radians.

46. Find the radius of a circle if a central angle of 1.4 radians intercepts an arc of 20 inches.

EXAMPLE 5. If θ is an acute angle expressed in radians, simplify the expression $\sin(\pi + \theta)$.

SOLUTION. $\sin(\pi + \theta) = \sin(180° + \theta)$
From page 132, $\sin(\pi + \theta) = -\sin\theta.$

If θ is an acute angle expressed in radians, simplify the following:

47. $\sin(\pi - \theta)$ **52.** $\tan\left(\dfrac{\pi}{2} + \theta\right)$ **57.** $\cos\left(\dfrac{3\pi}{2} - \theta\right)$

48. $\cos(\pi + \theta)$ **53.** $\tan\left(\dfrac{\pi}{2} - \theta\right)$ **58.** $\tan\left(\dfrac{3\pi}{2} - \theta\right)$

49. $\tan(\pi + \theta)$ **54.** $\sin\left(\dfrac{\pi}{2} - \theta\right)$ **59.** $\sin\left(\dfrac{3\pi}{2} + \theta\right)$

50. $\sin\left(\dfrac{\pi}{2} + \theta\right)$ **55.** $\cos\left(\dfrac{\pi}{2} - \theta\right)$ **60.** $\cos\left(\dfrac{3\pi}{2} + \theta\right)$

51. $\cos\left(\dfrac{\pi}{2} + \theta\right)$ **56.** $\sin\left(\dfrac{3\pi}{2} - \theta\right)$ **61.** $\tan\left(\dfrac{3\pi}{2} + \theta\right)$

Length of an Arc [A]

Let θ = the number of radians in a central angle that intercepts an arc s on the circle with radius r. In the same circle draw arc AB having

a central angle of one radian. Then $\dfrac{s}{\theta} = \dfrac{r}{1}$, because

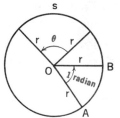

in the same circle, or in equal circles, central angles are proportional to their intercepted arcs.

Then $\qquad\qquad\qquad s = r\theta$

This formula can be expressed as follows:

The length of an arc of a circle is equal to the product of the radius and the number of radians in its central angle.

Note that the formula $s = r\theta$ contains three variables and that any one of them is a function of the other two and can be found when the values of the other two are known. For example, θ can be computed by $\theta = \dfrac{s}{r}$ or r can be computed by $r = \dfrac{s}{\theta}$.

EXERCISES

A

Find:

1. s when $r = 12$ and $\theta = \frac{1}{2}\pi$.
2. s when $r = 18.4$ and $\theta = \frac{3}{4}\pi$.
3. r when $s = 16.4$ and $\theta = \frac{2}{3}\pi$.
4. r when $s = 27.6$ and $\theta = \pi$.
5. θ when $r = 10$ and $s = 27$.
6. θ when $r = 16.3$ and $s = 81$.

7. Find the number of degrees in the central angle of a circle with radius of 20 inches if the angle subtends an arc of 13 inches.

8. Find the length of a degree on the equator considering the diameter of the equator to be 7912 miles.

9. The end of a 29-inch pendulum swings through a 4-inch arc. What is the size of the angle through which the pendulum swings?

10. If a 30-centimeter pendulum swings 2° 15′ on each side of its vertical position, what is the length of the arc through which the end of the pendulum swings?

11. A bicycle has a 28-inch wheel. How many revolutions will the wheel make when the bicycle travels one mile?

B

12. What is the length of a degree of longitude on the fortieth parallel? Assume that the earth is a sphere with a diameter of 7912 miles.

13. Find the length of a degree of longitude on the 45th parallel, assuming that the diameter of the earth is 7912 miles.

14. Prove that the area of a sector of a circle is $\frac{1}{2}r^2\theta$, θ being the angle at the center of the circle expressed in radians.

Linear and Angular Velocity [A]

When a body moves with a constant velocity v in time t, the distance s which the body travels is expressed by the formula $s = vt$. Solving this formula for v, we have $v = \frac{s}{t}$. The fraction $\frac{s}{t}$ expresses the *linear velocity* of the body. For example, if a boy runs 100 yards in 10 seconds, his average linear velocity is $\frac{100}{10}$, or 10 yards per second. The formula $s = vt$ is true regardless of the path of the moving body.

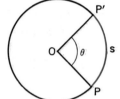

Now let a point P move on a circle O with a constant velocity v and let s be the distance traveled in time t. Then the linear velocity of the point is $\frac{s}{t}$. As the point P moves on the circle with constant velocity, the radius OP generates the central angle θ. If θ is generated in time t, then $\frac{\theta}{t}$ is the *angular velocity* of the point P.

From page 147, the arc s is given by the formula $s = r\theta$, θ being expressed in radians. Dividing both members of the equation $s = r\theta$ by t, we get $\frac{s}{t} = \frac{r\theta}{t}$. But $\frac{s}{t}$ is the linear velocity of P and $\frac{\theta}{t}$ is the angular velocity of P.

Now if we let the Greek letter ω (omega) stand for the angular velocity of P, the equation $\frac{s}{t} = \frac{r\theta}{t}$ becomes $v = r\omega$.

The linear velocity is equal to the radius times the angular velocity.

Two other forms of the formula $v = r\omega$ are $\omega = \frac{v}{r}$ and $r = \frac{v}{\omega}$. When using any of these formulas, you should remember that ω is expressed in radians.

EXERCISES [A]

1. If the angular velocity of a body is 300 revolutions per minute, what is the value ω?

2. The angular velocity of a flywheel is 500 radians per minute. Find the greatest linear velocity of any point on the flywheel if its diameter is 2 feet.

3. A flywheel makes 240 revolutions per minute. What is its angular velocity in radians?

4. A flywheel makes 20 revolutions per minute. What is the time required for the wheel to turn through π radians?

5. How many revolutions per minute does a wheel make if its angular velocity is 50π radians per second?

6. A bicycle wheel moves with an angular velocity of 8 radians per second. Find the linear velocity of the wheel if its diameter is 28 inches.

7. The propeller of an airplane is 9 feet in diameter. What is the linear velocity of the tip of a propeller blade if the angular velocity of the propeller is 50 radians per second?

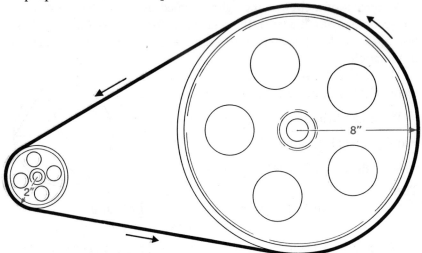

8. A wheel with an 8-inch radius is driven with a belt by a wheel with a 2-inch radius. What is the angular velocity of the larger wheel if the angular velocity of the smaller wheel is 250π radians per second?

9. As the minute hand of a large clock forms an angle of 52°, the end of the minute hand traverses a distance of 23.5 inches. Find the length of the minute hand.

10. The linear velocity of a point on a circle having a radius of 14 inches is 12 inches per second. Find the angular velocity of the point.

Areas of Sectors and Segments of Circles [A]

A *sector* is the figure formed by two radii and an arc of a circle. In the figure at the right OAB is a sector. In plane geometry it is shown that the area of a sector is equal to one half the product of the radius and the arc.

Then   area of sector $= \frac{1}{2}rs$.

But $s = r\theta$.

Then, by substitution,

     Area $OAB = \frac{1}{2}r(r\theta) = \frac{1}{2}r^2\,\theta$.

The area of a sector of a circle is given by the formula $K = \frac{1}{2}r^2\,\theta$, θ *being expressed in radians.*

A *segment* of a circle is the figure formed by a chord and its arc. In the accompanying diagram, the segment ADB encloses the shaded portion of the circle. The area of the segment is the area of the shaded part of the circle.

The area of the segment equals the area of the sector OAB minus the area of the triangle AOB.

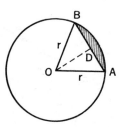

The area of the sector $= \frac{1}{2}r^2\theta$.

From page 111, Chapter IV,

     the area of $\triangle AOB = \frac{1}{2}r^2 \sin \theta$.

Then

         area of segment $AB = \frac{1}{2}r^2\theta - \frac{1}{2}r^2 \sin \theta$
                        $= \frac{1}{2}r^2(\theta - \sin \theta)$.

The area of a segment of a circle with radius r *and central angle* θ *is expressed by the formula* $K = \frac{1}{2}r^2(\theta - \sin \theta)$.

State how you would find the area of a segment of a circle when only the radius and chord are given.

EXAMPLE 1. Find the area of a sector of a circle if its central angle is 32° and the radius of the circle is 18 inches.

SOLUTION BY GEOMETRY.

$$K = \frac{32}{360} \times \pi r^2$$

$$K = \frac{32}{360} \times 3.1416 \times 18^2$$

$K = 90.478$ square inches, or 90 square inches

SOLUTION BY TRIGONOMETRY.

$K = \frac{1}{2} r^2 \theta$

π radians $= 180°$

$1° = \dfrac{\pi}{180}$ radian

$32° = \dfrac{32\pi}{180}$ radian

$K = \frac{1}{2} r^2 \theta$

$K = \frac{1}{2} \times 18^2 \times \dfrac{32\pi}{180} = \dfrac{18^2 \times 32\pi}{360}$

log 18 =	1.25527
log 18² =	2.51054
log 32 =	1.50515
log π =	0.49715
	4.51284
log 360 =	2.55630
log K =	1.95654
K =	90.478

The area is 90.478 square inches, or 90 square inches.

EXERCISES

A

1. Find the area of a sector of a circle whose central angle is $\frac{1}{2}\pi$ and whose diameter is 25 inches. Leave the answer in terms of π.

2. Find the area of a sector of a circle if its radius is 12.35 inches and the central angle is .3426 radian.

3. Find the area of a sector of a circle if the central angle is 53° and the radius of the circle is 15.3 inches.

4. Find the area of a sector of a circle if its central angle is 40° and the diameter of the circle is 24 inches.

5. A regular hexagon is inscribed in a circle with radius 18 inches. Find the area of each of the six segments.

6. A regular octagon is inscribed in a 20-inch circle. Find the area of the circle not enclosed by the octagon.

B

7. Two parallel chords on the same side of the center of a 24-inch circle are 10 inches and 6 inches long. Find the area of the part of the circle between the chords.

8. In a 20-inch circle, two parallel chords on opposite sides of the center are 6 inches and 8 inches long. Find the area of the portion of the circle between the chords.

9. A cylindrical gasoline tank 18 feet long has a diameter of 60 inches. The tank is buried in the ground in a horizontal position. Find the number of gallons of gasoline in the tank if it is filled to a depth of 16 inches. (V = area of segment $\times$ length, 1 cu. ft. = $7\frac{1}{2}$ gallons.)

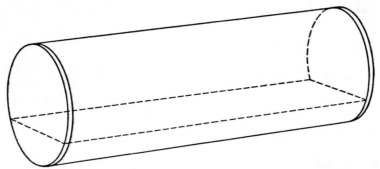

10. The area of a sector of a circle is 18 π. Find the radius of the circle if the central angle of the sector is $\frac{1}{6}\pi$.

11. Find the area of the smaller segment of a circle with diameter 30 inches if the chord of the segment is 26 inches.

12. The area of a sector of a circle is 100 square inches. Find the central angle if the radius of the circle is 12 inches.

Mil Measure [A]

The *mil* is used by the armed forces when measuring angles in computing firing data, mapping, reconnaisance, and sketching. The instruments used in measuring angles in the artillery are graduated in mils.

The mil (abbreviated $\not{m}$) is a unit for measuring angles and is $\frac{1}{6400}$ of a complete revolution.

Since 360° = 6400 mils,
$$1° = \frac{160}{9} \text{ mils,}$$
or $$1° = 17\frac{7}{9} \text{ mils.}$$

Since 6400 mils = 360°,
$$1 \text{ mil} = .05625°.$$

Since one radian $= 57.30°$ and 1000 mils $= 56.25°$, we see that

1000 mils $= 1$ radian, approximately.

The word *mil* means one thousandth.

The formula for the length s of an arc of a circle is $s = r\theta$, θ being in radian measure. If the measurement of the arc is made in mils, we must divide the mil measure by 1000 to obtain the radian measure.

Then $\qquad\qquad s = \dfrac{r \, m}{1000}$, approximately.

When the arc is small, $s = \dfrac{r \, m}{1000}$ can be used to find the arc s. The formula simplifies computation and enables one to find s quickly.

Since the distance between two points is usually measured on a straight line connecting the points instead of on the arc joining them, let us consider the chord AB in Fig. 1. When angle O is very small and the radius OA is large, the chord AB is almost equal to the arc AB. So the formula

$$\text{chord } AB = s = \frac{r \, m}{1000}$$

is approximately true.

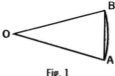

Fig. 1

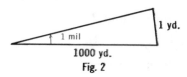

1 mil
1000 yd.
1 yd.
Fig. 2

According to the formula $s = \dfrac{r \, m}{1000}$, $s = 1$ yard when the angle is 1 mil and the distance is 1000 yards. (See Fig. 2.) Then *a mil subtends a yard at a distance of* 1000 *yards*. The army uses this statement for quick computations in the field.

EXAMPLE 1. Find the length of a target if at a right angle to the line of sight it subtends an angle of 25 mils at a range of 200 yards.

SOLUTION 1. $\qquad s = \dfrac{r \, m}{1000}$. $\quad s = \dfrac{200 \times 25}{1000} = 5$, the number of yards

SOLUTION 2. One mil subtends one yard at 1000 yards. Then 25 mils subtend 25 yards at 1000 yards. At 200 yards, 25 mils subtend $\frac{1}{5}$ of 25 yards, or 5 yards.

EXAMPLE 2. If two points, A and B, are 50 yards apart and are 5000 yards from an observer, how many mils do they subtend?

SOLUTION.
$$s = \frac{r\,m}{1000}$$

$$50 = \frac{5000\,m}{1000}$$

Solving, $m = 10$, the number of mils.

EXAMPLE 3. A target 24 feet long and perpendicular to the line of sight subtends an angle of 6 mils. Find the distance between the target and observer.

SOLUTION.
$$s = \frac{r\,m}{1000}$$

$$24 = \frac{r \times 6}{1000}$$

Solving, $r = 4000$, the number of feet.

EXERCISES [A]

1. Change to mils:

   a. 4°   **b.** 20°   **c.** 12°   **d.** 4′

2. Change to degrees:

   a. $17\frac{7}{9}$ mils   **b.** 1600 mils   **c.** 42 mils

3. Express in radians to the nearest integer:

   a. 31416 mils   **b.** 745 mils   **c.** 1625 mils

4. Which is larger, a radian or 1500 mils?

5. Which is larger, an angle of 57° or a radian?

6. Which is larger, an angle of 3° or a mil?

7. An observer reports to the gunner that the shots are falling 30 yards to the right of the target. If the range is 5000 yards, what correction in mils should the gunner make?

8. An airplane with a wing span of 80 feet is flying toward an observer. What is the distance of the plane from the observer when the plane subtends 8 mils?

9. Four guns in a battery of light artillery numbered 1, 2, 3, and 4 are spaced at intervals of 10 yards. The observer in front of the guns finds that the angle subtended by guns 1 and 3 is 12 mils. How far is the observer from the battery?

10. From an observation point 3000 yards away a barn whose length is 80 feet has its 80-foot side perpendicular to the line of sight. How many mils does the barn subtend at the observer?

CHAPTER REVIEW

1. What is the unit in the circular system of measurement? in the sexagesimal system?

2. Which is larger, a radian or an angle of an equilateral triangle?

3. Change to radians:

   a. 27°   b. 180°   c. 90°   d. 45°

4. Change the following radians to degrees:

   a. π b. 2π c. 2   d. .7854

5. Find the arcs when:

   a. $r = 14$ b. $r = 276$ c. $r = 7.2$

   $\theta = \dfrac{\pi}{3}$ $\theta = \dfrac{2\pi}{3}$ $\theta = \dfrac{\pi}{6}$

6. Find the radius of a circle when the arc is 16 inches and the central angle is $\dfrac{\pi}{8}$.

7. An arc of a circle is $\frac{1}{6}\pi$ and its central angle is $\frac{2}{3}\pi$. Find the radius of the circle.

8. The radius of a circle is 8 inches. Find the number of degrees in the central angle of the circle which intercepts an arc of:

   a. 3 inches   b. 4 inches   c. 14 inches

9. If the radius of a circle is 16 inches, find the arc of the circle which is intercepted by a central angle of:

   a. $\dfrac{\pi}{2}$ b. 60°   c. 24°

10. Through how many radians does the minute hand of a clock turn in 3 hours?

11. A spoke of a wheel makes 32 revolutions while the wheel is going 425 feet. Find the diameter of the wheel.

12. A bicycle whose wheels are 28 inches in diameter is going 20 m.p.h. How many revolutions per minute does each wheel make?

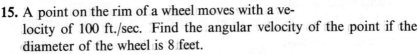

13. Use the drawing at the right to show that a radian is less than 60°.

14. The angular velocity of a point on a circle with radius of 8 feet is 10π radians per second. Find the linear velocity of the point.

15. A point on the rim of a wheel moves with a velocity of 100 ft./sec. Find the angular velocity of the point if the diameter of the wheel is 8 feet.

16. Simplify: **a.** $\sin (\pi + \theta)$.   **b.** $\tan \left(\dfrac{\pi}{2} - \theta \right)$.   **c.** $\cos \left(\dfrac{\pi}{2} + \theta \right)$.

17. Find the area of a segment of a circle if the central angle is 40° and the radius is 18 inches.

CHAPTER VII

LINE VALUES AND GRAPHS
OF FUNCTIONS

Δ

Representing Functions by Lines [A]

In Chapter I each of the six trigonometric functions was defined as the ratio of two line segments associated with the angle. Then in Chapter V these definitions were extended so as to include angles of any size, both positive and negative.

We can better understand and remember the behavior of these functions if we can represent them graphically. We know that any fraction whose denominator is 1 is equal to its numerator.

Thus, $\frac{4}{1} = 4$, $\frac{5.3}{1} = 5.3$, and $\frac{AB}{1} = AB$.

Now if we can express each trigonometric function as a ratio of two line segments and have the value of the second term of each ratio equal to one, then the first term of each ratio will represent a function. This first term, being a directed line segment, will represent the function both in magnitude and in direction.

Directed line segments which represent functions are called *line values* of the functions. Now let us see how we can draw the line values of the functions.

Line Values of the Functions of an Acute Angle [A]

Draw the horizontal axis OX and the vertical axis OY, as shown in the diagram on page 159. Let θ be any acute angle having its initial side lying on OX. With O as the center draw a circle whose radius is one unit in length. (A circle whose radius is one unit in length is called a *unit circle*.)

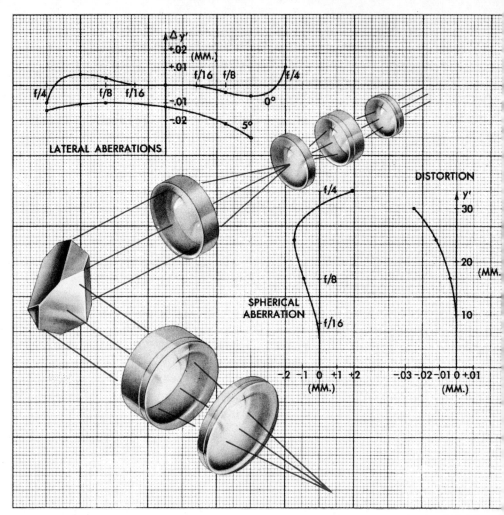

$\Delta y'$ +.02 (MM.)
+.01 f/16 f/8 f/4
0°
f/4 f/8 f/16
−.01
−.02 5°

LATERAL ABERRATIONS

DISTORTION
y'
30

20 (MM.

f/4

SPHERICAL
ABERRATION

f/8

f/16

10

−2 −1 0 +1 +2
(MM.)

−.03 −.02 −.01 0 +.01
(MM.)

Mathematics in Optics

Scientists designed the special optical system sketched above for use
with an elaborate machine tool. The curves shown predict the lens
performance

A and F are points of intersection of the circle with the axes. Draw $AB \perp OA$, $DC \perp OA$, and $EF \perp OF$, as shown in the diagram. Remember that $OA = OD = OF = 1$ and that $\angle OEF = \angle COD$.

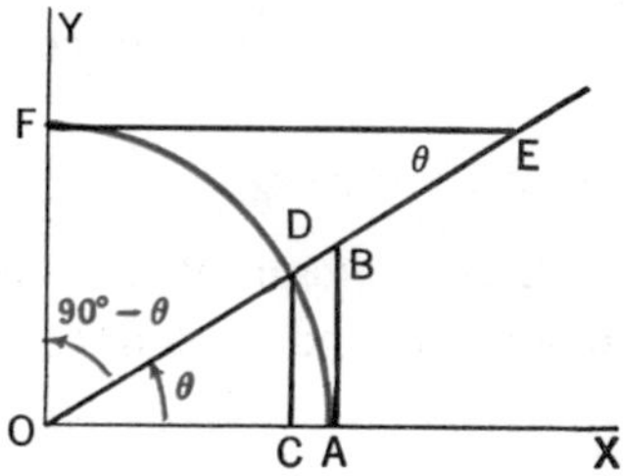

Then, $\sin \theta = \dfrac{CD}{OD} = \dfrac{CD}{1} = CD$

$\cos \theta = \dfrac{OC}{OD} = \dfrac{OC}{1} = OC$

$\tan \theta = \dfrac{AB}{OA} = \dfrac{AB}{1} = AB$

$\text{ctn } \theta = \tan (90° - \theta) = \dfrac{FE}{OF} = \dfrac{FE}{1} = FE$

$\sec \theta = \dfrac{OB}{OA} = \dfrac{OB}{1} = OB$

$\csc \theta = \sec (90° - \theta) = \dfrac{OE}{OF} = \dfrac{OE}{1} = OE$

EXERCISES

A

1. Can you suggest a way of remembering that AB represents the tangent of θ? that FE represents the cotangent of θ? that OB represents the secant of θ? that OE represents the cosecant of θ?

2. What two functions are represented by the legs of $\triangle OCD$?

B

3. Look up the definitions of versed sine, coversed sine, haversine, external secant, and subversed sine in Chapter I. Copy the figure above and draw $DH \perp OY$. Then show that:

CA represents versed sine θ
HF represents coversed sine θ
$\frac{1}{2} CA$ represents haversine θ
DB represents external secant θ
$OA + OC$ represents subversed sine θ

Line Values of the Functions in the Four Quadrants [A]

The four figures on the following page show the angle θ having its terminal side falling in each of the four quadrants. Figure 1 is like the figure above.

In each of the four quadrants,

$$CD = \sin \theta \qquad\qquad FE = \text{ctn } \theta$$
$$OC = \cos \theta \qquad\qquad OB = \sec \theta$$
$$AB = \tan \theta \qquad\qquad OE = \csc \theta$$

In each quadrant these line segments represent the functions both in magnitude and in sign, the length of the segment giving the magnitude

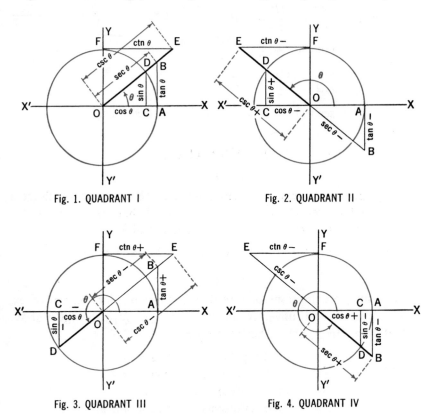

Fig. 1. QUADRANT I   Fig. 2. QUADRANT II

Fig. 3. QUADRANT III   Fig. 4. QUADRANT IV

and the direction of the line giving the sign of the function. Let us explain these statements.

In agreement with the definitions of the functions given in Chapter V, a horizontal line directed to the right is positive and one directed to the left is negative; a vertical line directed upward is positive and one directed downward is negative; and the terminal side of the angle is positive. In the diagrams OD is the terminal side of θ. Line segments measured on OD are positive if they have the same direction as OD and they are negative if they have a direction opposite to that of OD. For example, OE (csc θ) in quadrant III is negative because it is opposite in direction to OD.

Do you see that vertical line segments above the x-axis are positive and vertical line segments below the x-axis are negative? Do you see that horizontal line segments to the right of the y-axis are positive and horizontal line segments to the left of the y-axis are negative?

EXERCISES [A]

The following exercises refer to the four figures on page 160.

1. What is the sign of OB in each of the four quadrants? of OC? of OE? of OD?

2. Which functions are represented by vertical line segments? by horizontal line segments?

3. Which functions are represented by portions of the radius vector?

4. In which quadrant are all six functions positive?

Complete these statements:

5. Only the _? and its reciprocal function are positive in the second quadrant.

6. Only the _?_ and its reciprocal function are positive in the third quadrant.

7. Only the _?_ and its reciprocal function are positive in the fourth quadrant.

8. The sine, cosine, and tangent have the same signs as their _?_.

9. The _?_ and _?_ functions never have values greater than $+1$ or less than -1.

10. The _?_ and _?_ functions never have positive values less than 1.

11. The _?_ and _?_ functions may have very large positive values and very large negative values.

Variations of the Sine and Cosine [A]

The four figures below show the sine and cosine functions of θ in all four quadrants. The other functions are omitted for ease in studying the variation in the sine and cosine as the angle increases or decreases.

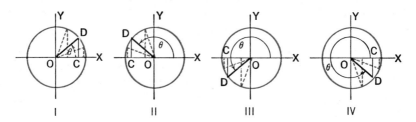

I   II   III   IV

The ordinate CD represents sin θ. Note that sin θ is positive in the first and second quadrants and negative in the third and fourth quadrants. CD may equal zero but its absolute value is never greater than the radius (1) of the unit circle.

In the first quadrant as θ becomes smaller CD becomes smaller; and as θ becomes larger, CD becomes larger. As θ approaches zero as a limit, CD, or sin θ, approaches zero as its limit; and as θ approaches 90° as a limit, CD approaches OD (which is 1) as its limit. So as θ increases from 0° to 90°, sin θ is positive and changes from 0 to 1.

As θ (in quadrant II) changes from 90° to 180°, sin θ is positive and decreases from 1 to 0.

As soon as θ becomes greater than 180° (in quadrant III), sin θ becomes negative. As θ increases from 180° to 270°, sin θ is negative and decreases from 0 to −1.*

As θ increases from 270° to 360°, sin θ is negative and increases from −1 to 0.

In the same four figures OC represents the cosine of θ. Again observe that the cosine is positive only in the first and fourth quadrants. Use these figures to observe the changes in the cosine as θ changes from 0° to 360°.

As θ approaches zero as a limit, OC approaches OD as its limit; and as θ approaches 90° as a limit, OC approaches zero as its limit. As θ increases from 0° to 90°, cos θ is positive and decreases from 1 to 0. As soon as θ becomes greater than 90°, cos θ becomes negative. And as θ

---

* The value of a negative number increases when its absolute value decreases, and decreases when its absolute value increases. Thus, −4 is greater than −5.

increases from 90° to 180°, cos θ is negative and decreases from 0 to -1. As θ increases from 180° to 270°, cos θ is negative and increases from -1 to 0. As θ increases from 270° to 360°, cos θ is positive and increases from 0 to 1.

Have you observed that neither the sine nor the cosine has any values greater than $+1$ or any values less than -1? We can express these facts as follows: $-1 \leqq \sin \theta \leqq +1$ and $-1 \leqq \cos \theta \leqq +1$.

Variations of Tangent and Secant [A]

In the four figures below, AB represents tan θ and OB represents sec θ. In quadrant I, when θ approaches zero, AB, or tan θ, approaches zero and OB, or sec θ, approaches 1. Now as θ increases from zero, both AB

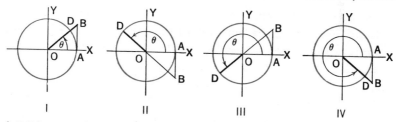

and OB become larger. When θ approaches very near 90°, both AB and OB become very large. When θ becomes 90°, OB and AB are parallel, never meeting in a finite point. However, we think of parallel lines as meeting at infinity. So as θ increases from 0° to 90°, tan θ is positive and increases from 0 to ∞ (infinity) and sec θ is positive and increases from 1 to ∞.

Just as soon as θ extends into the second quadrant, that is, becomes greater than 90°, both AB and OB become negative. Note that when θ passes through 90°, both tan θ and sec θ change from an infinitely large positive number to an infinitely large negative number, that is, from $+\infty$ to $-\infty$. As we shall see later, the graphs of these two functions are not smooth and continuous like the sine and cosine curves but have breaks in them.

As θ increases from 90° to 180°, both tan θ and sec θ are negative, tan θ increases from $-\infty$ to 0, and sec θ increases from $-\infty$ to -1. As θ increases from 180° to 270°, tan θ is positive, increasing from 0 to ∞, and sec θ is negative, decreasing from -1 to $-\infty$. As θ increases from 270° to 360°, tan θ is negative, increasing from $-\infty$ to 0, and sec θ is positive, decreasing from $+\infty$ to $+1$.

Variations in Cotangent and Cosecant [A]

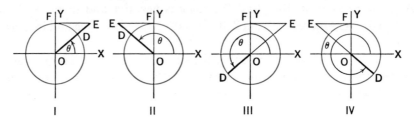

In the figures above *FE* represents the cotangent of θ and *OE* the cosecant of θ. You should follow the changes in ctn θ and csc θ as θ changes from 0° to 360°. Then check your results with the table below.

Summary of Changes of Functions [A]

The following table is a summary of the changes of the trigonometric functions as the angle changes from 0° to 360°.

ANGLE	FUNCTION					
	SINE	COSINE	TANGENT	COTANGENT	SECANT	COSECANT
0° to 90°	INCREASE 0 to +1	DECREASE +1 to 0	INCREASE 0 to +∞	DECREASE +∞ to 0	INCREASE +1 to +∞	DECREASE +∞ to +1
90° to 180°	DECREASE +1 to 0	DECREASE 0 to −1	INCREASE −∞ to 0	DECREASE 0 to −∞	INCREASE −∞ to −1	INCREASE +1 to +∞
180° to 270°	DECREASE 0 to −1	INCREASE −1 to 0	INCREASE 0 to +∞	DECREASE +∞ to 0	DECREASE −1 to −∞	INCREASE −∞ to −1
270° to 360°	INCREASE −1 to 0	INCREASE 0 to +1	INCREASE −∞ to 0	DECREASE 0 to −∞	DECREASE +∞ to +1	DECREASE −1 to −∞

Facts to Remember [A]

A study of the table above discloses some interesting facts:

1. In the first quadrant the sine, tangent, and secant functions increase as the angle increases and their cofunctions decrease as the angle increases. The sine, secant, and tangent are *increasing functions* and the cosine, cosecant, and cotangent are *decreasing functions* in this quadrant.

2. The values of the sine and cosine range from −1 to +1.

3. The values of the secant and cosecant range from $+1$ to $+\infty$ and from -1 to $-\infty$, having no values between -1 and $+1$.

4. The tangent and cotangent can have any value from $-\infty$ to $+\infty$.

5. All functions change signs as they pass through the values 0 and ∞.

6. The tangent always increases, except where it changes from $+\infty$ to $-\infty$.

7. The cotangent always decreases, except when it changes from $-\infty$ to $+\infty$.

EXERCISES

A

1. Using the unit circle construct the line function of:

    a. sin 45°   **c.** tan 60°   **e.** sin 270°   **g.** tan 270°

    b. cos 30°   **d.** sec 0°   **f.** sec 180°   **h.** csc 135°

2. As θ increases from 0° to 360° which function always increases (one exception)?

3. What is the range of values of each of the six functions?

4. If θ is less than 90°, show which is greater,

    a. sin θ or tan θ **c.** cos θ or ctn θ

    b. tan θ or sec θ **d.** csc θ or ctn θ

5. Of the angles 40°, 120°, 210°, 300°, 80°, and 350°,

    a. Which have negative sines?

    b. Which have positive cosines?

    c. Which have positive tangents?

6. Using unit circles, show that:

    a. sin 160° = sin 20°   **c.** tan 60° = −ctn 330°

    b. cos 135° = −cos 45°   **d.** csc 300° = −sec 30°

7. Show that tangents of angles less than 90° are less than ∞.

8. Which function decreases in each of the four quadrants?

9. Using unit circles, show that for θ in the first quadrant:

    a. $\sin^2 \theta + \cos^2 \theta = 1$

    b. $\sec^2 \theta = 1 + \tan^2 \theta$ **c.** $\tan \theta = \dfrac{\sin \theta}{\cos \theta}$

10. Which trigonometric functions pass through zero?

B

11. Name the quadrants, if any, in which the following changes occur as θ increases:
    a. Both sine and cosine increase.
    b. Sine increases and tangent increases.
    c. Tangent increases and sine decreases.
    d. Tangent decreases and secant decreases.

12. Which trigonometric functions pass through infinity?

13. Show which is the greater:
    a. sin $(180° - \theta)$ or tan θ
    b. tan $(180° + \theta)$ or tan θ

14. Explain why the sine and cosecant of any angle have the same sign.

Graphs of Functions [A]

Thus far in your study of mathematics you have learned how to graph functions like $2x + 3$ and $x^2 - 6x$. The graph of $y = 2x + 3$ is a straight line and the graph of $y = x^2 - 6x$ is a parabola.

x	-1	0	1	2
y	1	3	5	7

x	-1	1	0	3	5	6	7
y	7	-5	0	-9	-5	0	7

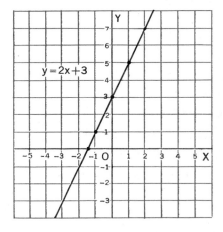

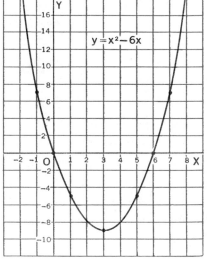

In the equation $y = 2x + 3$, the binomial $2x + 3$ is a function of x; and in the equation $y = x^2 - 6x$, the binomial $x^2 - 6x$ is a function of x. Is y a function of $2x + 3$? Is y a function of $x^2 - 6x$?

Trigonometric functions are graphed in a manner similar to the method used above. In graphing trigonometric functions we choose convenient values for the angles and use the table of natural functions to find the functions of these angles. We tabulate these pairs of values and plot the points, using co-ordinate axes. In graphing trigonometric functions we shall use x instead of θ to denote the angle.

The Graph of sin x [A]

To draw the graph of $y = \sin x$, we prepare a table of values of $\sin x$ from $0°$ to $360°$. We choose to let x have values of $0°$, $30°$, $60°$, $90°$, etc. We use Table X to find the values of $\sin x$ for these values.

We draw the perpendicular axes. On the x-axis we let each space equal $30°$ and on the y-axis we let each space represent .25 units. Then we plot the points whose co-ordinates are in the table. Then we draw

x	0°	30°	60°	90°	120°	150°	180°	210°	240°	270°	300°	330°	360°
sin x	0	.5	.9	1	.9	.5	0	−.5	−.9	−1	−.9	−.5	0

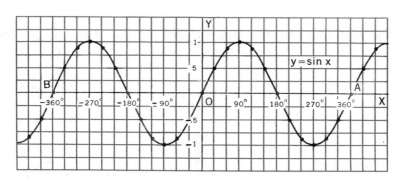

a smooth curve through the points. The curve is an S-shaped wave extending from the origin to A.

Now we let x take negative values. Since $\sin(-x) = -\sin x$, we can use the above table for graphing the curve from $0°$ to $-360°$.

Plotting the points and drawing a smooth curve through them, we obtain the curve from the origin to B. If we extend the graph, letting x

take values greater than 360° and less than −360°, it will continue to repeat itself every 360°. Since the function repeats itself, it is called a *periodic function*. The period of the sine function is 360°, or 2 π.

EXERCISES [A]

Complete the statements in Exs. 1–4. Use the graph of sin x for these exercises.

1. As *x* increases from 0° to 90°, sin *x* increases from _?_ to _?_.
As *x* increases from 90° to 270°, sin *x* decreases from _?_ to _?_.
As *x* increases from 270° to 360°, sin *x* increases from _?_ to _?_.

2. As *x* decreases from 0° to −90°, sin *x* decreases from _?_ to _?_.
As *x* decreases from −90° to −270°, sin *x* _?_ from _?_ to _?_.
As *x* decreases from −270° to −360°, sin *x* _?_ from _?_ to _?_.

3. The graph of sin *x* _?_ itself every 360°.

4. The maximum value of sin *x* is _?_ and the minimum value of sin *x* is _?_.

5. What is the approximate value of sin 45°?   of sin (−75°)?

6. If *x* is less than 90°, show by the graph that:
  a. sin (180° + *x*) = −sin *x*.   **b.** sin (180° − *x*) = sin *x*.

The Graph of cos *x* [A]

The method used in graphing the sine function is used in graphing the other functions. The graph of the cosine function is shown below.

x	0°	30°	60°	90°	120°	150°	180°	210°	240°	270°	300°	330°	360°
cos *x*	1	.9	.5	0	−.5	−.9	−1	−.9	−.5	0	.5	.9	1

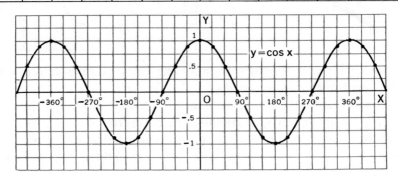

Notice that the cosine graph has the same shape as the sine graph but that it is moved either 90° to the left or 270° to the right.

EXERCISES

A

1. Tell why the cosine function is periodic.
2. What is the period of cos x?
3. How does the cosine of x change when x changes from 0° to 180°? from 180° to 360°?
4. Show that $\cos x = \cos(-x)$.
5. What is the maximum value of cos x?   the minimum value of cos x?
6. Show that for acute $\angle x$,

   a. $\cos(180° + x) = -\cos x$ **b.** $\cos(180° - x) = -\cos x$

B

7. On the same set of axes, draw the graphs of sin x and cos x. Then by adding the values of y, draw the graph of $y = \sin x + \cos x$. Is $\sin x + \cos x$ periodic?

The Graphs of tan x and ctn x [A]

The graph of tan x is shown below and that of ctn x on the next page. Notice that each graph consists of a series of parallel curves.

x	0°	30°	60°	90°	120°	150°	180°	210°	240°	270°	300°	330°	360°
tan x	0	.6	1.7	∞	−1.7	−.6	0	.6	1.7	∞	−1.7	−.6	0

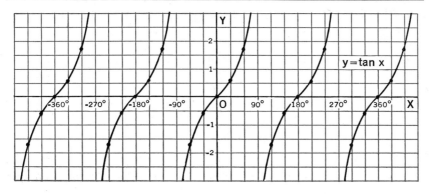

x	0°	30°	60°	90°	120°	150°	180°	210°	240°	270°	300°	330°	360°
ctn x	∞	1.7	.6	0	−.6	−1.7	∞	1.7	.6	0	−.6	−1.7	∞

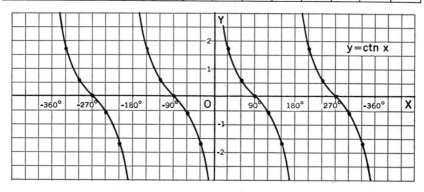

EXERCISES

A

Complete the sentences in exercises 1–5.

1. As an angle increases from 0° to 45°, its tangent increases from _?_ to _?_.

2. As an angle increases from 45° to 90°, its tangent increases from _?_ to _?_.

3. As an angle passes through 90°, the tangent jumps from _?_ to _? .

4. The period of tan x is _?_ degrees.

5. The period of ctn x is _?_ degrees.

6. Find four angles each of whose tangents equals 1; −1.

7. What is the approximate value of tan 15°? of tan 135°?

8. Show that tan $(180° − x) = −\tan x$.

9. Show that tan $(180° + x) = \tan x$.

B

10. Draw the graph of tan $x +$ ctn x.

The Graphs of sec x and csc x [B]

The graphs of sec x and csc x are shown on page 171. See how they compare with the graphs of the other four trigonometric functions.

x	0°	30°	60°	75°	90°	105°	120°	150°	180°	210°	240°	270°
sec x	1	1.2	2	4	∞	−4	−2	−1.2	−1	−1.2	−2	− ∞

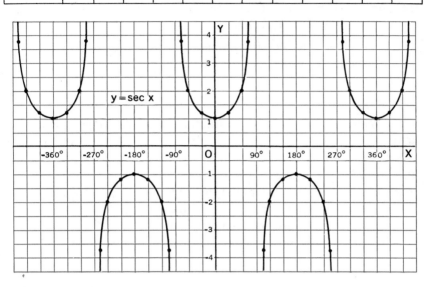

x	0°	15°	30°	60°	90°	120°	150°	165°	180°	195°	210°	240°	270°
csc x	∞	4	2	1.2	1	1.2	2	4	∞	−4	−2	−1.2	−1

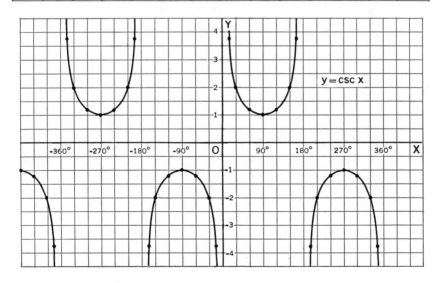

EXERCISES [B]

1. What is the period of sec x? of csc x?

2. Complete: The values of sec x and csc x are equal to or greater than _?_, but equal to or less than _?_.

3. One angle contains 89° 30′ and another angle is 1° larger. Compare their secants as to size.

Slope of a Curve [B]

The *slope of a line* is equal to the tangent of the angle that the line makes with the horizontal axis.

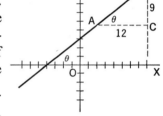

In the figure, the slope of the line $AB =$ tan $\theta = \frac{3}{4}$. AB is the graph of $y = \frac{3}{4} x + 3$. From the figure it can be seen that the slope of a line is equal to the increase of the function $\frac{3}{4} x + 3$ or y, divided by the increase of the independent variable x. Thus the slope of $AB = \dfrac{CB}{AC} = \dfrac{3}{4}$. Do you see that all segments of a given line have the same slope?

The *direction of a curve* at any point on it is the direction of the tangent to the curve at that point. Then the *slope of a curve* at any point of the curve is the slope of the tangent to the curve at this point. The slope of the tangent at a point on the curve gives the rate of change of the function at this point. At point A

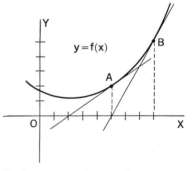

in the figure at the right, the slope of the curve is $\frac{2}{3}$. This means that the function $f(x)$ increases $\frac{2}{3}$ as fast as x at this point. At point B the rate of increase of the function is $\frac{5}{3}$. At A the slope of the tangent is $\frac{2}{3}$ and at B it is $\frac{5}{3}$.

In order that a graph may give a true picture of a function, the same unit must be used on both axes. If the same unit is not used on both axes, the graph does not picture the correct rate of change of the function at all points. For example, the graph of $y = x^2 - 6 x$ on page 166 is not a true picture of the relation between y and x since one unit on the y-axis does not have the same length as a unit on the *x*-axis. The graph pictures the ratio of the rate of change of *y* to the rate of change of *x* as larger than it really is. Here a smaller unit was used on the *y*-axis to save space on the page.

Radian Measure in Graphing [A]

In making the graphs of the trigonometric functions in the preceding pages, the unit on the *y*-axis and the unit on the *x*-axis were arbitrarily chosen and were independent of each other.

In order to obtain a true picture of these functions, we must use the same unit for the independent variable as we use for the dependent variable. For example, in graphing $y = \sin x$, we must use the same unit for measuring angle *x* as we use in measuring *y*, or sin *x*.

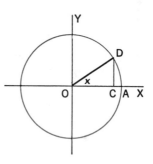

Now consider the function $y = \sin x$. Draw *CD*, the line representation of sin *x*. Since *O* is a unit circle, $OD = 1$. We know that *CD* is measured with reference to *OD*, or 1. Then we wish to measure ∠*x* by *OD*, or 1. We can measure ∠*x* by *OD* when we express *x* in radians. This is so because the number of radians in *x* is found by dividing the arc *AD* by the radius *OD*. Thus when the radius of the unit circle is used as a unit of length on the *y*-axis, it is the length of a radian on the *x*-axis.

Since the radius of the unit circle can be chosen arbitrarily, we can use any length as the unit on the *y*-axis. Then if we use this same unit to represent a radian on the *x*-axis, we can draw the graph which shows the correct relation between the angle and its sine.

In like manner it can be shown that radian measure can be used to obtain true pictures of the other functions.

To find the functions, first convert the radians to degrees, using Table IV. Then use the table of natural functions.

x in radians	0	.5	1	1.5	2	2.5	3	4	5	6
sin *x*	0	.5	.8	1.	.9	.6	.1	−.8	−1.	−.3
cos *x*	1	.9	.5	.1	−.4	−.8	−1	−.7	.3	1.

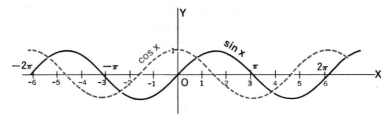

The solid curve is the graph of sin x and the broken-line curve is the graph of cos x. If the sine curve is moved $\frac{1}{2}\pi$ radians to the left, it will coincide with the cosine curve.

EXERCISES

A

1. Using the graphs above, find five angles whose sines equal the cosines.

2. Find four angles for each of which sin x + cos x = 0.

3. Between what values of x is cos x an increasing function?   a decreasing function?

4. Between what values of x is sin x an increasing function?   a decreasing function?

B

5. Choose any point P on the sine curve. Find the approximate slope of the curve at this point. Plot the point whose abscissa is that of P and whose ordinate equals the slope of the curve at P. Where does this point lie? Do the same for other points of the sine curve. What is your conclusion?

Amplitudes and Periods of Functions [B]

The maximum value of sin x is $+1$ and the minimum value is -1. Since the maximum value of $y = $ sin x is $+1$, the maximum value of $y = 2$ sin x is $+2$, the maximum value of $y = 5$ sin x is $+5$, and the maximum value of $y = n$ sin x is n. The minimum values of these functions are -1, -2, -5, and $-n$ respectively.

The *amplitude* of a periodic function (or curve) is the greatest numerical value that the function may have. It is the distance of the high points and low points of the curve from the x-axis. Then the amplitudes of $y = $ cos x, $y = 3$ cos x, $y = m$ cos x are 1, 3, and m respectively. Note that the coefficients of sin x and cos x affect the ordinate of the curve. The amplitudes of tan x, ctn x, sec x, and csc x are infinite.

From what has been said, you will see that any change in the coefficient of sin x or of cos x produces a change in the amplitude of the function. Now let us see how a change in the coefficient of x affects the function.

As explained on page 168, the *period* of sin x is 360°, or 2π. Since the sine of any angle repeats itself every 360° (2π), the sine of $2x$ repeats itself when $2x = 360°$, or when $x = 180°$, or π. Likewise, sin $3x$ repeats itself when $x = 120°$, or $\dfrac{2\pi}{3}$, and sin ax repeats itself when $x = \dfrac{2\pi}{a}$. Then the period of sin $2x$ is $\dfrac{2\pi}{2}$, of sin $3x$ is $\dfrac{2\pi}{3}$, and of sin ax is $\dfrac{2\pi}{a}$. Likewise, the period of sin $\frac{1}{2}x$ is $\dfrac{2\pi}{\frac{1}{2}} = 4\pi$; of sin $\frac{2}{5}x$ is $\dfrac{2\pi}{\frac{2}{5}} = 5\pi$.

The periods of the other five trigonometric functions are affected in like manner. Thus, the period of tan $\frac{2}{3}x$ is $\pi \div \frac{2}{3} = \frac{3}{2}\pi$ and the period of tan $\frac{3}{4}x = \pi \div \frac{3}{4} = \frac{4}{3}\pi$.

Now let us apply what we have just learned to graphing.

EXAMPLE. Graph $y = 2 \sin 3x$.

SOLUTION. Since the amplitude of the sine is 1, the amplitude of twice the sine is 2. The period of sin $3x$ is $\dfrac{2\pi}{3}$. We shall lay off on the y-axis a convenient unit. Then we shall lay off π on the x-axis equal to 3.14. Then we shall divide the π distances into 3 equal parts. Since the period is $\frac{2}{3}\pi$, the curve crosses the x-axis at 0, $\frac{1}{3}\pi$, $\frac{2}{3}\pi$, π, $\frac{4}{3}\pi$, $\frac{5}{3}\pi$, 2π, etc. The graph of 2 sin 3 x is shown below.

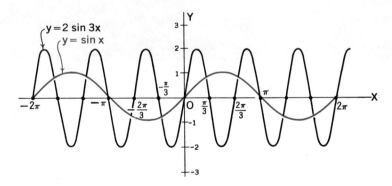

Photo by Howard Modavis, courte
Life; © *Time,* Incorporat

Solid Sound

Scientists at Bell Telephone Laboratories have developed a method of representing spoken words in three dimensions. Shown above are models of three-dimensional graphs of five of the digits. Such models enable engineers to study the sound patterns of speech and to improve the use of existing telephone transmission lines and coaxial cables

Importance of Periodic Functions [B]

A periodic function is one that repeats itself at regular intervals. It is one in which equal values occur in the same order when the variable is uniformly increased or decreased. As you have already learned, all six trigonometric functions are periodic.

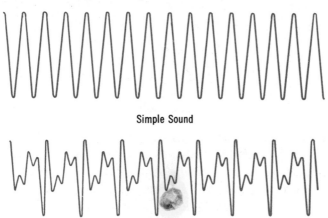

Simple Sound

ō as in Low

Periodic functions are important because they characterize so many relations existing among the forces and movements in nature.

As you know, sound travels in waves. If a sound is a pure tone, it can be represented by a sine curve. Sounds that are pleasing to the ear can be represented by complex periodic functions. Curves representing noises are irregular.

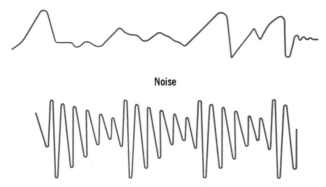

Noise

Musical Note

The sine curve occurs often in the study of electricity because the sine wave is the fundamental wave form of all alternating currents. The equations $y = a \sin bx$ and $y = a \cos bx$ are the foundations of the mathematics of wave motion.

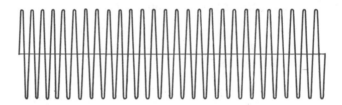

Carrier Wave

The carrier waves in radio transmission are sine waves. These waves are modulated by sound waves so as to change either their amplitude or their frequency. In the drawing shown below, the carrier waves are modulated by a change in their amplitude. The envelope of the modulated carrier wave has the same shape as the sound wave. In radio frequency modulation (RFM) the amplitude of the carrier wave is kept constant and the sound wave changes the frequency.

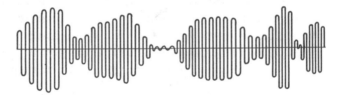

Carrier Curve Modulated by Voice Wave

Any uniform motion on a circle produces a harmonic motion on a diameter of the circle which can be represented by a sine wave. Thus, as the point P moves around the circle with uniform speed, its projection P' on the diameter AB oscillates along AB in simple harmonic motion.

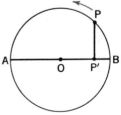

Many other natural phenomena have periodic properties. For example, the rotation of the earth on its axis and its movement around the sun are periodic.

EXERCISES[B]

State the periods and amplitudes of the following functions and draw their graphs:

1. $y = \sin 3x$ **3.** $y = 3 \cos 2x$ **5.** $y = \sec 2x$

2. $y = \sin 2x$ **4.** $y = 4 \cos 3x$ **6.** $y = 3 \tan 3x$

7. a. On the same set of axes draw the graphs of $\sin x$ and $\cos x$.
   b. Use the graph to show that $\cos x = \sin (90° - x)$.
   c. By adding the ordinates of the graphs of (**a**), graph the equation $y = \sin x + \cos x$.

8. At the right is a graph of a function of x. What is the slope of the tangent at P?

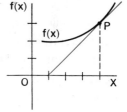

9. Compare the increase in the function with the increase in x.

10. Without the use of a table of sines, draw the graph of $\sin x$ from $0°$ to $360°$.

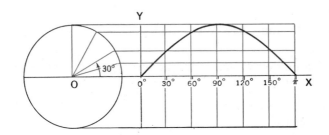

11. On the same set of axes draw the graphs of $\cos x$ and $\sec x$. For what value of x between $0°$ and $360°$ does $\cos x = \sec x$?

12. Graph $\sin x$ and $\sin (x + 90°)$ upon the same set of axes.

13. Graph $\cos x$ and $\cos (x + 90°)$ upon the same set of axes.

14. WLW (Cincinnati, Ohio) broadcasting station transmits on a frequency of 700 kilocycles (per second). If radio waves travel 186,000 miles per second, what is WLW's wave length?

15. If a radio station uses a wave length of 188 meters, what frequency does it use?

CHAPTER REVIEW

A

1. Tell which of the following statements are true and which are false:
   a. The tangent increases in the third quadrant.
   b. The cosecant increases in the third and fourth quadrants.
   c. If sin x and cos x are graphed on the same set of axes, the points of intersection of the curves give the solutions of sin x = cos x.
   d. The greatest value of sin x is +1.

2. Describe the variations of cos x as x increases from 0° to 360°.

3. Describe the variations of tan x as x increases from 0° to 360°.

4. Which functions increase in the first quadrant? Which decrease in this quadrant?

5. Which functions are positive in the second quadrant? in the third quadrant? in the fourth quadrant?

6. How should the units on the x-axis and y-axis be chosen so that the graphs of the trigonometric functions will show the correct slopes?

7. Which of the functions have maximum and minimum values?

8. Which functions never have values between −1 and +1?

9. Which functions have discontinuous curves, that is, breaks in the curves?

10. Draw a unit circle and draw the line segments representing the six trigonometric functions.

11. How can you tell the signs of the line segments that represent the trigonometric functions?

12. The sine of a certain angle is negative and the tangent of the angle is positive. In which quadrant is the angle?

13. If tan x is negative, what is the sign of ctn x?

14. What can you say about the signs of sec x and cos x?

15. In which quadrants does the tangent increase? the cotangent decrease?

16. On the same set of axes graph sin x and csc x. For what values of x between 0° and 360° does sin x = csc x?

17. Which of the following angles have positive cosines: 30°, 162°, 274°, 183°, −40°?

B

18. State which of the following statements are true and which are false:

a. The graph of sec x is a continuous curve.

b. The amplitude of sin θ is 1.

c. The period of cos θ is 360°.

d. There are 2π radians in a circle.

e. The slope of a curve at any point on it gives the rate of increase of the function at this point.

f. The period of $y = 3 \sin \dfrac{x}{6}$ is 4π.

19. Using the unit circle, show that in the first quadrant $\cos \theta = \dfrac{1}{\sec \theta}$.

20. Using the unit circle, show that $\tan^2 \theta = \sec^2 \theta - 1$.

21. What are the amplitude and period of $y = \frac{3}{5} \sin 2x$?

22. What are the amplitude and period of $y = 4 \cos \dfrac{x}{4}$?

23. Plot the graph of $y = \sin x - \cos x$.

24. Graph the function $y = \sin \left(x + \dfrac{\pi}{2} \right)$ and compare the graph with that of $y = \cos x$.

THE COLORADO-BIG THOMPSON PROJECT

Due to the westerly winds, the amount of rainfall on the eastern slopes of the Rocky Mountains is not sufficient for successful farming. When surveys were made, it was found that the upper Colorado River and its tributaries carried more water than was needed on the western slopes of the Rocky Mountains. Plans were made to carry the surplus water of the upper Colorado River by a tunnel through the mountains to the eastern slope, where it could be used in power plants, for irrigation, and for drinking-water supply. This project, called the Colorado-Big Thompson Project, is part of the work of the Bureau of Reclamation, United States Department of the Interior.

The Granby Dam and Reservoir were constructed on the Colorado River near the southwest corner of the Rocky Mountain National Park: The Granby Pumping Plant was constructed near the Granby Reservoir. This plant houses three 6,000 horsepower pumps which lift water from the reservoir 185 feet to supplement the water in Shadow Mountain and Grand Lakes.

From Grand Lake the water flows beneath the Rocky Mountain National Park through the Alva B. Adams Tunnel to the eastern slope of the mountains. On its descent to the South Platte River and its tributaries, the water is used to furnish power in six power plants, irrigate thousands of acres of land, fill reservoirs, and supply drinking water.

The Alva B. Adams Tunnel is a testimonial to engineering skill and the application of trigonometry to surveying. It is the world's longest irrigation tunnel. It was found that the eastern portal was 13.07 miles from the western portal and 107 feet lower. Exceeding care was needed in determining the course of the tunnel because of the terrain and magnetic declination.

The tunnel construction was started at both ends in 1940. The two crews blasting through solid rock began working toward each other. When the two crews met four years later, they were about three fourths of a mile beneath the Continental Divide. The two headings were within ¾ of an inch in grade and within ⁷⁄₁₆ of an inch in alignment. As you can appreciate, this was a remarkable engineering feat. It took two more years to line the tunnel, but in June, 1947, it was completed and the water ran through.

Alva B. Adams Tunnel
—East Portal

Granby Pumping Plant during Construction

Novitt, United States Bureau of Reclamation

FUNDAMENTAL RELATIONS

Δ

Identities [A]

Equations such as $(x + y)^2 = x^2 + 2xy + y^2$ and $x^2 + 5x = x(x + 5)$, which are true for all permissible values of the variables, are called *identical equations* or simply *identities*. The identity symbol ≡ is sometimes used, as in $(x + y)^2 \equiv x^2 + 2xy + y^2$. Equations such as $x + 3 = 5$ and $x^2 - x - 20 = 0$ are true only for certain values of the variables and are called *conditional equations*. In practice we usually refer to identical equations as identities and to conditional equations as equations.

There are eight fundamental identities or relations between the functions of any angle that are very important in mathematics. These relations and their proofs, as given below, should be thoroughly learned.

The Reciprocal Relations [A]

By definition (see diagram, page 128), we have

$$\sin\theta = \frac{y}{r} \quad \text{and} \quad \csc\theta = \frac{r}{y}$$

$$\cos\theta = \frac{x}{r} \quad \text{and} \quad \sec\theta = \frac{r}{x}$$

$$\tan\theta = \frac{y}{x} \quad \text{and} \quad \text{ctn}\,\theta = \frac{x}{y}$$

Hence, by multiplication, we have

$$\sin\theta \, \csc\theta = 1 \quad \text{or} \quad \sin\theta = \frac{1}{\csc\theta} \quad \text{or} \quad \csc\theta = \frac{1}{\sin\theta}. \qquad [1]$$

$$\cos\theta \, \sec\theta = 1 \quad \text{or} \quad \cos\theta = \frac{1}{\sec\theta} \quad \text{or} \quad \sec\theta = \frac{1}{\cos\theta}. \qquad [2]$$

$$\tan\theta \, \text{ctn}\,\theta = 1 \quad \text{or} \quad \tan\theta = \frac{1}{\text{ctn}\,\theta} \quad \text{or} \quad \text{ctn}\,\theta = \frac{1}{\tan\theta}. \qquad [3]$$

You should be able to use the three reciprocal relations in any one of the nine forms given.

The Quotient Relations [A]

By definition, we have

$$\sin \theta = \frac{y}{r} \quad \text{and} \quad \cos \theta = \frac{x}{r}.$$

By division, we have

$$\frac{\sin \theta}{\cos \theta} = \frac{\frac{y}{r}}{\frac{x}{r}} = \frac{y}{x} = \tan \theta$$

or

$$\tan \theta = \frac{\sin \theta}{\cos \theta} \qquad\qquad [4]$$

$$\frac{\cos \theta}{\sin \theta} = \frac{\frac{x}{r}}{\frac{y}{r}} = \frac{x}{y} = \text{ctn } \theta$$

or

$$\text{ctn } \theta = \frac{\cos \theta}{\sin \theta} \qquad\qquad [5]$$

The Pythagorean Relations [A]

Three important relations belong under this heading. The <u>first</u> is

$$\sin^2 \theta + \cos^2 \theta = 1 \qquad\qquad [6]$$

PROOF. Let θ be an angle in any quadrant. By the Pythagorean theorem,

$$y^2 + x^2 = r^2.$$

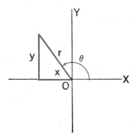

Dividing by r^2, we have

$$\frac{y^2}{r^2} + \frac{x^2}{r^2} = 1.$$

By definition, $\frac{y}{r} = \sin \theta$ or $\frac{y^2}{r^2} = \sin^2 \theta$,

and $\frac{x}{r} = \cos \theta$ or $\frac{x^2}{r^2} = \cos^2 \theta.$

By substitution, $\sin^2 \theta + \cos^2 \theta = 1.$

A <u>second</u> Pythagorean relation is

$$1 + \tan^2 \theta = \sec^2 \theta \qquad [7]$$

PROOF. Using the same figure,

$$x^2 + y^2 = r^2.$$

Dividing by x^2,
$$1 + \frac{y^2}{x^2} = \frac{r^2}{x^2}.$$

By definition, $\qquad \tan \theta = \frac{y}{x} \quad$ or $\quad \tan^2 \theta = \frac{y^2}{x^2}$,

and $\qquad \sec \theta = \frac{r}{x} \quad$ or $\quad \sec^2 \theta = \frac{r^2}{x^2}.$

By substitution, $\qquad 1 + \tan^2 \theta = \sec^2 \theta.$

The <u>third</u> of these relations is

$$1 + \operatorname{ctn}^2 \theta = \csc^2 \theta \qquad [8]$$

PROOF. $\qquad\qquad y^2 + x^2 = r^2$

Dividing by y^2,
$$1 + \frac{x^2}{y^2} = \frac{r^2}{y^2}$$

By definition, $\qquad \operatorname{ctn} \theta = \frac{-x}{y} \quad$ or $\quad \operatorname{ctn}^2 \theta = \frac{x^2}{y^2}$

and $\qquad \csc \theta = \frac{r}{y} \quad$ or $\quad \csc^2 \theta = \frac{r^2}{y^2}$

By substitution, $\qquad 1 + \operatorname{ctn}^2 \theta = \csc^2 \theta.$

We should be able to use the Pythagorean relations in any of the following forms:

$\sin^2 \theta + \cos^2 \theta = 1 \quad$ or $\quad \sin^2 \theta = 1 - \cos^2 \theta \quad$ or $\quad \cos^2 \theta = 1 - \sin^2 \theta.$

$1 + \tan^2 \theta = \sec^2 \theta \quad$ or $\quad 1 = \sec^2 \theta - \tan^2 \theta \quad$ or $\quad \tan^2 \theta = \sec^2 \theta - 1.$

$1 + \operatorname{ctn}^2 \theta = \csc^2 \theta \quad$ or $\quad 1 = \csc^2 \theta - \operatorname{ctn}^2 \theta \quad$ or $\quad \operatorname{ctn}^2 \theta = \csc^2 \theta - 1.$

The Functions of an Angle in Terms of Any Other Function of the Angle [A]

By using the fundamental relations we can express all the functions of an angle in terms of one function of the angle.

EXAMPLE. Express the other functions of ϕ in terms of $\sin \phi$.

SOLUTION. From [6], $\cos \phi = \pm \sqrt{1 - \sin^2 \phi}$.

From [4] and [6], $\quad \tan \phi = \dfrac{\sin \phi}{\cos \phi} = \pm \dfrac{\sin \phi}{\sqrt{1 - \sin^2 \phi}}$.

From [5] and [6], $\quad \text{ctn } \phi = \dfrac{\cos \phi}{\sin \phi} = \pm \dfrac{\sqrt{1 - \sin^2 \phi}}{\sin \phi}$.

From [2] and [6], $\quad \sec \phi = \dfrac{1}{\cos \phi} = \pm \dfrac{1}{\sqrt{1 - \sin^2 \phi}}$.

From [1], $\qquad\qquad \csc \phi = \dfrac{1}{\sin \phi}$.

EXERCISES [A]

Express the other functions of ϕ in terms of the given function:

1. $\cos \phi$ **2.** $\tan \phi$ **3.** $\text{ctn } \phi$ **4.** $\sec \phi$ **5.** $\csc \phi$

Express each of the following as a monomial:

6. $\csc^2 \phi - \text{ctn}^2 \phi$ **9.** $\tan \phi \text{ ctn } \phi + \sin^2 \phi + \cos^2 \phi$

7. $1 - \sin^2 \phi$ **10.** $\cos^2 \phi \tan^2 \phi + \sin^2 \phi \text{ ctn}^2 \phi$

8. $\sec^2 \phi - 1$ **11.** $\cos 70° + \sin 20°$

12. Prove the Pythagorean relations for a third-quadrant angle.

Simplification of Trigonometric Expressions [A]

In dealing with trigonometric expressions it is always desirable to reduce them to their simplest form. Trigonometric expressions are simplified by means of the eight fundamental identities and indicated algebraic reductions. An expression is simplified when it involves the least number of different functions. If no other substitution is apparent, transform the expression into one involving only sines and cosines. Avoid the use of radicals.

EXAMPLE 1. Simplify $\cos x + \sin x \tan x$.

SOLUTION. From [4], [6], and [1] we obtain

$$\cos x + \sin x \tan x = \cos x + \sin x \frac{\sin x}{\cos x}$$

$$= \frac{\cos^2 x + \sin^2 x}{\cos x} = \frac{1}{\cos x} = \sec x.$$

EXAMPLE 2. Simplify $\dfrac{ctn^2\ x}{1 - sin^2\ x}$.

SOLUTION. $\qquad \dfrac{ctn^2\ x}{1 - sin^2\ x} = \dfrac{ctn^2\ x}{cos^2\ x}$ (From [6], $cos^2\ x = 1 - sin^2\ x$)

$$= \dfrac{\dfrac{cos^2\ x}{sin^2\ x}}{cos^2\ x} \qquad \left(\text{From [5]}, \dfrac{cos^2\ x}{sin^2\ x} = ctn^2\ x\right)$$

$$= \dfrac{1}{sin^2\ x} \qquad \text{(Simplifying by algebra)}$$

$$= csc^2\ x. \qquad \left(\text{From [1]}, \dfrac{1}{sin^2\ x} = csc^2\ x\right)$$

Since $csc^2\ x$ is a single function and integral, it is simpler than the original expression, which contains two functions and is fractional.

EXAMPLE 3. Simplify $\dfrac{csc\ y - ctn\ y}{tan\ y + ctn\ y}$.

SOLUTION. Since no other substitution is apparent, we transform the expression so that it contains only sines and cosines. From the reciprocal and quotient relations we can write

$$\dfrac{csc\ y - ctn\ y}{tan\ y + ctn\ y} = \dfrac{\dfrac{1}{sin\ y} - \dfrac{cos\ y}{sin\ y}}{\dfrac{sin\ y}{cos\ y} + \dfrac{cos\ y}{sin\ y}}.$$

Multiplying both numerator and denominator by $sin\ y\ cos\ y$, we obtain

$$\dfrac{cos\ y - cos^2\ y}{sin^2\ y + cos^2\ y}.$$

Then substituting 1 for $sin^2\ y + cos^2\ y$, we find that

$$\dfrac{csc\ y - ctn\ y}{tan\ y + ctn\ y} = cos\ y - cos^2\ y.$$

EXERCISES
A

Simplify each of the following expressions:

1. $cos\ \theta\ tan\ \theta$

2. $csc\ A - sin\ A$

3. $cos\ x(1 + tan^2\ x)$

4. $sin\ x(1 + ctn^2\ x)$

5. $sec\ \theta\ ctn\ \theta$

6. $\dfrac{ctn^2\ x}{1 + ctn^2\ x}$

7. $tan\ x - sec\ x$

8. $cos\ \theta\ ctn\ \theta + sin\ \theta$

9. $cos\ \theta\ ctn\ \theta - tan\ \theta$

10. $\tan \phi \, (\csc^2 \phi - 1)$

11. $\sec y \cos y - \cos^2 y$

12. $(\sin \alpha + \cos \alpha)^2 - 1$

13. $(\operatorname{ctn} \beta + 1)^2 - 2 \operatorname{ctn} \beta$

14. $\dfrac{\tan^2 x}{1 + \tan^2 x}$

15. $(1 - \cos^2 A) \, (1 + \operatorname{ctn}^2 A)$

16. $\cos^2 \theta \operatorname{ctn}^2 \theta + \sin^2 \theta \operatorname{ctn}^2 \theta$

Simplify:

B

17. $\dfrac{\tan^2 A + 1}{\operatorname{ctn}^2 A + 1}$

18. $\dfrac{\cos^2 \beta}{1 - \sin \beta}$

19. $\dfrac{1 - \tan^2 \theta}{1 + \tan^2 \theta}$

20. $\dfrac{\sec \alpha}{\operatorname{ctn} \alpha + \tan \alpha}$

21. $\dfrac{\tan^2 x}{\sec^2 x} + \dfrac{\operatorname{ctn}^2 x}{\csc^2 x}$

22. $\dfrac{\sin \theta + \tan \theta}{1 + \sec \theta}$

23. $\dfrac{\sin A}{\tan A} - \dfrac{\tan A}{\sec A}$

24. $\dfrac{\sin \beta}{\csc \beta + \operatorname{ctn} \beta}$

25. $\dfrac{\sec^2 \phi - \tan^2 \phi}{\csc^2 \phi}$

Proving Identities [A]

Identities have a very important part in the applications of mathematics to electricity, radio, heat conduction, and engineering in general. It is frequently necessary to change an expression involving trigonometric functions to another form more suitable for a particular purpose. Practice in proving identities will enable you to develop the required skills.

Proving an identity consists in transforming one member into the other or transforming both members into the same expression or two expressions known to be equivalent. The student is cautioned not to confuse an identity with a conditional equation. The processes used in solving conditional equations do not always hold in identities.

No general method for proving identities can be given. However, the following suggestions will prove helpful:

1. *Transform the more complicated member so that it reduces to the simpler member.*
2. *Make substitutions from one or more of the eight fundamental relations when indicated.*
3. *Always keep the expression simplified by means of algebraic reductions.*
4. *If no other attack is indicated, express all functions in terms of sines and cosines.*
5. *Do not introduce radicals.*

EXAMPLE 1. Prove that $\tan \theta \sin \theta + \cos \theta = \sec \theta$.

SOLUTION. Evidently the left member is the more complicated.

Substituting $\dfrac{\sin \theta}{\cos \theta} = \tan \theta$ from [4], we have

$$\tan \theta \sin \theta + \cos \theta = \frac{\sin^2 \theta}{\cos \theta} + \cos \theta.$$

Now an algebraic addition is indicated. Adding, we have

$$\frac{\sin^2 \theta}{\cos \theta} + \cos \theta = \frac{\sin^2 \theta + \cos^2 \theta}{\cos \theta}.$$

Then substituting $1 = \sin^2 \theta + \cos^2 \theta$ from [6], we have

$$\frac{\sin^2 \theta + \cos^2 \theta}{\cos \theta} = \frac{1}{\cos \theta}.$$

From [2], $\qquad\qquad\qquad \dfrac{1}{\cos \theta} = \sec \theta.$

The completed proof without explanation should appear in the following form:

$$\begin{array}{c|c}
\tan \theta \sin \theta + \cos \theta & \\[2mm]
\dfrac{\sin^2 \theta}{\cos \theta} + \cos \theta & \\[2mm]
\dfrac{\sin^2 \theta + \cos^2 \theta}{\cos \theta} & \\[2mm]
\dfrac{1}{\cos \theta} & \sec \theta
\end{array}$$

This form is very important in proving identities. The arrangement prevents us from treating the identity as a conditional equation.

EXAMPLE 2. Prove that $\dfrac{\cos A}{1 + \sin A} + \dfrac{1 + \sin A}{\cos A} = 2 \sec A.$

SOLUTION. The left member is more complicated than the right member and addition of fractions is indicated.

Then $\qquad \dfrac{\cos A}{1 + \sin A} + \dfrac{1 + \sin A}{\cos A} = \dfrac{\cos^2 A + 1 + 2 \sin A + \sin^2 A}{\cos A(1 + \sin A)}.$

Substituting $1 = \cos^2 A + \sin^2 A$ in the numerator, we have

$$\frac{2 + 2 \sin A}{\cos A(1 + \sin A)}.$$

Factoring the numerator and reducing, we have

$$\frac{2(1 + \sin A)}{\cos A \,(1 + \sin A)} = \frac{2}{\cos A} = 2 \sec A.$$

The complete solution without explanation should appear as follows:

$$\dfrac{\cos A}{1 + \sin A} + \dfrac{1 + \sin A}{\cos A}$$

$$\dfrac{\cos^2 A + 1 + 2 \sin A + \sin^2 A}{\cos A(1 + \sin A)}$$

$$\dfrac{2 + 2 \sin A}{\cos A(1 + \sin A)}$$

$$\dfrac{2(1 + \sin A)}{\cos A(1 + \sin A)}$$

$$\dfrac{2}{\cos A} \qquad\qquad 2 \sec A$$

EXAMPLE 3. Prove that $\dfrac{\tan \theta - 1}{\tan \theta + 1} = \dfrac{1 - \text{ctn } \theta}{1 + \text{ctn } \theta}$.

SOLUTION. Since the members appear equally complicated, we shall transform both members to equivalent expressions.

$$\dfrac{\tan \theta - 1}{\tan \theta + 1} \qquad\qquad \dfrac{1 - \text{ctn } \theta}{1 + \text{ctn } \theta}$$

Changing to sines and cosines, we have

$$\dfrac{\dfrac{\sin \theta}{\cos \theta} - 1}{\dfrac{\sin \theta}{\cos \theta} + 1}$$

Changing to sines and cosines, we have

$$\dfrac{1 - \dfrac{\cos \theta}{\sin \theta}}{1 + \dfrac{\cos \theta}{\sin \theta}}$$

Simplifying the complex fraction,

$$\dfrac{\sin \theta - \cos \theta}{\sin \theta + \cos \theta}$$

Simplifying the complex fraction,

$$\dfrac{\sin \theta - \cos \theta}{\sin \theta + \cos \theta}$$

Since both members reduce to identical expressions the identity is proved.

EXERCISES

A

Prove the following identities:

1. $\sin \theta \sec \theta = \tan \theta$

2. $\sin \phi \sec \phi \, \text{ctn } \phi = 1$

3. $\cos^2 \alpha - \sin^2 \alpha = 1 - 2 \sin^2 \alpha$

4. $\text{ctn } \beta \sec \beta = \csc \beta$

5. $\cos^2 x + \cos^2 x \tan^2 x = 1$

6. $\sin^2 y + \sin^2 y \, \text{ctn}^2 y = 1$

7. $\cos^2 A - \sin^2 A = 2 \cos^2 A - 1$

8. $\sec B - \cos B = \sin B \tan B$

9. $\tan C + \operatorname{ctn} C = \sec C \csc C$

10. $\cos^4 \theta - \sin^4 \theta = \cos^2 \theta - \sin^2 \theta$

11. $\cos \phi \tan \phi \csc \phi = 1$

12. $\tan^2 \alpha - \sin^2 \alpha = \sin^2 \alpha \tan^2 \alpha$

13. $\sec^2 \beta + \csc^2 \beta = \sec^2 \beta \csc^2 \beta$

14. $\csc^4 \theta - \operatorname{ctn}^4 \theta = 1 + 2 \operatorname{ctn}^2 \theta$

15. $(\operatorname{ctn} A + 1)^2 = \csc^2 A + 2 \operatorname{ctn} A$

16. $(\tan B + \operatorname{ctn} B)^2 = \sec^2 B + \csc^2 B$

17. $\sec \theta - \cos \theta = \sin \theta \tan \theta$

18. $\csc A \operatorname{ctn} A \cos A + 1 = \csc^2 A$

19. $\tan \phi \sin \phi + \cos \phi = \sec \phi$

20. $\operatorname{ctn}^2 \beta - \cos^2 \beta = \cos^2 \beta \operatorname{ctn}^2 \beta$

B

21. $\dfrac{1 + \tan^2 \theta}{1 + \operatorname{ctn}^2 \theta} = \tan^2 \theta$

22. $\dfrac{1}{\sin \phi} - \sin \phi = \dfrac{\cos \phi}{\tan \phi}$

23. $\dfrac{1 - \sin^2 \alpha}{1 - \cos^2 \alpha} = \operatorname{ctn}^2 \alpha$

24. $\dfrac{1 + \tan^2 \beta}{\tan^2 \beta} = \csc^2 \beta$

25. $\dfrac{\csc^2 A - 1}{\sec^2 A - 1} = \operatorname{ctn}^4 A$

26. $\dfrac{\sin \theta - 1}{\cos \theta} = \tan \theta - \sec \theta$

27. $\dfrac{\operatorname{ctn}^2 \phi + 1}{\operatorname{ctn} \phi} = \tan \phi + \operatorname{ctn} \phi$

28. $\dfrac{1 + \sin A}{\cos A} = \dfrac{\cos A}{1 - \sin A}$

29. $\dfrac{\cos^2 B}{1 - \sin B} = 1 + \sin B$

30. $\dfrac{1 - 2 \cos^2 \alpha}{\sin \alpha \cos \alpha} = \tan \alpha - \operatorname{ctn} \alpha$

31. $\dfrac{\cos \theta + \sin \theta}{1 + \tan \theta} = \cos \theta$

32. $\dfrac{1 + \operatorname{ctn} \phi}{\csc \phi} = \dfrac{1 + \tan \phi}{\sec \phi}$

33. $\dfrac{\sec^2 x}{2 + \tan^2 x} = \dfrac{1}{1 + \cos^2 x}$

34. $\dfrac{\sin y}{1 + \cos y} = \dfrac{1 - \cos y}{\sin y}$

35. $\dfrac{1 + \csc \alpha}{\sec \alpha} = \operatorname{ctn} \alpha + \cos \alpha$

36. $\dfrac{1 + \sec \beta}{1 - \sec \beta} = \dfrac{\cos \beta + 1}{\cos \beta - 1}$

37. $\dfrac{1 - \tan^2 \theta}{1 - \operatorname{ctn}^2 \theta} = 1 - \sec^2 \theta$

38. $\dfrac{1}{\sec \phi + \tan \phi} = \sec \phi - \tan \phi$

39. $\dfrac{\tan A + \tan B}{\operatorname{ctn} A + \operatorname{ctn} B} = \tan A \tan B$

40. $\dfrac{\cos \theta}{\cos \theta - \sin \theta} = \dfrac{1}{1 - \tan \theta}$

41. $(\tan \phi + \text{ctn } \phi)(\sec \phi - \cos \phi) = \sec \phi \tan \phi$

42. $\sin^6 x + \cos^6 x = 1 - 3 \sin^2 x \cos^2 x$

43. $\sin y \text{ ctn } y \csc^2 y = \cos y + \cos y \text{ ctn}^2 y$

44. $\sin A + \cos A - \sin^3 A - \cos^3 A = \sin A \cos^2 A + \sin^2 A \cos A$

45. $(1 - \cos \theta)(1 + \sec \theta) = \sin \theta \tan \theta$

46. $\sin^3 \phi \cos \phi - \sin^5 \phi \cos \phi = \sin^3 \phi \cos^3 \phi$

47. $(1 + \sin \alpha)(\sec \alpha - \tan \alpha) = \cos \alpha$

48. $1 - \sec^2 \beta + \sec^2 \beta \tan^2 \beta = \tan^4 \beta$

49. $\sec^2 x - \csc^2 x = \dfrac{\csc^2 x - \text{ctn}^2 x \csc^2 x}{\text{ctn}^2 x}$

50. $\dfrac{2 - \sin^2 y}{\sin^3 y} = \csc^3 y + \text{ctn}^2 y \csc y$

51. $\dfrac{2}{\tan A - \text{ctn } A} = \dfrac{2 \tan A}{\tan^2 A - 1}$

52. $\dfrac{\sec A + \sec B}{\tan A - \tan B} = \dfrac{\tan A + \tan B}{\sec A - \sec B}$

53. $\dfrac{\cos z \text{ ctn } z - \tan z}{\csc z} = \dfrac{\cos z}{\sec z} - \dfrac{\sin z}{\text{ctn } z}$

54. $\dfrac{1 + \sin \phi}{1 - \sin \phi} - \dfrac{1 - \sin \phi}{1 + \sin \phi} = 4 \tan \phi \sec \phi$

Trigonometric Equations [A]

A *conditional trigonometric equation* is an expression of equality involving trigonometric functions of one or more unknown angles. Any value of angle for which the equality is true is a *solution* of the equation. A trigonometric equation, in general, has an unlimited number of solutions. We shall deal only with positive angles less than 360° that satisfy the equation.

While trigonometric equations belong to a class of equations known as transcendental and are not algebraic, we can apply our knowledge gained in solving algebraic equations to their solution. The methods of solution will be illustrated by examples.

EXAMPLE 1. Solve $2 \sin x = 1$

SOLUTION. $2 \sin x = 1$

$\sin x = \frac{1}{2}$

We have to find the angle or angles whose sine is $\frac{1}{2}$. Since the sine is positive in the first and second quadrants, there are two positive angles less than 360° whose sines are $\frac{1}{2}$. Angles of 30° and 150° have sines equal to $\frac{1}{2}$.

Hence $x = 30° \text{ or } 150°$

In case the angles are not special angles whose values we know, we can find their magnitude from Table X.

EXAMPLE 2. Solve $3 \tan^2 x - 1 = 0$

SOLUTION. $3 \tan^2 x = 1$

$\tan^2 x = \frac{1}{3}$

This equation is in quadratic form. Extracting the square root of both members of the equation, we have,

$$\tan x = \pm\tfrac{1}{3}\sqrt{3}.$$

Since the tangent is positive in the first and third quadrants and negative in the second and fourth, there are four values that satisfy x. The reference angle for $\pm\frac{1}{3}\sqrt{3}$ is 30°.

Then $x = 30°, 150°, 210°, \text{ and } 330°.$

EXAMPLE 3. Solve $2 \cos^2 x = 4 \cos x - 1$

SOLUTION. $2 \cos^2 x = 4 \cos x - 1$

$2 \cos^2 x - 4 \cos x + 1 = 0$

This equation is in quadratic form. Since it cannot be factored when the left member is equated to zero, we can solve either by completing the square or by using the quadratic formula. Using the formula, we have

$$\cos x = \frac{4 \pm \sqrt{16 - 8}}{4} = \frac{2 \pm \sqrt{2}}{2} = 1.7071 \text{ or } .2929$$

Since the value of the cosine of an angle does not exceed 1, there is no angle corresponding to $\cos x = 1.7071$, and this value is therefore discarded. For $\cos x = .2929$, we find, from Table X, $x = 72° 58'$. Since the cosine is positive in the first and fourth quadrants, the angles are

$$72° 58' \text{ and } 287° 2'.$$

EXAMPLE 4. Solve $\tan^2 \theta + 3 = 3 \sec \theta$

SOLUTION. Transforming to a single function by substituting $\sec^2 \theta - 1$ for $\tan^2 \theta$, we have

$$\sec^2 \theta + 2 = 3 \sec \theta$$
$$\sec^2 \theta - 3 \sec \theta + 2 = 0$$

Factoring, $\longrightarrow$ $(\sec \theta - 2)(\sec \theta - 1) = 0$

$$\sec \theta - 2 = 0 \qquad\qquad \sec \theta - 1 = 0$$
$$\sec \theta = 2 \qquad\qquad \sec \theta = 1$$
$$\theta = 60°, 300° \qquad\qquad \theta = 0°$$

EXAMPLE 5. Solve $2 \sin \phi \cos \phi = \sin \phi$

SOLUTION. While both members of the equation are divisible by $\sin \phi$, we should lose values for the angle by this operation. As in algebra, we cannot divide both members of the equation by a quantity involving the unknown. Instead, we transpose and factor:

$$2 \sin \phi \cos \phi - \sin \phi = 0$$
$$\sin \phi (2 \cos \phi - 1) = 0$$

$$\sin \phi = 0 \qquad\qquad 2 \cos \phi = 1$$
$$\phi = 0°, 180° \qquad\qquad \cos \phi = \tfrac{1}{2}$$
$$\phi = 60°, 300°$$

The roots are $0°, 60°, 180°, 300°$.

EXAMPLE 6. Solve $\sin x + \cos x = 1$

SOLUTION. To transform to a single function and avoid radicals, we transpose $\cos x$ and square both members:

$$\sin^2 x = 1 - 2 \cos x + \cos^2 x$$

Substituting,

$$1 - \cos^2 x = 1 - 2 \cos x + \cos^2 x$$
$$2 \cos^2 x - 2 \cos x = 0$$

Factoring, $\longrightarrow$ $2 \cos x (\cos x - 1) = 0$

$$\cos x = 0 \qquad\qquad \cos x = 1$$
$$x = 90°, 270° \qquad\qquad x = 0°$$

Since we squared the equation, we must check the solutions.

For $x = 90°$,	For $x = 270°$,	For $x = 0°$,
$\sin 90° + \cos 90° = 1$	$\sin 270° + \cos 270° = 1$	$\sin 0° + \cos 0° = 1$
if $\qquad 1 + 0 = 1$.	if $\qquad -1 + 0 = 1$.	if $\qquad 0 + 1 = 1$.
Since $\qquad 1 + 0 = 1$,	Since $\qquad -1 \neq 1$,	Since $\qquad 1 = 1$,
$90°$ is a solution.	$270°$ is not a solution.	$0°$ is a solution.

We now state the following directions for solving trigonometric equations:

1. *If possible, reduce the equation to simpler equations by factoring. When factoring, all the terms of the equation must be in one member and the other member must be zero.*
2. *If the equation involves more than one function, reduce all functions to one function by means of the fundamental identities.*
3. *Do not divide both members by a variable. In doing so, you may lose a solution.*
4. *Multiplying both members by a variable or raising both members to a power usually leads to extraneous solutions. If these operations are performed, the solutions must be checked for extraneous values.*

EXERCISES

A

Solve the following equations for all positive values less than $360°$:

1. $2 \cos \theta + 1 = 0$

2. $4 \sin^2 \theta = 1$

3. $\operatorname{ctn}^2 \phi - 3 = 0$

4. $3 \tan^2 x = 1$

5. $2 \sin^2 x - \cos^2 x = 2$

6. $2 \cos y + \sqrt{2} = 1$

7. $\sqrt{3} \tan \alpha = 1$

8. $\cos \beta - \sec \beta = 0$

9. $\tan \theta - \operatorname{ctn} \theta = 0$

10. $\sec^2 \phi - 1 = \tan \phi$

11. $3 \operatorname{ctn} x + \sqrt{3} = 0$

12. $4 \cos A = 3$

13. $\operatorname{ctn}^3 \theta - 3 \operatorname{ctn} \theta = 0$

14. $4 \cos^3 \phi = 3 \cos \phi$

15. $\tan^2 \beta = 4$

16. $\sec x = 4 \csc x$

17. $\sec^2 y - 2 \tan y = 0$

18. $\operatorname{ctn}^2 A + 3 = 3 \csc A$

19. $\tan \theta - 3 \operatorname{ctn} \theta = 0$

20. $(2 \sin \theta - 1)(\tan \theta + \sqrt{3}) = 0$

21. $(\sin \phi + 1)(2 \cos^2 \phi - 1) = 0$

22. $(\sec^2 \alpha - 2)(\csc \alpha + 1) = 0$

23. $\cos^2 \theta - 4 \sin^2 \theta = 0$

24. $\operatorname{ctn} \phi + \csc \phi = 2$

25. $\csc y - 3 \sin y + 2 = 0$

26. $\sec^4 \alpha - 2 \tan^2 \alpha + 1 = 0$

27. $3 \cos^2 \beta + 5 \cos \beta = 2$

28. $\csc^2 \theta - 3 = 6 \operatorname{ctn} \theta$

29. $\tan x = \sin x \cos x$

30. $\csc \phi = \operatorname{ctn} \phi + 1$

31. $2 \cos^2 \alpha + \sqrt{3} \sin \alpha + 1 = 0$

32. $\tan \beta \cos \beta - \cos \beta = 0$

33. $\tan y - \operatorname{ctn} y = 2 \sec y$

34. $\cos^2 A - \sin^2 A = \frac{1}{2}$

35. $4 \sec^2 \phi - 7 \tan^2 \phi = 3$

36. $\tan^2 z + \operatorname{ctn}^2 z = 2$

B

37. $\sin \theta - \cos \theta = 1$

38. $\cos x + \sin x = \sqrt{2}$

39. $\sin y + \sqrt{3} \cos y = 1$

40. $4 \sec^2 \beta - 15 \tan \beta = 8$

41. $2 \sin^4 x = 3 \sin^2 x - 1$

42. $3 \tan^4 y = 1 - 4 \tan^2 y$

43. $\sin^2 \phi - 2 \sin \phi \cos \phi = \cos^2 \phi$

44. $2 \sin^3 \theta - 2 \cos^3 \theta = \sin \theta - \cos \theta$

45. $3 \cos \phi - 4 \cos^3 \phi - 1 = 0$

46. $4 \sin^3 \phi - 3 \sin \phi - 1 = 0$

47. $4 \sin A \tan A - \cos A \, \text{ctn} \, A = 0$

48. $\csc z - 2 \sin z - \text{ctn} \, z = 0$

Simultaneous Trigonometric Equations in Two Variables When One Variable Is Linear and the Other Is an Angle [B]

We apply our knowledge of algebra to the solution of this type of problem.

EXAMPLE 1. Solve $r = 2 \cos \theta$ (1)

$r^2 = 3 + 3 \sin \theta$ (2)

SOLUTION. Substituting $r = 2 \cos \theta$ from equation (1) in equation (2), we have

$$4 \cos^2 \theta = 3 + 3 \sin \theta$$
$$4 - 4 \sin^2 \theta = 3 + 3 \sin \theta$$
$$4 \sin^2 \theta + 3 \sin \theta - 1 = 0$$
$$(4 \sin \theta - 1)(\sin \theta + 1) = 0$$

$4 \sin \theta = 1$

$\sin \theta = \frac{1}{4}$

$\theta = 14° 29', 165° 31'$

$\sin \theta = -1$

$\theta = 270°$

Substituting $\theta = 270°$ in (1),

$r = 0$

To find the values of r when $\theta = 14° 29'$ and $\theta = 165° 31'$, we first draw a figure, as shown, computing the third side of the triangle.

Then when $\sin \theta = \frac{1}{4}$, $\cos \theta = \pm\frac{1}{4}\sqrt{15}$.

From (1),

When $\theta = 14° 29'$,

$r = 2(\frac{1}{4}\sqrt{15}) = \frac{1}{2}\sqrt{15}$

When $\theta = 165° 31'$,

$r = 2(-\frac{1}{4}\sqrt{15}) = -\frac{1}{2}\sqrt{15}$.

The solutions are:

$\theta = 14° 29'$	$\theta = 165° 31'$	$\theta = 270°$
$r = \frac{1}{2}\sqrt{15}$	$r = -\frac{1}{2}\sqrt{15}$	$r = 0$

EXERCISES [B]

1. $r = 2 \sin \theta$
   $r = \tan \theta$

2. $r = 1 - \cos \theta$
   $r = \cos \theta$

3. $r = 2 \sin \theta$
   $r = \cos \theta$

4. $r^2 = \sin \theta$
   $r = 1 - \sin \theta$

5. $r \cos \theta = 1$
   $r^2 \sin^2 \theta = 3$

6. $r = 3 - \frac{1}{4} \tan \theta$
   $r^2 = \tan \theta$

Trigonometric Equations of the Type $x - \cos x = 0$ [B]

In this type of an equation in which x is a number and also an angle, the angle is given in radians.

EXAMPLE. Solve $x = \cos x$.

SOLUTION. We let $y = x$. Then
   $y = \cos x$.

We solve graphically the equations

$$y = x$$
and $$y = \cos x.$$

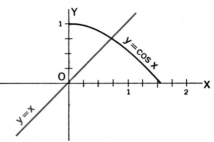

$y = x$ (straight line)			
x	0	2	etc.
y	0	2	

$y = \cos x$ (cosine curve)							
x	0	.25	.50	.75	1.00	1.25	1.50
y	1	.97	.88	.73	.54	.31	.07

The values for $\cos x$ were obtained from Table X, x in radians.
The graphs of the two equations intersect at $x = .74$, approximately. Hence $x = .74$ is the solution.

EXERCISES [B]

Solve for x *graphically. Obtain the values for the functions by referring to the radians in Table X.*

1. $2x = \cos x$ **3.** $x^2 = \cos x$ **5.** $\sin x = \log x$

2. $x - 1 = \sin x$ **4.** $\tan x = 1 - x$ **6.** $e^x = \cos x$ $(e = 2.71828\ldots)$

GENERAL REVIEW [A]

1. Express as the same function of a positive acute angle:

   a. $\sin 96°$ **c.** $\tan 212°$ **e.** $\sin (-144°)$ **g.** $\cos 333°$
   b. $\cos (-102°)$ **d.** $\operatorname{ctn} 766°$ **f.** $\csc 185°$ **h.** $\sec 100°$

2. Express as the co-function of a positive acute angle.
   a. tan (−160°)   c. sin 150°   e. sec 170°   g. csc (−115°)
   b. ctn 192°   d. cos (−210°)   f. tan 200°   h. cos (−95°)

3. Change the following radian values to degrees:

   a. $\dfrac{\pi}{6}$ c. $\dfrac{2\pi}{3}$ e. $\dfrac{7\pi}{8}$ g. $-\dfrac{2}{3}\pi$ i. $-\dfrac{\pi}{4}$

   b. $\dfrac{3\pi}{4}$ d. $\dfrac{5\pi}{6}$ f. 5π h. $\dfrac{7\pi}{6}$ j. 2

4. Change the following to radians in terms of π:
   a. 135°   b. 210°   c. 120°   d. 15°   e. 270°

5. Express as functions of θ:

   a. $\sin(\pi - \theta)$ d. $\operatorname{ctn}\left(\dfrac{\pi}{2} - \theta\right)$ g. $\csc(2\pi - \theta)$

   b. $\cos(\pi + \theta)$ e. $\sin\left(\dfrac{3\pi}{2} + \theta\right)$ h. $\sin\left(\theta - \dfrac{\pi}{2}\right)$

   c. $\tan\left(\dfrac{\pi}{2} + \theta\right)$ f. $\sec\left(\dfrac{3\pi}{2} - \theta\right)$ i. $\cos(-\pi - \theta)$

6. Find the area of the segment of a circle of radius 2, if the central angle of the arc of the segment is 1 radian.

7. A flywheel 8 feet in diameter makes 88 r.p.m. Find the linear velocity of a point on the rim of the wheel.

   Solve for x:
8. $2^x = 64$ *10. $\ln(x - 3) = 1 - \ln x$ 12. $3^{\frac{1}{x}} = 12$
9. $e^x = 3$ 11. $\log(x + 3) = 1 - \log x$ 13. $e^x + e^{-x} = 4$

14. An airplane leaving an airport rises at an angle of 8°. By how many feet will it clear a barrier 160 feet high at a distance of 1500 feet from the take-off?

15. Solve the right triangle ABC if one leg is 63.7 feet long and its adjacent acute angle is 33° 17′.

16. Find the radius of the incircle of a regular decagon whose radius is 4 inches.

   * You will recall that "ln" means "logarithm to base e."

ENGINEERING AS A CAREER

Analyze carefully your qualities to ascertain whether you may hope to succeed in engineering pursuits.

1. Do you like to try to understand the principles controlling the operation of processes or devices?
2. Do you enjoy reading about the industrial applications of chemistry, physics, and mathematics?
3. Are you inclined to read scientific literature without having it assigned to you?
4. Are you ambitious to make a contribution to the advancement of civilization?
5. Do you feel the urge to extend materially the scope of your technical knowledge?

Become acquainted with and seek the counsel of as many professional engineers as possible.

Make very certain that your preparatory training in arithmetic, algebra, plane geometry, solid geometry, and trigonometry is extensive and thorough.

A mastery of such courses as chemistry and physics is essential.

Do not specialize too soon. Apply yourself earnestly to such courses as English, economics, history, civics and government, which enable you to understand the society in which you live.

Strive with all earnestness to acquire knowledge and to be a superior student.

Courtesy of The Engineering Institute of Canada.

CHAPTER IX

FUNCTIONS OF TWO ANGLES

Δ

In Chapter VIII we dealt with the relations of the functions of one angle. In many applications of trigonometry it is desirable to express the functions of two or more angles in terms of the functions of the separate angles. In this chapter we shall derive several of these relations, some of which will have immediate application in later chapters.

In deriving these formulas, we shall consider only cases of two angles whose sum is less than a right angle. However, it can be proved that the formulas hold for any two angles regardless of magnitude.

The Sine of the Sum of Two Angles[A]

In the figure, let θ, ϕ, and $(\theta + \phi)$ be acute angles. θ is in standard position, and the initial side of ϕ coincides with the terminal side of θ. From P, any point on the terminal side of $(\theta + \phi)$, draw PA perpendicular to the initial side of ϕ and PB perpendicular to the initial side of θ. From A draw AC perpendicular to OB, and AD perpendicular to PB. Then $\angle APD = \theta$. Why? $DA = BC$. Why? By definition,

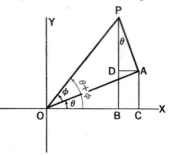

$$\sin(\theta + \phi) = \frac{PB}{OP} = \frac{AC + PD}{OP} = \frac{AC}{OP} + \frac{PD}{OP}.$$

The ratios $\dfrac{AC}{OP}$ and $\dfrac{PD}{OP}$ are not functions of either θ or ϕ. To obtain functions of these angles, we multiply $\dfrac{AC}{OP}$ by $\dfrac{OA}{OA} = 1$, and we multiply $\dfrac{DP}{OP}$ by $\dfrac{PA}{PA} = 1$. Then,

$$\sin (\theta + \phi) = \frac{AC}{OP} \cdot \frac{OA}{OA} + \frac{PD}{OP} \cdot \frac{PA}{PA}$$

$$= \frac{AC}{OA} \cdot \frac{OA}{OP} + \frac{PD}{PA} \cdot \frac{PA}{OP}$$

Therefore, $\sin (\theta + \phi) = \sin \theta \cos \phi + \cos \theta \sin \phi$ [9]

The Cosine of the Sum of Two Angles [A]

From the figure on page 201 we have, by definition,

$$\cos (\theta + \phi) = \frac{OB}{OP} = \frac{OC - DA}{OP} = \frac{OC}{OP} - \frac{DA}{OP}$$

$$= \frac{OC}{OP} \cdot \frac{OA}{OA} - \frac{DA}{OP} \cdot \frac{PA}{PA}$$

$$= \frac{OC}{OA} \cdot \frac{OA}{OP} - \frac{DA}{PA} \cdot \frac{PA}{OP}$$

Therefore, $\cos (\theta + \phi) = \cos \theta \cos \phi - \sin \theta \sin \phi$ [10]

The Tangent of the Sum of Two Angles [A]

We derive the formula for $\tan (\theta + \phi)$ by making use of formulas [4], [9], and [10].

$$\tan (\theta + \phi) = \frac{\sin (\theta + \phi)}{\cos (\theta + \phi)} = \frac{\sin \theta \cos \phi + \cos \theta \sin \phi}{\cos \theta \cos \phi - \sin \theta \sin \phi}$$

Dividing each term of the numerator and denominator of the last fraction by $\cos \theta \cos \phi$, we obtain

$$\tan (\theta + \phi) = \frac{\dfrac{\sin \theta \cos \phi}{\cos \theta \cos \phi} + \dfrac{\cos \theta \sin \phi}{\cos \theta \cos \phi}}{\dfrac{\cos \theta \cos \phi}{\cos \theta \cos \phi} - \dfrac{\sin \theta \sin \phi}{\cos \theta \cos \phi}}$$

$$= \frac{\dfrac{\sin \theta}{\cos \theta} + \dfrac{\sin \phi}{\cos \phi}}{1 - \dfrac{\sin \theta \sin \phi}{\cos \theta \cos \phi}}$$

Therefore, $\tan (\theta + \phi) = \dfrac{\tan \theta + \tan \phi}{1 - \tan \theta \tan \phi}$ [11]

The Subtraction Formulas [A]

The formulas for $\sin (\theta + \phi)$, $\cos (\theta + \phi)$, and $\tan (\theta + \phi)$ are known as the addition formulas. The formulas for $\sin (\theta - \phi)$, $\cos (\theta - \phi)$, and $\tan (\theta - \phi)$ are called the subtraction formulas. Since the addition formulas are true for all angles, positive or negative, the subtraction formulas may be derived as follows:

$$\sin (\theta - \phi) = \sin [\theta + (-\phi)]$$
$$= \sin \theta \cos (-\phi) + \cos \theta \sin (-\phi)$$

Substituting $\cos \phi = \cos (-\phi)$, and $\sin (-\phi) = -\sin \phi$, we have

$$\mathbf{\sin (\theta - \phi) = \sin \theta \cos \phi - \cos \theta \sin \phi} \qquad [12]$$

In like manner,

$$\cos (\theta - \phi) = \cos [\theta + (- \phi)]$$
$$= \cos \theta \cos (-\phi) - \sin \theta \sin (- \phi)$$

or $\qquad \mathbf{\cos (\theta - \phi) = \cos \theta \cos \phi + \sin \theta \sin \phi} \qquad [13]$

Also,

$$\tan (\theta - \phi) = \tan [\theta + (-\phi)] = \frac{\tan \theta + \tan (-\phi)}{1 - \tan \theta \tan (-\phi)}$$

or $\qquad \mathbf{\tan (\theta - \phi) = \dfrac{\tan \theta - \tan \phi}{1 + \tan \theta \tan \phi}} \qquad [14]$

Applications of the Addition and Subtraction Formulas* [A]

These formulas can be used to compute exact values of certain angles, to derive other needed formulas, and to make necessary transformations of expressions.

The addition and subtraction formulas are not given for the cotangent, secant, and cosecant, as they have few applications. The derivations of the cotangent formulas are inserted as exercises.

EXAMPLE 1. Find the exact value of $\sin 75°$.

SOLUTION. $\quad \sin 75° = \sin (45° + 30°)$
$$= \sin 45° \cos 30° + \cos 45° \sin 30°$$
$$= \tfrac{1}{2}\sqrt{2} \cdot \tfrac{1}{2}\sqrt{3} + \tfrac{1}{2}\sqrt{2} \cdot \tfrac{1}{2}$$
$$= \tfrac{1}{4}(\sqrt{6} + \sqrt{2})$$

* All the formulas of this chapter are given on pages 334-336 for reference. However, the formulas should be memorized so that such reference will be unnecessary.

EXAMPLE 2. Given $\sin \theta = -\frac{3}{5}$, θ being a third-quadrant angle, and $\tan \phi = -\frac{7}{24}$, ϕ a second-quadrant angle. Find $\sin (\theta + \phi)$, $\cos (\theta + \phi)$, and $\tan (\theta + \phi)$.

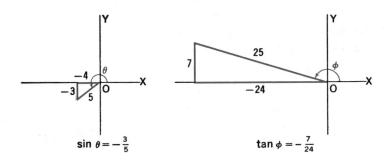

$$\sin \theta = -\frac{3}{5} \qquad\qquad \tan \phi = -\frac{7}{24}$$

SOLUTION. In the diagrams, θ and ϕ are in standard position.

Then
$$\sin (\theta + \phi) = \sin \theta \cos \phi + \cos \theta \sin \phi$$
$$= -\tfrac{3}{5} \cdot (-\tfrac{24}{25}) - \tfrac{4}{5} \cdot \tfrac{7}{25} = \tfrac{72}{125} - \tfrac{28}{125} = \tfrac{44}{125}$$

$$\cos (\theta + \phi) = \cos \theta \cos \phi - \sin \theta \sin \phi$$
$$= -\tfrac{4}{5} \cdot (-\tfrac{24}{25}) + \tfrac{3}{5} \cdot \tfrac{7}{25} = \tfrac{96}{125} + \tfrac{21}{125} = \tfrac{117}{125}$$

$$\tan (\theta + \phi) = \frac{\tan \theta + \tan \phi}{1 - \tan \theta \tan \phi}$$

$$= \frac{\tfrac{3}{4} - \tfrac{7}{24}}{1 - \tfrac{3}{4} \cdot (-\tfrac{7}{24})} = \frac{72 - 28}{96 + 21} = \frac{44}{117}$$

In what quadrant would $(\theta + \phi)$ be?

EXERCISES

A

1. Using the functions of 60° and 45° and the addition formulas, find the sine, cosine, and tangent of 105°.

2. Using the functions of 30° and 45° and the subtraction formulas, find the sine, cosine, and tangent of 15°.

3. Derive these formulas:

   a. $\operatorname{ctn} (\theta + \phi) = \dfrac{\operatorname{ctn} \theta \operatorname{ctn} \phi - 1}{\operatorname{ctn} \theta + \operatorname{ctn} \phi}$ b. $\operatorname{ctn} (\theta - \phi) = \dfrac{\operatorname{ctn} \theta \operatorname{ctn} \phi + 1}{\operatorname{ctn} \phi - \operatorname{ctn} \theta}$

4. Simplify the following expressions:

a. $\sin (30° + A)$ c. $\tan (60° + A)$ e. $\sin (45° - A)$

b. $\cos (45° + A)$ d. $\tan (30° - A)$ f. $\cos (60° - A)$

g. $\sin (B - 30°) + \cos (B - 60°)$

h. $\cos (B + 30°) - \sin (B - 60°)$

i. $\tan (B + 45°) + \text{ctn} (B - 45°)$

j. $\tan (\pi + \alpha) + \tan (\pi - \alpha)$

k. $\cos (60° + A + B) + \sin (30° - A - B)$

5. Given $\sin \theta = -\frac{5}{13}$ in the third quadrant, and $\tan \phi = -\frac{8}{15}$ in the second quadrant, find the sine, cosine, and tangent of the following:

a. $(\theta + \phi)$ b. $(\theta - \phi)$ c. $(\pi + \theta)$ d. $(\pi - \phi)$

6. If $\tan \alpha = \frac{1}{3}$ and $\tan \beta = 3$, find $\tan (\alpha - \beta)$.

7. Given $\cos \theta = -\frac{24}{25}$, $\sin \phi = \frac{3}{5}$, θ and ϕ second-quadrant angles, find

a. $\sin (\theta + \phi)$ b. $\cos (\theta + \phi)$ c. $\tan (\theta - \phi)$ d. $\sin (\theta - \phi)$

8. Express as functions of a single angle:

a. $\sin 40° \cos 15° + \cos 40° \sin 15°$

b. $\sin 50° \cos 20° - \sin 20° \cos 50°$

c. $\cos 10° \cos 40° - \sin 10° \sin 40°$

d. $\dfrac{\tan 25° + \tan 40°}{1 - \tan 25° \tan 40°}$

B

Show that

9. $\sin (A + B + C) = \sin A \cos B \cos C + \cos A \sin B \cos C + \cos A \cos B \sin C - \sin A \sin B \sin C$.

10. $\cos (A + B + C) = \cos A \cos B \cos C - \cos A \sin B \sin C - \sin A \cos B \sin C - \sin A \sin B \cos C$.

11. $\tan (A + B + C) = \dfrac{\tan A + \tan B + \tan C - \tan A \tan B \tan C}{1 - \tan B \tan C - \tan A \tan C - \tan A \tan B}$.

12. Find the value of $\sin (\theta + 60°) \cos A - \cos (\theta + 60°) \sin A$.

13. Express as the single function of an angle:

a. $\sin (2\theta + 3\phi) \cos (3\phi + \theta) - \cos (2\theta + 3\phi) \sin (3\phi + \theta)$.

b. $\cos (3\alpha + \beta) \cos (2\alpha + \beta) + \sin (3\alpha + \beta) \sin (2\alpha + \beta)$.

14. If $\tan A = 2$ and $A + B = 135°$, find $\tan B$.

15. If $\tan \theta = \dfrac{x}{x + 1}$ and $\tan \phi = \dfrac{1}{2x + 1}$, find $\tan (\theta + \phi)$.

Functions of Twice an Angle [A]

The functions of twice an angle can be derived from the addition formulas in the following manner:

$$\sin 2\theta = \sin(\theta + \theta) = \sin\theta\cos\theta + \cos\theta\sin\theta$$

Then $$\sin 2\theta = 2\sin\theta\cos\theta \qquad [15]$$

Also $$\sin\theta = 2\sin\tfrac{1}{2}\theta\cos\tfrac{1}{2}\theta.$$

These formulas may be expressed in words as follows:

The sine of an angle is equal to twice the sine of half the angle times the cosine of half the angle.

We may also write

$$\cos 2\theta = \cos(\theta + \theta) = \cos\theta\cos\theta - \sin\theta\sin\theta$$

Then $$\cos 2\theta = \cos^2\theta - \sin^2\theta \qquad [16]$$

By using the identity $\sin^2\theta + \cos^2\theta = 1$, this formula may be expressed in terms of the sine or the cosine as follows:

$$\cos 2\theta = 1 - 2\sin^2\theta \quad \text{or} \quad \cos 2\theta = 2\cos^2\theta - 1$$

The student should remember and be able to use all three forms of formula [16]. This formula may also be used to express $\cos\theta$ in terms of half angles as follows:

$$\cos\theta = \cos^2\tfrac{1}{2}\theta - \sin^2\tfrac{1}{2}\theta = 2\cos^2\tfrac{1}{2}\theta - 1 = 1 - 2\sin^2\tfrac{1}{2}\theta$$

We also have

$$\tan 2\theta = \tan(\theta + \theta) = \frac{\tan\theta + \tan\theta}{1 - \tan\theta\tan\theta}$$

Then $$\tan 2\theta = \frac{2\tan\theta}{1 - \tan^2\theta} \qquad [17]$$

Formulas [15], [16], [17], may be applied to any multiple of an angle.

Examples are

(1) $\sin 4A = 2\sin 2A\cos 2A$ (3) $\cos 6A = \cos^2 3A - \sin^2 3A$

(2) $\tan B = \dfrac{2\tan\tfrac{1}{2}B}{1 - \tan^2\tfrac{1}{2}B}$ (4) $\cos\tfrac{2}{3}A = 2\cos^2\tfrac{1}{3}A - 1$

Functions of Half Angles [A]

The formulas for $\sin \frac{1}{2} \theta$ and $\cos \frac{1}{2} \theta$ may be derived from formula [16] as follows:

$$\cos \theta = 1 - 2 \sin^2 \tfrac{1}{2} \theta$$

Solving for $\sin \frac{1}{2} \theta$, we have

$$2 \sin^2 \tfrac{1}{2} \theta = 1 - \cos \theta$$

$$\sin^2 \tfrac{1}{2} \theta = \frac{1 - \cos \theta}{2}$$

$$\sin \tfrac{1}{2} \theta = \pm \sqrt{\frac{1 - \cos \theta}{2}} \qquad [18]$$

This formula may also be used in the form

$$\sin \theta = \pm \sqrt{\frac{1 - \cos 2\theta}{2}}$$

Solving the identity

$$\cos \theta = 2 \cos^2 \tfrac{1}{2} \theta - 1$$

for $\cos \frac{1}{2} \theta$, we have

$$2 \cos^2 \tfrac{1}{2} \theta = 1 + \cos \theta$$

$$\cos^2 \tfrac{1}{2} \theta = \frac{1 + \cos \theta}{2}$$

$$\cos \tfrac{1}{2} \theta = \pm \sqrt{\frac{1 + \cos \theta}{2}} \qquad [19]$$

Also

$$\cos \theta = \pm \sqrt{\frac{1 + \cos 2\theta}{2}}$$

The formula for $\tan \frac{1}{2} \theta$ is obtained from formulas [18] and [19] by division.

$$\frac{\sin \tfrac{1}{2} \theta}{\cos \tfrac{1}{2} \theta} = \frac{\pm \sqrt{\dfrac{1 - \cos \theta}{2}}}{\pm \sqrt{\dfrac{1 + \cos \theta}{2}}} = \pm \sqrt{\frac{1 - \cos \theta}{1 + \cos \theta}}.$$

That is,

$$\tan \tfrac{1}{2} \theta = \pm \sqrt{\frac{1 - \cos \theta}{1 + \cos \theta}} \qquad [20]$$

Also,

$$\tan \theta = \pm \sqrt{\frac{1 - \cos 2\theta}{1 + \cos 2\theta}}$$

The sign to be taken in formulas [18], [19], [20], depends upon the quadrant of the angle.

Formula [20] has two other forms that it is convenient to know. If we rationalize the radical in [20], we obtain

$$\tan \tfrac{1}{2}\,\theta = \pm\sqrt{\frac{1 - \cos\theta}{1 + \cos\theta} \cdot \frac{1 + \cos\theta}{1 + \cos\theta}} = \pm\sqrt{\frac{1 - \cos^2\theta}{(1 + \cos\theta)^2}}$$

Then
$$\tan \tfrac{1}{2}\,\theta = \frac{\sin\theta}{1 + \cos\theta}$$

Also, if we multiply both numerator and denominator of the radicand by $1 - \cos\theta$, we obtain

$$\tan \tfrac{1}{2}\,\theta = \frac{1 - \cos\theta}{\sin\theta}$$

The student should remember formula [20] in all three forms.

In the last two formulas, $1 - \cos\theta$ and $1 + \cos\theta$ will always be positive or zero and $\sin\theta$ and $\tan\tfrac{1}{2}\,\theta$ will always have the same sign. Therefore the $\pm$ sign is not needed in the formulas. If θ is a first-quadrant angle, $\sin\theta$ and $\tan\tfrac{1}{2}\,\theta$ are both positive. If θ is a second-quadrant angle, $\tfrac{1}{2}\,\theta$ is in the first quadrant and $\sin\theta$ and $\tan\tfrac{1}{2}\,\theta$ are both positive. If θ is a third- or fourth-quadrant angle, $\tfrac{1}{2}\,\theta$ is in the second quadrant and $\sin\theta$ and $\tan\tfrac{1}{2}\,\theta$ are both negative.

Examples of the application of formulas [18], [19], and [20] are:

1. $\sin 2\,\theta = \pm\sqrt{\dfrac{1 - \cos 4\,\theta}{2}}$

2. $\cos 3\,\theta = \pm\sqrt{\dfrac{1 + \cos 6\,\theta}{2}}$

3. $\tan 15° = \pm\sqrt{\dfrac{1 - \cos 30°}{1 + \cos 30°}}$

4. $\tan 75° = \dfrac{\sin 150°}{1 + \cos 150°}$

EXERCISES

A

1. From the cosine of 30°, find the sine, cosine, and tangent of 15°.

2. From the cosine of 150°, find the sine, cosine, and tangent of 75°.

3. If θ is in the first quadrant, and $\sin\theta = \tfrac{4}{5}$, find the

   a. sine, cosine, and tangent of $2\,\theta$.

   b. sine, cosine, and tangent of $\tfrac{1}{2}\,\theta$.

4. By the double-angle formulas, find the sine, cosine, and tangent of
   a. 60°   **b.** 120°   **c.** 240°   **d.** 300°

5. Using the half-angle formulas, find the sine, cosine, and tangent of
   a. $22\frac{1}{2}°$ **b.** 105°   **c.** $67\frac{1}{2}°$ **d.** 150°

6. Derive the formula $\operatorname{ctn} 2\ \theta = \dfrac{\operatorname{ctn}^2 \theta - 1}{2 \operatorname{ctn} \theta}$.

7. Derive the formulas

$$\operatorname{ctn} \tfrac{1}{2}\theta = \pm\sqrt{\frac{1 + \cos \theta}{1 - \cos \theta}} = \frac{1 + \cos \theta}{\sin \theta} = \frac{\sin \theta}{1 - \cos \theta}.$$

8. Given $\sin \theta = -\frac{7}{25}$, θ in the third quadrant, find
   a. $\sin 2\ \theta$ **b.** $\cos 2\ \theta$ **c.** $\tan 2\ \theta$ **d.** $\cos \frac{1}{2}\ \theta$ **e.** $\tan \frac{1}{2}\ \theta$

9. Given $\cos \theta = -\frac{8}{17}$, θ in the second quadrant, find
   a. $\sin 2\ \theta$ **b.** $\tan 2\ \theta$ **c.** $\tan \frac{1}{2}\ \theta$ **d.** $\sin \frac{1}{2}\ \theta$ **e.** $\cos \frac{1}{2}\ \theta$

10. Given $\tan \theta = 2$, θ in the third quadrant, find
    a. $\tan 2\ \theta$ **b.** $\tan \frac{1}{2}\ \theta$ **c.** $\sin 2\ \theta$ **d.** $\cos 2\ \theta$ **e.** $\cos \frac{1}{2}\ \theta$

B

11. Express in terms of the same function of θ:
    a. $\sin 3\ \theta$ **b.** $\cos 3\ \theta$ **c.** $\tan 3\ \theta$ **d.** $\sin 4\ \theta$

12. Given right triangle ABC, $C = 90°$, show that

    a. $\sin 2A = \dfrac{2\ ab}{c^2}$ **b.** $\cos 2A = \dfrac{b^2 - a^2}{c^2}$ **c.** $\tan 2A = \dfrac{2\ ab}{b^2 - a^2}$

    d. $\sin (A - B) = \cos 2B$ **e.** $\cos (A - B) = \sin 2A$

13. Prove that $\sec 2\ x = \dfrac{\sec^2 x}{2 - \sec^2 x}$; that $\csc 2\ x = \frac{1}{2} \sec x \csc x$.

The Product Formulas [A]

The products of the sines and cosines of two angles can be derived from the addition and subtraction formulas.

From [9], [12], [10], and [13] respectively,

$$(1)\ \sin (A + B) = \sin A \cos B + \cos A \sin B$$
$$(2)\ \sin (A - B) = \sin A \cos B - \cos A \sin B$$
$$(3)\ \cos (A + B) = \cos A \cos B - \sin A \sin B$$
$$(4)\ \cos (A - B) = \cos A \cos B + \sin A \sin B$$

Adding and then subtracting the corresponding members of equations (1) and (2) on the preceding page, we have

$$\sin (A + B) + \sin (A - B) = 2 \sin A \cos B \qquad [21]$$

$$\sin (A + B) - \sin (A - B) = 2 \cos A \sin B \qquad [22]$$

Adding and then subtracting the corresponding members of equations (3) and (4), we have

$$\cos (A + B) + \cos (A - B) = 2 \cos A \cos B \qquad [23]$$

$$\cos (A + B) - \cos (A - B) = -2 \sin A \sin B \qquad [24]$$

These four formulas are needed for transformations in the calculus and also to derive the next four formulas.

The Sum and Difference of Two Sines or Two Cosines [A]

If we let
$$A + B = \theta$$
$$A - B = \phi$$

and solve the two equations for A and B, we obtain

$$A = \tfrac{1}{2} (\theta + \phi)$$
and
$$B = \tfrac{1}{2} (\theta - \phi).$$

Making these four substitutions in formulas [21], [22], [23], and [24], we have

$$\sin \theta + \sin \phi = 2 \sin \tfrac{1}{2}(\theta + \phi) \cos \tfrac{1}{2}(\theta - \phi) \qquad [25]$$

$$\sin \theta - \sin \phi = 2 \cos \tfrac{1}{2}(\theta + \phi) \sin \tfrac{1}{2}(\theta - \phi) \qquad [26]$$

$$\cos \theta + \cos \phi = 2 \cos \tfrac{1}{2}(\theta + \phi) \cos \tfrac{1}{2}(\theta - \phi) \qquad [27]$$

$$\cos \theta - \cos \phi = -2 \sin \tfrac{1}{2}(\theta + \phi) \sin \tfrac{1}{2}(\theta - \phi) \qquad [28]$$

EXAMPLE 1.   Express $2 \sin 3 A \cos A$ as the sum or difference of two sines or two cosines.

SOLUTION.   From Formula [21],
$$2 \sin 3 A \cos A = \sin (3 A + A) + \sin (3 A - A)$$
$$= \sin 4 A + \sin 2 A$$

EXAMPLE 2.   Express $\cos 5 \theta - \cos 3 \theta$ as a product involving sines or cosines.

SOLUTION.   From Formula [28],
$$\cos 5 \theta - \cos 3 \theta = - 2 \sin \tfrac{1}{2}(5 \theta + 3 \theta) \sin \tfrac{1}{2}(5 \theta - 3 \theta)$$
$$= -2 \sin 4 \theta \sin \theta$$

EXERCISES [A]

Express each of the following as the sum or difference of sines or cosines:

1. $2 \cos 6 A \sin 2 A$ 4. $\sin 4 \alpha \cos \alpha$ 7. $\cos \theta \sin \frac{1}{2} \theta$

2. $2 \cos 5 A \cos 3 A$ 5. $\cos 2 \beta \sin 4 \beta$ 8. $\sin \frac{3}{2} \phi \cos \frac{1}{2} \phi$

3. $2 \sin 3 \phi \sin 2 \phi$ 6. $\cos \frac{1}{4} x \sin \frac{3}{4} x$ 9. $\sin 4 z \sin 2 z$

Express each of the following as a product involving sines and cosines:

10. $\sin 4 \theta + \sin 2 \theta$ 13. $\cos 3 \alpha + \cos \alpha$ 16. $\cos \theta + \cos 2 \theta$

11. $\cos 5 \theta - \cos 3 \theta$ 14. $\sin 3 \beta - \sin 5 \beta$ 17. $\sin 5 \theta + \sin \theta$

12. $\sin 6 \theta - \sin 2 \theta$ 15. $\cos \frac{3}{2} \phi - \cos \frac{1}{2} \phi$ 18. $\sin \frac{3}{2} A - \sin \frac{1}{2} A$

Without using tables find the value of

19. $\cos 75° + \cos 15°$ 20. $\sin 105° - \sin 45°$ 21. $\cos 165° - \cos 105°$

Identities [A]

Proving identities involving the formulas of this chapter will be illustrated by several examples.

EXAMPLE 1. Prove that $\dfrac{\sin (\theta - \phi)}{\sin (\theta + \phi)} = \dfrac{\operatorname{ctn} \phi - \operatorname{ctn} \theta}{\operatorname{ctn} \phi + \operatorname{ctn} \theta}$.

SOLUTION. Since the left member involves the sum and difference of two angles, we try to transform it into the right member.

$$\frac{\sin (\theta - \phi)}{\sin (\theta + \phi)}$$

From formulas [12] and [9],

$$\frac{\sin \theta \cos \phi - \cos \theta \sin \phi}{\sin \theta \cos \phi + \cos \theta \sin \phi}$$

Dividing both numerator and denominator by $\sin \theta \sin \phi$,

$$\frac{\dfrac{\sin \theta \cos \phi}{\sin \theta \sin \phi} - \dfrac{\cos \theta \sin \phi}{\sin \theta \sin \phi}}{\dfrac{\sin \theta \cos \phi}{\sin \theta \sin \phi} + \dfrac{\cos \theta \sin \phi}{\sin \theta \sin \phi}} \qquad \dfrac{\operatorname{ctn} \phi - \operatorname{ctn} \theta}{\operatorname{ctn} \phi + \operatorname{ctn} \theta}$$

EXAMPLE 2. Prove that $\tan A + \operatorname{ctn} 2A = \csc 2A$.

SOLUTION. We shall transform both members so that they contain only functions of A.

$$\tan A + \operatorname{ctn} 2A \qquad\qquad\qquad \csc 2A$$

$$\tan A + \frac{1}{\tan 2A} \qquad\qquad\qquad \frac{1}{\sin 2A}$$

$$\tan A + \frac{1}{\dfrac{2\tan A}{1 - \tan^2 A}} \qquad\qquad\qquad \frac{1}{2\sin A \cos A}$$

Simplifying the complex fraction,

$$\tan A + \frac{1 - \tan^2 A}{2\tan A}$$

Simplifying by addition,

$$\frac{1 + \tan^2 A}{2\tan A}$$

$$\frac{\sec^2 A}{2\tan A}$$

Changing to sines and cosines,

$$\frac{\dfrac{1}{\cos^2 A}}{\dfrac{2\sin A}{\cos A}}$$

Simplifying,

$$\frac{1}{2\sin A \cos A}$$

Since both members reduce to the same expression the identity is proved.

EXAMPLE 3. Prove that $\dfrac{\sin 7\alpha - \sin 5\alpha}{\cos 7\alpha + \cos 5\alpha} = \tan \alpha$

SOLUTION. We shall transform the left member into the same expression as the right member.

$$\frac{\sin 7\alpha - \sin 5\alpha}{\cos 7\alpha + \cos 5\alpha}$$

Transforming the numerator and denominator by formulas [26] and [27] respectively,

$$\frac{2\cos 6\alpha \sin \alpha}{2\cos 6\alpha \cos \alpha}$$

$$\frac{\sin \alpha}{\cos \alpha} \qquad\qquad\qquad \tan \alpha$$

EXERCISES

A

Prove the following identities:

1. $\tan \theta \tan \frac{1}{2} \theta = \sec \theta - 1$

2. $\sin 2 \theta = \dfrac{2 \tan \theta}{1 + \tan^2 \theta}$

3. $(\sin \theta - \cos \theta)^2 = 1 - \sin 2 \theta$

4. $\dfrac{\sin 2 \theta}{1 + \cos 2 \theta} = \tan \theta$

5. $\tan (\theta + 45°) = \dfrac{1 + \tan \theta}{1 - \tan \theta}$

6. $\cos^4 A - \sin^4 A = \cos 2 A$

7. $(1 - \cos^2 \alpha) \cos^2 \alpha = \frac{1}{4} \sin^2 2 \alpha$

8. $\dfrac{\cos (\alpha + \beta)}{\cos (\alpha - \beta)} = \dfrac{1 - \tan \alpha \tan \beta}{1 + \tan \alpha \tan \beta}$

9. $\dfrac{\sin 2 \phi}{\sin \phi} + \dfrac{\cos 2 \phi + 1}{\cos \phi} = 4 \cos \phi$

10. $\dfrac{\tan \theta - \sin \theta}{\tan \theta + \sin \theta} = \tan^2 \frac{1}{2} \theta$

11. $\dfrac{1 - \tan^2 \frac{1}{2} \theta}{1 + \tan^2 \frac{1}{2} \theta} = \cos \theta$

12. $\operatorname{ctn} \frac{1}{2} \theta - \tan \frac{1}{2} \theta = 2 \operatorname{ctn} \theta$

13. $\tan 2 \phi = \dfrac{2}{\operatorname{ctn} \phi - \tan \phi}$

14. $2 \cos x \csc 2 x = \csc x$

15. $\operatorname{ctn} \alpha \sin 2 \alpha = 1 + \cos 2 \alpha$

16. $\dfrac{\sin 2 \theta}{\sin \theta} - \dfrac{\cos 2 \theta}{\cos \theta} = \sec \theta$

17. $\sin 3 x = 3 \sin x - 4 \sin^3 x$

18. $\cos 3 x = 4 \cos^3 x - 3 \cos x$

19. $\tan 3 x = \dfrac{3 \tan x - \tan^3 x}{1 - 3 \tan^2 x}$

20. $\dfrac{2 \tan \alpha}{\tan 2 \alpha} = 1 - \tan^2 \alpha$

21. $\sin 3 \theta + \sin \theta = 2 \sin 2 \theta \cos \theta$

22. $\tan^2 \phi + 2 \operatorname{ctn} 2 \phi \tan \phi = 1$

23. $2 \csc \alpha \tan \frac{1}{2} \alpha - 1 = \tan^2 \frac{1}{2} \alpha$

24. $\cos^4 \beta + \sin^4 \beta = 1 - 2 \sin^2 \beta \cos^2 \beta$

25. $\dfrac{\sin 3\,\theta + \sin \theta}{\sin 3\,\theta - \sin \theta} = \dfrac{2}{1 - \tan^2\theta}$

26. $1 + \sin \phi = (\sin \tfrac{1}{2}\phi + \cos \tfrac{1}{2}\phi)^2$

27. $\sin\left(\dfrac{\pi}{6} + x\right) = \cos\left(\dfrac{\pi}{3} - x\right)$

28. $(\sin y - \cos y)^2 = 1 - \cos\left(\dfrac{\pi}{2} - 2\,y\right)$

29. $\cos(\theta + \phi)\cos(\theta - \phi) = \cos^2\phi - \sin^2\theta$

30. $\sin\left(\alpha + \dfrac{\pi}{3}\right) + \sin\left(\alpha - \dfrac{\pi}{3}\right) = \sin \alpha$

31. $\tan \tfrac{1}{2}(A + B) = \dfrac{\sin A + \sin B}{\cos A + \cos B}$

32. $\sin(\theta + \phi)\cos \phi - \cos(\theta + \phi)\sin \phi = \sin \theta$

33. $\sin\left(\dfrac{\pi}{3} + \theta\right) - \cos\left(\dfrac{\pi}{6} + \theta\right) = \sin \theta$

34. $\dfrac{1 + \cos \alpha + \cos 2\,\alpha}{\sin \alpha + \sin 2\,\alpha} = \operatorname{ctn} \alpha$

35. $\dfrac{2 \sin \theta - \sin 2\,\theta}{2 \sin \theta + \sin 2\,\theta} = \tan^2 \tfrac{1}{2}\,\theta$

B

36. $\sin 2\,\theta\,(4 \cos^4 \theta - 4 \cos^2 \theta)^2 = \sin^5 2\,\theta$

37. $\dfrac{(\cos \theta + \sin \theta)^3}{\cos 2\,\theta} = \dfrac{1 + \sin 2\,\theta}{\cos \theta - \sin \theta}$

38. $\sin x + 2 \sin 3\,x + \sin 5\,x = 4 \cos^2 x \sin 3\,x$

If A, B, C are the angles of a triangle, prove that

39. $\sin 2\,A + \sin 2\,B + \sin 2\,C = 4 \sin A \sin B \sin C$

40. $\cos 2\,A + \cos 2\,B + \cos 2\,C = -1 - 4 \cos A \cos B \cos C$

41. $\cos^2 A + \cos^2 B + \cos^2 C = 1 - 2 \cos A \cos B \cos C$

42. $\sin^2 A + \sin^2 B + \sin^2 C = 2\,(1 + \cos A \cos B \cos C)$

43. $\sin^2 \tfrac{1}{2}A + \sin^2 \tfrac{1}{2}B + \sin^2 \tfrac{1}{2}C = 1 - 2 \sin \tfrac{1}{2}A \sin \tfrac{1}{2}B \sin \tfrac{1}{2}C$

44. $\operatorname{ctn} A \operatorname{ctn} B + \operatorname{ctn} B \operatorname{ctn} C + \operatorname{ctn} A \operatorname{ctn} C = 1$

Equations [A]

No general method for solving equations involving two angles or multiple angles can be given. However, the following suggestions will be helpful:

1. *If possible, reduce the equation to simpler equations by factoring.*
2. *Transform the functions of different angles to functions of the same angle by means of known formulas.*
3. *Transform the equation so as to involve only the same function of this angle.*
4. *If any operations are performed that might produce extraneous roots, all roots must be checked.*

EXAMPLE 1. Solve $4 \cos^2 \theta \sin 2\theta - 1 = 2 \sin 2\theta - 2 \cos^2 \theta$.

SOLUTION. $4 \cos^2 \theta \sin 2\theta - 1 = 2 \sin 2\theta - 2 \cos^2 \theta$
Transposing, $4 \cos^2 \theta \sin 2\theta + 2 \cos^2 \theta - 2 \sin 2\theta - 1 = 0$
Factoring, $2 \cos^2 \theta (2 \sin 2\theta + 1) - (2 \sin 2\theta + 1) = 0$
$(2 \cos^2 \theta - 1)(2 \sin 2\theta + 1) = 0$

$2 \cos^2 \theta - 1 = 0$	$2 \sin 2\theta + 1 = 0$
$\cos^2 \theta = \frac{1}{2}$	$\sin 2\theta = -\frac{1}{2}$
$\cos \theta = \pm \frac{1}{2}\sqrt{2}$	$2\theta = 210°, 330°, 570°, 690°$
$\theta = 45°, 135°, 225°, 315°$	$\theta = 105°, 165°, 285°, 345°$

$\therefore \theta = 45°, 105°, 135°, 165°, 225°, 285°, 315°, 345°$.

Notice that when we obtain θ from 2θ, we must find all positive values of 2θ up to 720° to obtain values of θ up to 360°.

EXAMPLE 2. Solve $\cos 3\theta - 2 \cos 2\theta + \cos \theta = 0$.

SOLUTION. Rearranging the equation,
$$(\cos 3\theta + \cos \theta) - 2 \cos 2\theta = 0$$
Transposing $(\cos 3\theta + \cos \theta)$ by [27],
$$2 \cos 2\theta \cos \theta - 2 \cos 2\theta = 0$$
$$2 \cos 2\theta (\cos \theta - 1) = 0$$

$\cos 2\theta = 0$	$\cos \theta = 1$
$2\theta = 90°, 270°, 450°, 630°$	$\theta = 0°$
$\theta = 45°, 135°, 225°, 315°$	

$\therefore \theta = 0°, 45°, 135°, 225°, 315°$.

EXAMPLE 3. Solve $\sin 2x = \cos 3x$.

SOLUTION. $\sin 2x = \cos 3x$

Transposing, $\sin 2x - \cos 3x = 0$

We first change $\cos 3x$ to functions of $2x$ and x.

$$\sin 2x - \cos (2x + x) = 0$$
$$\sin 2x - \cos 2x \cos x + \sin 2x \sin x = 0$$

The left member of this equation will not factor, so we change the functions of $2x$ to functions of x.

$$2 \sin x \cos x - \cos x (1 - 2 \sin^2 x) + 2 \sin^2 x \cos x = 0$$
$$2 \sin x \cos x - \cos x + 2 \sin^2 x \cos x + 2 \sin^2 x \cos x = 0$$
$$2 \sin x \cos x - \cos x + 4 \sin^2 x \cos x = 0$$

Factoring, $\cos x (2 \sin x - 1 + 4 \sin^2 x) = 0$

$\cos x = 0$ $2 \sin x - 1 + 4 \sin^2 x = 0$

$x = 90°, 270°$ $4 \sin^2 x + 2 \sin x - 1 = 0$

Solving by the quadratic formula,

$$\sin x = \frac{-2 \pm \sqrt{4 + 16}}{8} = \frac{-1 \pm \sqrt{5}}{4}$$
$$= \frac{-1 \pm 2.2361}{4}$$

$\sin x = .3090$ or $-.8090$

From Table X,

$x = 18°, 162°,$ or $234°, 306°$

Therefore $x = 18°, 90°, 162°, 234°, 270°, 306°$

EXERCISES

A

Solve the following equations for all positive values less than $360°$:

1. $\sin 2\theta = 2 \sin \theta$

2. $\sin 2\alpha = \cos \alpha$

3. $\cos \beta = \sin \dfrac{\beta}{2}$

4. $\tan 2\phi = 2 \sin \phi$

5. $\sin^2 \theta = 1 - \sin 2\theta$

6. $\sin 2x + 2 \cos 2x = 1$

7. $\sin 2y = \tan y$

8. $\sin 3z + \sin z = 0$

9. $\tan 2\phi = \text{ctn } \phi$

10. $2 \sin^2 \frac{1}{2} \theta - \cos \theta = 2$

11. $25 \cos^4 x - 25 \sin^4 x = 7$

12. $\cos 2\theta + 2\sin^2 \frac{1}{2}\theta = 1$

13. $\sin A + \cos 2A = 1$

14. $4\sin^2 2\phi - 4\sin^2 \phi = 1$

15. $\tan \alpha \tan 2\alpha = 1$

16. $\sin \beta - \cos 2\beta = \sin 3\beta$

17. $\cos 4x + \cos 2x = 0$

18. $2\operatorname{ctn} 2\theta = \csc \theta$

19. $\tan 4\phi = 3\tan 2\phi$

20. $\sin 4z + \sqrt{3}\cos 2z = 0$

21. $\cos 4\theta + 2\cos^2 2\theta = 0$

22. $\sec 2y = 2\cos y - 1$

23. $2\sin^2 \theta + \sin 2\theta - 1 + 2\cos^2 \theta = 0$

24. $\sin^2 x - \cos^2 x - \cos 2x = 1$

25. $\sin 4A + \sin 2A + \sin 3A = 0$

26. $2\tan^2 4\theta - \sec 4\theta - 4 = 0$

27. $\cos 3\phi \cos \phi + \sin 3\phi \sin \phi + 1 = 0$

28. $\cos 2z \sec z + \sec z + 1 = 0$

29. $\tan y + \tan 2y - \tan 3y = 0$

30. $\sin \frac{1}{2} x \cos 2x (1 - \tan^2 x) = 0$

B

31. $\sin 3\alpha \cos 2\alpha + 2\sin \alpha \cos^2 \alpha + \sin \alpha \cos 2\alpha = 0$

32. $\tan \theta + \tan 2\theta = 1 - \tan \theta \tan 2\theta$

33. $\cos y - \cos 5y + 2\sin 3y = 0$

34. $\sec x \sec 2x - \tan x - \tan 2x = 0$

35. $\operatorname{ctn} x - \operatorname{ctn} 3x = \csc 3x$

36. $\cos 6\theta - 3\cos 3\theta = 0$

37. $\sin 2\phi - \sin \phi = 4\cos^2 \frac{1}{2}\phi - 3$

38. $\sin 3y - \cos 2y + 1 = 0$

39. $2\sin (x - 30°) = \sqrt{3} \sin x$

40. $\sin A + 2\sin 2A + 3\sin 3A = 0$

Antenna on Top of Radio-Relay Tower at Creston, Wyoming

This station is one of over a hundred on the Long Lines Transcontinental Radio-Relay System—an example of the many achievements of electrical engineers

CHAPTER X

OBLIQUE TRIANGLES

Δ

An *oblique triangle* is one that does not contain a right angle. The term includes both acute and obtuse triangles. If any three parts of a triangle, one of which is a side, are known, the other parts can be computed, that is, the triangle can be solved. If only the three angles of a triangle are known, no triangle is determined because an unlimited number of similar triangles having the given angles are possible.

The method used in solving an oblique triangle depends upon the parts of the triangle that are given. The four possible cases follow:

CASE I.   Given one side and two angles.
CASE II.   Given two sides and an angle opposite one of them.
CASE III.   Given two sides and the included angle.
CASE IV.   Given the three sides.

In Case I the third angle can be found by subtracting the sum of the two given angles from 180°. Then the triangle is determined because *two triangles are congruent if two angles and the included side of one are equal respectively to two angles and the included side of the other* (A.S.A. = A.S.A.).

In Case II the triangle is not always determined, as we shall see later.

In Case III the triangle is determined because S.A.S. = S.A.S.

In Case IV the triangle is determined because S.S.S. = S.S.S.

Any oblique triangle can be solved by drawing a perpendicular from one of the vertices to the opposite side to form two right triangles and then solving the two right triangles. This method is often laborious and sometimes difficult. We shall therefore learn more direct methods. The very important *law of sines*, which can be used to solve Case I and Case II and which can be used with the law of cosines or the law of tangents to solve Case III, will now be developed.

Law of Sines [A]

This law may be stated as follows:

In any triangle, the sides are proportional to the sines of their opposite angles.

PROOF.

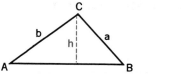 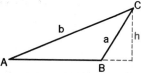

Let ABC be any oblique triangle. From C, draw the altitude h to AB.

In each triangle,
$$\frac{h}{b} = \sin A$$

and
$$\frac{h}{a} = \sin B.$$

By division,
$$\frac{a}{b} = \frac{\sin A}{\sin B}.$$

By alternation,
$$\frac{a}{\sin A} = \frac{b}{\sin B}.\;*$$

Likewise, by drawing the altitude from A, we can prove that
$$\frac{b}{\sin B} = \frac{c}{\sin C}.$$

Then
$$\frac{a}{\sin A} = \frac{b}{\sin B} = \frac{c}{\sin C},$$

or
$$\frac{a}{b} = \frac{\sin A}{\sin B}; \; \frac{a}{c} = \frac{\sin A}{\sin C}; \; \frac{b}{c} = \frac{\sin B}{\sin C}.$$

Either the natural functions or the logarithms of natural functions may by used in solving triangles by this law.

In order to apply the law of sines in the solution of a triangle, the following parts must be known:

a. Two angles and a side opposite one of them, or

b. Two sides and an angle opposite one of them.

* If $A = 90°$, $h = b$ and $\frac{a}{1} = \frac{b}{\sin B}$; if $B = 90°$, $h = a$ and $\frac{a}{\sin A} = \frac{b}{1}$.

Solution of Case I—Given One Side and Two Angles[A]

When two angles and one side of a triangle are given, the third angle can be computed. Then the law of sines can be used to find the remaining sides.

Thus if A, B, and c are known, we can use the formula $A + B + C = 180°$ to find C and then use the law of sines to find a and b.

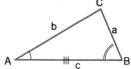

EXAMPLE 1. Solve the triangle ABC, given

$$a = 31.42, A = 34° 18', \text{ and } C = 75° 22' 30''$$

SOLUTION.

GIVEN		REQUIRED
$a = 31.42$		$B = 70° 19' 30''$
$A = 34° 18'$		$b = 52.502$
$C = 75° 22' 30''$		$c = 53.951$

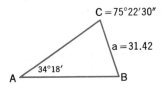

1. To find B:

$$B = 180° - A - C$$
$$= 180° - 34° 18' - 75° 22' 30''$$
$$= 70° 19' 30''$$

2. To find b:

$$\frac{b}{\sin B} = \frac{a}{\sin A}$$

$$b = \frac{a \sin B}{\sin A}$$

$$b = \frac{31.42 \times \sin 70° 19' 30''}{\sin 34° 18'}$$

$$
\begin{aligned}
\log 31.42 &= 1.49721 \\
\log \sin 70° 19' 30'' &= 9.97388 - 10 \\
\hline
& 11.47109 - 10 \\
\log \sin 34° 18' &= 9.75091 - 10 \\
\hline
\log b &= 1.72018 \\
b &= 52.502
\end{aligned}
$$

3. To find c:

$$\frac{c}{\sin C} = \frac{a}{\sin A}$$

$$c = \frac{a \sin C}{\sin A}$$

$$c = \frac{31.42 \times \sin 75° 22' 30''}{\sin 34° 18'}$$

$$
\begin{aligned}
\log 31.42 &= 1.49721 \\
\log \sin 75° 22' 30'' &= 9.98570 - 10 \\
\hline
& 11.48291 - 10 \\
\log \sin 34° 18' &= 9.75091 - 10 \\
\hline
\log c &= 1.73200 \\
c &= 53.951
\end{aligned}
$$

If A, C, and a are found by measurement, $B = 70° 20'$, $b = 52.50$, and $c = 53.95$.

Checking Solutions of Triangles [A]

One method of checking a solution is to repeat the solution. It is better, however, to solve the problem again, by a method which is independent of the first, or to apply a formula containing the unknown parts.

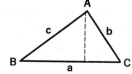

The formula $a = b \cos C + c \cos B$ can be used to check Cases I and II but it is not a check adapted to logarithms. Mollweide's formulas, which will be developed below, are suggested for checking Cases I, II, and III because they contain all six parts of the triangle, are easily remembered, and are easy to apply. They may be used for Case IV, in which the angles of the triangle are to be found, but $A + B + C = 180°$ is a shorter check and is sufficient if the angles are found independently of each other.

In any triangle ABC,

$$\frac{a - b}{c} = \frac{\sin \frac{1}{2}(A - B)}{\cos \frac{1}{2} C}$$

and

$$\frac{a + b}{c} = \frac{\cos \frac{1}{2}(A - B)}{\sin \frac{1}{2} C},$$

which are known as Mollweide's formulas.

PROOF. By the law of sines,

$$\frac{a}{c} = \frac{\sin A}{\sin C} \text{ and } \frac{b}{c} = \frac{\sin B}{\sin C} \tag{1}$$

By the subtraction axiom,

$$\frac{a - b}{c} = \frac{\sin A - \sin B}{\sin C} \tag{2}$$

From page 210,

$$\sin A - \sin B = 2 \sin \frac{1}{2}(A - B) \cos \frac{1}{2}(A + B)$$

and from page 206

$$\sin C = 2 \sin \frac{1}{2} C \cos \frac{1}{2} C.$$

Substituting these values in (2), we have

$$\frac{a - b}{c} = \frac{2 \sin \frac{1}{2}(A - B) \cos \frac{1}{2}(A + B)}{2 \sin \frac{1}{2} C \cos \frac{1}{2} C} \tag{3}$$

Since $C = 180° - (A + B)$,

$$\tfrac{1}{2} C = 90° - \tfrac{1}{2}(A + B).$$

Then $\sin \frac{1}{2} C = \sin [90° - \frac{1}{2}(A + B)] = \cos \frac{1}{2}(A + B)$.

Substituting the value of $\sin \frac{1}{2}C$ in (3), we have

$$\frac{a - b}{c} = \frac{2 \sin \frac{1}{2}(A - B) \cos \frac{1}{2}(A + B)}{2 \cos \frac{1}{2}(A + B) \cos \frac{1}{2} C} \tag{4}$$

Simplifying,

$$\frac{a - b}{c} = \frac{\sin \frac{1}{2}(A - B)}{\cos \frac{1}{2} C} \tag{5}$$

If b is larger than a, use the form

$$\frac{b - a}{c} = \frac{\sin \frac{1}{2}(B - A)}{\cos \frac{1}{2} C}$$

The proof of

$$\frac{a + b}{c} = \frac{\cos \frac{1}{2}(A - B)}{\sin \frac{1}{2} C} \tag{6}$$

is left to the student.

We shall now use one of Mollweide's equations to check the solution of the Example on page 221.

Check by $\qquad \dfrac{b - a}{c} = \dfrac{\sin \frac{1}{2}(B - A)}{\cos \frac{1}{2} C}$

$$\begin{aligned} b &= 52.502 \\ a &= 31.420 \\ \hline b - a &= 21.082 \\ c &= 53.951 \end{aligned} \qquad\qquad \begin{aligned} B &= 70° \ 19' \ 30'' \\ A &= 34° \ 18' \\ \hline B - A &= 36° \ 1' \ 30'' \\ \tfrac{1}{2}(B - A) &= 18° \ 0' \ 45'' \\ \tfrac{1}{2} C &= 37° \ 41' \ 15'' \end{aligned}$$

$$\frac{b - a}{c} = \frac{\sin \frac{1}{2}(B - A)}{\cos \frac{1}{2} C}$$

$$\begin{aligned} \log (b - a) &= 11.32391 - 10 \\ \log c &= 1.73200 \\ \hline \log \text{quotient} &= 9.59191 - 10 \end{aligned} \qquad \begin{aligned} \log \sin \tfrac{1}{2}(B - A) &= 19.49027 - 20 \\ \log \cos \tfrac{1}{2} C &= 9.89838 - 10 \\ \hline \log \text{quotient} &= 9.59189 - 10 \end{aligned}$$

The two quotients check sufficiently.

Check by $\qquad a = b \cos C + c \cos B$

Using Table X for $\cos C$ and $\cos B$,

$$a = 52.502 \times .2525 + 53.951 \times .3366$$
$$a = 13.2568 + 18.1599$$
$$a = 31.42, \text{ to four significant figures.}$$

EXERCISES [A]

Solve the following triangles and check each solution by using one of Mollweide's formulas:

1. $a = 28.34$
$\quad B = 71° 30'$
$\quad C = 46° 45'$

2. $a = 1.843$
$\quad B = 63° 20'$
$\quad C = 54° 30'$

3. $b = 1.435$
$\quad A = 50° 15'$
$\quad B = 71° 45'$

4. $b = 3.124$
$\quad A = 59° 17'$
$\quad B = 34° 23'$

5. $b = 7.8541$
$\quad A = 63° 18' 20''$
$\quad C = 41° 30' 45''$

6. $c = 4.3274$
$\quad A = 18° 25' 10''$
$\quad C = 51° 35' 10''$

7. $c = 1009$
$\quad B = 13° 15'$
$\quad C = 100° 50'$

8. $a = 14.06$
$\quad A = 100° 24'$
$\quad C = 27° 10'$

9. $a = 8.400$
$\quad A = 78° 20'$
$\quad B = 33° 46'$

Solution of Case II—Given Two Sides and An Angle Opposite One of Them [A]

Since the law of sines gives the relation between two sides of a triangle and the angles opposite them, it can be used to find the second angles of the triangle. For example, if A, a, and b are known, we can use the law of sines to find B. After the second angle has been found, we can find the third angle. Then we can use the law of sines to find the third side.

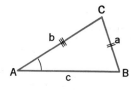

The solution of a triangle, given two sides and an angle opposite one of them, requires considerable thought and care. However, it should not be too difficult if you will study the following discussion carefully.

Let us construct $\triangle ABC$, given A, a, and b.

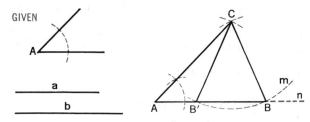

First we construct $\angle A$ and on one of its sides we lay off $AC = b$. Then with C as the vertex and a radius equal to a we describe arc m intersecting the other side n of $\angle A$ in the point B. Then we draw BC, and ABC is the required triangle. The arc *m* may intersect *n* in one point, two points, or in no point, depending upon the length of *a*. Therefore, we may have one solution, two solutions, or no solution.

Let us consider all the possible constructions and solutions. There are nine possible combinations, one of which has three possible constructions, making in all eleven possible constructions or solutions. We shall now consider all of them.

A. *If the longer of the two given sides is opposite the given angle, there is one solution and only one.*

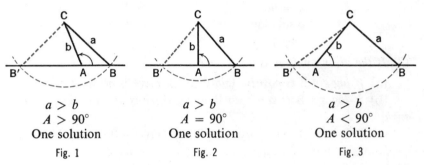

$a > b$	$a > b$	$a > b$
$A > 90°$	$A = 90°$	$A < 90°$
One solution	One solution	One solution
Fig. 1	Fig. 2	Fig. 3

In Fig. 1, $\triangle ABC$ is the required triangle. The $\triangle AB'C$ is not a solution because it does not contain $\angle A$. In Fig. 2, $\triangle ABC$ is the required triangle since $\triangle AB'C$ is congruent to $\triangle ABC$ and is not considered a separate solution. In Fig. 3 $\triangle ABC$ is the only solution. Why is not $\triangle AB'C$ a solution?

B. *If the two given sides are equal and*

(1) *If the given angle is not acute, there is no solution;*

(2) *If the given angle is acute, there is one solution only and the triangle is isosceles.*

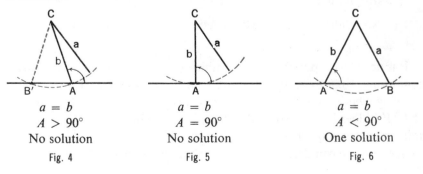

$a = b$	$a = b$	$a = b$
$A > 90°$	$A = 90°$	$A < 90°$
No solution	No solution	One solution
Fig. 4	Fig. 5	Fig. 6

C. *If the shorter of the two given sides is opposite the given angle, and*

(1) *If the given angle is a right angle or an obtuse angle, there is no solution.*

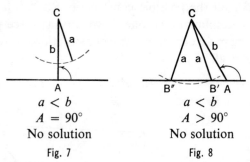

$a < b$ $a < b$
$A = 90°$ $A > 90°$
No solution   No solution
Fig. 7   Fig. 8

(2) *If the given angle* A *is acute and*

(a) *If log sin* B *is positive (sin* B > 1), *there is no solution;*

(b) *If log sin* B *is zero (sin* B = 1), *there is one solution, a right triangle;*

(c) *If log sin* B *is negative (sin* B *lies between 0 and 1), there are two solutions, one acute triangle and one obtuse triangle.*

The three figures below include all the possibilities when $a < b$ and $A < 90°$.

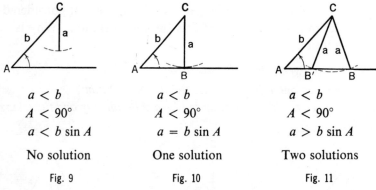

$a < b$ $a < b$ $a < b$
$A < 90°$ $A < 90°$ $A < 90°$
$a < b \sin A$ $a = b \sin A$ $a > b \sin A$

No solution   One solution   Two solutions

Fig. 9   Fig. 10   Fig. 11

It is not always possible to determine by a drawing which of the three conditions (Figures 9, 10, 11) exists, since we cannot always tell by a drawing whether the arc with radius = a will intersect the other side of ∠A. If it does intersect the other side, it is not always possible to determine by a drawing whether it will cut the side in one point or two. Let us see how we can determine which of the three possibilities exists.

When we solve for B by the law of sines, we have $\sin B = \dfrac{b \sin A}{a}$. The sine of any angle of a triangle is positive. Why? The sine of any angle is never greater than unity.

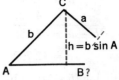

Now if in a solution we find that $a < b \sin A$, or $\sin B > 1$ (or $\log \sin B > 0$), there is no solution. In this case $a < b \sin A$ as in Fig. 9.

If we find that $\sin B = 1$ ($\log \sin B = 0$), then $\angle B$ is a right angle and $a = b \sin A$ (Fig. 10).

If we find that $\sin B >$ zero but < 1 ($\log \sin B$ is negative), $\angle B$ has two values. This is so because an acute angle and its supplement have the same sine. When $\sin B$ has a value between 0 and 1, $a > b \sin A$. Figure 11 shows the two solutions, $\triangle ABC$ and $\triangle AB'C$. This is known as the *ambiguous case*, meaning that there is more than one solution.

EXAMPLE 1. Solve $\triangle ABC$ if $a = 4.927$, $b = 8.413$, and $B = 21° 41'$.

SOLUTION.

GIVEN		REQUIRED
$a = 4.927$		$A = 12° 29' 47''$
$b = 8.413$		$C = 145° 49' 13''$
$B = 21° 41'$		$c = 12.792$

There is one solution, by Case II, A.

1. To find A:

$$\sin A = \frac{a \sin B}{b}$$

$$\sin A = \frac{4.927 \sin 21° 41'}{8.413}$$

$\log 4.927 = 0.69258$
$\log \sin 21° 41' = 9.56759 - 10$
$ \overline{10.26017 - 10}$
$\log 8.413 = .92495$
$\overline{\log \sin A = 9.33522 - 10}$
$ A = 12° 29' 47''$

2. To find C: $\quad C = 180° - B - A$
$ C = 180° - 21° 41' - 12° 29' 47''$
$ C = 145° 49' 13''$

3. To find c:

$$c = \frac{b \sin C}{\sin B}$$

$$c = \frac{8.413 \sin 145° 49' 13''}{\sin 21° 41'}$$

$\log 8.413 = 0.92495$
$\log \sin 145° 49' 13'' = 9.74957 - 10$
$ \overline{10.67452 - 10}$
$\log \sin 21° 41' = 9.56759 - 10$
$\overline{ \log c = 1.10693}$
$ c = 12.792$

If the given data are found by measurement, $A = 12° 30'$, $C = 145° 49'$, and $c = 12.79$.

Check by Mollweide's formula: $\dfrac{b-a}{c} = \dfrac{\sin \frac{1}{2}(B-A)}{\cos \frac{1}{2}C}$

$b =$ 8.413	$B = 21° 41'$
$a =$ 4.927	$A = 12° 29' 47''$
$b - a =$ 3.486	$\frac{1}{2}(B - A) = 4° 35' 36''$
$c = 12.792$	$\frac{1}{2}C = 72° 54' 36''$
$\log (b - a) = 10.54233 - 10$	$\log \sin \frac{1}{2}(B - A) = 18.90354 - 20$
$\log c = 1.10693$	$\log \cos \frac{1}{2}C = 9.46816 - 10$
log quotient $= 9.43540 - 10$	log quotient $= 9.43538 - 10$

The logarithms of the quotients in the check differ by 2 in the last decimal place. In a check the logarithms usually differ by one unit in the last decimal place but a difference of 3 in the last decimal place is permitted in a check.

EXAMPLE 2.   Solve the triangle ABC, given $b = 128$, $c = 145$, and $B = 21° 18'$.

SOLUTION.

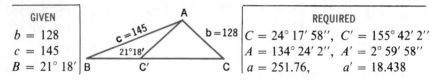

GIVEN
$b = 128$
$c = 145$
$B = 21° 18'$

REQUIRED
$C = 24° 17' 58''$, $C' = 155° 42' 2''$
$A = 134° 24' 2''$, $A' = 2° 59' 58''$
$a = 251.76$, $a' = 18.438$

This problem is of the type IIC, (2).

1. To find C and C':

$$\frac{\sin C}{\sin B} = \frac{c}{b}$$

$$\sin C = \frac{c \sin B}{b}$$

$$\sin C = \frac{145 \sin 21° 18'}{128}$$

$\log 145 =$	2.16137
$\log \sin 21° 18' =$	9.56021 − 10
	11.72158 − 10
$\log 128 =$	2.10721
$\log \sin C =$	9.61437 − 10

Since $\log \sin C$ is negative, C has two values, $C = 24° 17' 58''$ and $C' = 155° 42' 2''$.

2. To find A and A':

$A = 180° - B - C$
$A = 180° - 21° 18' - 24° 17' 58''$
$A = 134° 24' 2''$
$A' = 180° - B - C'$
$A' = 180° - 21° 18' - 155° 42' 2''$
$A' = 2° 59' 58''$

3. To find a and a':

$$\frac{a}{b} = \frac{\sin A}{\sin B} \qquad\qquad \frac{a'}{b} = \frac{\sin A'}{\sin B}$$

$$a = \frac{b \sin A}{\sin B} \qquad\qquad a' = \frac{b \sin A'}{\sin B}$$

$$a = 128\,\frac{\sin 134° 24' 2''}{\sin 21° 18'} \qquad\qquad a' = \frac{128 \sin 2° 59' 58''}{\sin 21° 18'}$$

log 128 =	2.10721		log 128 =	2.10721
log sin 134° 24' 2'' =	9.85399 − 10		log sin 2° 59' 58'' =	8.71872 − 10
	11.96120 − 10			10.82593 − 10
log sin 21° 18' =	9.56021 − 10		log sin 21° 18' =	9.56021 − 10
log a =	2.40099		log a' =	1.26572
a =	251.76		a' =	18.438

If the given data are found by measurement, the values of a and a' should be rounded off to three significant figures and the values of A, A', C, and C' should be rounded off to the nearest 10 minutes.

Check by Mollweide's formula.

$$
\begin{array}{ll}
a = 251.76 & A = 134° 24' 2'' \\
b = 128.00 & B = 21° 18' \\
\overline{a - b = 123.76} & \overline{\tfrac{1}{2}(A - B) = 56° 33' 1''} \\
c = 145 & \tfrac{1}{2}C = 12° 8' 59''
\end{array}
$$

$$\frac{a - b}{c} = \frac{\sin \tfrac{1}{2}(A - B)}{\cos \tfrac{1}{2}C}$$

log $(a - b)$ = 12.09258 − 10		log sin $\tfrac{1}{2}(A - B)$ = 19.92136 − 20
log c = 2.16137		log cos $\tfrac{1}{2}C$ = 9.99016 − 10
log quotient = 9.93121 − 10		log quotient = 9.93120 − 10

EXERCISES

A

Test the data in Exercises 1–9 and determine in each case whether the triangle ABC *is solvable. If the triangle is solvable, determine the number of solutions.*

1. $a = 40$	**2.** $a = 18$	**3.** $a = 44$	**4.** $b = 15$	**5.** $a = 12$
$b = 30$	$c = 18$	$b = 60$	$c = 25$	$b = 18$
$A = 70°$	$A = 90°$	$A = 100°$	$C = 110°$	$A = 30°$

6. $a = 10$	**7.** $a = 15$	**8.** $a = 50$	**9.** $a = 25$
$b = 40$	$b = 30$	$b = 48$	$b = 25$
$A = 70°$	$A = 30°$	$B = 60°$	$A = 40°$

Solve the following triangles if they are solvable, checking the solutions by a Mollweide formula:

10. $a = 23.47$	**12.** $b = 37.24$	**14.** $a = 55.94$
$b = 16.81$	$c = 23.45$	$b = 143.72$
$A = 74° 18'$	$C = 34° 23'$	$A = 30° 14' 15''$

11. $a = 4.186$	**13.** $a = 33.69$	**15.** $b = 17.141$
$b = 3.625$	$b = 52.44$	$c = 9.842$
$A = 44° 25'$	$A = 21° 43'$	$B = 110° 42' 45''$

16. The diagonal of a parallelogram is 42.36 feet long and forms angles of 29° 14′ and 32° 46′ with the sides. Find the lengths of the sides.

17. In $\triangle ABC$, $\angle A = 62° 24'$, $\angle B = 41° 38'$, and $BC = 7.41$ inches. Find the length of the bisector of $\angle C$.

18. In order that a 25-foot ladder may reach a certain window it must make an angle of 62° with the ground. What angle must a 30-foot ladder make with the ground to reach the same window?

B

19. *A* and *B*, when on the same meridian and 92° 24′ apart, observed that the zenith angles of the moon were 47° 25′ and 46° 21′ respectively. How far was each observer from the moon? Assume the radius of the earth to be 3956 miles.

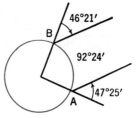

20. A boat is steaming northeast at 15 miles an hour. At 2 P.M. a lighthouse bears N 10° W and at 4 P.M. it bears W 31° S. How far was the boat from the lighthouse at 2 P.M.?

21. A cruiser is steaming southwest at 16 knots. At 8 A.M. a landmark bears N 24° W and at 11 A.M. it bears N 28° 20′ E. How far from the cruiser was the landmark at 8 A.M.? (A knot is a speed of one nautical mile an hour. A nautical mile is about 6080 feet.)

22. An airplane was flying a course at 6500 feet altitude. When at the point A, the angle of depression of the point C was 75°. When it

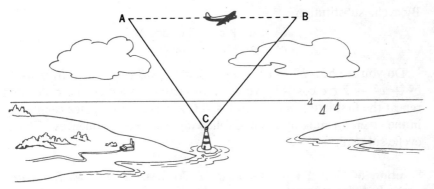

reached the point B, 10 seconds later, the angle of depression of C was 50° 30′. Find the ground speed of the plane in miles an hour.

The Law of Cosines[A]

This important law may be stated as follows:

The square of any side of a triangle is equal to the sum of the squares of the two other sides minus twice the product of these two sides multiplied by the cosine of their included angle.

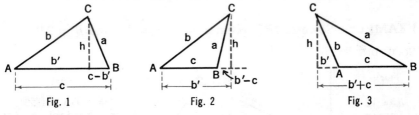

| Fig. 1 | Fig. 2 | Fig. 3 |

The three cases for expressing the side a of $\triangle ABC$ in terms of b, c, and A are illustrated above.

For Fig. 1, $a^2 = h^2 + (c - b')^2 = h^2 + c^2 - 2 c b' + b'^2$
For Fig. 2, $a^2 = h^2 + (b' - c)^2 = h^2 + c^2 - 2 c b' + b'^2$
For Fig. 3, $a^2 = h^2 + (b' + c)^2 = h^2 + c^2 + 2 c b' + b'^2$

For each figure, $h^2 + b'^2 = b^2$. By substituting b^2 for $h^2 + b'^2$, we have for Fig. 1 and Fig. 2, $a^2 = b^2 + c^2 - 2 c b'$ and for Fig. 3, $a^2 = b^2 + c^2 + 2 c b'$. For Fig. 1 and Fig. 2, $b' = b \cos A$ and for Fig. 3, $b' = -b \cos A$.

Substituting the values just found for b', we have for all three figures,

$$a^2 = b^2 + c^2 - 2\,bc \cos A$$

By cyclic substitution,

$$b^2 = a^2 + c^2 - 2\,ac \cos B$$
$$c^2 = a^2 + b^2 - 2\,ab \cos C$$

Do you see how $b^2 = a^2 + c^2 - 2\,a\,c \cos B$ is obtained from $a^2 = b^2 + c^2 - 2\,b\,c \cos A$? We write the letters in alphabetic order and repeat the first letter: $a\,b\,c\,a$ and $A\,B\,C\,A$. Then we replace each letter in the given formula by the one following it in these sequences. This is cyclic substitution.

Solution of Case III by the Law of Cosines. *Given Two Sides and the Included Angle* [A]

As you remember, the law of sines can be used to solve Case I and Case II. The law of cosines can be used to solve Case III and Case IV. In Case III the law of cosines, in the form $a^2 = b^2 + c^2 - 2\,bc \cos A$, can be used to find the third side a of the triangle, and then the law of sines can be used to find the two remaining angles. The law of cosines could be used to find the two angles, but the computation is too long. This law is not adapted to a solution by logarithms because the right member of the formula consists of terms and not of factors.

EXAMPLE. Solve $\triangle ABC$, given $a = 12$, $c = 10$, and $B = 24°$.

SOLUTION.

GIVEN		REQUIRED
$a = 12$		$b = 4.975$, or 5.0
$c = 10$		$A = 101°\ 10'$, or $101°$
$B = 24°$		$C = 54°\ 50'$, or $55°$

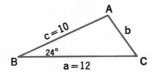

1. To find b:

$$b^2 = a^2 + c^2 - 2\,ac \cos B$$

$$\begin{aligned}
a^2 &= 144 \\
c^2 &= 100 \\
\hline
a^2 + c^2 &= 244 \\
2\,ac \cos B &= 219.25 \\
\hline
b^2 &= 24.75 \\
b &= 4.975
\end{aligned}$$

2. To find C:

We first find C because it is smaller than A, being opposite the smaller side.

$$\frac{\sin C}{c} = \frac{\sin B}{b}$$

$$\sin C = \frac{c \sin B}{b}$$

$$\sin C = \frac{10 \sin 24°}{4.975}$$

$$\begin{array}{rl}
\log 10 = & 1.00000 \\
\log \sin 24° = & 9.60931 - 10 \\
\hline
 & 10.60931 - 10 \\
\log 4.975 = & .69679 \\
\hline
\log \sin C = & 9.91252 - 10 \\
C = & 54° 50'
\end{array}$$

The value of C was rounded off to the nearest minute because a four-place table was used to find b.

3. To find A:

$$\frac{\sin A}{a} = \frac{\sin B}{b}$$

$$\sin A = \frac{a \sin B}{b}$$

$$\sin A = \frac{12 \sin 24°}{4.975}$$

$$\begin{array}{rl}
\log 12 = & 1.07918 \\
\log \sin 24° = & 9.60931 - 10 \\
\hline
 & 10.68849 - 10 \\
\log 4.975 = & .69679 \\
\hline
\log \sin A = & 9.99170 - 10 \\
A = & 101° 10'
\end{array}$$

This value of A is taken because A is obtuse.

$$\begin{array}{rl}
Check: \quad A = & 101° 10' \\
B = & 24° \\
C = & 54° 50' \\
\hline
A + B + C = & 179° 60'
\end{array}$$

EXERCISES [A]

Solve the following triangles and check your solutions:

1. $a = 14$
   $b = 10$
   $C = 46° 18'$

2. $a = 20$
   $b = 14$
   $C = 110° 40'$

3. $b = 25$
   $c = 20$
   $A = 76° 50'$

4. $b = 64$
   $c = 48$
   $A = 62° 14'$

5. $b = 30$
   $c = 20$
   $A = 45°$

6. $a = 32$
   $b = 40$
   $C = 71° 45'$

Solution of Case IV by the Law of Cosines. *Given the Three Sides* [A]

If we solve the formulas $a^2 = b^2 + c^2 - 2bc \cos A$, $b^2 = a^2 + c^2 - 2ac \cos B$, and $c^2 = a^2 + b^2 - 2ab \cos C$ for $\cos A$, $\cos B$, and $\cos C$ respectively, we obtain

$$\cos A = \frac{b^2 + c^2 - a^2}{2bc}$$

$$\cos B = \frac{a^2 + c^2 - b^2}{2ac} \qquad \cos C = \frac{a^2 + b^2 - c^2}{2ab}$$

These formulas can be used to find the angles of a triangle when the sides of the triangle are given.

EXAMPLE. Solve $\triangle ABC$, given $a = 18$, $b = 14$, and $c = 10$.

SOLUTION.

GIVEN
$a = 18$
$b = 14$
$c = 10$

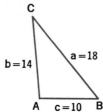

REQUIRED
$A = 95°\ 44'$, or $96°$
$B = 50°\ 42'$, or $51°$
$C = 33°\ 34'$, or $34°$

1. To find A:

$$\cos A = \frac{b^2 + c^2 - a^2}{2\ bc}$$

$$\cos A = \frac{196 + 100 - 324}{280}$$

$$\cos A = -.1000$$
$$A = 95°\ 44'$$

2. To find B:

$$\cos B = \frac{a^2 + c^2 - b^2}{2\ ac}$$

$$\cos B = \frac{324 + 100 - 196}{360}$$

$$\cos B = .6333$$
$$B = 50°\ 42'$$

3. To find C:

$$\cos C = \frac{a^2 + b^2 - c^2}{2\ ab}$$

$$\cos C = \frac{324 + 196 - 100}{504}$$

$$\cos C = .8333$$
$$C = 33°\ 34'$$

$Check:$ $A = 95°\ 44'$
$B = 50°\ 42'$
$C = 33°\ 34'$
$\overline{}$
$A + B + C = 180°\ 0'$

EXERCISES [A]

Solve the following triangles and check your solutions:

1. $a = 30$
$b = 20$
$c = 25$

2. $a = 16$
$b = 20$
$c = 28$

3. $a = 70$
$b = 80$
$c = 90$

4. $a = 70$
$b = 240$
$c = 250$

5. $a = 800$
$b = 1500$
$c = 1700$

6. $a = 185$
$b = 125$
$c = 153$

The Four Cases [A]

We have now learned how to solve any oblique plane triangle. The law of sines was used to find a side in Case I and a side and angle in Case II. The law of cosines was used to find a side in Case III and angles in Case IV. Since the law of cosines is not adapted to logarithms, we shall develop formulas adapted to logarithms for Cases III and IV. For Case III we shall use the law of tangents.

The Law of Tangents [A]

The statement and proof of this law are as follows:

In any triangle the difference of any two sides is to their sum as the tangent of half the difference of the angles opposite these sides is to the tangent of half their sum.

PROOF. In any $\triangle ABC$, $\dfrac{a}{\sin A} = \dfrac{b}{\sin B}$ (1)

Then $\dfrac{a}{b} = \dfrac{\sin A}{\sin B}$ (2)

Then $\dfrac{a - b}{a + b} = \dfrac{\sin A - \sin B}{\sin A + \sin B}$. Why? (3)

From page 210, $\sin A - \sin B = 2 \cos \frac{1}{2}(A + B) \sin \frac{1}{2}(A - B)$

and $\sin A + \sin B = 2 \sin \frac{1}{2}(A + B) \cos \frac{1}{2}(A - B)$

Substituting in (3), we have

$$\frac{a - b}{a + b} = \frac{2 \cos \frac{1}{2}(A + B) \sin \frac{1}{2}(A - B)}{2 \sin \frac{1}{2}(A + B) \cos \frac{1}{2}(A - B)} \quad (4)$$

$$\frac{a - b}{a + b} = \text{ctn} \, \tfrac{1}{2}(A + B) \tan \tfrac{1}{2}(A - B) \quad (5)$$

$$\therefore \frac{a - b}{a + b} = \frac{\tan \frac{1}{2}(A - B)}{\tan \frac{1}{2}(A + B)} \quad (6)$$

If b is greater than a,

$$\frac{b - a}{b + a} = \frac{\tan \frac{1}{2}(B - A)}{\tan \frac{1}{2}(B + A)}$$

Since we use the law of tangents to find the angles of a triangle, we write the formulas in the form

$$\frac{\tan \frac{1}{2}(A - B)}{\tan \frac{1}{2}(A + B)} = \frac{a - b}{a + b} \quad \text{and} \quad \frac{\tan \frac{1}{2}(B - A)}{\tan \frac{1}{2}(B + A)} = \frac{b - a}{b + a}$$

Solution of Case III by the Law of Tangents. *Given Two Sides and the Included Angle*[A]

The law of tangents is preferable to the law of cosines for Case III when large numbers are involved and when it is desired to use logarithms.

In using the law of tangents for Case III, one half the sum of A and B is found by plane geometry and one half the difference by the law of tangents. Then by addition and subtraction, A and B are found. The third side of the triangle is found by the law of sines.

EXAMPLE. Solve $\triangle ABC$, given $a = 143.7$, $b = 114.1$, and $C = 42° 15'$.

SOLUTION.

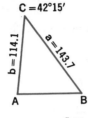

$C = 42°15'$
$b = 114.1$
$a = 143.7$
$A \quad\quad B$

GIVEN
$a = 143.7$
$b = 114.1$
$C = 42° 15'$

REQUIRED
$A = 85° 25' 33''$, or $85° 26'$
$B = 52° 19' 27''$, or $52° 19'$
$c = 96.930$, or 96.93

$$a = 143.7$$
$$\underline{b = 114.1}$$
$$a + b = 257.8$$
$$a - b = \quad 29.6$$

$$\tfrac{1}{2}(A + B) = \tfrac{1}{2}(180° - C)$$
$$= 68° 52' 30''$$

1. To find A and B:

$$\frac{\tan \tfrac{1}{2}(A - B)}{\tan \tfrac{1}{2}(A + B)} = \frac{a - b}{a + b}$$

$$\tan \tfrac{1}{2}(A - B) = \frac{(a - b) \tan \tfrac{1}{2}(A + B)}{a + b}$$

$$= \frac{29.6 \tan 68° 52' 30''}{257.8}$$

$$\log 29.6 = \quad 1.47129$$
$$\log \tan 68° 52' 30'' = \underline{10.41300 - 10}$$
$$11.88429 - 10$$
$$\log 257.8 = \underline{\quad 2.41128}$$
$$\overline{\log \tan \tfrac{1}{2}(A - B) = \quad 9.47301 - 10}$$
$$\tfrac{1}{2}(A - B) = 16° 33' 3''$$
$$\tfrac{1}{2}(A + B) = 68° 52' 30''$$
$$\overline{A = 85° 25' 33''}$$
$$B = 52° 19' 27''$$

2. To find c:

$$\frac{c}{\sin C} = \frac{b}{\sin B}$$

$$c = \frac{b \sin C}{\sin B}$$

$$c = \frac{114.1 \sin 42° 15'}{\sin 52° 19' 27''}$$

$$
\begin{aligned}
\log 114.1 &= 2.05729 \\
\log \sin 42° 15' &= 9.82761 - 10 \\
\hline
&\ \ 11.88490 - 10 \\
\log \sin 52° 19' 27'' &= 9.89844 - 10 \\
\hline
\log c &= 1.98646 \\
c &= 96.930
\end{aligned}
$$

Check by Mollweide's formula:

$$\frac{a - c}{b} = \frac{\sin \frac{1}{2}(A - C)}{\cos \frac{1}{2}B}$$

$a =$	143.7	$A =$	85° 25' 33''
$c =$	96.930	$C =$	42° 15'
$a - c =$	46.770	$\frac{1}{2}(A - C) =$	21° 35' 16''
$b =$	114.1	$\frac{1}{2} B =$	26° 9' 44''
$\log (a - c) =$	11.66997 − 10	$\log \sin \frac{1}{2}(A - C) =$	19.56576 − 20
$\log b =$	2.05729	$\log \cos \frac{1}{2} B =$	9.95306 − 10
$\log$ quotient $=$	9.61268 − 10	$\log$ quotient $=$	9.61270 − 10

EXERCISES [A]

Solve the following triangles, using the law of tangents:

1. $a = 407$
$b = 513$
$C = 66° 34'$

2. $a = 78.3$
$b = 62.7$
$C = 82° 55'$

3. $b = 46.34$
$c = 75.19$
$A = 73° 27'$

4. $b = 5.217$
$c = 8.46$
$A = 34° 25'$

5. $a = 19.78$
$b = 24.54$
$C = 121° 30'$

6. $a = 46.37$
$c = 29.42$
$B = 140° 40'$

7. $b = 72.143$
$c = 53.465$
$A = 42° 18' 40''$

8. $b = 127.18$
$c = 135.44$
$A = 78° 27' 15''$

9. $a = 27.961$
$c = 34.215$
$B = 94° 16' 40''$

Half-Angle Formulas[A]

The half-angle formulas are useful in solving Case IV by logarithms.

(1) *Formula for* $\tan \frac{1}{2} A$

From page 207, $\tan \frac{1}{2} A = \sqrt{\dfrac{1 - \cos A}{1 + \cos A}}$ (1)

By the law of cosines, $\cos A = \dfrac{b^2 + c^2 - a^2}{2\,b\,c}$.

Then $1 - \cos A = 1 - \dfrac{b^2 + c^2 - a^2}{2\,b\,c}$

$$= \frac{2\,b\,c - (b^2 + c^2 - a^2)}{2\,b\,c}$$

$$= \frac{a^2 - (b^2 - 2\,b\,c + c^2)}{2\,b\,c} = \frac{a^2 - (b - c)^2}{2\,b\,c}$$

$$1 - \cos A = \frac{(a + b - c)(a - b + c)}{2\,b\,c} \tag{2}$$

Similarly, it can be shown that

$$1 + \cos A = \frac{(b + c - a)(b + c + a)}{2\,b\,c} \tag{3}$$

From equations (1), (2), and (3), we get

$$\tan \tfrac{1}{2} A = \sqrt{\frac{(a + b - c)(a - b + c)}{(b + c - a)(b + c + a)}} \tag{4}$$

Now let $a + b + c = 2\,s$ (5)

Then
$$a + b - c = 2\,s - 2\,c = 2\,(s - c) \tag{6}$$
$$a - b + c = 2\,(s - b) \tag{7}$$
$$b + c - a = 2\,(s - a) \tag{8}$$

Substituting in equation 4,

$$\tan \tfrac{1}{2} A = \sqrt{\frac{(s - b)(s - c)}{s(s - a)}} \tag{9}$$

Similarly,

$$\tan \tfrac{1}{2} B = \sqrt{\frac{(s - a)(s - c)}{s(s - b)}} \quad \text{and} \quad \tan \tfrac{1}{2} C = \sqrt{\frac{(s - a)(s - b)}{s(s - c)}}$$

(2) Another Formula for tan ½ A

Let O be the center of the circle inscribed in $\triangle ABC$. Let r denote the radius of the circle. Denote the perimeter of the triangle by $2\,s$ and let x, y, and z represent the tangents to the circle from A, B, and C respectively.

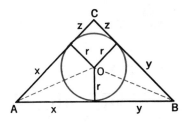

From the figure, $\tan \frac{1}{2} A = \dfrac{r}{x}$ (1)

$$2x + 2y + 2z = 2s$$

Then $$x + y + z = s$$

$$x = s - y - z = s - (y + z)$$

Then $$x = s - a$$ (2)

From (1) and (2), $$\tan \tfrac{1}{2} A = \dfrac{r}{s - a}$$ (3)

Likewise $$\tan \tfrac{1}{2} B = \dfrac{r}{s - b} \text{ and } \tan \tfrac{1}{2} C = \dfrac{r}{s - c}$$

(3) Formulas for sin ½ A and cos ½ A

By using formulas $\sin \frac{1}{2} A = \sqrt{\dfrac{1 - \cos A}{2}}$ and $\cos \frac{1}{2} A = \sqrt{\dfrac{1 + \cos A}{2}}$

and following the general plan used in proving

$$\tan \tfrac{1}{2} A = \sqrt{\dfrac{(s - b)(s - c)}{s(s - a)}},$$

we can show that $$\sin \tfrac{1}{2} A = \sqrt{\dfrac{(s - b)(s - c)}{bc}}$$

and $$\cos \tfrac{1}{2} A = \sqrt{\dfrac{s(s - a)}{bc}}$$

Formula for the Radius of the Incircle [A]

The two formulas for $\tan \frac{1}{2} A$ are

$$\tan \tfrac{1}{2} A = \sqrt{\frac{(s-b)(s-c)}{s(s-a)}} \text{ and } \tan \tfrac{1}{2} A = \frac{r}{s-a}.$$

Hence

$$\frac{r}{s-a} = \sqrt{\frac{(s-b)(s-c)}{s(s-a)}}$$

Solving,

$$r = (s-a)\sqrt{\frac{(s-b)(s-c)}{s(s-a)}}$$

$$r = \sqrt{\frac{(s-a)(s-b)(s-c)}{s}}^{*}$$

Solution of Case IV by Half-Angle Formula. *Given the Three Sides* [A]

When the three sides of a triangle are given, we can find the angles by any of the half-angle formulas:

$$\tan \tfrac{1}{2} A = \sqrt{\frac{(s-b)(s-c)}{s(s-a)}} \qquad \sin \tfrac{1}{2} A = \sqrt{\frac{(s-b)(s-c)}{bc}}$$

$$\cos \tfrac{1}{2} A = \sqrt{\frac{s(s-a)}{bc}}$$

However, in this text we shall first find r and then use the formula

$$\tan \tfrac{1}{2} A = \frac{r}{s-a}.$$

To solve $\triangle ABC$, given a, b, and c:

1. Find r by the formula
$$r = \sqrt{\frac{(s-a)(s-b)(s-c)}{s}}$$

2. Then find A, B, and C by

$$\tan \tfrac{1}{2} A = \frac{r}{s-a} \qquad \tan \tfrac{1}{2} B = \frac{r}{s-b} \qquad \tan \tfrac{1}{2} C = \frac{r}{s-c}$$

3. Check by $A + B + C = 180°$

* This formula can be easily developed by equating the values of the area K in the formulas $K = rs$ and $K = \sqrt{s(s-a)(s-b)(s-c)}$. Since you may not be familiar with these formulas and we have not developed them in the preceding work, we did not use them in the proof above.

EXAMPLE. Solve $\triangle ABC$, given $a = 157$, $b = 170$, and $c = 126.6$.

SOLUTION.

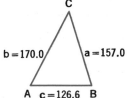

GIVEN
$a = 157$
$b = 170$
$c = 126.6$

REQUIRED
$A = 61°\ 53'\ 38''$ or $61°\ 50'$
$B = 72°\ 46'\ 4''$, or $72°\ 50'$
$C = 45°\ 20'\ 20''$, or $45°\ 20'$

$$a = 157$$
$$b = 170$$
$$\underline{c = 126.6}$$
$$\overline{2\,s = 453.6}$$
$$s = 226.8$$

$$s - a = 69.8$$
$$s - b = 56.8$$
$$s - c = 100.2$$

1. To find r:

$$r = \sqrt{\frac{(s-a)(s-b)(s-c)}{s}}$$

$$r = \sqrt{\frac{69.8 \times 56.8 \times 100.2}{226.8}}$$

$$\log 69.8 = 1.84386$$
$$\log 56.8 = 1.75435$$
$$\log 100.2 = \underline{2.00087}$$
$$5.59908$$
$$\log 226.8 = \underline{2.35564}$$
$$\log \text{radical} = 3.24344$$
$$\log r = 1.62172$$

2. To find A:

$$\tan \tfrac{1}{2} A = \frac{r}{s-a}$$

$$= \frac{r}{69.8}$$

$$\log r = 11.62172 - 10$$
$$\log 69.8 = \underline{1.84386}$$
$$\log \tan \tfrac{1}{2} A = 9.77786 - 10$$

$$\tfrac{1}{2} A = 30°\ 56'\ 49''$$
$$A = 61°\ 53'\ 38''$$

3. To find B:

$$\tan \tfrac{1}{2} B = \frac{r}{s-b}$$

$$= \frac{r}{56.8}$$

$$\log r = 11.62172 - 10$$
$$\log 56.8 = \underline{1.75435}$$
$$\log \tan \tfrac{1}{2} B = 9.86737 - 10$$

$$\tfrac{1}{2} B = 36°\ 23'\ 2''$$
$$B = 72°\ 46'\ 4''$$

4. To find C:

$$\tan \tfrac{1}{2} C = \frac{r}{s-c}$$

$$= \frac{r}{100.2}$$

$$\log r = 11.62172 - 10$$
$$\log 100.2 = \underline{2.00087}$$
$$\log \tan \tfrac{1}{2} C = 9.62085 - 10$$

$$\tfrac{1}{2} C = 22°\ 40'\ 10''$$
$$C = 45°\ 20'\ 20''$$

Since the three angles are found independently, we may check by the formula
$A + B + C = 180°$.

EXERCISES

A

Solve the following triangles and check your solutions:

1. $a = 73.8$
   $b = 64.2$
   $c = 58.9$

2. $a = 29.4$
   $b = 38.2$
   $c = 25.3$

3. $a = 94.81$
   $b = 72.46$
   $c = 100.73$

4. $a = 1254$
   $b = 3006$
   $c = 3507$

5. $a = 50.42$
   $b = 94.79$
   $c = 107.11$

6. $a = 172.8$
   $b = 172.8$
   $c = 215.3$

7. $a = 24.18$
   $b = 17.26$
   $c = 13.49$

8. $a = 35.19$
   $b = 84.72$
   $c = 91.76$

9. $a = 2347$
   $b = 2096$
   $c = 1548$

B

10. Prove by the method used on page 238 that $\sin \frac{1}{2} A = \sqrt{\dfrac{(s-b)(s-c)}{bc}}$.

11. Prove by the method suggested on page 238 that $\cos \frac{1}{2} A = \sqrt{\dfrac{s(s-a)}{bc}}$.

12. Using the formulas $K = rs$ and $K = \sqrt{s(s-a)(s-b)(s-c)}$, prove that $r = \sqrt{\dfrac{(s-a)(s-b)(s-c)}{s}}$.

Summary of the Four Cases

CASE	GIVEN	SOLUTION BY	CHECK
I	Two angles and one side	Law of sines	Mollweide's formula or $a = b \cos C + c \cos B$
II	Two sides and one opposite angle	Law of sines	Mollweide's formula
III	Two sides and in-cluded angle	Law of cosines or Law of tangents	Mollweide's formula
IV	Three sides	Law of cosines or Half-angle formulas	$A + B + C = 180°$

EXERCISES[A]

Solve the following triangles and check your solutions:

1. $c = 125.4$
$\quad A = 72° 41'$
$\quad B = 60° 32'$

2. $b = 7.15$
$\quad c = 18.24$
$\quad C = 95° 27'$

3. $a = 24.16$
$\quad b = 15.38$
$\quad A = 40° 15'$

4. $a = 73.84$
$\quad b = 61.07$
$\quad C = 52° 21'$

5. $a = 15.374$
$\quad b = 18.946$
$\quad C = 24° 18' 48''$

6. $a = 134.72$
$\quad b = 104.68$
$\quad c = 120.24$

EXERCISES (APPLICATIONS)

A

1. Find the sides of a parallelogram if one of its diagonals is 18.31 feet long and makes angles of 28° 34' and 52° 26' with the sides.

2. Two ships sail from the same port, one N.E. 60 miles and the other S 20° E 42 miles. What is the bearing of the second ship from the first after they have gone the above distances?

3. Prove by the law of sines: "If two sides of a triangle are equal, the angles opposite these sides are equal."

4. Prove by the law of sines: "If two angles of a triangle are equal, the sides opposite these angles are equal."

5. A fir tree stands upright on a mountainside which rises uniformly at an angle of 16° 20'. The tree breaks at a point 30 feet from the ground, the top striking down the slope of the mountain 26 feet from the foot of the tree. How high was the tree before it broke?

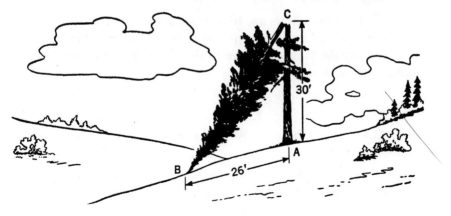

6. The radius of a circle is 23.45 inches. Find the length of a chord of the circle whose central angle is 72° 18′.

7. Two airplanes start at the same time from two airports, A and B, 210 miles apart and having the same latitude. One plane flies from A on course 22° 40′ and the other flies from B on course 322° 20′. How far from A will their tracks intersect? (The track is the path and the course is the direction of the track, measured clockwise from N.)

8. AB is a 26-inch chord of a circle whose diameter is 38 inches. Find the angle subtended at the center of the circle.

9. Find the radius of the largest circular flower bed which can be made on a triangular plot of ground whose sides are 33′, 38′, and 27′, if the bed is to lack one foot of touching each of the three sides.

10. An airplane was flying on a straight level course toward an airport at a height of 20,000 feet when the altimeter failed to indicate the height. The navigator observed that the angle of depression of the airport was 18°. Two minutes later he observed that the angle of depression of the airport was 41°. What was the speed of the plane?

11. The distance between points A and B could not be measured directly. To find the distance a point C was selected and the following measurements were then made: $AC = 490.3$ feet; $BC = 724.8$ feet; $\angle ACB = 73° 10′$. Find the distance AB.

12. Prove by the law of sines: The bisector of an angle of a triangle divides the opposite side into segments which are proportional to the adjacent sides.

13. The radii of two circles are 10.0 inches and 26.0 inches, respectively, and the distance between their centers is 26.0 inches. Find the angle formed by the tangents drawn to the circles at one of the points of their intersection.

B

14. In $\triangle ABC$, $a = 26$, $b = 30$, and $c = 42$. Find the length of the bisector of $\angle C$.

15. In $\triangle ABC$, $a = 46$, $b = 38$, and $c = 52$. Find the length of the median to the side c.

16. The bearing of a ship at C was north from A and N 61° W from B. Later when the ship was at D, its bearing was N 53° E from A and N 10° W from B. If A and B are 6200 feet apart and B is directly east of A, how far apart are C and D?

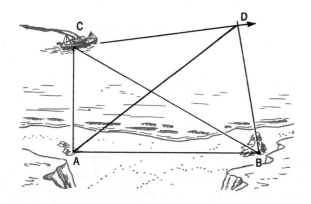

17. From two stations, A and B, 4800 feet apart on level ground, observations were made on a stationary balloon. From A the angle of elevation of the balloon was 42° 34′. The angle formed by the vertical plane through A and P and the vertical plane through A and B was 20° 42′. The angle formed by the vertical plane through B and P and the vertical plane through B and A was 35° 10′. How high was the balloon?

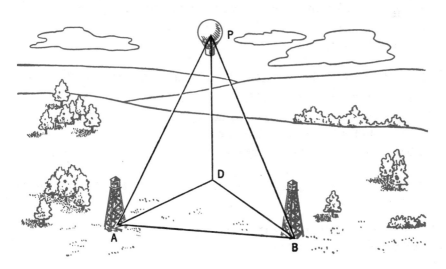

18. Two telescopes were mounted 340 feet apart on a carrier. An object was sighted at the same time by both telescopes. The angular deviation of the object from the line joining the telescopes was 112° at one telescope and 67° at the other. How far from the nearer telescope was the object?

19. *Prove* $D = \dfrac{a}{\sin A}$, where D = diameter of circumcircle.

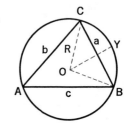

SUGGESTIONS: $\angle A = \angle BOY$,
                  $\frac{1}{2} a = R \sin BOY$

Areas of Oblique Triangles[A]

In plane geometry you proved that the area of a triangle is equal to one half the product of its base and altitude ($A = \frac{1}{2} bh$). In this text we shall use K for area since we use A so often to represent an angle. The formula $K = \frac{1}{2} bh$ is sufficient when the base and altitude of a triangle are known but it cannot be applied directly to any of the four cases summarized on page 242. We shall now consider methods of finding the areas of triangles in the four cases.

CASE I. To find the area of a triangle, given two angles and a side.

When two angles and a side of the triangle are given, the law of sines can be used to find a second side. Then we can use the method of Case III, stated below, to find the area.

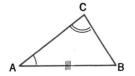

CASE II. To find the area of a triangle, given two sides and an angle opposite one of them.

In this case we use the law of sines to find the angle included by the two given sides. Then we use the formula in Case III, below.

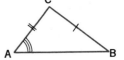

CASE III. To find the area of a triangle, given two sides and the included angle.

The area of a triangle is equal to one half the product of any two sides and the sine of the included angle.

PROOF: Let K = the area of $\triangle ABC$. Draw the altitude h to the side AC.

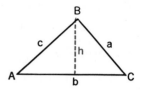

Then $K = \frac{1}{2} bh$.

But $\dfrac{h}{c} = \sin A$. Then $h = c \sin A$.

By substitution, $\qquad K = \frac{1}{2} bc \sin A$

By cyclic substitution, $\qquad K = \frac{1}{2} ac \sin B$

and $\qquad\qquad\qquad K = \frac{1}{2} ab \sin C$

CASE IV. To find the area of a triangle, given the three sides a, b, and c.

The area of a triangle with sides a, b, *and* c *is given by the formulas*

$$K = rs \quad \text{and} \quad K = \sqrt{s(s-a)(s-b)(s-c)}$$

where $s = \frac{1}{2}(a + b + c)$.

PROOF.

To prove $K = rs$.

Inscribe circle O in the given $\triangle ABC$. Draw the radii OD, OE, and OF to the points of tangency. Draw AO, BO, and CO.

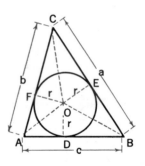

$K = \triangle AOB + \triangle BOC + \triangle AOC$

$K = \frac{1}{2} cr + \frac{1}{2} ar + \frac{1}{2} br$

$K = \frac{1}{2} r (a + b + c)$

But $\quad a + b + c = 2s$

Then $\qquad\qquad K = \frac{1}{2} r (2s)$

and $\qquad\qquad K = rs$

To prove $K = \sqrt{s(s-a)(s-b)(s-c)}$

From page 240, $r = \sqrt{\dfrac{(s-a)(s-b)(s-c)}{s}}$

Substituting this value of r in the formula $K = rs$, we get

$$K = \sqrt{\dfrac{(s-a)(s-b)(s-c)}{s}} \times s$$

$$K = \sqrt{s(s-a)(s-b)(s-c)}$$

This formula is known as Hero's formula. You may have proved it in plane geometry.

Radius of a Circumcircle [A]

On page 240 it was shown that the inradius of a triangle is given by the formula $r = \sqrt{\dfrac{(s-a)(s-b)(s-c)}{s}}$.

We shall now derive a formula for the radius of the circumcircle of the triangle.

Let O be the center of the circumcircle of $\triangle ABC$ and let R denote its radius and D its diameter. Draw $ON \perp AB$.

$\widehat{AN} = \frac{1}{2}\widehat{AB}$. Why?   (1)

$\angle C \overset{\circ}{=} \frac{1}{2}\widehat{AB}$ and $\angle O \overset{\circ}{=} \frac{1}{2}\widehat{AB}$. Give proof.   (2)

$\therefore \angle C = \angle O$ and $\sin C = \sin O$ (3)

$$\sin O = \frac{AE}{R} \qquad (4)$$

But $AE = \frac{1}{2}c$ (5)

Then $\sin C = \dfrac{\frac{1}{2}c}{R} = \dfrac{c}{2R}$ (6)

and $2R = \dfrac{c}{\sin C}$ (7)

Then $D = 2R = \dfrac{a}{\sin A} = \dfrac{b}{\sin B} = \dfrac{c}{\sin C}$ (8)

Other Area Formulas [A]

To find the area of a triangle in Case I, we find a second side and then use the formula in Case III. We shall now combine these two operations.

Suppose that A, B, and c are the given parts of $\triangle ABC$. By Case III, $K = \frac{1}{2}bc \sin A$.   (1)

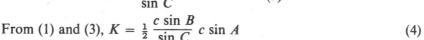

Since $\dfrac{b}{c} = \dfrac{\sin B}{\sin C}$,   (2)

$$b = \frac{c \sin B}{\sin C} \qquad (3)$$

From (1) and (3), $K = \frac{1}{2}\dfrac{c \sin B}{\sin C}\,c \sin A$ (4)

Then $K = \dfrac{c^2 \sin A \sin B}{2 \sin C}$ (5)

Likewise, $K = \dfrac{a^2 \sin B \sin C}{2 \sin A} = \dfrac{b^2 \sin A \sin C}{2 \sin B}$

Another formula for the area is $K = \dfrac{abc}{4R}$. The proof of it follows:

From (5), $\qquad K = \dfrac{c^2 \sin A \sin B}{2 \sin C}$ $\hfill (6)$

Since $2R = \dfrac{a}{\sin A} = \dfrac{b}{\sin B} = \dfrac{c}{\sin C}$ (see page 248), $\hfill (7)$

$\qquad \sin A = \dfrac{a}{2R},\ \sin B = \dfrac{b}{2R},$ and $\sin C = \dfrac{c}{2R}$ $\hfill (8)$

From (6) and (8), $\qquad K = \dfrac{c^2 \times \dfrac{a}{2R} \times \dfrac{b}{2R}}{2\left(\dfrac{c}{2R}\right)}$ $\hfill (9)$

Then $\qquad\qquad\qquad K = \dfrac{abc}{4R}$ $\hfill (10)$

EXERCISES (AREAS)

A

Find the area of each of the following triangles:

1. $a = 78$
$\quad b = 34$
$\quad c = 66$

2. $a = 123$
$\quad b = 250$
$\quad c = 200$

3. $b = 31.4$
$\quad c = 21.7$
$\quad A = 34°\ 29'$

4. $a = 2700$
$\quad c = 3500$
$\quad B = 86°\ 22'$

5. $a = 92.75$
$\quad b = 86.14$
$\quad A = 72°\ 40'$

6. $a = 4.832$
$\quad c = 6.371$
$\quad B = 41°\ 34'$

7. $a = 132.3$
$\quad b = 274.5$
$\quad B = 100°\ 45'$

8. $a = 724.16$
$\quad A = 69°\ 27'\ 30''$
$\quad B = 50°\ 18'\ 15''$

9. $c = 132.78$
$\quad A = 79°\ 18'\ 10''$
$\quad B = 18°\ 34'\ 50''$

10. Find the area of a triangle having two sides of 31.14 feet and 25.63 feet and the included angle $35°\ 10'$.

11. Two sides of a triangle are 135 and 265. Find the area of the triangle if the angle included by the two sides is $41°$.

12. $ABCD$ is a quadrilateral. Find its area if $AB = 30$, $BC = 40$, $CD = 28$, $AD = 24$, and $A = 106°$.

13. The sides of a triangle are 16, 20, and 24. Find the radius of its incircle.

14. The sides of a triangle are 30, 40, and 48. Find the radius of its incircle.

15. Find the radius of the circle circumscribed about the triangle whose sides are 5, 12, and 13.

16. Find the diameter of the circle circumscribed about $\triangle ABC$ if $b = 15$ inches and $\angle B = 60°$.

17. How many acres are there in a tract of land with sides 27.81 rods, 35.28 rods, and 60.23 rods?

18. In $\triangle ABC$, $a = 42$, $b = 36$, and $A = 67°$. Find r.

19. The area of a rectangular field is 80 acres. One side of the field is 20 chains. Find the adjacent sides. (1 chain = 4 rods.)

20. The area of a triangular field is 8.27 acres. Two of the sides are 74.6 rods and 62.5 rods. Find the angle included by these sides.

21. The sides of a triangle are 16 feet, 18 feet, and 20 feet. Find the area of the inscribed circle.

22. The sides of a triangle are 12″, 15″, and 21″. Find the area of the circumscribed circle.

23. Each side of a rhombus is 40 inches and one of its angles is 54°. Find its area.

24. Find the area of a regular hexagon having a side of 14 inches.

25. Find the area of a parallelogram if its two diagonals are 12.43 inches and 28.16 inches and intersect each other at an angle of 49° 40′.

26. The sides of a triangle are 12.0 inches, 10.0 inches, and 15.6 inches, and its area is 60 square inches. Find the radius of its circumcircle.

B

27. Find the area of the segment ABC of $\odot\ O$ having given $OA = 18″$ and $AB = 12″$.

28. Two triangles are determined by $a = 8$, $b = 10$, and $A = 30°$. Find the difference in area of the two triangles without finding the area of either of them.

29. Prove that the area of any quadrilateral is equal to one-half the product of its two diagonals and the sine of their included angle.

30. Prove that the area of $\triangle ABC$ is equal to $bc \sin \frac{1}{2} A \cos \frac{1}{2} A$.

31. Prove that the radii of the incircle and circumcircle of $\triangle ABC$ have the relation $rR = \dfrac{abc}{2(a + b + c)}$.

32. Find the number of square yards of canvas in a conical tent with a circular base if the vertical angle is 62° and the center pole is 14 feet high.

33. Two streets intersect at an angle of 78° 36'. A corner lot facing the two streets has a frontage of 196.2 feet on one of the streets and 104.7 feet on the other. The lot is a convex quadrilateral with the other two equal sides forming a right angle. Find the area of the lot.

Vector Representation [A]

If you have studied physics, you know that a *force* is that which changes or tends to change the state of rest or the motion of a body. Any force has magnitude and direction. For example, when a boy pushes a lawn mower, the force is exerted on the handle in the direction of the mower.

To describe a force we must give both its magnitude and direction. We can represent a force by a straight line segment drawn to scale with an arrow point at one end to show its direction. In the figure, AB and AC represent two forces acting on a particle at A. The line segments AB and AC are called *vectors. Vectors* are line segments which represent quantities having both magnitude and direction. Forces, velocities, and accelerations are vector quantities.

Parallelogram Law of Forces [A]

When two or more forces act on a body at a point, the single force which would produce the same effect upon the body is called their *resultant*. For example, if two boys are pulling on a rope in the same direction, one boy pulling with a force of 30 pounds, and the other with a force of 20 pounds, their resultant is a force of 50 pounds in the same direction.

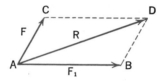

Let AB and AC represent two forces F_1 and F_2 acting on a particle at A. AB and AC are drawn to scale and the arrows show the directions of the forces. To find the resultant of F_1 and F_2, we construct the parallelogram $ABDC$. Then we draw the diagonal AD with the arrow point at D. AD represents the resultant R of F_1 and F_2. The single force R has the same effect on the body at A as the combined effects of F_1 and F_2. The forces F_1 and F_2 are called the *components* of R.

If two forces F_1 *and* F_2 *acting at a point* A *are represented by two line segments* AB *and* AC, *their resultant force* R *is represented by the diagonal* AD *of the parallelogram* ABDC.

If AB and AC have the same direction, the parallelogram degenerates into a straight line segment and AD is the arithmetic sum of AB and AC.

If AB and AC have opposite directions, the parallelogram degenerates into a straight line segment; the resultant AD is the arithmetic difference of AB and AC and has the direction of the larger of the two forces.

The resultant of two forces acting at a point can be found graphically by constructing the parallelogram and measuring the diagonal. The direction of the resultant can be found with a protractor. However, since the graphic method does not give a high degree of accuracy in results, the analytic method is usually preferable. Let us now discuss the analytic method of finding the resultant.

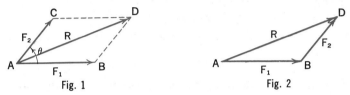

Fig. 1   Fig. 2

In Fig. 1, $AC = BD$. Then the two component forces and the resultant force are represented by vectors which form the triangle ABD (Figs. 1 and 2). $\angle B$ is the supplement of $\angle BAC$. Since AB, BD, and $\angle B$ are known, the solution of the triangle ABD falls into Case III. Both the law of cosines and the law of tangents apply. By the law of cosines,

$$\overline{AD}^2 = \overline{AB}^2 + \overline{BD}^2 - 2\,\overline{AB} \cdot \overline{BD}\,\cos B.$$

$AB = F_1$ and $BD = F_2$. Since $\angle B$ is the supplement of $\angle BAC$, or θ, $\cos B = -\cos \theta$. Then the equation above reduces to

$$R^2 = F_1{}^2 + F_2{}^2 + 2\,F_1F_2 \cos \theta.$$

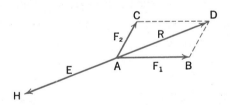

The force equal in magnitude to AD but opposite in direction is called the *equilibrant* of F_1 and F_2. The three forces F_1, F_2, and E balance each other and their resultant is zero. Can you show by drawings that each of the forces F_1, F_2, and E is the equilibrant of the other two?

Resolution of Forces [A]

By reversing the process of finding the resultant of two component forces, we can resolve any force into two component forces.

Let AB represent a given force F. Suppose that we wish to find two forces which act at right angles to each other and whose resultant is AB. Through A draw two lines l_1 and l_2 which are perpendicular to each other. Through B draw lines parallel to l_1 and l_2, forming the parallelogram $ACBD$. The components of AB are AC and AD.

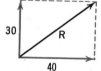

If AB makes $\angle\theta$ with AC, the rectangular components of F are:

$$x = F \cos \theta \qquad\qquad y = F \sin \theta$$

EXAMPLE 1. Two forces, one of 30 pounds and the other of 40 pounds, act at a point on a body at right angles to each other. What single force would have the same effect on the body?

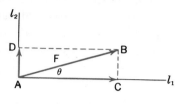

SOLUTION. $R^2 = 30^2 + 40^2$
$R^2 = 2500$
$R = 50$. The single force is 50 pounds.

EXAMPLE 2. Two forces, one of 150 pounds and the other of 200 pounds, act at a point of a body and form an angle of 42° 20′ with each other. Find the magnitude of their resultant.

SOLUTION. We can use either the parallelogram or the triangle.

Using Fig. 2, $B = 180° - 42° 20'$; $B = 137° 40'$

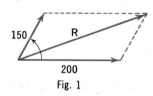

Fig. 1

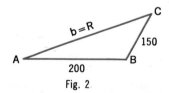

Fig. 2

By the law of cosines,

$b^2 = a^2 + c^2 - 2\,ac \cos B$, or $R^2 = F_1{}^2 + F_2{}^2 + 2\,F_1F_2 \cos \theta$
$b^2 = 150^2 + 200^2 - 2(150)\,(200) \cos 137° 40'$
$b = 326.88$
$R = 326.9$ pounds, or about 327 pounds

We can also find b by the law of tangents followed by the law of sines.

The direction of R can now be found by the law of sines.

EXAMPLE 3. Resolve a force of 10 pounds into two equal components, one of them making an angle of 45° with the force.

SOLUTION. In the figure, $AB = BC$ since $F_1 = F_2$. Then $\angle ACB = 45°$, and $\angle B = 90°$.

$$F_1 = F_2 = 10 \div \sqrt{2} = 7.07.$$

Then each component is about 7 pounds.

EXAMPLE 4. A block of wood weighing 6 pounds rests on an inclined plane that makes an angle of 20° with the horizontal. How much of the friction force is needed to prevent the block from sliding down the plane?

SOLUTION. The weight of the block is 6 pounds. This force, represented by DG, is perpendicular to the horizontal line AC. We wish to resolve this force into the force DE parallel to AB and the force DF which is perpendicular to AB, the face of the plane. The block is kept from sliding down the plane by the equilibrant force DK, which is equal in magnitude but opposite in direction to DE.

$\triangle DFG \sim \triangle ACB$. (Prove.)

$$\frac{FG}{6} = \sin 20°$$

$$FG = 6 \times .3420 = 2.052$$

But $DK = DE = FG$

$\therefore$ The force DK is 2.052, or about 2 pounds.

EXERCISES (FORCES AND VECTORS)

A

1. Two forces, one of 10 pounds and one of 8 pounds, act at a point on a body at right angles. Find the resultant force and the angles which it makes with the two components.

2. Two forces act at right angles at a point on a body. One of the forces is 120 pounds and the other is 160 pounds. Find the resultant of the two forces and the angles formed by the resultant and the components.

3. Two forces, one of 325 pounds and the other of 400 pounds, act at a point on a body at an angle of 45° with each other. Find the resultant and the angles it makes with the two components.

4. Resolve a force of 32 pounds into two components, each of which makes an angle of 30° with it.

5. An office safe was lowered from an office building by two cables attached to buildings on opposite sides of a street. At one time the cables formed angles of 42° and 76° with the buildings. Find the pull on each of the cables if the safe weighed 1250 pounds.

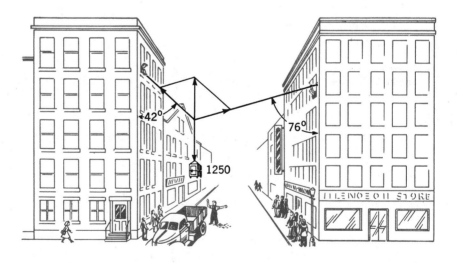

6. What weight can be supported by two wires each making an angle of 70° with the horizontal and able to sustain a pull of 320 pounds?

7. A switch engine on one track pulls a freight car on another parallel track by a cable. If a force of 3200 pounds on the cable is needed to start the car when the cable is taut and forms angles of 30° with the tracks, what force would be needed to start the car when the engine is coupled to the car?

8. When a boy pulls his sled with a rope, the rope makes an angle of 35° with the horizontal. If a pull of 16 pounds on the rope is needed to move the sled, what is the horizontal component force?

9. The resultant of two forces acting at a point at right angles to each other is 40 pounds. If one of the forces is 30 pounds, what is the other force and what angle does it make with the resultant?

10. A force of 300 pounds is resolved into components of 200 pounds and 250 pounds. What angle do the components make with each other?

B

11. If two equal forces F and F act at a point at an angle of $2\,\theta$, show that their resultant equals $2\,F\cos\theta$.

12. Two equal forces act at a point. Through what angle must one of them be turned so that their resultant is turned through 90°?

13. Show that as the angle between two concurrent forces is increased, their resultant is decreased.

14. Three forces of 54.2 pounds, 86.1 pounds, and 110.4 pounds act at angles of 48° 15′, 123° 30′, and 56° 15′ respectively, with the horizontal. Find the sum of their horizontal components and the sum of their vertical components.

15. Two forces, of 140 pounds and 260 pounds respectively, act at a point on a body at an angle of 78° 20′. Find their resultant and the angle the resultant makes with the smaller component force.

16. An iron ball weighing 10 pounds rests on two smooth plane-surfaced boards which are inclined at respectively 30° and 60° to the horizontal. What is the pressure on each board?

Hint. The pressures on the boards are perpendicular to the boards.

Parallelogram Law of Velocities [A]

Although we often attach the same meaning to the words "speed" and "velocity," they have different meanings. *Velocity* is the rate at which a moving point changes its position. It implies both magnitude and direction. *Speed* is the magnitude of a velocity. So velocity includes speed and direction.

Two velocities can be combined in the same manner that we combine two forces.

Suppose that an airplane is flying east at 100 m.p.h. and that the wind is blowing northwest at 40 m.p.h. In 15 minutes the plane would have gone through still air from A to B' but the wind carries the plane to C'; in 30 minutes, the plane would have gone through still air 50 miles to B'' but the movement of the air has caused the plane to be at C''; and

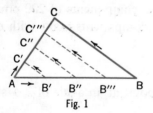

Fig. 1

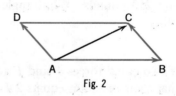

Fig. 2

in one hour the plane would have gone through still air 100 miles from A to B but the wind has carried the plane a distance of 40 miles from B to C. So the actual path of the plane is AC. If AB represents the velocity of the plane in still air and AD represents the velocity of the wind, then *AC*, the diagonal of the parallelogram *ABCD*, represents the velocity of the plane in reference to the ground.

This is an example of the application of the parallelogram law of velocities, which is as follows:

If two instantaneous velocities of a body are represented by two line segments AB *and* AD, *their resultant is represented by the diagonal* AC *of the parallelogram* ABCD.

Terms used in Aviation [A]

The parallelogram of velocities is used in solving many problems in aviation. Before we proceed with the solutions of these problems, we should learn the meanings of words often used in aviation.

The *knot* is one nautical mile per hour and a *nautical mile* is a distance of 6080.27 feet. A nautical mile is the length of one minute of arc on the earth's equator.

You should remember that the words "per hour" never follow the word "knot." The expression "15 knots" means "15 nautical miles per hour." The knot is used for giving velocities in military aviation, and it may be adopted also by civil authorities.

The *heading* of an airplane is the direction in which the plane is pointed. Due to the wind a plane does not always go in the direction it is pointed.

The *track* of a plane is its actual path.

The *course* of a plane is the direction of its path.

The *air speed* of a plane is its speed in still air.

The *ground speed* of a plane is its speed relative to the ground or water over which it flies.

A *tail wind* is one that blows in the same general direction of the flight.

A *head wind* is one that blows opposite the general direction of flight.

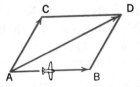

The air speed *AB*, as shown in the drawing, combined with the wind velocity *AC*, gives *AD*, the ground speed and direction of flight.

The angle *BAD* is called the *drift angle*.

EXAMPLE 1. Find the course, ground speed, and drift angle of an airplane headed at 140° when flying at an air speed of 240 m.p.h. if there is a 30-mile wind blowing from direction 40°.

SOLUTION. Let OA denote the direction and air speed of the plane and OB the speed of the wind and the direction in which it is blowing. Draw $\square OBCA$. Then the diagonal OC gives the ground speed and course of the plane.

$\angle AOC$ is the drift angle.
$\angle AOB = (40° + 180°) - 140° = 80°$. Then
$\angle OAC = 100°$.
$OA = 240$ and $AC = OB = 30$.

Using $\triangle OAC$,

$$\overline{OC}^2 = \overline{AC}^2 + \overline{OA}^2 - 2\,\overline{AC} \times \overline{OA} \cos A$$
$$\overline{OC}^2 = 30^2 + 240^2 - 2 \times 30 \times 240\,(-.1736)$$

Solving,

$$OC = 247.0$$

$$\frac{\sin COA}{30} = \frac{\sin 100°}{247.0}$$

$$\frac{\sin COA}{30} = \frac{.9848}{247}$$

$$\sin COA = \frac{30 \times .9848}{247}$$
$$= .1196$$
$$\angle COA = 6°\ 52', \text{ or } 7°$$

The ground speed is 250 m.p.h., the drift angle is 7°, and the course is 147°

EXAMPLE 2. A pilot is to fly on course 74° in a wind blowing 40 knots from direction 132°. If he is to fly an air speed of 220 knots, in what direction must he head his plane and what will his ground speed be?

SOLUTION. Draw OE in direction 74° to give the direction of flight. Draw OA opposite in direction to 132° to represent 40 knots. With A as the center and a radius $= 5\frac{1}{2}$ centimeters describe an arc intersecting OE in C. Complete the $\square OBCA$. We used 1 cm. $= 40$ knots. OB represents the air speed and OC represents the ground speed. The heading of the plane is in direction OB.

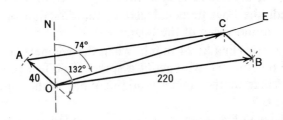

Using $\triangle OBC$, $BC = 40$, $OB = 220$, and $C = 122°$.

$$\frac{\sin O}{40} = \frac{\sin 122°}{220}$$

$$\sin O = \frac{40 \sin 122°}{220}$$

$$
\begin{array}{rl}
\log 40 = & 1.60206 \\
\log \sin 122° = & 9.92842 - 10 \\
\hline
& 11.53048 - 10 \\
\log 220 = & 2.34242 \\
\hline
\log \sin O = & 9.18806 - 10 \\
O = & 8° \, 52' \, 12''
\end{array}
$$

The wind-correction angle is $8° \, 52' \, 12''$.

Then the heading $= 74° + 8° \, 52' \, 12''$
$\qquad\qquad\quad = 82° \, 52' \, 12''$ or $83°$

To find OC

$$
\begin{aligned}
B &= 180° - C - O \\
&= 180° - 122° - 8° \, 52' \, 12'' \\
&= 49° \, 7' \, 48''
\end{aligned}
$$

$$\frac{OC}{\sin B} = \frac{BO}{\sin C}$$

$$OC = \frac{BO \sin B}{\sin C}$$

$$= \frac{220 \sin 49° \, 7' \, 48''}{\sin 122°}$$

$$
\begin{array}{rl}
\log 220 = & 2.34242 \\
\log \sin 49° \, 7' \, 48'' = & 9.87864 - 10 \\
\hline
& 12.22106 - 10 \\
\log \sin 122° = & 9.92842 - 10 \\
\hline
\log OC = & 2.29264 \\
OC = & 196.17
\end{array}
$$

The ground speed is 196.17 knots or 200 knots.

EXERCISES [A]

1. A river is flowing at the rate of 2.4 miles an hour when a boy rows across it. If the boy rows at a still-water speed of 3.1 miles an hour and heads the boat perpendicular to the direction of the current, find the ground speed of the boat.

2. A train is traveling at 24 m.p.h. when the engineer throws a small package out the cab window at a speed of 60 feet per second and perpendicular to the train's motion. What is the initial speed of the package?

3. An airplane with a speed of 160 knots is headed east while a 24-knot wind is blowing from 240°. Find the course and ground speed of the plane.

4. An airplane with a speed of 215 knots is headed at 230° while a wind is blowing from 90° at 24 knots. Find the course and ground speed of the plane.

5. An airplane is headed at 230° at 320 knots when a 15-knot wind is blowing from 50°. Find the ground speed of the plane and the wind-correction angle.

6. A pilot is to fly on course 95° at 110 m.p.h. when the wind is blowing from direction 200° at 18 m.p.h. In what direction should he head the plane?

7. A pilot wishes to fly on course 290° with an air speed of 300 knots when the wind blows from direction 224° at 18 knots. Find the wind-correction angle.

8. A plane is headed in direction 130° with an air speed of 180 knots. The course is 105° with a ground speed of 110 knots. Find the direction of the wind.

9. A plane is headed in direction 58° with an air speed of 150 m.p.h. The course is 72°, with a ground speed of 130 m.p.h. Find the speed and direction of the wind.

10. In what direction must a pilot head his plane to have a course of 45° if its air speed is 240 m.p.h. and a 40 m.p.h. wind is blowing from direction 280°?

11. A pilot wishes to fly on course 70° when the wind is blowing 30 m.p.h. from direction 145°. If he plans an air speed of 125 m.p.h., what wind correction angle must he use?

12. A plane was headed in direction 62° at 140 knots when the wind was blowing from direction 105°. After flying one hour the plane was over a point whose bearing from the starting point was 40°. Find the speed of the wind.

13. Find the speed of an east wind if a plane flies at an air speed of 200 m.p.h. headed in direction 145° on course 161°.

CHAPTER REVIEW

1. State which parts of the triangle are given in each of the four cases of solution of oblique triangles.

2. Which checks are suggested in this text for the four cases?

3. Which cases can be solved in part by the law of sines?

4. State the law of sines; the law of cosines; the law of tangents.

5. Complete:
  a. In Case I we use the law of sines to find the _?_ of a triangle.
  b. In Case II we first use the law of sines to find a (an) _?_ of the triangle.

6. Show by a drawing the ambiguous case.

7. Write the Mollweide formula which we use in this text.

8. Is a triangle determined, given a, b, and A with $a > b$?

9. How many triangles are determined, given a, b, and A with $a = b \sin A$?

10. Find side c of $\triangle ABC$, given $a = 10$, $b = 8$, and $A = 46° 34'$.

11. Find $\angle A$ of $\triangle ABC$, given $a = 24$, $b = 28$, and $c = 32$.

12. Determine whether $\angle A$ is acute, right, or obtuse, given $a = 74$, $b = 23$, and $c = 75$.

13. The common chord of two intersecting circles is 6.1 inches long and the radii of the circles are 9.2 inches and 8.4 inches. Find the distance between the centers of the circles.

14. Find the area of a triangle whose sides are 24", 36", and 48".

15. Find the area of a triangle if two sides are 114.2 inches and 17.4 inches and the included angle is 40° 35'.

16. The altitude of an isosceles triangle is equal to the base of the triangle. How large is each of the angles of the triangle?

17. Find the apothem of a regular decagon inscribed in a 10-inch circle.

18. Find the area of a regular octagon circumscribed about an 18-inch circle.

19. Solve $\triangle ABC$, given $A = 74.2°$, $a = 126$, and $b = 84$.

20. Solve $\triangle ABC$, given $a = 320.14$, $c = 275.64$, and $B = 67° 24' 40''$.

21. Solve $\triangle ABC$, given $a = 108.4$, $b = 114.0$, and $c = 129.2$.

22. Find the radius of the circle inscribed in the triangle whose sides are 20, 30, and 40.

23. Find the radius of the circle circumscribed about the triangle whose sides are 8, 15, and 17.

24. Find the radius of the circle circumscribed about the triangle whose sides are 16'', 16'', and 20''.

25. A pilot is flying course 34° at 480 m.p.h. How fast is he going east?

26. An airplane is headed in direction 118° at an air speed of 220 m.p.h. Find his course and ground speed if the wind is blowing from direction 234° at 20 m.p.h.

27. A pilot wishes to fly course 320° when a 30 m.p.h. wind is blowing from direction 170°. In what direction should he head his plane if it will have an air speed of 350 m.p.h.?

28. A speedboat has a speed of 61 m.p.h. on still water. How fast can it go downstream on a river that flows 4 m.p.h.? How fast can it go upstream? How fast can it go when crossing the river at an angle of 20° with the direction of the current?

29. Two boats move so that each has a constant bearing with the other. If they continue this relationship, what will be the result?

30. Find the resultant of two concurrent forces, one of 1420 pounds and the other of 1280 pounds, if they act at an angle of 37° 48'.

31. A force of 647 pounds acts on an object lying on the ground and makes an angle of 20° with the ground. How many pounds of the force are used in lifting the object?

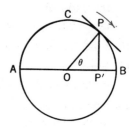

32. In the figure, point P has a uniform speed of 120 feet per second on circle O. P' is the projection of P on AB. As P moves from C to B, how fast is P' moving from O to B?

CAA Technical Development and Evaluation Center, Weir Cook Airport

Science Applied to Agriculture

Atomic energy may soon go to work for the nation's farmers, say CAA
engineers who are testing new equipment designed to determine the
moisture content and density of soils

CHAPTER XI

INVERSE FUNCTIONS

Δ

Meaning of Inverse Functions [A]

In the equation $y = x^2$, y is said to be a function of x. If x and y are interchanged in $y = x^2$ and the equation is solved for y, $y = \pm\sqrt{x}$. The functions $y = x^2$ and $y = \pm\sqrt{x}$ are inverse functions. For every value assigned to x in the equation $y = x^2$ there is a single corresponding value of y and therefore y is a *single-valued* function of x. For every positive real value assigned to x in the equation $y = \pm\sqrt{x}$, there are two corresponding values of y, and y is called a *multiple-valued* function of x. Other examples of inverse functions are $y = 10^x$ and $y = \log x$; $y = 2x + 3$ and $y = \dfrac{x - 3}{2}$.

In like manner, $y = \tan x$ and $y = \text{arc tan } x$ are inverse functions. The expression $y = \text{arc tan } x$* is read "y is the angle whose tangent is x"; it may also be read "inverse tangent of x" or "anti-tangent of x." The other five inverse trigonometric functions are $y = \text{arc sin } x$, $y = \text{arc cos } x$, $y = \text{arc ctn } x$, $y = \text{arc sec } x$, and $y = \text{arc csc } x$.

An inverse trigonometric function has infinitely many values corresponding to each value of x. For example, there are two positive angles less than $360°$ whose tangent is $\sqrt{3}$, namely $60°$ and $240°$. Any angle obtained from these by adding or subtracting multiples of $360°$ has a tangent equal to $\sqrt{3}$. This may be written $\text{arc tan } \sqrt{3} = 60° + n \cdot 180°$ where n is an integer. If radian measure is used, $\text{arc tan } \sqrt{3} = \dfrac{\pi}{3} + \pi n$.

Thus the inverse trigonometric functions are *multiple-valued* while the direct trigonometric functions are *single-valued*.

---

* Another notation for $y = \text{arc tan } x$ sometimes used is $y = \tan^{-1} x$. The -1 should not be confused with an exponent.

EXAMPLE 1. Find the positive angles less than 360° for arc sin $(-\frac{1}{2})$.

SOLUTION. The sine of an angle is negative in the third and fourth quadrants. The reference angle associated with $\frac{1}{2}$ is 30°. Hence the angles are 210° and 330°.

EXAMPLE 2. Solve $y = 5 \tan 3 x$ for x.

SOLUTION. Since $5 \tan 3 x = y$, $\tan 3 x = \frac{1}{5} y$ and $3 x = \text{arc tan } \frac{1}{5} y$. Then $x = \frac{1}{3} \text{ arc tan } \frac{1}{5} y$.

EXAMPLE 3. Solve $y = \text{arc cos } 3 x$ for x.

SOLUTION. Since $\text{arc cos } 3 x = y$, $3 x = \cos y$ and $x = \frac{1}{3} \cos y$.

EXERCISES [A]

Find the positive angles less than 360° represented by the following:

1. arc tan 1

2. arc sin $(\pm\frac{1}{2})$

3. arc ctn $(-\sqrt{3})$

4. arc cos $(-\frac{1}{2}\sqrt{2})$

5. arc sec 2

6. arc csc $(\pm\sqrt{2})$

7. arc cos (-1)

8. arc tan (-1)

9. arc cos $(\frac{1}{2}\sqrt{2})$

10. arc sec $\frac{3}{2}$

11. arc sin .0175

12. arc tan $(-.0699)$

Solve each of the following equations for x:

13. $y = \sin 2 x$

14. $y = \frac{1}{2} \tan 4 x$

15. $y = 2 \sec 2 x$

16. $y = 1 + \tan \pi x$

17. $y = \text{arc cos } 5 x$

18. $y = \text{arc sin } \frac{1}{2} x$

19. $y = 2 \text{ arc ctn } 2 x$

20. $y = \text{arc sec } 4 x$

21. $3 y = 4 \text{ arc csc } 5 x$

22. If θ is an acute angle and $\theta = \text{arc tan } y$, represent θ as a first-quadrant angle with any point P on the terminal side of the angle having an ordinate y and an abscissa $= 1$. That is, $\tan \theta = \frac{y}{1} = y$. Find the radius vector in terms of y and represent all the inverse functions of θ in terms of y.

If θ is an acute angle, represent all the other inverse functions of θ, given

23. $\theta = \text{arc sin } (x + 1)$

24. $\theta = \text{arc cos } (x - 1)$

25. $\theta = \text{arc tan } \dfrac{\sqrt{1 - x^2}}{x}$

26. $\theta = \text{arc sec } \dfrac{a^2 + 1}{a^2 - 1}$

27. $\theta = \text{arc sin } e^x$

28. $\theta = \text{arc ctn } \dfrac{m + 1}{m - 1}$

Principal Values of the Inverse Trigonometric Functions [A]

In applications involving inverse functions it is necessary to select *one special value* of the many values of a function. This special value is called the *principal value*. The following definitions of the principal values of the inverse functions (if they exist) were selected to meet the requirements of advanced mathematics. In each case a is a positive number.

1. The principal value of arc sin a, arc cos a, arc tan a, arc ctn a, arc sec a, or arc csc a, is zero or a positive angle no greater than 90°.

2. The principal value of arc sin $(-a)$ or arc tan $(-a)$ is a negative angle no less than −90°.

3. The principal value of arc cos $(-a)$ or arc ctn $(-a)$ is a positive angle from 90° to 180° inclusive.

4. The principal value of arc sec $(-a)$ or arc csc $(-a)$ is a negative angle from −90° to −180° inclusive.

The inverse trigonometric functions do not exist for all values of a. For example, there in no angle y such that y = arc sin 2. The inverse functions are defined for the following range of values for a, a being a real number:

$$\text{arc sin } a \text{ and arc cos } a \text{ for } -1 \leq a \leq 1$$
$$\text{arc tan } a \text{ and arc ctn } a \text{ for all values of } a$$
$$\text{arc sec } a \text{ and arc csc } a \text{ for } a \leq -1 \text{ and } a \geq 1$$

The principal value is denoted by capitalizing the word *arc*. Thus Arc sin x* means the principal value of the angle whose sine is x. However, in practice this designation is not always used, since we know from the problem whether the principal value or more values are indicated.

EXERCISES [A]

Find the values of:

1. Arc sin $\frac{1}{2} \sqrt{2}$ **5.** Arc sec $(-\sqrt{2})$ **9.** Arc tan $(-\sqrt{3})$

2. Arc cos $\frac{1}{2}$ **6.** Arc csc 2   **10.** Arc ctn (-1)

3. Arc tan (-1) **7.** Arc sin $(-\frac{1}{2})$ **11.** Arc sec 2

4. Arc ctn $\sqrt{3}$ **8.** Arc cos (-1) **12.** Arc csc $(-\sqrt{2})$

* When the form sin⁻¹ x is used the principal value is denoted by Sin⁻¹ x.

Find the values of the following:

13. Arc sin $\left(\cos \dfrac{\pi}{6} \right)$

14. Arc cos $\left(\tan \dfrac{\pi}{4} \right)$

15. Arc tan (sec π)

16. Arc ctn $\left(\sin \dfrac{\pi}{6} \right)$

17. Arc sec $\left(\text{ctn } \dfrac{\pi}{4} \right)$

18. Arc sec $\left(\sin \dfrac{3\pi}{4} \right)$

19. sec (Arc sec 2)

20. sin (Arc tan [−1])

21. cos (Arc sec$\sqrt{2}$)

22. tan (Arc ctn [−1])

23. ctn (Arc cos $\tfrac{1}{2}$)

24. csc (Arc csc [−2])

Graphs of Inverse Functions [A]

The graph of the equation $y = $ arc sin x in which y is expressed in radians is given in Figure 1 on the next page. The graph of $y = $ arc sin x is the graph of the sine curve on the y-axis. The graphs of the other inverse functions are given in Figures 2–6, the principal values being indicated by the heavier part of the curves. This part of the curve giving the principal values is called the **principal branch** of the curve. Notice that the principal branch is that continuous part of the curve (except in the secant and cosecant) nearest the origin which gives an equal range for positive and negative values of x.

EXERCISES [B]

Sketch the graphs for

1. $y = $ arc sin $2x$ **3.** $y = $ arc cos $2x$ **5.** $y = \tfrac{1}{2}$ arc sec x

2. $y = $ arc sin $\tfrac{1}{2} x$ **4.** $y = 2$ arc tan $\tfrac{1}{2} x$ **6.** $y = \tfrac{1}{2}$ arc ctn $2x$

Identities and Equations involving Inverse Functions [A]

In proving identities involving inverse functions, we must be careful to prove that, for every admissible value of the variable, a value of each inverse function exists which makes the identity valid. While it is not necessary that these values be the principal values of the functions, we shall restrict our work to principal values.

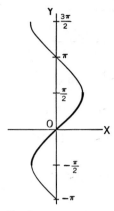

Fig. 1. $y = \text{arc sin } x$

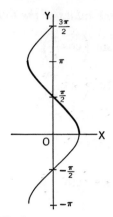

Fig. 2. $y = \text{arc cos } x$

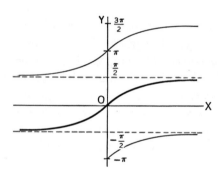

Fig. 3. $y = \text{arc tan } x$

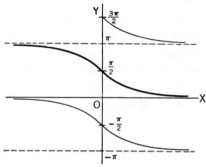

Fig. 4. $y = \text{arc ctn } x$

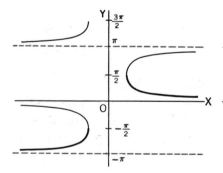

Fig 5. $y = \text{arc csc } x$

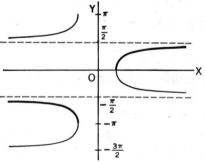

Fig. 6. $y = \text{arc sec } x$

In solving equations involving inverse functions, the roots must always be checked by substituting in the original equation.

EXAMPLE 1. Prove that Arc tan $\frac{1}{2}$ + Arc tan $\frac{1}{3}$ = $\frac{\pi}{4}$.

SOLUTION. Let Arc tan $\frac{1}{2}$ = A and Arc tan $\frac{1}{3}$ = B. Then tan A = $\frac{1}{2}$ and tan B = $\frac{1}{3}$. If we substitute A = Arc tan $\frac{1}{2}$ and B = Arc tan $\frac{1}{3}$ in the given equation, we have to prove that $A + B = \frac{\pi}{4}$.

Now
$$\tan (A + B) = \frac{\tan A + \tan B}{1 - \tan A \tan B}$$

Substituting the numerical values for tan A and tan B, we have

$$\tan (A + B) = \frac{\frac{1}{2} + \frac{1}{3}}{1 - \frac{1}{6}} = 1$$

or
$$A + B = \text{Arc tan } 1$$

$$\therefore \text{Arc tan } \tfrac{1}{2} + \text{Arc tan } \tfrac{1}{3} = \frac{\pi}{4}$$

EXAMPLE 2. Prove that Arc tan x = Arc cos $\dfrac{1}{\sqrt{1 + x^2}}$ when x is positive.

SOLUTION. Let A = Arc tan x, making tan A = x,

and
$$B = \text{Arc cos } \frac{1}{\sqrt{1 + x^2}}, \text{ making cos } B = \frac{1}{\sqrt{1 + x^2}}$$

We have to prove A = B.

From the relation sin B = $\sqrt{1 - \cos^2 B}$, we obtain

$$\sin B = \sqrt{1 - \frac{1}{1 + x^2}} = \sqrt{\frac{x^2}{1 + x^2}} = \frac{x}{\sqrt{1 + x^2}}$$

Then $\tan B = \dfrac{\sin B}{\cos B} = \dfrac{\dfrac{x}{\sqrt{1 + x^2}}}{\dfrac{1}{\sqrt{1 + x^2}}}$ = x or Arc tan x = B.

Since A = Arc tan x and B = Arc tan x, A and B being first-quadrant angles, we have

$$A = B$$

$$\therefore \text{Arc tan } x = \text{Arc cos } \frac{1}{\sqrt{1 + x^2}}$$

EXAMPLE 3. Find the value of sin [Arc sec (-2) — Arc sin $(-\frac{3}{5})$].

SOLUTION. Let θ = Arc sec (-2) and ϕ = Arc sin $(-\frac{3}{5})$.

Then representing θ and ϕ by figures in the proper quadrants, we can write directly all the functions of θ and ϕ.

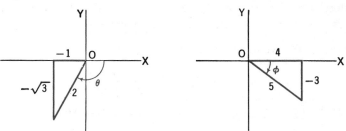

Substituting θ = Arc sec (-2) and ϕ = Arc sin $(-\frac{3}{5})$ in the original expression, we have to find sin $(\theta - \phi)$.

$$\sin (\theta - \phi) = \sin \theta \cos \phi - \cos \theta \sin \phi$$
$$= -\tfrac{1}{2} \sqrt{3} \cdot \tfrac{4}{5} + \tfrac{1}{2}(-\tfrac{3}{5})$$
$$= -\tfrac{4}{10} \sqrt{3} - \tfrac{3}{10}$$
$$= -\tfrac{1}{10}(4 \sqrt{3} + 3) \text{ or } -.9928$$

∴ sin [Arc sec (-2) — Arc sin $(-\frac{3}{5})$] = $-\tfrac{1}{10}(4 \sqrt{3} + 3)$ or $-.9928$

EXAMPLE 4. Solve Arc tan $3x$ + Arc tan $x = \dfrac{\pi}{2}$.

SOLUTION. Let θ = Arc tan $3x$ and ϕ = Arc tan x

Then   tan $\theta = 3x$ and tan $\phi = x$

Substituting θ and ϕ in the equation, we have

$$\theta + \phi = \frac{\pi}{2}$$

Since we are dealing with principal values and the sum of the angles is $\dfrac{\pi}{2}$ radians, the angles are both first-quadrant angles. They are represented in the figures.

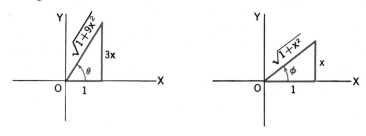

If two angles are equal, the same function of the angles are equal.

We take
$$\sin (\theta + \phi) = \sin \frac{\pi}{2}$$

$$\sin \theta \cos \phi + \cos \theta \sin \phi = 1$$

Substituting from the figures,

$$\frac{3 x}{\sqrt{1 + 9 x^2}} \cdot \frac{1}{\sqrt{1 + x^2}} + \frac{1}{\sqrt{1 + 9 x^2}} \cdot \frac{x}{\sqrt{1 + x^2}} = 1$$

$$\frac{4 x}{\sqrt{1 + 10 x^2 + 9 x^4}} = 1$$

$$4 x = \sqrt{1 + 10 x^2 + 9 x^4}$$

Squaring,
$$16 x^2 = 1 + 10 x^2 + 9 x^4$$

$$9 x^4 - 6 x^2 + 1 = 0$$

$$(3 x^2 - 1) (3 x^2 - 1) = 0$$

$3 x^2 - 1 = 0$	$3 x^2 - 1 = 0$
$3 x^2 = 1$	$3 x^2 = 1$
$x = \pm\frac{1}{3} \sqrt{3}$	$x = \pm\frac{1}{3} \sqrt{3}$

Substituting $x = \frac{1}{3} \sqrt{3}$ in the original equation

$$\text{Arc tan } 3 x + \text{Arc tan } x = \frac{\pi}{2}$$

$$\text{Arc tan } \sqrt{3} + \text{Arc tan } \frac{1}{3} \sqrt{3} = \frac{\pi}{2}$$

$$\frac{\pi}{3} + \frac{\pi}{6} = \frac{\pi}{2}$$

$$\frac{\pi}{2} = \frac{\pi}{2}$$

$$\therefore x = \frac{1}{3} \sqrt{3} \text{ is a solution.}$$

We know that $-\frac{1}{3} \sqrt{3}$ is not a solution, because it would give two negative angles whose sum could not be $\frac{\pi}{2}$ radians.

EXERCISES

A

Evaluate the following expressions:

1. $\sin (\text{Arc sin } \frac{2}{3} + \text{Arc cos } \frac{1}{2})$

2. $\cos (\text{Arc tan } \frac{3}{4} - \text{Arc sin } \frac{1}{2})$

3. $\tan (\text{Arc tan } \frac{1}{2} + \text{Arc tan } 1)$

4. $\text{ctn} (\text{Arc tan } [-\frac{2}{3}] + \text{Arc tan } \frac{1}{2})$

Prove the following statements true:

5. Arc tan $2 -$ Arc tan $1 =$ Arc tan $\frac{1}{3}$

6. Arc sin $1 -$ Arc tan $1 = \dfrac{\pi}{4}$

7. Arc tan $5 -$ Arc tan $2 =$ Arc tan $\frac{3}{11}$

8. Arc sin $\frac{4}{5} +$ Arc sin $\frac{5}{13} =$ Arc cos $\frac{16}{65}$

9. Arc tan $\frac{1}{4} +$ Arc tan $\frac{2}{9} = \frac{1}{2}$ Arc sec $\frac{5}{3}$

10. Arc sin $\frac{8}{17} +$ Arc sin $\frac{3}{5} =$ Arc sin $\frac{77}{85}$

11. Arc tan $\frac{1}{7} - \dfrac{\pi}{4} = 2$ Arc tan $\left(-\frac{1}{3}\right)$

12. Arc sin $\frac{4}{5} = \pi - 2$ Arc tan 2

13. Arc tan $\frac{5}{11} +$ Arc tan $\frac{3}{8} =$ Arc tan 1

B

14. Arc tan $\frac{1}{3} =$ Arc tan $\frac{4}{7} -$ Arc tan $\frac{1}{5}$

15. Arc sin $\frac{5}{13} +$ Arc sin $\frac{4}{5} +$ Arc sin $\frac{16}{65} =$ Arc sin 1

16. Arc tan $\frac{1}{2} +$ Arc tan $\frac{1}{5} +$ Arc tan $\frac{1}{8} =$ Arc tan 1

17. Arc tan $\frac{1}{2} -$ Arc tan $\frac{1}{11} =$ Arc tan $\frac{5}{6} -$ Arc tan $\frac{1}{3}$

18. Arc tan $x +$ Arc tan $y =$ Arc tan $\dfrac{x + y}{1 - xy}$

19. Arc cos $x +$ Arc sin $x = \dfrac{\pi}{2}$

20. Arc tan $x +$ Arc ctn $x = \dfrac{\pi}{2}$

21. Arc sin $x +$ Arc tan $\dfrac{\sqrt{1 - x^2}}{x} = \dfrac{\pi}{2}$

Solve and check the following equations:

22. Arc tan $(x + \sqrt{3}) -$ Arc tan $(x - \sqrt{3}) =$ Arc tan $\sqrt{3}$

23. Arc tan $3x +$ Arc tan $2x = \dfrac{\pi}{4}$

24. Arc tan $x = 2$ Arc tan $\frac{1}{2} -$ Arc tan $\frac{1}{7}$

25. Arc tan $\frac{1}{2} x$ + Arc ctn $\frac{5}{3}$ = $\frac{\pi}{4}$

26. Arc cos 2 x + Arc cos x = Arc cos $\frac{1}{2}$

27. Arc sin $\dfrac{1}{x}$ − Arc sin $\frac{4}{5}$ = 2 Arc tan $\frac{1}{2}$

28. Arc sin $\frac{1}{2} x$ + 2 Arc tan x = π

29. Arc tan x − Arc sin $\frac{1}{2} x$ = 0

30. Arc sin 2 x + Arc sin x = $\dfrac{\pi}{2}$

31. Arc cos 4 x − Arc sin 3 x = 0

32. Arc tan 2 x = Arc tan (x + 1) + Arc tan (x − 1)

Symmetric Graphs

By interchanging x and y in the relation $y = \sin x$ we get the relation $x = \sin y$, which can be stated "$y = $ arc sin x" or "y is an angle whose sin is x."

The graph of $y = \sin x$ for x having real values from $-\dfrac{\pi}{2}$ to $\dfrac{\pi}{2}$ inclusive and the graph of $y = $ arc sin x for x having values from -1 to $+1$ inclusive are shown at the right on the same set of axes. The graph of $y = x$ is on this set of axes.

For any point (a, b) on the graph of $y = \sin x$ there is a point (b, a) on the graph of $y = $ arc sin x; and conversely. It can be proved that the line $y = x$ is the perpendicular bisector of the line segment joining the points (b, a) and (a, b) and that the graphs of $y = \sin x$ and $y = $ Arc sin x are symmetric with respect to the line $y = x$. The same discussion applies to the other trigonometric functions.

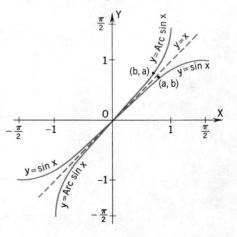

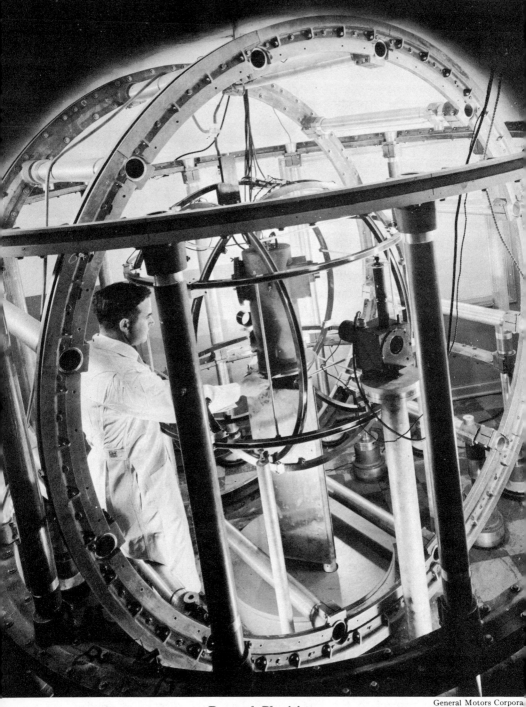

Research Physicist

The equipment shown is used for very delicate and precise measurements of magnetic phenomena

CHAPTER XII

COMPLEX NUMBERS
AND HYPERBOLIC FUNCTIONS

Δ

In previous chapters we have confined our work to real numbers. In this chapter we shall study imaginary and complex numbers and their use in trigonometry. Many of the applications of trigonometry in engineering and the physical sciences involve imaginary and complex numbers.

Imaginary Numbers [A]

The imaginary unit is $\sqrt{-1}$. It is convenient and desirable to represent $\sqrt{-1}$ by the symbol i. The imaginary number was first needed in the solution of the pure quadratic equation. For example, in solving $x^2 = -7$, we have $x = \pm\sqrt{-7} = \pm i\sqrt{7}$. We can use the letter i just as we use any other letter in algebra. We should learn to know the values of the smaller powers of i as given in the following table:

$$i = \sqrt{-1} = i \qquad\qquad i^5 = i^4 \cdot i = i$$
$$i^2 = (\sqrt{-1})^2 = -1 \qquad i^6 = i^4 \cdot i^2 = -1$$
$$i^3 = i^2 \cdot i = -i \qquad\qquad i^7 = i^4 \cdot i^3 = -i$$
$$i^4 = i^2 \cdot i^2 = 1 \qquad\qquad i^8 = i^4 \cdot i^4 = 1$$

Notice that the values of i repeat every four terms.

The necessity for writing $\sqrt{-7}$ as $i\sqrt{7}$ is illustrated in the following: $\sqrt{-7} \cdot \sqrt{-3} = -\sqrt{21}$, not $\sqrt{21}$. It should be written $i\sqrt{7} \cdot i\sqrt{3} = -\sqrt{21}$.

Complex Numbers [A]

A *complex number* is an expression consisting of the algebraic sum of a real number and an imaginary number. A complex number may

277

be represented in symbols by $a + bi$, where a and b are real numbers. If $b = 0$ and $a \neq 0$, the complex number becomes a real number. If $a = 0$ and $b \neq 0$, the complex number becomes an imaginary number. If $a = b = 0$, the complex number is equal to zero.

In a complete quadratic equation like $x^2 + 2x + 3 = 0$, the roots are complex numbers. Solving $x^2 + 2x + 3 = 0$ by the quadratic formula,

$$x = \frac{-2 \pm \sqrt{4 - 12}}{2}$$

$$x = -1 \pm i\sqrt{2}$$

Conjugate complex numbers are two complex numbers which differ only in the sign of their imaginary parts. $a + bi$ and $a - bi$ represent two conjugate complex numbers.

Two complex numbers can be equal only when their real parts are equal and their imaginary parts are equal. This is true since an imaginary number cannot equal a real number.

If you have studied complex numbers in algebra, the exercises that follow will serve as a review. If you have not had much work on complex numbers, you will need to study the examples carefully.

EXAMPLE 1. Subtract $3 + \sqrt{-2}$ from $8 - \sqrt{-8}$.

SOLUTION. Changing to the $a + bi$ form, $3 + \sqrt{-2} = 3 + i\sqrt{2}$ and $8 - \sqrt{-8} = 8 - 2i\sqrt{2}$

Then
$$8 - 2i\sqrt{2}$$
$$\underline{3 + i\sqrt{2}}$$
$$5 - 3i\sqrt{2} \quad \textit{Answer}$$

EXAMPLE 2. Multiply $2 + \sqrt{-9}$ by $3 - \sqrt{-16}$.

SOLUTION. Writing the problem as the product of two binomials,
$$(2 + 3i)(3 - 4i) = 6 + i - 12i^2 = 6 + i + 12 = 18 + i.$$

EXAMPLE 3. Divide $4 + 3i$ by $3 + 2i$.

SOLUTION. We write the indicated division as a fraction and rationalize the denominator by multiplying both numerator and denominator by the conjugate of the denominator. Thus,

$$\frac{4 + 3i}{3 + 2i} \cdot \frac{3 - 2i}{3 - 2i} = \frac{12 + i - 6i^2}{9 - 4i^2} = \frac{12 + i + 6}{13} = \frac{18 + i}{13}$$

EXAMPLE 4. Expand $(5 - i \sqrt{3})^2$.

SOLUTION. $(5 - i \sqrt{3})^2 = 25 - 10 \, i \sqrt{3} + 3 \, i^2$
$$= 22 - 10 \, i \sqrt{3}$$

EXAMPLE 5. Find the square root of $-16 + 30 \, i$.

SOLUTION. Represent the square root of $-16 + 30 \, i$ by $a + bi$. Then
$$a + bi = \sqrt{-16 + 30 \, i}$$
Squaring, $\qquad a^2 + 2 \, abi - b^2 = -16 + 30 \, i$

Equating the real parts and imaginary parts,
$$a^2 - b^2 = -16$$
$$ab = 15$$

Solving these two simultaneous quadratic equations for a and b, we have $a = 3$, $b = 5$ or $a = -3$, $b = -5$. Then the two square roots are $3 + 5 \, i$ and $-3 - 5 \, i$. (In solving the two simultaneous equations two extraneous roots were also found due to squaring the equation.)

EXAMPLE 6. Find the value of x and y in the equation
$$3 \, x + 2 \, iy - 3 + 4 \, i = 0.$$

SOLUTION. Transposing to form two equal complex numbers, we have $3 \, x + 2 \, iy = 3 - 4 \, i$. Equating the real parts and the imaginary parts,
$$3 \, x = 3 \text{ or } x = 1$$
and $\qquad 2 \, iy = -4 \, i \text{ or } y = -2$

EXERCISES [A]

Write the conjugate of the following complex numbers:

1. $3 + 4 \, i$ $\qquad\qquad$ **3.** $7 - i \sqrt{3}$ $\qquad\qquad$ **5.** $\sqrt{3} + i$

2. $-2 + i$ $\qquad\qquad$ **4.** $-2 + i \sqrt{5}$ $\qquad\qquad$ **6.** $x + iy$

Simplify and express in terms of i:

7. $\sqrt{-16}$ $\qquad$ **9.** $\sqrt{-8}$ $\qquad\qquad$ **11.** $3 \sqrt{-25}$

8. $\sqrt{-5}$ $\qquad$ **10.** $\sqrt{-27 \, a^2}$ $\qquad$ **12.** $3 \sqrt{-32} + 2 \sqrt{-8}$

13. $5\sqrt{-108} - 2\sqrt{-48}$ **14.** $2i + 7 - 3i$

15. $\sqrt{-45} + \sqrt{-5}$ **16.** $\sqrt{-9} \cdot \sqrt{-4}$ **17.** $(\sqrt{-\frac{2}{3}})^2$

Do as indicated:

18. $(3 - 2i) + (-4 + 5i)$ **22.** $(\sqrt{3} + \sqrt{-4})^2$

19. $(3 - 2i)(2 - 3i)$ **23.** $(3 + i\sqrt{2})^2$

20. $(3 + 4i) \div (1 + 2i)$ **24.** $(x + iy)(x - iy)$

21. $(\sqrt{5} + i) \div (\sqrt{2} - i)$ **25.** $(2 - i)^3$

Find the values of x and y:

26. $3x + iy + 3(2 - i) = 0$ **28.** $2(x - 4) + iy = 0$

27. $x\sqrt{2} + 9i + 3iy - \sqrt{6} = 0$ **29.** $3x = 5i(y - 4)$

Find the square roots of:

30. $-1 - 4i\sqrt{3}$ **31.** $23 - 10i\sqrt{2}$ **32.** $-2i$

Solve the following equations:

33. $x^2 + 12 = 0$ **36.** $x^2 - 2x + 2 = 0$

34. $4x^2 + 9 = 0$ **37.** $x^3 - 1 = 0$. (Factor the left member

35. $x^2 + x + 1 = 0$ and set each factor equal to zero.)

Graphical Representation of Complex Numbers[A]

We can represent every complex number $a + bi$ by a point in a plane; and conversely, every point in a plane can be represented by a complex number. To do this we make use of the rectangular system of coordinates by letting points on the x-axis represent real numbers and

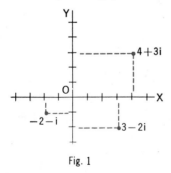

Fig. 1

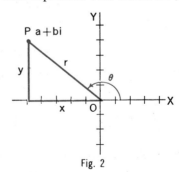

Fig. 2

points on the y-axis represent imaginary numbers. The x-axis is the axis of real numbers and the y-axis is the axis of imaginary numbers.

In Figure 1, $4 + 3i$ is represented by a point 4 units to the right of the y-axis and 3 units above the x-axis. Likewise, $-2 - i$ and $3 - 2i$ are represented in Figure 1. In Figure 2, if P represents any complex number $a + bi$, the directed line segment OP or radius vector r is called the **modulus** (or **absolute value**) of the complex number. The positive angle θ, measured counterclockwise from the positive end of the x-axis, is the **amplitude** (or **argument**) of the complex number.

$$\text{Modulus} = r = \sqrt{x^2 + y^2} \text{ and amplitude} = \theta = \arctan\frac{y}{x}.$$

The modulus of $4 + 3i = \sqrt{16 + 9} = 5$ and the amplitude of $4 + 3i = \theta \arctan\frac{3}{4}$.

Graphical Addition and Subtraction of Complex Numbers [A]

To add two complex numbers, as $3 + 2i$ and $-2 + 5i$, graphically, we plot the points A and B representing the complex numbers respectively and draw the vectors OA and OB. Then construct $BC \parallel OA$ and $AC \parallel OB$. Draw OC, the diagonal of parallelogram $OACB$. Then point C or vector OC represents the sum of $3 + 2i$ and $-2 + 5i$.

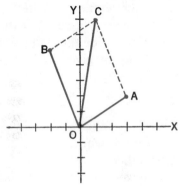

If we wish to subtract $-2 + 5i$ from $3 + 2i$ graphically, we change the subtrahend to $2 - 5i$ and add $3 + 2i$ and $2 - 5i$ graphically.

EXERCISES [A]

Plot the points representing the numbers:

1. $3 - 4i$
2. $2 + 3i$
3. $-5 - 12i$

4. $-6 + 8i$
5. $-3 + i$
6. $-1 - i$

7. $4 - 5i$
8. $2 + 7i$
9. $-2 + 2i$

10. 6
11. $3i$
12. $-2i$

Add graphically:

13. $5 + 2i$ and $2 + 5i$
14. $3 + 4i$ and $-2 + 6i$

15. $-2 - 3i$ and $4 + 9i$
16. 4 and $-3i$

Subtract graphically:

17. $2 - 3i$ from $3 + 5i$

18. $1 - i$ from $4 - 3i$

Polar Co-ordinates[A]

Two systems of co-ordinates are in common use in mathematics, the rectangular and the polar. Some problems easily solved by using one system are very difficult to solve using the other system. For that reason we use the system that makes our work less difficult for a given problem.

In the polar system of co-ordinates the position of a point is described with reference to a fixed point, O, called the **pole or origin,** and a fixed, positively directed line, OA, called the polar axis or initial line. The position of point P is given by (r, θ), called polar co-ordinates. The angle θ when measured counterclockwise from OA to OP is positive and when measured clockwise from OA to OP is negative. When r lies on the terminal side of θ it is positive, but when r lies on the extension of

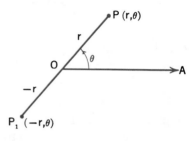

the terminal side through the pole it is negative. Thus the co-ordinates of P_1 may be given as $(-r, \theta)$. Since any point in the plane can be designated by positive polar co-ordinates, we shall restrict our work to positive values of r and θ.

Polar Form of a Complex Number[A]

Since we frequently need to change from one system of co-ordinates to the other, it is customary to superimpose the rectangular system on the polar system. In the figure, O is the origin of both systems, OX is the polar axis of the polar system, and the y-axis is referred to as the $\dfrac{\pi}{2}$ axis of the polar system. The complex number $x + yi$ is represented by $P(x, y)$ in the rectangular system and by $P(r, \theta)$ in the polar system.

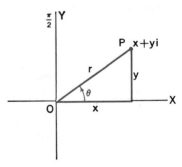

Then

$$\frac{x}{r} = \cos\theta \quad \text{or} \quad x = r\cos\theta \tag{1}$$

and

$$\frac{y}{r} = \sin\theta \quad \text{or} \quad y = r\sin\theta. \tag{2}$$

If we multiply both members of equation (2) by i, we have

$$yi = ri \sin \theta \qquad (3)$$

Adding (1) and (3), $x + yi = r \cos \theta + ri \sin \theta = r (\cos \theta + i \sin \theta)$. The expression $r (\cos \theta + i \sin \theta)$ is the polar form of the complex number $x + yi$. r is the modulus and θ is the amplitude. r and θ are taken as positive. $\cos \theta + i \sin \theta$ may be abbreviated by the symbol **cis θ**. Thus $r (\cos \theta + i \sin \theta) = r$ cis θ.

To express a complex number in polar form, we have, from the figure,

$$r = \sqrt{x^2 + y^2} \text{ and } \theta = \text{arc tan } \frac{y}{x}.$$

We must be careful to obtain the correct quadrant angle for θ. For example,

$$\theta = \text{arc tan } \frac{-y}{x} \text{ is a fourth-quadrant angle,}$$

$$\theta = \text{arc tan } \frac{-y}{-x} \text{ is a third-quadrant angle,}$$

and

$$\theta = \text{arc tan } \frac{y}{-x} \text{ is a second-quadrant angle.}$$

In the beginning, at least, you should plot $x + yi$ to obtain the correct quadrant for θ.

EXAMPLE 1. Express $-3 + 4 i$ in polar form.

.SOLUTION. $-3 + 4 i$ is represented by point P in the figure.

Then $x = -3, y = 4$.

$$r = \sqrt{x^2 + y^2} = \sqrt{9 + 16} = 5.$$

$$\theta = \text{arc tan } \left(\frac{4}{-3}\right) = 126° \, 52', \quad \theta \text{ being}$$

found from Table X to the nearest minute. Then r cis θ = 5 cis 126° 52'.

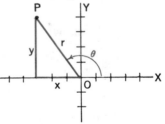

EXAMPLE 2. Express 8 cis 240° in rectangular form.

SOLUTION. Represent 8 cis 240° by point P.

$x = r \cos \theta = 8 \cos 240° = 8(-\frac{1}{2}) = -4$

$y = r \sin \theta = 8 \sin 240°$

$$= 8(-\frac{1}{2} \sqrt{3}) = -4 \sqrt{3}$$

Then $x + iy = -4 - 4 i \sqrt{3}$.

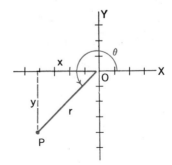

EXERCISES [A]

Draw the directed line segments which represent each of the following and express in polar form:

1. $1 + i$ **3.** $2 + 5i$ **5.** $-3 + 2i$ **7.** -4

2. $-2 - 3i$ **4.** $\sqrt{3} - 1$ **6.** $3i + 3\sqrt{3}$ **8.** $3i$

Draw the directed line segments which represent each of the following, and express in rectangular form:

9. 6 cis 30°   **11.** 3 cis 270°   **13.** 4 cis 210°   **15.** 2 cis 0°

10. 5 cis 330°   **12.** 8 cis 120°   **14.** 9 cis 330°   **16.** 5 cis π

The Product of Two Complex Numbers in Polar Form [A]

Let $\qquad z_1 = r_1 (\cos \theta_1 + i \sin \theta_1)$

and $\qquad z_2 = r_2 (\cos \theta_2 + i \sin \theta_2)$

be any two complex numbers in polar form.

Then, by multiplication, we have

$$z_1 z_2 = r_1 r_2 [(\cos \theta_1 \cos \theta_2 - \sin \theta_1 \sin \theta_2) + i (\sin \theta_1 \cos \theta_2 + \cos \theta_1 \sin \theta_2)]$$

$$= r_1 r_2 [\cos (\theta_1 + \theta_2) + i \sin (\theta_1 + \theta_2)]$$

or $\qquad\qquad z_1 z_2 = r_1 r_2 \text{ cis } (\theta_1 + \theta_2).$

This may be stated in the form of a theorem as follows:

The product of two complex numbers is a complex number whose modulus is the product of the moduli and whose amplitude is the sum of the amplitudes of the given complex numbers.

EXAMPLE. Find the product of $2\sqrt{3} + 2i$ and $-3 + 3i$.

SOLUTION. Changing $2\sqrt{3} + 2i$ to polar form, we have

$r_1 = \sqrt{12 + 4} = 4$ and

$\theta_1 = \arctan \dfrac{1}{\sqrt{3}} = 30°.$

Then $2\sqrt{3} + 2i = 4$ cis 30°.

Changing $-3 + 3i$ to polar form, we have $r_2 = \sqrt{9 + 9} = 3\sqrt{2}$

and $\theta_2 = \arctan (-1) = 135°.$

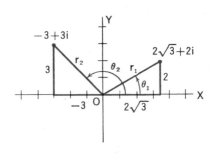

Then $-3 + 3i = 3\sqrt{2}\text{ cis }135°$.

Hence $(2\sqrt{3} + 2i)(-3 + 3i) = r_1 r_2 \text{ cis }(\theta_1 + \theta_2) = 12\sqrt{2}\text{ cis }165°$.

The Quotient of Two Complex Numbers in Polar Form [A]

Let
$$z_1 = r_1(\cos\theta_1 + i\sin\theta_1)$$

and
$$z_2 = r_2(\cos\theta_2 + i\sin\theta_2)$$

be any two complex numbers in polar form.

Then, by division, we have

$$\frac{z_1}{z_2} = \frac{r_1(\cos\theta_1 + i\sin\theta_1)}{r_2(\cos\theta_2 + i\sin\theta_2)}.$$

Multiplying both numerator and denominator of the right member by $\cos\theta_2 - i\sin\theta_2$, we have

$$\frac{z_1}{z_2} = \frac{r_1[(\cos\theta_1\cos\theta_2 + \sin\theta_1\sin\theta_2) + i(\sin\theta_1\cos\theta_2 - \cos\theta_1\sin\theta_2)]}{r_2(\cos^2\theta_2 + \sin^2\theta_2)}$$

$$= \frac{r_1}{r_2}[\cos(\theta_1 - \theta_2) + i\sin(\theta_1 - \theta_2)]$$

or
$$\frac{z_1}{z_2} = \frac{r_1}{r_2}\text{ cis }(\theta_1 - \theta_2).$$

This may be stated in theorem form as follows:

The quotient of two complex numbers is a complex number whose modulus is the modulus of the dividend divided by the modulus of the divisor and whose amplitude is the amplitude of the dividend minus the amplitude of the divisor.

EXAMPLE.   Divide 6 cis 150° by $2\sqrt{3}$ cis 60°.

SOLUTION. $\dfrac{6\text{ cis }150°}{2\sqrt{3}\text{ cis }60°} = \dfrac{6}{2\sqrt{3}}\text{ cis }90° = \sqrt{3}\text{ cis }90°$.

Powers and Roots of Complex Numbers in Polar Form.   De Moivre's Theorem. [A]

If we use the theorem on page 284 to multiply the complex number $r(\cos\theta + i\sin\theta)$ successively by itself, we have

$$[r(\cos\theta + i\sin\theta)]^2 = r^2(\cos 2\theta + i\sin 2\theta)$$
$$[r(\cos\theta + i\sin\theta)]^3 = r^3(\cos 3\theta + i\sin 3\theta)$$

and so on to

$$[r \,(\cos \theta + i \sin \theta)]^n = r^n \,(\cos n\,\theta + i \sin n\,\theta)$$
$$= r^n \; \text{cis } n\,\theta.$$

Stated in the form of a theorem,

The nth power of a complex number is a complex number whose modulus is the nth power of the modulus of the given number and whose amplitude is n times the amplitude of the given number.

This theorem is known as *De Moivre's Theorem*. It is also valid when *n* is negative or fractional. We shall use *n* fractional to obtain roots of numbers.

EXAMPLE 1. Find $(\sqrt{2} + i \sqrt{2})^4$.

SOLUTION. Writing $\sqrt{2} + i \sqrt{2}$ in polar form, we have 2 cis 45°. Then
$$[2 \text{ cis } 45°]^4 = 2^4 \text{ cis } 180° = 16\,(-1 + 0) = -16.$$

EXAMPLE 2. Find the cube root of $-4 + 4\,i \sqrt{3}$.

SOLUTION. $-4 + 4\,i \sqrt{3} = 8\,(\cos 120° + i \sin 120°)$

Then $[r \,(\cos \theta + i \sin \theta)]^{\frac{1}{3}} = [8\,(\cos 120° + i \sin 120°)]^{\frac{1}{3}}$
$$= 2\,(\cos 40° + i \sin 40°)$$

This is one cube root of $-4 + 4\,i \sqrt{3}$. But since the trigonometric functions of 120° are the same as those for 120° + any integral multiple of 360°, we may write the cube roots of $-4 + 4\,i \sqrt{3}$ as $(8 \text{ cis } 120°)^{\frac{1}{3}}$, $(8 \text{ cis } 480°)^{\frac{1}{3}}$, $(8 \text{ cis } 840°)^{\frac{1}{3}}$, and so on. However, when we evaluate these we find that after the first three, the values are repeated in cycles of three. This proves that a number (except 0) has three and only three distinct cube roots.

Every complex number except zero has n *and only* n *distinct nth roots.*

The *n* distinct *n*th roots of a number may be represented graphically by points on a circle whose center is at the origin and whose radius is the modulus of these roots. These points divide the circle into *n* equal arcs.

The other two cube roots of $-4 + 4\,i \sqrt{3}$ in polar form are

$$(8 \text{ cis } 480°)^{\frac{1}{3}} = 2 \text{ cis } 160°,$$
and $$(8 \text{ cis } 840°)^{\frac{1}{3}} = 2 \text{ cis } 280°.$$

EXAMPLE 3. Find the five distinct fifth roots of 1 and represent the points graphically.

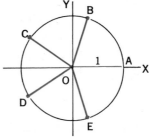

SOLUTION. $1 =$ cis $0°$, cis $360°$, cis $720°$, cis $1080°$, cis $1440°$. Then the fifth roots of 1 are cis $0°$, cis $72°$, cis $144°$, cis $216°$, and cis $288°$. The points A, B, C, D, and E represent the five fifth roots of 1.

The moduli of the points are 1. $\widehat{AB} = \widehat{BC} = \widehat{CD} = \widehat{DE} = \widehat{EA} = 72°$. Proceeding to find the roots in rectangular form, we have

cis $0° = 1 (\cos 0° + i \sin 0°) = 1$
cis $72° = 1 (\cos 72° + i \sin 72°) = .3090 + .9511 i$
cis $144° = 1 (\cos 144° + i \sin 144°) = -.8090 + .5878 i$
cis $216° = 1 (\cos 216° + i \sin 216°) = -.8090 - .5878 i$
cis $288° = 1 (\cos 288° + i \sin 288°) = .3090 - .9511 i$

Finding the 5 fifth roots of 1 is the same as solving the equation $x^5 - 1 = 0$.

EXERCISES

A

Perform the indicated operations, using the polar form of the complex numbers:

1. 2 cis $30° \cdot 3$ cis $150°$
2. 4 cis $25° \cdot 5$ cis $40°$
3. 3 cis $120° \div$ cis $30°$
4. 6 cis $210° \div 2$ cis $30°$
5. $(2 - 2 i)(1 + i \sqrt{3})$
6. $(7 - 24 i) \div (3 + 4 i)$
7. $(1 + i)^3$

8. $(2 - i \sqrt{3})^2$
9. $(3 i)^5$
10. $(2 - 2 i)^4$
11. $(\sqrt{3} - i)^6$
12. $(1 - i \sqrt{3})^5$
13. $(1 + i)^{\frac{1}{4}}$
14. $(1 - i)^{\frac{1}{5}}$

15. $(-2 + 2 i)^{\frac{1}{4}}$
16. $(3 - i \sqrt{3})^{\frac{1}{6}}$
17. $(27)^{\frac{1}{3}}$
18. $(-64)^{\frac{1}{3}}$
19. $(8)^{\frac{1}{3}}$
20. $(-7 + 24 i)^{\frac{1}{4}}$
21. $(-4 + i \sqrt{2})^{\frac{1}{2}}$

B

Solve the following equations:

22. $x^2 + 4 = 0$
23. $x^8 = 1$
24. $x^3 - 8 = 0$

25. $x^3 + i = 0$
26. $x^4 + 32 = 0$
27. $x^5 + 1 = 0$

28. $x^6 - 1 = 0$
29. $x^3 + 27 = 0$
30. $x^4 - 8 = 0$

Trigonometric and Exponential Series [B]

In more advanced mathematics it is proved that

$$\sin x = x - \frac{x^3}{3!} + \frac{x^5}{5!} - \frac{x^7}{7!} + \ldots \qquad \text{[I]}$$

$$\cos x = 1 - \frac{x^2}{2!} + \frac{x^4}{4!} - \frac{x^6}{6!} + \ldots \qquad \text{[II]}$$

$$e^x = 1 + x + \frac{x^2}{2!} + \frac{x^3}{3!} + \frac{x^4}{4!} + \ldots \qquad \text{[III]}$$

They are called the sine, cosine, and exponential series respectively. The x in $\sin x$ and $\cos x$ is in radians. 3! is read factorial 3 and means the product of all integers from 1 to 3 inclusive.

In [III], if we replace x by ix, we have

$$e^{ix} = 1 + ix + \frac{(ix)^2}{2!} + \frac{(ix)^3}{3!} + \frac{(ix)^4}{4!} + \frac{(ix)^5}{5!} + \ldots$$

$$e^{ix} = 1 + ix - \frac{x^2}{2!} - \frac{ix^3}{3!} + \frac{x^4}{4!} + \frac{ix^5}{5!} - \ldots$$

$$e^{ix} = \left(1 - \frac{x^2}{2!} + \frac{x^4}{4!} - \ldots\right) + i\left(x - \frac{x^3}{3!} + \frac{x^5}{5!} - \ldots\right)$$

Substituting $\sin x$ and $\cos x$ for the series in parentheses, we have

$$e^{ix} = \cos x + i \sin x. \qquad \text{[IV]}$$

This formula is very important as it shows the relation between the exponential and trigonometric functions.

Replacing x by $-x$ in [IV], we have

$$e^{-ix} = \cos x - i \sin x \qquad \text{[V]}$$

Subtracting [V] from [IV],

$$e^{ix} - e^{-ix} = 2 i \sin x$$

or $$\sin x = \frac{e^{ix} - e^{-ix}}{2 i} \qquad \text{[VI]}$$

Adding [IV] and [V],

$$e^{ix} + e^{-ix} = 2 \cos x$$

or $$\cos x = \frac{e^{ix} + e^{-ix}}{2} \qquad \text{[VII]}$$

Equations [VI] and [VII] are called **Euler's** equations, after the Swiss mathematician Euler (1707–1783) who discovered them. They define the trigonometric functions in terms of the exponential function.

Hyperbolic Functions [B]

If we replace x by ix in formulas [VI] and [VII], we have

$$\sin ix = i\frac{e^x - e^{-x}}{2} \qquad \text{[VIII]}$$

$$\cos ix = \frac{e^x + e^{-x}}{2} \qquad \text{[IX]}$$

The exponential functions $\dfrac{e^x - e^{-x}}{2}$ and $\dfrac{e^x + e^{-x}}{2}$ are defined as the **hyperbolic sine of** x and the **hyperbolic cosine of** x respectively. Written in symbols, they are

$$\sinh x = \frac{e^x - e^{-x}}{2}$$

and

$$\cosh x = \frac{e^x + e^{-x}}{2}.$$

The other hyperbolic functions are,

Hyperbolic tangent $x = \tanh x = \dfrac{\sinh x}{\cosh x} = \dfrac{e^x - e^{-x}}{e^x + e^{-x}}$,

Hyperbolic cotangent $x = \operatorname{ctnh} x = \dfrac{\cosh x}{\sinh x} = \dfrac{e^x + e^{-x}}{e^x - e^{-x}}$,

Hyperbolic secant $x = \operatorname{sech} x = \dfrac{1}{\cosh x} = \dfrac{2}{e^x + e^{-x}}$,

Hyperbolic cosecant $x = \operatorname{csch} x = \dfrac{1}{\sinh x} = \dfrac{2}{e^x - e^{-x}}$.

The hyperbolic functions are very important in the applications of mathematics. The trigonometric functions are often called circular functions. The circular, or trigonometric, functions are related to an arc connected with the circle in the same manner that the hyperbolic functions are related to an arc associated with the equilateral hyperbola.

The inverse hyperbolic functions are written $y = \sinh^{-1} x$, $y = \cosh^{-1} x$, $y = \tanh^{-1} x$, etc., and read "y is the number whose hyperbolic sine is x, etc." $y = $ arc sinh x is not used as the inverse function, since y is a number and not an angle.

From formulas [VIII] and [IX] and the definitions of the hyperbolic functions, we see that the relations between the circular and hyperbolic functions are as follows:

$$\sin ix = i \sinh x$$
$$\cos ix = \cosh x$$
and
$$\tan ix = i \tanh x$$

There are many relations between the hyperbolic functions that resemble the relations between the trigonometric functions.

EXAMPLE. Prove that $\cosh^2 x - \sinh^2 x = 1$.

SOLUTION.

$$\cosh^2 x - \sinh^2 x$$

$$\left(\frac{e^x + e^{-x}}{2}\right)^2 - \left(\frac{e^x - e^{-x}}{2}\right)^2 \quad \Bigg| \quad 1$$

$$\frac{e^{2x} + 2 + e^{-2x}}{4} - \frac{e^{2x} - 2 + e^{-2x}}{4}$$

$$\therefore \ \cosh^2 x - \sinh^2 x = 1$$

EXERCISES [B]

Using the first two terms of the sine series, page 288, and the first three terms of the cosine series, find the following and check with Table X:

1. $\sin 1$ **2.** $\cos 1$ **3.** $\tan 1$ **4.** $\sin \frac{1}{2}$ **5.** $\cos \frac{1}{2}$

6. Letting $x = 1$ in the series for e^x, find e correct to three decimal places.

Prove the following:

7. $\sinh(-x) = -\sinh x$ **13.** $\sinh \pi i = 0$

8. $\cosh(-x) = \cosh x$ **14.** $\cosh \pi i = -1$

9. $\tanh(-x) = -\tanh x$ **15.** $1 - \tanh^2 x = \text{sech}^2 x$

10. $\sinh 0 = 0$ **16.** $\text{ctnh}^2 x - 1 = \text{csch}^2 x$

11. $\cosh 0 = 1$ **17.** $\sinh 2x = 2 \sinh x \cosh x$

12. $\tanh 0 = 0$ **18.** $\cosh 2x = \cosh^2 x + \sinh^2 x$

19. $\sinh(x + y) = \sinh x \cosh y + \cosh x \sinh y$

20. $\cosh(x + y) = \cosh x \cosh y + \sinh x \sinh y$

21. $\sinh (x - y) = \sinh x \cosh y - \cosh x \sinh y$

22. $\cosh (x - y) = \cosh x \cosh y - \sinh x \sinh y$

23. $e^x = \cosh x + \sinh x$, and $e^{-x} = \cosh x - \sinh x$

24. $\cosh^{-1} x = \ln (x + \sqrt{x^2 - 1})$

25. $\tanh^{-1} x = \frac{1}{2} \ln \dfrac{1 + x}{1 - x}$

Using Table V, plot graphs of

26. $y = \sinh x$ **27.** $y = \cosh x$ **28.** $y = \tanh x$

Solve:

29. $e^{2x} - 3 e^x + 2 = 0$ **30.** $e^{2x} + 3 e^x - 10 = 0$

Gauss (1777–1855)

Karl Friedrich Gauss was born on April 30, 1777. He was a precocious child having an excellent memory and a great power for mental calculations, which he retained during the remainder of his life. Without being taught he learned to read at the age of three. At the age of ten he astonished Büttner, his teacher, when without any aid from his teacher or text, he quickly found the sum of a series like 32164 + 32370 + 32576 + ... + 52558.

Gauss made numerous advancements in various fields of mathematics. We shall mention a few of them. He was the first to prove that any algebraic equation has at least one root and that all roots of an algebraic equation are of the form $a + ib$, which is a complex number. He was one of the first to interpret a complex number as a point in a plane and to study functions of a complex variable. (If $f(z) = z^2$ and $z = x + iy$, then $f(z)$ is an example of a function of the complex variable z.)

Gauss was modest about his accomplishments and many of his discoveries were unknown by others before his death. For example, his posthumous papers showed that his work on quaternions preceded that of William R. Hamilton by thirty years.

Gauss is considered one of the three greatest mathematicians yet known, the other two being Archimedes and Newton.

GENERAL REVIEW EXERCISES

Δ

Chapters I–III

In exercises 1–20, tell which statements are true and which are false:

1. $\sin 24° < \sin 30°$
2. $\cos 32° < \cos 36°$
3. $\tan 40° < \tan 50°$
4. $\operatorname{ctn} 40° < \tan 50°$
5. If $a^2 + b^2 = c^2$, $\triangle ABC$ is a rt. $\triangle$.
6. $\log 524 = \log 52.4 + 1$
7. $\sin 27° = \cos 63°$
8. $\operatorname{ctn} 80° = \tan 10°$
9. $\sin 30° = \frac{1}{2}\sqrt{3}$
10. $\tan 45° = 1$
11. $\log_5 48 = \dfrac{\log_{10} 48}{\log_5 10}$
12. $\log 25 + \log 4 = 2$
13. If $\log 82.3 = 1.9154$, then $\log 823 = 2.9154$.
14. $\dfrac{\log x}{\log y} = \log x - \log y$
15. $\sin x$ and $\sec x$ are reciprocal functions.
16. $\sec x$ and $\cos x$ are reciprocal functions.
17. The approximate number 4703.2 has four significant figures.
18. The sum of two or more approximate numbers has no more significant figures than the least accurate addend.
19. The product of two approximate numbers should not contain more significant figures than either the multiplier or multiplicand.
20. The base of the common system of logarithms is 10.

21. Find the value of $\dfrac{76.341 \times 2.1846}{302.09}$ by the use of logarithms.

22. Express 0.000027 as a scientific number.

23. Express 17461 as a power of 10.

24. Find the value of $10^{\log 100}$.

25. Show that $10^{1 + \log 10} = 100$.

26. If $\sin x = \frac{3}{4}$, find without the use of a table the values of the other trigonometric functions of x.

27. If $\log 50 = 1.6990$, find $\log 20$.

28. $t = \pi \sqrt{\dfrac{l}{g}}$. Find t when $l = 31.4$ and $g = 32.2$.

29. $t = \pi \sqrt{\dfrac{l}{980}}$. Find l when $t = 3$.

30. $S = 4\pi r^2$. Find r when $S = 1000$.

Solve for x:

31. $2^x = 32$ **32.** $2^{x-3} = 9$ **33.** $14^{x+1} = 196$

34. $\log x + \log 2x = 6 + \log 5$.

35. $2 \log x = 2 + \log \left(\dfrac{x}{5} - 1 \right)$

Solve the following right triangles without the use of logarithms:

36. $B = 61°\ 32'$ **38.** $A = 41°\ 18'$
     $b = 246.1$ $c = 179.3$

37. $A = 32°\ 19'$ **39.** $a = 201.4$
     $b = 13.42$ $c = 392.8$

Chapters IV-VI

In exercises 1–10, tell which statements are true and which are false:

1. In the first quadrant all functions are positive.

2. The cosine is negative in the second and third quadrants.

3. The tangent is positive in the third quadrant.

4. In the second quadrant the sine and cosecant are positive.

5. The sine of 500° is negative.

6. In right $\triangle ABC$, $a = b \sin A$.

7. In right $\triangle ABC$, $c = a \csc A$.

8. π radians $= 360°$.

9. A radian is more than 60°.

10. At one hundred yards a mil subtends a chord of one yard.

11. Given ctn $A = \frac{1}{3}$ in the third quadrant, write the other functions of A.

12. If $\cos \theta = \frac{1}{2}\sqrt{2}$ and θ is a fourth-quadrant angle, give the other functions of θ.

13. Express as functions of positive acute angles:

   a. sin 135°   **d.** ctn 310°   **g.** csc 340° 12′

   b. cos 190°   **e.** sec 210°   **h.** sin 117° 13′

   c. tan $(-200°)$ **f.** cos $(-112°)$ **i.** tan 164° 37′

14. Express as functions of θ:

   a. sin $(180° - \theta)$ **d.** ctn $(270° + \theta)$ **g.** sin $(360° - \theta)$

   b. cos $(90° + \theta)$ **e.** sec $(180° + \theta)$ **h.** cos $(360° + \theta)$

   c. tan $(\theta + 90°)$ **f.** csc $(270° - \theta)$ **i.** tan $(180° - \theta)$

15. Change $\frac{\pi}{4}$ radians to degrees.

16. Change 34° 18′ to radians, having π in the answer.

17. Find the radius of a circle in which an arc of 25.14 inches has a central angle of 2.631 radians.

In exercises 18–21, θ is an acute angle expressed in radians. Simplify each expression:

18. $\sin (\pi + \theta)$ **20.** $\tan \left(\dfrac{\pi}{2} - \theta\right)$

19. $\cos (\pi + \theta)$ **21.** $\sin \left(\dfrac{\pi}{2} + \theta\right)$

22. The angular velocity of a flywheel is $100\,\pi$ radians per second. Find the velocity of a point on the outer rim of the wheel if the diameter of the wheel is 3 feet.

Use logarithms in solving the right $\triangle ABC$, given

23. $a = 461.32$ **24.** $A = 46° 18′ 40″$

     $b = 235.18$ $a = 23.478$

25. Find the area of right $\triangle ABC$, given $A = 33°\ 32'$ and $a = 141.7$.

26. Find the area of right $\triangle ABC$, given $B = 27°\ 19'\ 30''$ and $c = 42.134$.

27. Find the area of a sector of a circle if its central angle is $32°\ 20'$ and the radius of the circle is 18.31 inches.

28. The arc of a circle is $\dfrac{3\,\pi}{4}$ and its central angle is $\dfrac{\pi}{4}$. Find the radius of the circle.

29. Through how many radians does the minute hand of a clock turn in 10 hours?

30. Change to degrees:
   a. 800 mils   **b.** 64 mils   **c.** 320 mils

31. Change to mils:
   a. $8°$ **b.** $12°$ **c.** $40°$

32. Does $\sin (A - B) = -\sin (B - A)$?

33. Complete: $\tan 120° = -\operatorname{ctn}\ \underline{\ ?\ }$.

34. Give the values of the sine, cosine, and tangent of each of the following angles:
   a. $0°$ **b.** π **c.** $\dfrac{\pi}{6}$ **d.** $\dfrac{\pi}{4}$ **e.** $\dfrac{\pi}{3}$ **f.** $\dfrac{4\,\pi}{3}$

35. How many mils are there in the sum of the angles of a triangle? of a quadrilateral?

36. The length of a propeller blade is 48 inches. What is the speed in miles an hour of the tip of the blade when the propeller revolves 3240 times a minute?

Chapters VII–IX

1. Which line segment in the drawing represents the sine function? the cosine function? the cotangent function? the secant function? the cosecant function?

2. In which quadrants are the sine functions positive? In which quadrants are the tangent functions positive? In which quadrants are the cosine functions positive?

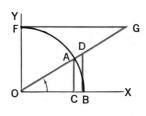

3. Name the pairs of functions which always have the same signs.

4. Describe the variation of the sine function as the angle increases from 0° to 360°.

5. Which functions range in value from -1 to $+1$?

6. Which functions never have values from -1 to $+1$?

7. Which functions have values from $-\infty$ to $+\infty$?

8. Which functions have continuous graphs?

9. Show that $\tan(\pi - x) = -\tan x$.

10. Show that $\sin(\pi + x) = -\sin x$.

11. Draw the graph of $y = \sin x$ from $-\pi$ to $+\pi$.

Determine the period and amplitude and draw the graph of:

12. $y = \sin 2x$

13. $y = 2 \sin x$

14. $y = 2 \cos 4x$

15. $y = 2 \tan 3x$

Prove the following identities:

16. $\dfrac{1}{1 - \cos \alpha} + \dfrac{1}{1 + \cos \alpha} = 2 \csc^2 \alpha$

17. $\dfrac{\operatorname{ctn} \theta + 1}{\operatorname{ctn} \theta - 1} = \dfrac{\cos \theta + \sin \theta}{\cos \theta - \sin \theta}$

18. $\dfrac{\sin x}{\csc x - \operatorname{ctn} x} = 1 + \cos x$

19. $\dfrac{1 + \sec \beta}{\csc \beta} = \sin \beta + \tan \beta$

20. $(\tan y + \operatorname{ctn} y)^2 \cos^2 y - 1 = \operatorname{ctn}^2 y$

21. $\dfrac{\sec \theta}{1 - \tan \theta} + \dfrac{\csc \theta}{1 + \tan \theta} = \dfrac{\csc \theta}{1 - 2 \sin^2 \theta}$

22. $\dfrac{\sin x + \cos y}{\csc x + \sec y} = \sin x \cos y$

23. $1 + (\operatorname{ctn} x + \csc x)^2 - 2 \csc x \operatorname{ctn} x = 2 \csc^2 x$

Solve the following equations:

24. $\tan \theta = 2 \sin \theta$

25. $\operatorname{ctn} x - \csc x = 1$

26. $\cos^2 \theta = \cos \theta$

27. $\tan x + \sec x = 1$

28. $\sec \alpha \tan \alpha - \sin \alpha = \sin^3 \alpha$

29. $\cos^4 \theta - \sin^4 \theta = \frac{1}{2}$

30. $\cos x \, \text{ctn} \, x + \cos x = \csc x \, \text{ctn} \, x$

Prove:

31. $\cos 4 x = \sin^4 x - 6 \sin^2 x \cos^2 x + \cos^4 x$

32. $\tan \left(y + \dfrac{\pi}{4} \right) + \tan \left(y - \dfrac{\pi}{4} \right) = 2 \tan 2 y$

33. $\dfrac{\sin 3 A}{\cos A} + \dfrac{\cos 3 A}{\sin A} = 2 \, \text{ctn} \, 2 A$

34. $\dfrac{1 + \tan C}{1 - \tan C} = \tan 2 C + \sec 2 C$

35. $\dfrac{\sin \theta + \sin 3 \theta}{\cos \theta - \cos 3 \theta} = \text{ctn} \, \theta$

Solve:

36. $\csc 2 x = 2 \sin 2 x$

37. $4 \sin^2 \frac{1}{2} x = 2 - \cos^2 x$

38. $\tan \frac{1}{2} x + \sin x = 0$

39. $\sin 2 \theta = \sin 4 \theta$

40. $\tan (\phi + 45°) = 1 - \sin 2 \phi$

Chapter X

In exercises 1–12 tell which of the statements are true and which are false:

1. There are only four cases of solution of plane oblique triangles.

2. The law of sines can be used to solve a triangle when one side and two angles of the triangle are given.

3. Mollweide's formulas are used to solve triangles in Case III.

4. A nautical mile is about 800 feet longer than a statute mile.

5. The law of cosines is expressed by the formula
$$a^2 = b^2 + c^2 + 2 \, bc \cos A.$$

6. $\dfrac{a - b}{c} = \dfrac{\sin \frac{1}{2}(A - B)}{\cos \frac{1}{2} C}$ is a Mollweide formula.

7. The law of tangents can be used to find the remaining angles of a triangle when two sides and the included angle are given.

8. If in $\triangle ABC$, $b = 25$, $a = 20$, and $A = 65°$, there is one solution of the triangle.

9. $\tan \frac{1}{2} A = \dfrac{r}{s - a}$ is a half-angle formula.

10. $K = \sqrt{(s - a)(s - b)(s - c)}$ is Hero's formula, used to find the area of a triangle.

11. The formula $K = \frac{1}{2} bc \sin A$ can be used to find the area of a triangle.

12. $D = \dfrac{c}{\sin C}$ is a formula that can be used to find the diameter of the circle circumscribed about $\triangle ABC$.

13. Give the formulas you would use to solve an oblique triangle, given:
  a. Two angles and one side.
  b. Two sides and an angle opposite one of them.
  c. Two sides and their included angle.
  d. The three sides.

14. When is the law of tangents preferable to the law of cosines in solving a triangle, given two sides and the included angle?

15. Express by a formula:
  a. The law of sines
  b. The law of cosines
  c. The law of tangents
  d. The value of $\tan \frac{1}{2} A$

16. Give one of Mollweide's formulas.

17. In $\triangle ABC$, $\sin A = \frac{5}{7}$, $\sin B = \frac{4}{5}$, and $a = 1230$. Find b.

18. In $\triangle ABC$, $b = 840$, $c = 720$, and $\sin B = .1726$. Find $\sin C$.

19. A plane flying at a speed of 430 m.p.h. is climbing at an angle of 12°. Find the rate of climb.

20. Two sides of a triangular lot are 134.1 feet and 880.4 feet respectively. The angle opposite the greater side is 51° 24′. Find the third side of the triangle.

Find the area of △ABC, *if*

21. $a = 471.3$, $b = 236.2$, and $C = 47°\ 18'$.

22. $a = 423$, $b = 726$, and $c = 514$.

23. Find the area of parallelogram *ABCD* in which *AB* = 12.43 inches, ∠*DBC* = 61° 45′, and ∠*ABD* = 40° 30′.

For exercises 24–26, use the figure below.

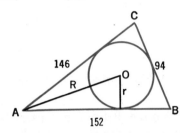

24. Find *R* in the figure.

25. Find *r* in the figure.

26. Find ∠*BAO* in the figure.

27. Find the three angles of △*ABC* given $a = 200.0$, $b = 300.0$, and $c = 400.0$.

28. Solve △*ABC*, given $A = 100°\ 17'\ 34''$, $b = 1413.7$, and $c = 2439.1$.

29. Solve △*ABC*, given $B = 41°\ 32'\ 20''$, $c = 4147.8$, and $b = 3218.9$.

30. Two planes start at the same time from the same airport. One flies on course 42° 18′ at 320 knots and the other on course 274° 35′ at 284 knots. How far apart will they be in 80 minutes?

31. A plane is headed in direction 134° 15′ at an air speed of 295 m.p.h. Find its ground speed and course if the wind is blowing from direction 40° 40′ at 20 m.p.h.

32. Find the resultant of two forces, one of 72 pounds and the other of 56 pounds, if they act at a point at an angle of 37°.

33. An airplane flies in direction 62° 18′ at 470 m.p.h. Find its velocities north and east.

34. A plane with an air speed of 300 m.p.h. is to fly course 210°. In which direction must the plane be headed if the wind is blowing 25 m.p.h. from direction 110°?

35. Two observers, one at A and the other at B, were 1760 yards apart when they observed the flash of an enemy gun at C. If $\angle A$ was 38° and $\angle B$ was 61°, how far was each observer from the enemy gun?

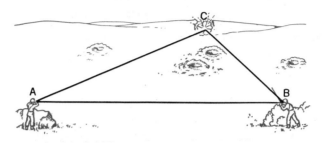

36. An enemy battery at 7000 yards subtends an angle of 8 mils. How wide is the battery?

37. An observer finds that the shells of his battery fall 6 mils to the right of the target. If the range of the target is 8300 yards and the observer is in a tree at his battery, how far from the target did the shells land?

Chapters XI–XII

1. Find the positive angles less than 360° for arc cos $\frac{1}{2}$.

2. Add $3 + 5i$ and $-4 - 2i$.

3. Express $4 + 2i$ in polar form.

4. Using the polar form, multiply $1 - i$ by $3 + 2i$.

5. Find the value of Arc tan $\left(\cos \frac{\pi}{4} \right)$.

6. Solve Arc tan $\frac{x}{2}$ + Arc ctn $\frac{5}{3} = \frac{\pi}{4}$.

7. Using De Moivre's Theorem, find the three cube roots of 8.

8. Complete: $x + iy = $ _?_ $(\cos \theta + i \sin \theta) = re^?$

9. Express e^x by a series.

10. Form an equation whose roots are 3, $\dfrac{1 + i\sqrt{3}}{2}$, and $\dfrac{1 - i\sqrt{3}}{2}$.

11. Show that sinh $(\pi i) = 0$.

SPHERICAL TRIGONOMETRY

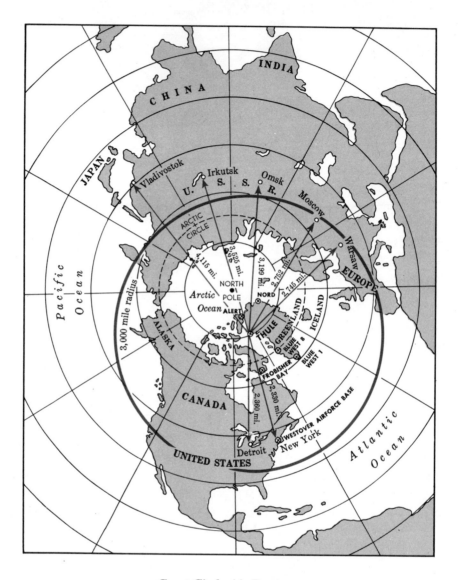

Great-Circle Air Routes

The great-circle air lanes shown on the map provide short routes over Arctic wastes from the United States and Canada to Europe and Asia. The military base at Thule may one day become an important commercial airport

THE RIGHT SPHERICAL TRIANGLE

Δ

Spherical trigonometry deals with the relations between the angles and sides of a spherical triangle.

In finding distances and directions involving small areas, the surface of the earth is assumed to be a plane, and plane trigonometry is sufficient for the solution of problems that arise. When distances are so large that the curvature of the earth must be taken into consideration, it is necessary to use spherical triangles. Spherical trigonometry is needed in the study of geodesy, air and marine navigation, and astronomy.

Definitions and Propositions from Solid Geometry

The study of spherical trigonometry is based on the geometry of the sphere. The following facts from solid geometry will have an immediate application in the work that follows and are stated here for reference:

1. A line perpendicular to a plane is perpendicular to any line in the plane passing through its foot.

2. Through a given point there can be one plane, and only one, perpendicular to a given line.

3. If a line is perpendicular to a given plane, every plane which contains this line is perpendicular to the given plane.

4. If two intersecting planes are perpendicular to a third plane, their intersection is also perpendicular to that plane.

5. A *great circle* of a sphere is the intersection of the sphere and a plane through the center of the sphere. A *small circle* of a sphere is the intersection of the sphere and a plane not passing through the center of the sphere.

6. The *axis* of a circle of a sphere is the diameter of the sphere which is perpendicular to the plane of the circle. The extremities of the axis are the *poles* of the circle.

7. The sides of a spherical polygon are arcs of great circles. The angles of the polygon are the spherical angles formed by the sides of the polygon.

8. A spherical angle is equal in degrees to the arc of the great circle which has the vertex of the angle as a pole and is included between the sides of the angle, extended if necessary.

9. Each side of a spherical triangle is less than the sum of the other two sides.

10. The sum of the sides of a spherical polygon is less than 360°.

11. The shortest line between two points on a sphere is the minor arc of a great circle through these points.

12. If the vertices of one spherical triangle are the poles of the sides of another spherical triangle, the second triangle is called the *polar triangle* of the first.

13. If one spherical triangle is the polar triangle of another, then the second is the polar triangle of the first.

14. In two polar triangles each angle of one is the supplement of the opposite side of the other.

15. The sum of the angles of a spherical triangle is greater than 180° and less than 540°.

16. If two sides of a spherical triangle are equal, the angles opposite these sides are equal; and conversely.

17. If two sides of a spherical triangle are unequal, the angle opposite the greater side is the greater; and conversely.

18. A *lune* is a spherical figure composed of two great semicircles.

Solution of Special Right Spherical Triangles [A]

In general, a spherical triangle can be solved if any three of its six parts are given.

In a trirectangular spherical triangle each side is a quadrant, or 90°. If the spherical triangle is birectangular, the sides opposite the right angles are quadrants and the third side is equal in degrees to the third angle. If either the third side or the third angle is given, the solution is known; otherwise the solution is indeterminate. Therefore in developing formulas to solve right spherical triangles we need only to consider triangles having one right angle.

One or more sides or angles of a spherical triangle may be greater than 180°. In practice it is customary to solve such triangles by reference triangles in which each side and each angle is less than 180°. Hence we shall consider only triangles in which each side and each angle is less than 180°.

Formulas for the Solution of Right Spherical Triangles[A]

Let O be the center of a sphere, ABC a right spherical triangle with C the right angle, $B < 90°$, and $A < 90°$.

Then OA, OB, and OC are radii of the sphere, and $a \doteq \angle BOC$, $b \doteq \angle AOC$, and $c \doteq \angle AOB$.

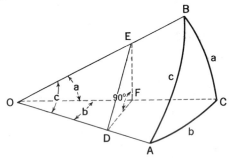

Through any point E in OB pass plane $DEF \perp OA$, intersecting planes OBC, OAC, and OBA in straight lines EF, DF, and DE respectively.

DE and $DF \perp OA$. $\therefore \angle EDF$ is the plane angle of dihedral $\angle B\text{-}OA\text{-}C$, and $\angle EDF \doteq \angle A$. Plane $DEF \perp$ plane OAC. $\angle B\text{-}OC\text{-}A \doteq \angle C$. $\therefore \angle B\text{-}OC\text{-}A$ is a right dihedral angle and plane $OBC \perp$ plane OAC. $\therefore EF \perp OF$ and FD.

Then we have four right angles, ODE, ODF, EFO, and EFD.

$$\frac{OD}{OE} = \frac{OD}{OF} \cdot \frac{OF}{OE}. \quad \cos c = \frac{OD}{OE}, \cos b = \frac{OD}{OF}, \cos a = \frac{OF}{OE}.$$

Then $$\cos c = \cos b \cos a \qquad [1]$$

$$\frac{EF}{OE} = \frac{EF}{ED} \cdot \frac{ED}{OE}. \quad \sin a = \frac{EF}{OE}, \sin A = \frac{EF}{ED}, \sin c = \frac{ED}{OE}.$$

Then $$\sin a = \sin A \sin c \qquad [2]$$

By analogy, interchanging A and B, and a and b, we have

$$\sin b = \sin B \sin c \tag{3}$$

$$\frac{DF}{OD} = \frac{DF}{ED} \cdot \frac{ED}{OD}. \quad \tan b = \frac{DF}{OD}, \quad \cos A = \frac{DF}{ED}, \quad \tan c = \frac{ED}{OD}.$$

Then

$$\tan b = \cos A \tan c \tag{4}$$

Interchanging A and B, and a and b, we have

$$\tan a = \cos B \tan c \tag{5}$$

$$\frac{EF}{OF} = \frac{EF}{FD} \cdot \frac{FD}{OF}. \quad \tan a = \frac{EF}{OF}, \quad \tan A = \frac{EF}{FD}, \quad \sin b = \frac{FD}{OF}.$$

Then

$$\tan a = \tan A \sin b \tag{6}$$

Interchanging A and B, and a and b, we have

$$\tan b = \tan B \sin a \tag{7}$$

From [6] and [7], by multiplication,

$$\tan a \tan b = \tan A \tan B \sin a \sin b$$

Dividing both members of the equation by $\sin a \sin b$,

$$\frac{1}{\cos a \cos b} = \tan A \tan B$$

Substituting $\cos c = \cos a \cos b$ [1], we have

$$\frac{1}{\cos c} = \tan A \tan B \text{ or } \frac{1}{\cos c} = \frac{1}{\operatorname{ctn} A \operatorname{ctn} B}$$

Then

$$\cos c = \operatorname{ctn} A \operatorname{ctn} B \tag{8}$$

From [3] and [4], by multiplication,

$$\sin b \cos A \tan c = \tan b \sin B \sin c$$

or

$$\cos A = \frac{\tan b}{\sin b} \cdot \frac{\sin c}{\tan c} \cdot \sin B$$

$$= \frac{1}{\cos b} \cdot \cos c \cdot \sin B$$

Substituting $\cos a = \dfrac{\cos c}{\cos b}$ from [1],

$$\cos A = \cos a \sin B \tag{9}$$

Interchanging letters, we have

$$\cos B = \cos b \sin A \tag{10}$$

In deriving the ten formulas above it was assumed that a and b were less than 90°, but the formulas are valid when a and b are greater than 90°. These ten formulas are all that are necessary to find any one of the three remaining parts of a right spherical triangle when any two parts in addition to the right angle are given.

Napier's Rules of Circular Parts [A]

It is unnecessary to memorize these ten formulas. John Napier of Scotland, the inventor of logarithms, has given us a method of writing any formula needed. It is necessary to remember only two simple rules in connection with a symbolic triangle. A spher- 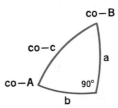 ical right triangle is labeled as shown in the figure. The letters on the hypotenuse, co–B, co–c, co–A, mean that the complementary function is to be used. Notice that C is omitted from the right angle. If any one of the five given parts is called the middle part, the two parts next to it are called the adjacent parts and the remaining two parts are called the opposite parts. Napier's rules are:

I. *The sine of any middle part is equal to the product of the tangents of the adjacent parts.*

II. *The sine of any middle part is equal to the product of the cosines of the opposite parts.*

In applying Rule I, if one of the adjacent parts is co–B, then tan co–B = ctn B. Similarly, in applying Rule II, cos co–c = sin c.

Some examples of Rule I are: sin a = tan b ctn B, cos B = tan a ctn c, and cos c = ctn B ctn A.

Examples of Rule II are: sin b = sin c sin B, cos A = cos a sin B, and cos c = cos a cos b.

Laws of Quadrants [A]

Inasmuch as a quadrant contains 90°, we shall refer to angles and arcs less than 90° as being in the first quadrant, and angles and arcs between 90° and 180° as being in the second quadrant.

The following *laws of quadrants*, often referred to as the *rule of species*, are true for all right spherical triangles and are helpful in deciding whether a required part is greater or less than 90°. They are very important if a required part is found from its sine. The laws are:

I. *An angle and its opposite side are in the same quadrant.*

II. *If any two of the three sides are in the same quadrant, the third side is in the first quadrant; if any two sides are in different quadrants, the third side is in the second quadrant.*

The first law is true because it follows from $\cos A = \cos a \sin B$, formula [9], that $\cos A$ and $\cos a$ must have the same sign since $\sin B$ is always positive. Hence both A and a must either be less than 90°, or both must have values between 90° and 180°.

The second law is true because it follows from formula [1], $\cos c = \cos b \cos a$, that if any two of the quantities $\cos c$, $\cos b$, $\cos a$ have the same sign, the third is positive; if any two have opposite signs, the third is negative.

Solution of Right Spherical Triangles [A]

In solving a right spherical triangle use the following directions:

---

1. Draw and letter a representative figure, placing rings or circles around the given parts.
2. To find the required parts, write formulas from *Napier's rules* each of which contains one required part and the two given parts.
3. Make a complete outline for logarithmic computation before looking up any logarithms.
4. Write the algebraic signs of the functions in front of and a little above each logarithmic function. From these signs determine the sign of the resulting function in order to determine the quadrant of the angle.
5. Check the solution by using a formula which contains the three required parts.

EXAMPLE. Solve the right spherical triangle ABC, given $A = 112°\ 24'$ and $b = 36°\ 18'$.

SOLUTION.

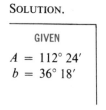

GIVEN
$A = 112°\ 24'$
$b = 36°\ 18'$

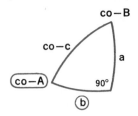

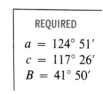

REQUIRED
$a = 124°\ 51'$
$c = 117°\ 26'$
$B = 41°\ 50'$

1. To find a. $\sin b = \tan a \operatorname{ctn} A$
   Solving for tan a, $\tan a = \sin b \tan A$
   Substituting, $\tan a = \sin 36° 18' \tan 112° 24'$

$$^+\log \sin 36° 18' = 9.77233 - 10$$
$$^-\log \tan 112° 24' = 0.38492$$
$$\overline{^-\log \tan a = 0.15725}$$

$$a = 180° - 55° 9' = 124° 51'$$

Since the value of log tan a is negative, a is a second-quadrant angle. This also agrees with the first law of quadrants that an angle and its opposite side are in the same quadrant.

2. To find c. $\cos A = \operatorname{ctn} c \tan b$
   Solving for ctn c, $\operatorname{ctn} c = \cos A \operatorname{ctn} b$
   Substituting, $\operatorname{ctn} c = \cos 112° 24' \operatorname{ctn} 36° 18'$

$$^-\log \cos 112° 24' = 9.58101 - 10$$
$$^+\log \operatorname{ctn} 36° 18' = 0.13397$$
$$\overline{^-\log \operatorname{ctn} c = 9.71498 - 10}$$

$$c = 180° - 62° 35' = 117° 25'$$

3. To find B. $\cos B = \sin A \cos b$
   Substituting, $\cos B = \sin 112° 24' \cos 36° 18'$

$$^+\log \sin 112° 24' = 9.96593 - 10$$
$$^+\log \cos 36° 18' = 9.90630 - 10$$
$$\overline{^+\log \cos B = 9.87223 - 10}$$

$$B = 41° 50'$$

4. Logarithmic check. $\cos B = \operatorname{ctn} c \tan a$

$$^-\log \operatorname{ctn} c = 9.71498 - 10$$
$$^-\log \tan a = 0.15725$$
$$\overline{^+\log \cos B = 9.87223 - 10}$$

Since the value of log cos B found in the check agrees with the value of log cos B in (3), the logarithmic work is correct. The logarithmic check should always be applied before the values of the sides and angles are found from the tables. Observe that any errors made in finding the required parts from their logarithms do not affect the check.

EXERCISES [A]

Solve the following right spherical triangles:

1. $A = 33° 20'$
$B = 72° 40'$

2. $a = 40° 27'$
$b = 51° 18'$

3. $a = 18° 22'$
$B = 24° 6'$

4. $a = 40° 25'$
$c = 70° 34'$

5. $a = 75° 16'$
$b = 130° 6'$

6. $c = 48° 12'$
$B = 24° 10'$

7. $b = 45° 45'$
$c = 112° 18'$

8. $c = 70° 26'$
$A = 52° 3'$

9. $b = 36° 30' 15''$
$A = 142° 7' 12''$

10. $a = 128° 12' 10''$
$b = 48° 56' 20''$

11. $A = 108° 12' 35''$
$B = 120° 4' 5''$

12. $b = 96° 20' 45''$
$A = 52° 8' 30''$

13. In exercises 1–8 find the lengths of the sides in feet if the radius of the sphere in each exercise is 10 feet.

14. In exercises 1–8 find the areas of the triangles in square feet if the radius of the sphere in each exercise is 12 feet. From solid geometry the area formula is $S = \dfrac{\pi r^2 E}{180}$, where E is the spherical excess; $E = (A + B + C) - 180°$.

15. Explain why none of the following sets of data can be used as parts of a right spherical triangle:

a. $b = 70°, B = 110°$

b. $A = 45°, B = 28°$

c. $a = 78°, b = 44°, c = 32°$

d. $a = 80°, b = 150°, c = 140°$

e. $a = 95°, b = 100°, c = 110°$

f. $a = 80°, A = 120°$

The Ambiguous Case of Right Spherical Triangles [A]

When the given parts of a right spherical triangle are a side and the angle opposite, two solutions are obtained. If we have given a and A in the right spherical triangle ABC, we can extend c and b to form the lune AA'. Since the angles of a lune are equal, we have the two triangles ABC and $A'BC$ formed with the same given data.

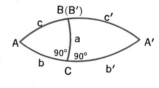

The sides of a lune are 180° and hence $c' = 180° - c$ and $b' = 180° - b$. Also $B' = 180° - B$. In solving the ambiguous case one triangle is referred to as ABC and the other as $A'B'C'$.

EXAMPLE. Solve the right spherical triangle ABC, given $a = 32°\ 20'$ and $A = 45°\ 33'$.

SOLUTION.

GIVEN
$a = 32°\ 20'$
$A = 45°\ 33'$

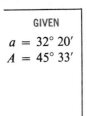
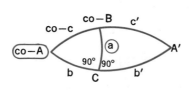

REQUIRED
$B = 55°\ 59'$
$c = 48°\ 31'$
$b = 38°\ 23'$
$B' = 124°\ 1'$
$c' = 131°\ 29'$
$b' = 141°\ 37'$

1. *To find B.*

$$\cos A = \sin B \cos a$$

Solving for sin B,

$$\sin B = \frac{\cos A}{\cos a}$$

Substituting,

$$\sin B = \frac{\cos 45°\ 33'}{\cos 32°\ 20'}$$

$$
\begin{aligned}
{}^+\log \cos 45°\ 33' &= 19.84528 - 20 \\
{}^+\log \cos 32°\ 20' &= \underline{\ 9.92683 - 10} \\
{}^+\log \sin B &= \ 9.91845 - 10
\end{aligned}
$$

$$B = 55°\ 59', \quad B' = 124°\ 1'$$

2. *To find c.*

$$\sin a = \sin c \sin A$$

Solving for sin c,

$$\sin c = \frac{\sin a}{\sin A}$$

Substituting,

$$\sin c = \frac{\sin 32°\ 20'}{\sin 45°\ 33'}$$

$$
\begin{aligned}
{}^+\log \sin 32°\ 20' &= 19.72823 - 20 \\
{}^+\log \sin 45°\ 33' &= \underline{\ 9.85361 - 10} \\
{}^+\log \sin c &= \ 9.87462 - 10
\end{aligned}
$$

$$c = 48°\ 31', \quad c' = 131°\ 29'$$

3. *To find b.*

$$\sin b = \operatorname{ctn} A \tan a$$

Substituting,

$$\sin b = \operatorname{ctn} 45°\ 33' \tan 32°\ 20'$$

$$
\begin{aligned}
{}^+\log \operatorname{ctn} 45°\ 33' &= 9.99166 - 10 \\
{}^+\log \tan 32°\ 20' &= \underline{9.80140 - 10} \\
{}^+\log \sin b &= 9.79306 - 10
\end{aligned}
$$

$$b = 38°\ 23'$$
$$b' = 141°\ 37'$$

4. *Logarithmic check.* $\qquad$ $\sin b = \sin c \sin B$

$$\frac{\begin{aligned}\log \sin c &= 9.87462 - 10\\ \log \sin B &= 9.91845 - 10\end{aligned}}{\log \sin b = 9.79307 - 10}$$

This value checks the value of log sin b found in part 3.

EXERCISES [A]

Solve the following right spherical triangles:

1. $A = 29° 11'$
$\quad a = 23° 56'$

2. $A = 79° 2'$
$\quad a = 72° 3'$

3. $B = 84° 14' 12''$
$\quad b = 78° 20' 36''$

4. $a = 126° 5' 20''$
$\quad A = 105° 55' 30''$

5. $a = 133° 21'$
$\quad A = 119° 28'$

6. $B = 111° 42'$
$\quad b = 127° 35'$

Isosceles Spherical Triangles [A]

An isosceles spherical triangle can be solved by dividing it into two symmetric right spherical triangles by an arc drawn from the vertex perpendicular to the base. If, in the figure, arc PC is drawn perpendicular to arc AB, $\widehat{AC}$ $= \widehat{CB}$ and $\angle APC = \angle BPC$. By solving one of the right spherical triangles we can obtain the required parts of the isosceles triangle.

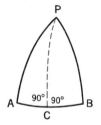

EXERCISES [A]

Solve the following isosceles spherical triangles:

1. $A = B = 80°$
$\quad C = 110°$

2. $A = C = 72° 10'$
$\quad b = 98° 16'$

3. $B = C = 56° 56'$
$\quad b = 82° 12'$

4. $a = b = c = 70° 36'$

5. $a = b = 83° 12' 50''$
$\quad c = 42° 24' 10''$

6. $a = b = 72° 18' 15''$
$\quad A = 57° 19' 20''$

7. $a = b = 116° 50' 25''$
$\quad C = 91° 10' 30''$

8. $A = B = C = 120° 8' 40''$.

Quadrantal Triangles [A]

A *quadrantal triangle* is a spherical triangle having one side equal to a quadrant, or 90°. The polar triangle of a quadrantal triangle is a right spherical triangle. The polar right triangle is solved to obtain the required parts of the quadrantal triangle. The method of solution will be illustrated by an example.

EXAMPLE. Solve the spherical $\triangle\,ABC$, given $c\,=\,$ 90°, $a\,=\,$ 72° 18′, $b\,=\,$ 63° 12′.

SOLUTION. Draw polar $\triangle\,A'B'C'$ of $\triangle\,ABC$.

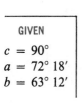

GIVEN
$c\,=\,$ 90°
$a\,=\,$ 72° 18′
$b\,=\,$ 63° 12′

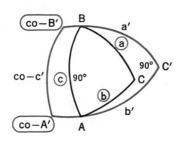

REQUIRED
$A\,=\,$ 70° 5′, or 70°
$B\,=\,$ 61° 45′, or 62°
$C\,=\,$ 99° 17′, or 99°

Then

$$C' = 180° - c = 90°$$
$$B' = 180° - b = 116° 48'$$
$$A' = 180° - a = 107° 42'$$

We now solve the right triangle $A'B'C'$.

1. *To find a′.* $\qquad\qquad\qquad \cos A' = \sin B' \cos a'$

Solving for $\cos a'$, $\qquad\qquad \cos a' = \dfrac{\cos A'}{\sin B'}$

Substituting, $\qquad\qquad\qquad \cos a' = \dfrac{\cos 107° 42'}{\sin 116° 48'}$

$$\begin{array}{r} {}^-\log \cos 107° 42' = 19.48292 - 20 \\ {}^+\log \sin\ 116° 48' = \ \ 9.95065 - 10 \\ \hline {}^-\log \cos a' = \ \ 9.53227 - 10 \end{array}$$

$$a' = 180° - 70° 5' = 109° 55'$$

This value satisfies the first law of quadrants.

2. *To find b′.* $\qquad\qquad\qquad \cos B' = \cos b' \sin A'$

Solving for $\cos b'$, $\qquad\qquad \cos b' = \dfrac{\cos B'}{\sin A'}$

(cont. on next page)

Substituting, $\qquad \cos b' = \dfrac{\cos 116° 48'}{\sin 107° 42'}$

$$\begin{array}{rl} {}^-\log \cos 116° 48' = & 19.65406 - 20 \\ {}^+\log \sin\ 107° 42' = & \ \ 9.97894 - 10 \\ \hline {}^-\log \cos b' = & \ \ 9.67512 - 10 \end{array}$$

$$b' = 180° - 61° 45' = 118° 15'$$

This value of b' satisfies the first law of quadrants.

3. *To find c'.* $\qquad\qquad \cos c' = \text{ctn } B'\ \text{ctn } A'.$

Substituting, $\qquad\qquad \cos c' = \text{ctn } 116° 48'\ \text{ctn } 107° 42'$

$$\begin{array}{rl} {}^-\log \text{ctn } 116° 48' = & 9.70341 - 10 \\ {}^-\log \text{ctn } 107° 42' = & 9.50398 - 10 \\ \hline {}^+\log \cos c' = & 9.20739 - 10 \end{array}$$

$$c' = 80° 43'$$

This value of c' satisfies the second law of quadrants.

4. *Logarithmic check.* $\qquad \cos c' = \cos a' \cos b'$

$$\begin{array}{rl} {}^-\log \cos a' = & 9.53227 - 10 \\ {}^-\log \cos b' = & 9.67512 - 10 \\ \hline {}^+\log \cos c' = & 9.20739 - 10 \end{array}$$

This value of log cos c' agrees with the value in (3).

Then $\qquad \begin{aligned} A &= 180° - a' = 180° - 109° 55' = 70° 5' \\ B &= 180° - b' = 180° - 118° 15' = 61° 45' \\ C &= 180° - c' = 180° - \ \ 80° 43' = 99° 17' \end{aligned}$

EXERCISES[A]

Solve the following quadrantal triangles:

1. $c = 90°$
   $A = 148° 44'$
   $b = 21° 14'$

2. $c = 90°$
   $a = 22° 11'$
   $B = 43° 52'$

3. $c = 90°$
   $a = 52° 6'$
   $b = 64° 50'$

4. $c = 90°$
   $B = 96° 40'$
   $A = 124° 25'$

5. $c = 90°$
   $a = 36° 20' 10''$
   $b = 108° 15' 15''$

6. $c = 90°$
   $B = 73° 16' 20''$
   $b = 79° 32' 45''$

7. Find the area of the triangles in exercises 1–4 if the radii of the spheres are 12 feet. See Ex. 14, page 310, for area formula.

CHAPTER XIV

THE GENERAL SPHERICAL TRIANGLE

Δ

The term *general spherical triangle* is commonly used in referring to oblique spherical triangles that are not isosceles or quadrantal. However, the formulas developed in this chapter are valid for all spherical triangles.

The Parts of a Spherical Triangle[A]

The three sides and the three angles of a spherical triangle are called its parts. The remaining parts of a spherical triangle can be found when any three are known. This gives rise to six possible cases as follows:

CASE   I. Given the three sides (S.S.S.).

CASE II. Given the three angles (A.A.A.).

CASE III. Given two sides and the included angle (S.A.S.).

CASE IV. Given two angles and the included side (A.S.A.).

CASE V. Given two sides and the angle opposite one of them (S.S.A.)

CASE VI. Given two angles and the side opposite one of them (A.A.S.)

Many different formulas may be derived to aid in the solution of the six cases. However, the derivations of some of the formulas are long and difficult, and the formulas themselves are not easy to remember. To save time and make the work simpler, we shall first develop two formulas and use them to solve and check solutions in Cases I–IV.

The Law of Sines[A]

Let ABC (page 317) be a spherical triangle. Draw $\overset{\frown}{CD} \perp \overset{\frown}{AB}$, forming the two right spherical triangles ADC and BDC.

Massachusetts Institute of Technol

Spherical Triangle in Architecture

This is a picture of the architect's model of the new auditorium at the Massachusetts Institute of Technology. The design is based on the shape of a spherical triangle whose area is one-eighth that of a sphere of the same radius. The spherical surface serves as the roof and part of the walls of the structure.

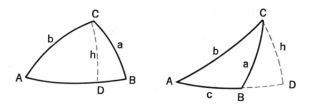

In the figure on the right, sin ABC = sin DBC. Then applying Napier's rules to right triangles ADC and BDC respectively, we have

$$\sin h = \sin b \sin A$$
$$\sin h = \sin a \sin B$$

Therefore $\sin a \sin B = \sin b \sin A$

or $\dfrac{\sin a}{\sin A} = \dfrac{\sin b}{\sin B}$

In like manner, $\dfrac{\sin b}{\sin B} = \dfrac{\sin c}{\sin C}$

Then $\dfrac{\sin a}{\sin A} = \dfrac{\sin b}{\sin B} = \dfrac{\sin c}{\sin C}$ [I]

Stated in words,

In any spherical triangle the sines of the sides are proportional to the sines of the opposite angles.

The Law of Cosines [A]

Let ABC be a spherical triangle. Draw $\overset{\frown}{CD} \perp \overset{\frown}{AB}$, forming rt. $\triangle ADC$ and BDC. Designate $\overset{\frown}{CD}$ by h and $\overset{\frown}{AD}$ by x.

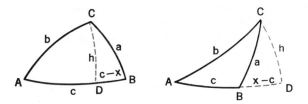

In either figure, cos $(c - x)$ = cos $(x - c)$. Applying Napier's rules to rt. $\triangle BDC$, we have

$$\cos a = \cos h \cos (c - x)$$

or $\cos a = \cos h \cos c \cos x + \cos h \sin c \sin x$ (1)

From rt. $\triangle ADC$, we have

$$\sin x = \tan h \operatorname{ctn} A, \tag{2}$$

$\cos b = \cos h \cos x$, or

$$\cos x = \frac{\cos b}{\cos h}, \tag{3}$$

and
$$\sin h = \sin b \sin A \tag{4}$$

Substituting (2) and (3) in (1), we obtain

$$\cos a = \cos h \cos c \cdot \frac{\cos b}{\cos h} + \cos h \sin c \tan h \operatorname{ctn} A,$$

or $\cos a = \cos b \cos c + \sin c \sin h \operatorname{ctn} A$ (5)

Substituting (4) in (5), we have

$$\cos a = \cos b \cos c + \sin c \sin b \sin A \operatorname{ctn} A,$$

or $\mathbf{\cos a = \cos b \cos c + \sin b \sin c \cos A}$ [II]

In like manner, by interchanging letters, we have

$\mathbf{\cos b = \cos a \cos c + \sin a \sin c \cos B,}$ [II]

and $\mathbf{\cos c = \cos a \cos b + \sin a \sin b \cos C.}$ [II]

These three formulas are known as the law of cosines for spherical triangles. Stated in words,

In any spherical triangle the cosine of any side is equal to the product of the cosines of the other two sides plus the product of the sines of these two sides by the cosine of their included angle.

Solution of Case I. [A]   *Given the three sides* (S.S.S.).

EXAMPLE. Solve $\triangle ABC$, given $a = 72° 12'$, $b = 105° 20'$, $c = 60° 36'$.

SOLUTION. The law of cosines is not readily adaptable to the use of logarithms but it saves time to use logarithms as much as possible in the computations. Since both natural and logarithmic functions will be used, it makes the work easier if we list these values at the beginning.

GIVEN	VALUES	
$a = 72° 12'$	$\cos a = .3057$	$^+\log \sin a = 9.97870 - 10$
$b = 105° 20'$	$\cos b = -.2644$	$^+\log \sin b = 9.98426 - 10$
$c = 60° 36'$	$\cos c = .4909$	$^+\log \sin c = 9.94012 - 10$
		$^+\log \cos a = 9.48529 - 10$
REQUIRED		$^-\log \cos b = 9.42232 - 10$
$A = 58° 47'$		$^+\log \cos c = 9.69100 - 10$
$B = 119° 59'$		
$C = 51° 29'$		

1. To find A. Solving the law of cosines for $\cos A$,

we have $$\cos A = \frac{\cos a - \cos b \cos c}{\sin b \sin c}$$

Let $x = \sin b \sin c$.

$^-\log \cos b = 9.42232 - 10$	$^+\log \sin b = 9.98426 - 10$
$^+\log \cos c = 9.69100 - 10$	$^+\log \sin c = 9.94012 - 10$
$^-\log \text{prod.} = 9.11332 - 10$	$^+\log x = 9.92438 - 10$

$$\text{product} = -.12981$$

Then $\cos A = \dfrac{.3057 + .12981}{x} = \dfrac{.43551}{x}$

$$
\begin{aligned}
^+\log .43551 &= 19.63900 - 20 \\
^+\log x &= 9.92438 - 10 \\
\hline
^+\log \cos A &= 9.71462 - 10
\end{aligned}
$$

$$A = 58° 47'$$

2. To find B. $$\cos B = \frac{\cos b - \cos a \cos c}{\sin a \sin c}$$

$^+\log \cos a = 9.48529 - 10$	$^+\log \sin a = 9.97870 - 10$
$^+\log \cos c = 9.69100 - 10$	$^+\log \sin c = 9.94012 - 10$
$^+\log \text{prod.} = 9.17629 - 10$	$^+\log x = 9.91882 - 10$

$$\text{product} = .15007$$

Then $\cos B = \dfrac{-.2644 - .15007}{x} = \dfrac{-.41447}{x}$

$$
\begin{aligned}
^-\log .41447 &= 19.61749 - 20 \\
^+\log x &= 9.91882 - 10 \\
\hline
^-\log \cos B &= 9.69867 - 10
\end{aligned}
$$

$$B = 180° - 60° 1' = 119° 59'$$

3. To find C. $$\cos C = \frac{\cos c - \cos a \cos b}{\sin a \sin b}$$

$^+\log \cos a = 9.48529 - 10$	$^+\log \sin a = 9.97870 - 10$
$^-\log \cos b = 9.42232 - 10$	$^+\log \sin b = 9.98426 - 10$
$^-\log \text{prod.} = 8.90761 - 10$	$^+\log x = 9.96296 - 10$

$$\text{product} = -.08084$$

Then $\cos C = \dfrac{.4909 + .08084}{x} = \dfrac{.57174}{x}$

$$\begin{aligned}
^+\log .57174 &= 19.75720 - 20 \\
^+\log x &= 9.96296 - 10 \\
\hline
^+\log \cos C &= 9.79424 - 10 \\
C &= 51° \, 29'
\end{aligned}$$

4. Checking by the law of sines,

$$\frac{\sin a}{\sin A} = \frac{\sin b}{\sin B} = \frac{\sin c}{\sin C}$$

$$\begin{array}{ll}
\log \sin a = 9.97870 - 10 & \qquad \log \sin b = 9.98426 - 10 \\
\underline{\log \sin A = 9.93207 - 10} & \qquad \underline{\log \sin B = 9.93760 - 10} \\
.04663 & \qquad .04666
\end{array}$$

$$\begin{aligned}
\log \sin c &= 9.94012 - 10 \\
\underline{\log \sin C} &= 9.89344 - 10 \\
&\,.04668
\end{aligned}$$

Since a 4-place table was used once in each computation the angles were given to the nearest minute. The check is valid if the logarithms do not differ by more than two in the fourth decimal place.

EXERCISES [A]

Solve the following spherical triangles:

1. $a = 56° \, 10'$
   $b = 52° \, 40'$
   $c = 93° \, 30'$

2. $a = 110° \, 15'$
   $b = 33° \, 20'$
   $c = 96° \, 50'$

3. $a = 54° \, 20'$
   $b = 96° \, 40'$
   $c = 122° \, 18'$

4. $a = 65° \, 15'$
   $b = 74° \, 25'$
   $c = 122° \, 10'$

5. $a = 75° \, 12'$
   $b = 58° \, 44'$
   $c = 106° \, 18'$

6. $a = 96° \, 54'$
   $b = 82° \, 6'$
   $c = 104° \, 36'$

Solution of Case II. [A]   *Given the three angles (A.A.A.).*

We can solve Case II by means of polar triangles and the law of cosines. First find the sides of the polar triangle from the given triangle. Second solve the polar triangle for its angles, using the law of cosines. Then find the sides of the given triangle from the angles of the polar triangle. Check the solution by the law of sines.

EXERCISES[A]

Solve the following spherical triangles:

1. $A = 130°$
   $B = 110°$
   $C = 85°$

2. $A = 61° 10'$
   $B = 88° 20'$
   $C = 48° 40'$

3. $A = 45° 15'$
   $B = 35° 30'$
   $C = 128° 20'$

4. $A = 98° 12'$
   $B = 124° 18'$
   $C = 72° 32'$

5. $A = 136° 4'$
   $B = 64° 14'$
   $C = 46° 29'$

6. $A = 98° 16'$
   $B = 82° 24'$
   $C = 38° 48'$

Solution of Case III. [A] *Given two sides and the included angle (S.A.S.).*

EXAMPLE. Solve spherical $\triangle ABC$, given $a = 76° 20'$, $b = 110° 18'$, and $C = 48° 52'$.

SOLUTION.

GIVEN		VALUES
$a = 76° 20'$	$\cos a = .2363$	$^+\log \cos a = 9.37341 - 10$
$b = 110° 18'$	$\cos b = -.3469$	$^-\log \cos b = 9.54025 - 10$
$C = 48° 52'$		$^+\log \cos C = 9.81810 - 10$
		$^+\log \sin a = 9.98753 - 10$
REQUIRED		$^+\log \sin b = 9.97215 - 10$
$c = 58° 50'$		
$A = 58° 47'$		
$B = 124° 21'$		

1. To find c. From the law of cosines,

$$\cos c = \cos a \cos b + \sin a \sin b \cos C.$$

$^+\log \cos a = 9.37341 - 10$
$^-\log \cos b = 9.54025 - 10$
$^-\overline{\log \text{ prod.}} = 8.91366 - 10$

   product $= -.08197$

$^+\log \sin a = 9.98753 - 10$
$^+\log \sin b = 9.97215 - 10$
$^+\log \cos C = 9.81810 - 10$
$^+\overline{\log \text{ prod.}} = 9.77778 - 10$

   product $= .59949$

Then $\cos c = -.08197 + .59949 = .51752$

             $\log \cos c = 9.71393 - 10$

                    $c = 58° 50'$

2. To find A.
$$\cos A = \frac{\cos a - \cos b \cos c}{\sin b \sin c}$$

$^-$log cos b = 9.54025 $-$ 10	$^+$log sin b = 9.97215 $-$ 10
$^+$log cos c = 9.71393 $-$ 10	$^+$log sin c = 9.93230 $-$ 10
$^-$log prod. = 9.25418 $-$ 10	$^+$log x = 9.90445 $-$ 10
product = $-$.17955	

Then $\cos A = \dfrac{.2363 + .17995}{x} = \dfrac{.41625}{x}$

$$
\begin{aligned}
^+\text{log } .41625 &= 19.61936 - 20 \\
^+\text{log } x &= \ \ 9.90445 - 10 \\
\hline
^+\text{log cos } A &= \ \ 9.71491 - 10
\end{aligned}
$$

$$A = 58° \, 45'$$

3. To find B.
$$\cos B = \frac{\cos b - \cos a \cos c}{\sin a \sin c}$$

$^+$log cos a = 9.37341 $-$ 10	$^+$log sin a = 9.98753 $-$ 10
$^+$log cos c = 9.71393 $-$ 10	$^+$log sin c = 9.93230 $-$ 10
$^+$log prod. = 9.08734 $-$ 10	$^+$log x = 9.91983 $-$ 10
product = .12228	

Then $\cos B = \dfrac{-.3469 - .12228}{x} = \dfrac{-.46918}{x}$

$$
\begin{aligned}
^-\text{log } .46918 &= 19.67134 - 20 \\
^+\text{log } x &= \ \ 9.91983 - 10 \\
\hline
^-\text{log cos } B &= \ \ 9.75151 - 10
\end{aligned}
$$

$$B = 180° - 55° \, 39' = 124° \, 21'$$

4. Checking by the law of sines,

log sin a = 9.98753 $-$ 10	log sin b = 9.97215 $-$ 10
log sin A = 9.93192 $-$ 10	log sin B = 9.91677 $-$ 10
.05561	.05538

$$
\begin{aligned}
\text{log sin } c &= 9.93230 - 10 \\
\text{log sin } C &= 9.87690 - 10 \\
\hline
&\ \ \ .05540
\end{aligned}
$$

The solution checks.

EXERCISES[A]

Solve the following spherical triangles:

1. $a = 122°\ 18'$
   $b = 88°\ 21'$
   $C = 100°\ 16'$

2. $b = 94°\ 18'$
   $c = 55°\ 6'$
   $A = 48°\ 30'$

3. $a = 68°\ 12'$
   $c = 135°\ 35'$
   $B = 76°\ 45'$

4. $a = 42°\ 5'$
   $b = 45°\ 15'$
   $C = 38°\ 40'$

5. $a = 77°\ 36'$
   $b = 110°\ 24'$
   $C = 47°\ 10'$

6. $b = 72°\ 58'$
   $c = 40°\ 45'$
   $A = 44°\ 32'$

Solution of Case IV.[A] *Given two angles and the included side (A.S.A.).*

Case IV is solved by means of polar triangles. First find two sides and the included angle of the polar triangle from the given triangle. Second, solve the polar triangle by Case III. Then find the required parts of the given triangle from the polar triangle.

EXERCISES[A]

Solve the following spherical triangles:

1. $A = 40°\ 15'$
   $B = 122°\ 40'$
   $c = 36°\ 10'$

2. $A = 127°\ 20'$
   $B = 105°\ 40'$
   $c = 124°\ 30'$

3. $B = 101°\ 20'$
   $C = 64°\ 30'$
   $a = 61°\ 10'$

4. $B = 128°\ 12'$
   $C = 32°\ 36'$
   $a = 41°\ 6'$

5. $A = 66°\ 30'$
   $C = 42°\ 12'$
   $b = 52°\ 50'$

6. $A = 140°\ 8'$
   $C = 71°\ 12'$
   $b = 133°\ 28'$

Solution of Case V.[B] *Given two sides and the angle opposite one of them (S.S.A.).*

Cases V and VI are the ambiguous cases of the general spherical triangle corrsponding to the ambiguous Case II of oblique plane triangles. There may be two, one, or no solutions.

To solve Case V we shall use the law of sines and two formulas selected from a group of formulas known as Napier's Analogies, which are given here without proof.

$$\frac{\tan \tfrac{1}{2} c}{\tan \tfrac{1}{2}(a - b)} = \frac{\sin \tfrac{1}{2}(A + B)}{\sin \tfrac{1}{2}(A - B)} \qquad \text{[III]}$$

$$\frac{\operatorname{ctn} \tfrac{1}{2} C}{\tan \tfrac{1}{2}(A - B)} = \frac{\sin \tfrac{1}{2}(a + b)}{\sin \tfrac{1}{2}(a - b)} \qquad \text{[IV]}$$

Two similar formulas can be written from each of Napier's Analogies by a proper change of letters.

We shall illustrate the method of solving Case V by an example.

EXAMPLE. Solve the spherical $\triangle ABC$, given $a = 56° 24'$, $b = 32° 36'$, $A = 102° 18'$.

SOLUTION.

We shall first solve for B by the law of sines. If log sin $B > 0$, there is no solution. If log sin $B = 0$, the triangle is right and there is one solution. If log sin $B < 0$, there may be one or two solutions; B is either an acute angle or its supplement or both. From solid geometry we know that if $A > B > C$, then $a > b > c$; and conversely. In the process of solving we can determine the number of solutions from this relation.

We begin by assuming two solutions and drawing a representative figure showing the two possible triangles ABC and $AB'C$.

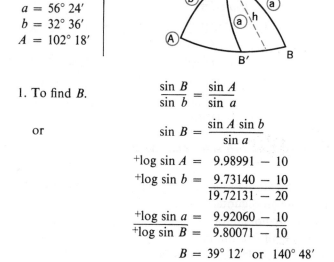

GIVEN
$a = 56° 24'$
$b = 32° 36'$
$A = 102° 18'$

REQUIRED
$B = 39° 12'$
$c = 41° 38'$
$C = 51° 12'$

1. To find B.

$$\frac{\sin B}{\sin b} = \frac{\sin A}{\sin a}$$

or

$$\sin B = \frac{\sin A \sin b}{\sin a}$$

$$
\begin{array}{ll}
{}^+\log \sin A = & 9.98991 - 10 \\
{}^+\log \sin b = & 9.73140 - 10 \\
\hline
& 19.72131 - 20 \\
{}^+\log \sin a = & 9.92060 - 10 \\
\hline
{}^+\log \sin B = & 9.80071 - 10
\end{array}
$$

$$B = 39° 12' \text{ or } 140° 48'$$

Since we have given $a > b$, we know that $A > B$. This relation is satisfied only when $B = 39° 12'$. Hence we know that there is only one solution.

2. To find c. From formula [III], page 323,

$$\tan \tfrac{1}{2} c = \frac{\tan \tfrac{1}{2}(a - b) \sin \tfrac{1}{2}(A + B)}{\sin \tfrac{1}{2}(A - B)}$$

$$a = 56° 24'$$
$$b = 32° 36'$$
$$a + b = 89°$$
$$a - b = 23° 48'$$
$$\tfrac{1}{2}(a + b) = 44° 30'$$
$$\tfrac{1}{2}(a - b) = 11° 54'$$

$$A = 102° 18'$$
$$B = 39° 12'$$
$$A + B = 141° 30'$$
$$A - B = 63° 6'$$
$$\tfrac{1}{2}(A + B) = 70° 45'$$
$$\tfrac{1}{2}(A - B) = 31° 33'$$

$$
\begin{aligned}
{}^+\log \tan \tfrac{1}{2}(a - b) &= 9.32373 - 10 \\
{}^+\log \sin \tfrac{1}{2}(A + B) &= 9.97501 - 10 \\
\hline
&\ 19.29874 - 20 \\
{}^+\log \sin \tfrac{1}{2}(A - B) &= 9.71870 - 10 \\
\hline
{}^+\log \tan \tfrac{1}{2} c &= 9.58004 - 10 \\
\tfrac{1}{2} c &= 20° 49.1' \\
c &= 41° 38'
\end{aligned}
$$

3. To find C. From formula [IV], page 323,

$$\operatorname{ctn} \tfrac{1}{2} C = \frac{\tan \tfrac{1}{2}(A - B) \sin \tfrac{1}{2}(a + b)}{\sin \tfrac{1}{2}(a - b)}$$

$$
\begin{aligned}
{}^+\log \tan \tfrac{1}{2}(A - B) &= 9.78817 - 10 \\
{}^+\log \sin \tfrac{1}{2}(a + b) &= 9.84566 - 10 \\
\hline
&\ 9.63383 - 10 \\
{}^+\log \sin \tfrac{1}{2}(a - b) &= 9.31430 - 10 \\
\hline
\log \operatorname{ctn} \tfrac{1}{2} C &= 0.31953 \\
\tfrac{1}{2} C &= 25° 36.1' \\
C &= 51° 12'
\end{aligned}
$$

4. Check by the law of sines.

We use $\dfrac{\sin a}{\sin A} = \dfrac{\sin c}{\sin C}$, since a and A were given and c and C were required.

$$
\begin{aligned}
\log \sin a &= 19.92060 - 20 \\
\log \sin A &= 9.98991 - 10 \\
\hline
&\ 9.93069 - 10
\end{aligned}
$$

$$
\begin{aligned}
\log \sin c &= 19.82240 - 20 \\
\log \sin C &= 9.89173 - 10 \\
\hline
&\ 9.93067 - 10
\end{aligned}
$$

Solution of Case VI. [8] *Given two angles and the side opposite one of them (A.A.S.).*

The side opposite one given angle is known. The method of solution is to find first the side opposite the other given angle by the law of sines. Then find the third side and the third angle by Napier's Analogies. Be on the alert for two, one, or no solutions. Check by the law of sines, using given data for one ratio and required data for the other ratio.

EXERCISES [B]

Solve the following spherical triangles:

1. $a = 44° 10'$
$b = 18° 20'$
$A = 64° 30'$

2. $a = 30° 40'$
$b = 32° 30'$
$A = 88° 2'$

3. $b = 80° 5'$
$c = 82° 55'$
$B = 85° 12'$

4. $B = 145° 9'$
$C = 72° 12'$
$b = 160° 21'$

5. $a = 148° 12'$
$c = 140° 33'$
$A = 152° 45'$

6. $A = 69° 50'$
$B = 120° 17'$
$b = 81° 11'$

7. $B = 116° 58'$
$C = 46° 4'$
$b = 75° 31'$

8. $A = 47° 15'$
$B = 80° 30'$
$b = 55° 18'$

Summary of Methods of Solving General Spherical Triangles

CASE I (S.S.S.).   *Law of cosines.*

CASE II (A.A.A.).   *Solve polar triangle by law of cosines.*

CASE III (S.A.S.). *Law of cosines.*

CASE IV (A.S.A.).   *Solve polar triangle by law of cosines.*

CASE V (S.S.A.).   *Law of sines and Napier's Analogies.*

CASE VI (A.A.S.).   *Law of sines and Napier's Analogies.*

CHECK.   *Law of sines.*

Area of a Spherical Triangle [A]

The area of a spherical triangle is found by the well-known formula from solid geometry

$$S = \frac{\pi r^2 E}{180},$$

where $E = (A + B + C) - 180°$.

E is called the spherical excess of the triangle. When E is in radians the formula becomes

$$S = r^2 E.$$

Using $E = (A + B + C) - 180°$ enables us to find the area when the three angles are known.

Other Formulas for E [B]

The spherical excess can also be found by two other formulas stated here without proof.

a. Lhuilier's Formula.

$\tan^2 \frac{1}{4} E = \tan \frac{1}{2} s \tan \frac{1}{2}(s - a) \tan \frac{1}{2}(s - b) \tan \frac{1}{2}(s - c)$, where $s = \frac{1}{2}(a + b + c)$, gives the value of E when three sides are known.

b. $\tan \frac{1}{2} E = \dfrac{\tan \frac{1}{2} a \tan \frac{1}{2} b \sin C}{1 + \tan \frac{1}{2} a \tan \frac{1}{2} b \cos C}$ gives the value of E when two sides and the included angle are known.

EXERCISES

A

Find the area in square feet of the following spherical triangles:

1. $A = 130°$	2. $A = 61° 10'$	3. $A = 45° 15'$
$B = 110°$	$B = 88° 20'$	$B = 35° 30'$
$C = 85°$	$C = 48° 40'$	$C = 128° 20'$
$r = 10$ ft.	$r = 12$ ft.	$r = 60$ ft.

B

4. $a = 56° 10'$	6. $a = 54° 20'$	8. $b = 94° 18'$
$b = 52° 40'$	$b = 96° 40'$	$c = 55° 6'$
$c = 93° 30'$	$c = 122° 18'$	$A = 48° 30'$
$r = 15$ ft.	$r = 60$ ft.	$r = 72$ ft.
5. $a = 110° 15'$	7. $a = 122° 18'$	9. $a = 68° 12'$
$b = 33° 20'$	$b = 88° 21'$	$c = 135° 35'$
$c = 96° 50'$	$C = 100° 16'$	$B = 76° 45'$
$r = 48$ ft.	$r = 90$ ft.	$r = 20$ ft.

Ships Sail on Great-Circle Routes
The *Queen Mary*, passing Lower Manhattan, is outward bound

THE TERRESTRIAL TRIANGLE

Δ

One of the main applications of spherical trigonometry pertains to marine and air navigation over large areas. In finding the distance between two points and the direction of one point from another, we assume that the earth is a sphere with a radius of 3960 miles.

The Terrestrial Sphere [A]

We shall first define some terms that must be known in order to solve problems in navigation. References are to the figure on this page.

1. The *axis* of the earth is the diameter *NS* about which the earth rotates. *N* and *S* denote the north and south poles respectively.

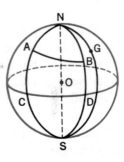

2. The *equator* is the great-circle section of the earth made by a plane perpendicular to the axis of the earth at its center.

3. *Meridians* are great circles passing through the poles. They are perpendicular to the equator. The meridian (denoted by *G*), passing through Greenwich, England, is the *prime*, or principal, meridian.

4. The *latitude* of any point is the number of degrees it lies north or south of the equator.

5. The *longitude* of any point is the number of degrees it lies east or west of the prime meridian from 0° to 180°.

Bearing and Track [A]

The bearing of any point *B* from *A* is the angle between the meridian through *A* and the great-circle arc through *A* and *B*. This angle may be measured in different ways. The usual method and the one we shall use is to measure the angle clockwise from NA to AB. The bearing of AB may also be given as N (so many degrees) E or S (so many degrees) E.

In navigation the arc AB is referred to as the *great-circle track*. The term *course* means the angle between the meridian and the center line of the vessel or plane. On account of wind conditions the course is the direction a plane must be "headed" in order to follow the track.

Nautical Mile [A]

The *nautical* mile is the length of an arc of one minute on a great circle of the earth. It is the standard unit for measuring distances in marine and air navigation. The international standard for the nautical mile is 6080 feet. Since the statute or land mile is 5280 feet, one nautical mile is 1.1515 statute miles.

The Terrestrial Triangle [A]

In the figure, the terrestrial triangle ANB is formed by the great-circle arc AB and the arcs AN and BN of the meridians through A and B, respectively. If the latitude and longitudes of A and B are known, then in $\triangle ANB$, $\widehat{AN} = 90° -$ (the latitude of A), $\widehat{BN} = 90° -$ (the latitude of B), $\angle ANB = \widehat{CD} =$ the difference of the longitudes of A and B. (Longitude west is usually considered as positive and longitude east as negative.) This gives us two sides and the included angle of triangle ANB, which is Case III in the solution of general spherical triangles. $\widehat{AB}$ can be found by the law of cosines, and $\angle NAB$ by the law of sines.

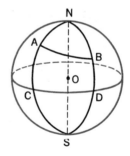

In case a point is south of the equator, 90° is added to the latitude of the point to find a side of the triangle. Likewise, if one point is east longitude and the other point is west longitude, we add the two longitudes to find $\angle NAB$. If the sum of the longitudes is greater than 180°, the sum is subtracted from 360°.

EXAMPLE. Find the length of the great-circle track and its bearing from Cherbourg (49° 40′ N, 1° 39′ W) to New York City (40° 46′ N, 73° 51′ W).

SOLUTION. In the terrestrial triangle ABN, A represents Cherbourg, and B New York City.

GIVEN		REQUIRED
$\widehat{AN} = b = 90° - 49° 40' = 40° 20'$		$n = 2978$ miles
$\widehat{BN} = a = 90° - 40° 46' = 49° 14'$		$B = 228° 45'$
$N = 73° 51' - 1° 39' = 72° 12'$		

1. To find n. $\cos n = \cos a \cos b + \sin a \sin b \cos N$.

$^+\log \cos a = 9.81490 - 10$ $^+\log \sin a = 9.87931 - 10$

$^+\log \cos b = 9.88212 - 10$ $^+\log \sin b = 9.81106 - 10$

$^+\log$ prod. $= 9.69702 - 10$ $^+\log \cos N = 9.48529 - 10$

  product $= .49776$ $\log$ prod. $= 9.17566 - 10$

              product $= .14985$

Then $\cos n = .49776 + .14985 = .64761$

        $\log \cos n = 9.81132 - 10$

            $n = 49° 38' = 2978' = 2978$ nautical miles.

The length of the great-circle track is 2978 nautical miles.

2. To find A. We use the law of sines. We can usually tell from a map whether the angle is acute or obtuse.

$$\frac{\sin A}{\sin a} = \frac{\sin N}{\sin n}$$

or $$\sin A = \frac{\sin a \sin N}{\sin n}$$

  $\log \sin a = \quad 9.87931 - 10$

  $\log \sin N = \quad 9.97870 - 10$

              $19.85801 - 20$

  $\log \sin n = \quad 9.88191 - 10$

  $\overline{\log \sin A} = \quad 9.97610 - 10$

        $A = 71° 10'. \quad 360° - 71° 10' = 289° 50'$

The bearing is $289° 50'$. The bearing may also be given as N $71° 10'$ W.

3. Check. By Napier's Analogies,

$$\frac{\tan \frac{1}{2}(n - a)}{\tan \frac{1}{2} b} = \frac{\sin \frac{1}{2}(N - A)}{\sin \frac{1}{2}(N + A)}$$

$n - a = 49° 38' - 49° 14' = 24'$	$N - A = 72° 12' - 71° 10' = 1° 2'$
$\frac{1}{2}(n - a) = 12'$	$\frac{1}{2}(N - A) = 31'$
$b = 40° 20'$	$N + A = 72° 12' + 71° 10' = 143° 22'$
$\frac{1}{2}b = 20° 10'$	$\frac{1}{2}(N + A) = 71° 41'$
$\log \tan \frac{1}{2}(n - a) = 17.54291 - 20$	$\log \sin \frac{1}{2}(N - A) = 17.95508 - 20$
$\log \tan \frac{1}{2}b = \underline{9.56498 - 10}$	$\log \sin \frac{1}{2}(N + A) = \underline{9.97742 - 10}$
$7.97793 - 10$	$7.97766 - 10$

The check differs by 2.7 in the fourth decimal place, which is sufficiently accurate considering the small angles involved.

EXERCISES [A]

Draw a representative figure for each exercise.

1. Find the length of the great-circle track from the Brooklyn Navy Yard (40° 42′ N, 73° 59′ W), to the point where the prime meridian crosses the equator.

2. Find the length and the initial bearing of the great-circle track from Pearl Harbor (21° 27′ N, 157° 57′ W) to San Francisco (37° 32′ N, 122° 13′ W).

3. A ship sails from Boston (42° 20′ N, 70° 53′ W) to Lisbon (38° 40′ N, 9° 18′ W). Find the distance of the great-circle track. Also find the bearing of the track when leaving Boston and when approaching Lisbon.

4. Find the length of the shortest air route between Cape Town (33° 56′ S, 18° 28′ E) and Dakar (14° 40′ N, 17° 25′ W). What is the bearing of this track as the plane leaves Cape Town.

5. Find the shortest distance between Greenwich (51° 29′ N) and New York City (40° 46′ N, 73° 51′ W). Also find the initial direction of the track.

6. What is the shortest distance from Moscow (55° 43′ N, 37° 34′ E) to London (51° 31′ N, 0° 6′ W)? Find the initial bearing of the track.

7. Find the shortest distance from Chicago (41° 50′ N, 87° 35′ W) to Paris (48° 50′ N, 2° 20′ E).

8. Find the shortest distance from New York (40° 46′ N, 73° 51′ W) to Moscow (55° 43′ N, 38° 34′ E).

9. Find the distance and initial bearing of the shortest route from Rio de Janeiro (22° 54′ S, 43° 10′ W) to Sydney (32° 52′ S, 151° 12′ E).

10. An airplane flies the great-circle track from Tokyo (35° 39′ N, 139° 45′ E) to Wellington (41° 17′ S, 174° 47′ E).

   a. Find the length and initial direction of the great-circle track.
   b. How far from Tokyo does the plane cross the equator and what is the longitude at the point of crossing?
   c. What is the bearing of the great-circle track as the plane crosses the equator?

11. A plane leaves Chicago (41° 50′ N, 87° 36′ W) on a great-circle track with an initial bearing of 63° 30′. What is the latitude and longitude of the plane after traveling 1000 miles (nautical)?

12. If you were to make a nonstop flight from the city of Dayton, Ohio (39° 46′ N, 84° 12′ W) to Tokyo (35° 39′ N, 139° 45′ E) by the shortest route, in which direction would you start your flight?

13. A plane leaves Los Angeles (34° 03′ N, 118° 14′ W) on a great-circle track with an initial bearing of 65°. Find the latitude and longitude of the plane when it has flown 1000 nautical miles.

SUMMARY OF IMPORTANT FORMULAS

Δ

Plane Trigonometry

I. Functions of a single angle

$$\sin \theta \csc \theta = 1, \text{ or } \sin \theta = \frac{1}{\csc \theta}, \text{ or } \csc \theta = \frac{1}{\sin \theta} \qquad [1]$$

$$\cos \theta \sec \theta = 1, \text{ or } \cos \theta = \frac{1}{\sec \theta}, \text{ or } \sec \theta = \frac{1}{\cos \theta} \qquad [2]$$

$$\tan \theta \operatorname{ctn} \theta = 1, \text{ or } \tan \theta = \frac{1}{\operatorname{ctn} \theta}, \text{ or } \operatorname{ctn} \theta = \frac{1}{\tan \theta} \qquad [3]$$

$$\tan \theta = \frac{\sin \theta}{\cos \theta} \qquad \operatorname{ctn} \theta = \frac{\cos \theta}{\sin \theta} \qquad [4, 5]$$

$$\sin^2 \theta + \cos^2 \theta = 1 \qquad [6]$$

$$1 + \tan^2 \theta = \sec^2 \theta \qquad [7]$$

$$1 + \operatorname{ctn}^2 \theta = \csc^2 \theta \qquad [8]$$

II. Functions of $\theta \pm \phi$

$$\sin (\theta + \phi) = \sin \theta \cos \phi + \cos \theta \sin \phi \qquad [9]$$

$$\cos (\theta + \phi) = \cos \theta \cos \phi - \sin \theta \sin \phi \qquad [10]$$

$$\tan (\theta + \phi) = \frac{\tan \theta + \tan \phi}{1 - \tan \theta \tan \phi} \qquad [11]$$

$$\sin (\theta - \phi) = \sin \theta \cos \phi - \cos \theta \sin \phi \qquad [12]$$

$$\cos (\theta - \phi) = \cos \theta \cos \phi + \sin \theta \sin \phi \qquad [13]$$

$$\tan (\theta - \phi) = \frac{\tan \theta - \tan \phi}{1 + \tan \theta \tan \phi} \qquad [14]$$

III. Functions of Twice an Angle

$$\sin 2\theta = 2 \sin \theta \cos \theta \qquad [15]$$

$$\cos 2\,\theta = \cos^2 \theta - \sin^2 \theta = 2\cos^2 \theta - 1 = 1 - 2\sin^2 \theta \quad [16]$$

$$\tan 2\,\theta = \frac{2\tan \theta}{1 - \tan^2 \theta} \qquad [17]$$

IV. Functions of Half an Angle

$$\sin \tfrac{1}{2}\theta = \pm \sqrt{\frac{1 - \cos \theta}{2}} \qquad \cos \tfrac{1}{2}\theta = \pm \sqrt{\frac{1 + \cos \theta}{2}} \qquad [18, 19]$$

$$\tan \tfrac{1}{2}\theta = \pm \sqrt{\frac{1 - \cos \theta}{1 + \cos \theta}} = \frac{\sin \theta}{1 + \cos \theta} = \frac{1 - \cos \theta}{\sin \theta} \qquad [20]$$

V. Sums and Differences of Functions

$$\sin (A + B) + \sin (A - B) = 2 \sin A \cos B \qquad [21]$$
$$\sin (A + B) - \sin (A - B) = 2 \cos A \sin B \qquad [22]$$
$$\cos (A + B) + \cos (A - B) = 2 \cos A \cos B \qquad [23]$$
$$\cos (A + B) - \cos (A - B) = -2 \sin A \sin B \qquad [24]$$
$$\sin \theta + \sin \phi = 2 \sin \tfrac{1}{2}(\theta + \phi) \cos \tfrac{1}{2}(\theta - \phi) \qquad [25]$$
$$\sin \theta - \sin \phi = 2 \cos \tfrac{1}{2}(\theta + \phi) \sin \tfrac{1}{2}(\theta - \phi) \qquad [26]$$
$$\cos \theta + \cos \phi = 2 \cos \tfrac{1}{2}(\theta + \phi) \cos \tfrac{1}{2}(\theta - \phi) \qquad [27]$$
$$\cos \theta - \cos \phi = -2 \sin \tfrac{1}{2}(\theta + \phi) \sin \tfrac{1}{2}(\theta - \phi) \qquad [28]$$

VI. Triangle Formulas

Law of Sines

$$\frac{a}{\sin A} = \frac{b}{\sin B} = \frac{c}{\sin C}$$

Law of Cosines

$$a^2 = b^2 + c^2 - 2\,bc \cos A*$$

Law of Tangents

$$\frac{a - b}{a + b} = \frac{\tan \tfrac{1}{2}(A - B)*}{\tan \tfrac{1}{2}(A + B)}$$

Half-Angle Formulas

$$\tan \tfrac{1}{2} A = \frac{r}{s - a}{}^*$$

$$s = \tfrac{1}{2}(a + b + c),\ r = \sqrt{\frac{(s - a)(s - b)(s - c)}{s}}$$

* Here and in the rest of the formulas, an asterisk is used when two other formulas may be obtained by changing the letters in cyclic order.

Mollweide's Equations

$$\frac{a + b}{c} = \frac{\cos \frac{1}{2}(A - B)}{\sin \frac{1}{2} C}$$

$$\frac{a - b}{c} = \frac{\sin \frac{1}{2}(A - B)}{\cos \frac{1}{2} C}$$

VII. *Areas*

Triangles. $\quad K = \frac{1}{2} hb \qquad K = \frac{1}{2} bc \sin A* \qquad K = rs$

$$K = \frac{abc}{4R} \qquad K = \sqrt{s (s - a)(s - b)(s - c)}$$

Sectors. $\quad K = \frac{1}{2} r^2 \theta$

Segments. $\quad K = \frac{1}{2} r^2 (\theta - \sin \theta)$

VIII. *Angular Measure*

Radian. $\quad \pi$ radians $= 180° \qquad s = r \theta$ (arc of circle with radius r)

$$1 \text{ radian} = \frac{180°}{\pi} \qquad 1° = \frac{\pi}{180} \text{ radian}$$

Mil. $\quad 1 \cancel{m} = \frac{9°}{160} \qquad 1° = \frac{160}{9} \cancel{m} \quad 1 \text{ radian} = 1000 \cancel{m}$

IX. *Complex Numbers*

$$x + yi = r (\cos \theta + i \sin \theta)$$

$$r^n (\cos \theta + i \sin \theta)^n = r^n (\cos n \theta + i \sin n \theta)$$

X. *Exponential Functions*

$$e^{i\theta} = \cos \theta + i \sin \theta \qquad\qquad e^{-i\theta} = \cos \theta - i \sin \theta$$

$$\sin \theta = \frac{e^{i\theta} - e^{-i\theta}}{2i} \qquad\qquad \cos \theta = \frac{e^{i\theta} + e^{-i\theta}}{2}$$

XI. *Hyperbolic Functions*

$$\sinh x = \frac{e^x - e^{-x}}{2} \qquad\qquad \cosh x = \frac{e^x + e^{-x}}{2}$$

Spherical Trigonometry

I. *Polar Triangles*

$$A + a' = 180° = A' + a*$$

II. *Right Spherical Triangles*

Napier's Rules

1. The sine of any middle part is equal to the product of the tangents of the adjacent parts.

2. The sine of any middle part is equal to the product of the cosines of the opposite parts.

III. *General Spherical Triangles*

Law of Sines

$$\frac{\sin a}{\sin A} = \frac{\sin b}{\sin B} = \frac{\sin c}{\sin C}$$

Law of Cosines

$$\cos a = \cos b \cos c + \sin b \sin c \cos A*$$

Napier's Analogies

$$\frac{\tan \frac{1}{2} c}{\tan \frac{1}{2}(a - b)} = \frac{\sin \frac{1}{2}(A + B)*}{\sin \frac{1}{2}(A - B)}$$

$$\frac{\operatorname{ctn} \frac{1}{2} C}{\tan \frac{1}{2}(A - B)} = \frac{\sin \frac{1}{2}(a + b)*}{\sin \frac{1}{2}(a - b)}$$

Area

$$S = \frac{\pi r^2 E}{180} \qquad E = (A + B + C) - 180°$$

TABLES

Δ

1

TABLE I

COMMON LOGARITHMS OF NUMBERS

100–150

N	0	1	2	3	4	5	6	7	8	9
100	00 000	00 043	00 087	00 130	00 173	00 217	00 260	00 303	00 346	00 389
101	432	475	518	561	604	647	689	732	775	817
102	860	903	945	988	01 030	01 072	01 115	01 157	01 199	01 242
103	01 284	01 326	01 368	01 410	452	494	536	578	620	662
104	703	745	787	828	870	912	953	995	02 036	02 078
105	02 119	02 160	02 202	02 243	02 284	02 325	02 366	02 407	02 449	02 490
106	531	572	612	653	694	735	776	816	857	898
107	938	979	03 019	03 060	03 100	03 141	03 181	03 222	03 262	03 302
108	03 342	03 383	423	463	503	543	583	623	663	703
109	743	782	822	862	902	941	981	04 021	04 060	04 100
110	04 139	04 179	04 218	04 258	04 297	04 336	04 376	04 415	04 454	04 493
111	532	571	610	650	689	727	766	805	844	883
112	922	961	999	05 038	05 077	05 115	05 154	05 192	05 231	05 269
113	05 308	05 346	05 385	423	461	500	538	576	614	652
114	690	729	767	805	843	881	918	956	994	06 032
115	06 070	06 108	06 145	06 183	06 221	06 258	06 296	06 333	06 371	06 408
116	446	483	521	558	595	633	670	707	744	781
117	819	856	893	930	967	07 004	07 041	07 078	07 115	07 151
118	07 188	07 225	07 262	07 298	07 335	372	408	445	482	518
119	555	591	628	664	700	737	773	809	846	882
120	07 918	07 954	07 990	08 027	08 063	08 099	08 135	08 171	08 207	08 243
121	08 279	08 314	08 350	386	422	458	493	529	565	600
122	636	672	707	743	778	814	849	884	920	955
123	991	09 026	09 061	09 096	09 132	09 167	09 202	09 237	09 272	09 307
124	09 342	377	412	447	482	517	552	587	621	656
125	09 691	09 726	09 760	09 795	09 830	09 864	09 899	09 934	09 968	10 003
126	10 037	10 072	10 106	10 140	10 175	10 209	10 243	10 278	10 312	346
127	380	415	449	483	517	551	585	619	653	687
128	721	755	789	823	857	890	924	958	992	11 025
129	11 059	11 093	11 126	11 160	11 193	11 227	11 261	11 294	11 327	361
130	11 394	11 428	11 461	11 494	11 528	11 561	11 594	11 628	11 661	11 694
131	727	760	793	826	860	893	926	959	992	12 024
132	12 057	12 090	12 123	12 156	12 189	12 222	12 254	12 287	12 320	352
133	385	418	450	483	516	548	581	613	646	678
134	710	743	775	808	840	872	905	937	969	13 001
135	13 033	13 066	13 098	13 130	13 162	13 194	13 226	13 258	13 290	13 322
136	354	386	418	450	481	513	545	577	609	640
137	672	704	735	767	799	830	862	893	925	956
138	988	14 019	14 051	14 082	14 114	14 145	14 176	14 208	14 239	14 270
139	14 301	333	364	395	426	457	489	520	551	582
140	14 613	14 644	14 675	14 706	14 737	14 768	14 799	14 829	14 860	14 891
141	922	953	983	15 014	15 045	15 076	15 106	15 137	15 168	15 198
142	15 229	15 259	15 290	320	351	381	412	442	473	503
143	534	564	594	625	655	685	715	746	776	806
144	836	866	897	927	957	987	16 017	16 047	16 077	16 107
145	16 137	16 167	16 197	16 227	16 256	16 286	16 316	16 346	16 376	16 406
146	435	465	495	524	554	584	613	643	673	702
147	732	761	791	820	850	879	909	938	967	997
148	17 026	17 056	17 085	17 114	17 143	17 173	17 202	17 231	17 260	17 289
149	319	348	377	406	435	464	493	522	551	580
150	17 609	17 638	17 667	17 696	17 725	17 754	17 782	17 811	17 840	17 869
N	0	1	2	3	4	5	6	7	8	9

150–200

N	0	1	2	3	4	5	6	7	8	9
150	17 609	17 638	17 667	17 696	17 725	17 754	17 782	17 811	17 840	17 869
151	898	926	955	984	18 013	18 041	18 070	18 099	18 127	18 156
152	18 184	18 213	18 241	18 270	298	327	355	384	412	441
153	469	498	526	554	583	611	639	667	696	724
154	752	780	808	837	865	893	921	949	977	19 005
155	19 033	19 061	19 089	19 117	19 145	19 173	19 201	19 229	19 257	19 285
156	312	340	368	396	424	451	479	507	535	562
157	590	618	645	673	700	728	756	783	811	838
158	866	893	921	948	976	20 003	20 030	20 058	20 085	20 112
159	20 140	20 167	20 194	20 222	20 249	276	303	330	358	385
160	20 412	20 439	20 466	20 493	20 520	20 548	20 575	20 602	20 629	20 656
161	683	710	737	763	790	817	844	871	898	925
162	952	978	21 005	21 032	21 059	21 085	21 112	21 139	21 165	21 192
163	21 219	21 245	272	299	325	352	378	405	431	458
164	484	511	537	564	590	617	643	669	696	722
165	21 748	21 775	21 801	21 827	21 854	21 880	21 906	21 932	21 958	21 985
166	22 011	22 037	22 063	22 089	22 115	22 141	22 167	22 194	22 220	22 246
167	272	298	324	350	376	401	427	453	479	505
168	531	557	583	608	634	660	686	712	737	763
169	789	814	840	866	891	917	943	968	994	23 019
170	23 045	23 070	23 096	23 121	23 147	23 172	23 198	23 223	23 249	23 274
171	300	325	350	376	401	426	452	477	502	528
172	553	578	603	629	654	679	704	729	754	779
173	805	830	855	880	905	930	955	980	24 005	24 030
174	24 055	24 080	24 105	24 130	24 155	24 180	24 204	24 229	254	279
175	24 304	24 329	24 353	24 378	24 403	24 428	24 452	24 477	24 502	24 527
176	551	576	601	625	650	674	699	724	748	773
177	797	822	846	871	895	920	944	969	993	25 018
178	25 042	25 066	25 091	25 115	25 139	25 164	25 188	25 212	25 237	261
179	285	310	334	358	382	406	431	455	479	503
180	25 527	25 551	25 575	25 600	25 624	25 648	25 672	25 696	25 720	25 744
181	768	792	816	840	864	888	912	935	959	983
182	26 007	26 031	26 055	26 079	26 102	26 126	26 150	26 174	26 198	26 221
183	245	269	293	316	340	364	387	411	435	458
184	482	505	529	553	576	600	623	647	670	694
185	26 717	26 741	26 764	26 788	26 811	26 834	26 858	26 881	26 905	26 928
186	951	975	998	27 021	27 045	27 068	27 091	27 114	27 138	27 161
187	27 184	27 207	27 231	254	277	300	323	346	370	393
188	416	439	462	485	508	531	554	577	600	623
189	646	669	692	715	738	761	784	807	830	852
190	27 875	27 898	27 921	27 944	27 967	27 989	28 012	28 035	28 058	28 081
191	28 103	28 126	28 149	28 171	28 194	28 217	240	262	285	307
192	330	353	375	398	421	443	466	488	511	533
193	556	578	601	623	646	668	691	713	735	758
194	780	803	825	847	870	892	914	937	959	981
195	29 003	29 026	29 048	29 070	29 092	29 115	29 137	29 159	29 181	29 203
196	226	248	270	292	314	336	358	380	403	425
197	447	469	491	513	535	557	579	601	623	645
198	667	688	710	732	754	776	798	820	842	863
199	885	907	929	951	973	994	30 016	30 038	30 060	30 081
200	30 103	30 125	30 146	30 168	30 190	30 211	30 233	30 255	30 276	30 298
N	0	1	2	3	4	5	6	7	8	9

COMMON LOGARITHMS

200–250

N	0	1	2	3	4	5	6	7	8	9
200	30 103	30 125	30 146	30 168	30 190	30 211	30 233	30 255	30 276	30 298
201	320	341	363	384	406	428	449	471	492	514
202	535	557	578	600	621	643	664	685	707	728
203	750	771	792	814	835	856	878	899	920	942
204	963	984	31 006	31 027	31 048	31 069	31 091	31 112	31 133	31 154
205	31 175	31 197	31 218	31 239	31 260	31 281	31 302	31 323	31 345	31 366
206	387	408	429	450	471	492	513	534	555	576
207	597	618	639	660	681	702	723	744	765	785
208	806	827	848	869	890	911	931	952	973	994
209	32 015	32 035	32 056	32 077	32 098	32 118	32 139	32 160	32 181	32 201
210	32 222	32 243	32 263	32 284	32 305	32 325	32 346	32 366	32 387	32 408
211	428	449	469	490	510	531	552	572	593	613
212	634	654	675	695	715	736	756	777	797	818
213	838	858	879	899	919	940	960	980	33 001	33 021
214	33 041	33 062	33 082	33 102	33 122	33 143	33 163	33 183	203	224
215	33 244	33 264	33 284	33 304	33 325	33 345	33 365	33 385	33 405	33 425
216	445	465	486	506	526	546	566	586	606	626
217	646	666	686	706	726	746	766	786	806	826
218	846	866	885	905	925	945	965	985	34 005	34 025
219	34 044	34 064	34 084	34 104	34 124	34 143	34 163	34 183	203	223
220	34 242	34 262	34 282	34 301	34 321	34 341	34 361	34 380	34 400	34 420
221	439	459	479	498	518	537	557	577	596	616
222	635	655	674	694	713	733	753	772	792	811
223	830	850	869	889	908	928	947	967	986	35 005
224	35 025	35 044	35 064	35 083	35 102	35 122	35 141	35 160	35 180	199
225	35 218	35 238	35 257	35 276	35 295	35 315	35 334	35 353	35 372	35 392
226	411	430	449	468	488	507	526	545	564	583
227	603	622	641	660	679	698	717	736	755	774
228	793	813	832	851	870	889	908	927	946	965
229	984	36 003	36 021	36 040	36 059	36 078	36 097	36 116	36 135	36 154
230	36 173	36 192	36 211	36 229	36 248	36 267	36 286	36 305	36 324	36 342
231	361	380	399	418	436	455	474	493	511	530
232	549	568	586	605	624	642	661	680	698	717
233	736	754	773	791	810	829	847	866	884	903
234	922	940	959	977	996	37 014	37 033	37 051	37 070	37 088
235	37 107	37 125	37 144	37 162	37 181	37 199	37 218	37 236	37 254	37 273
236	291	310	328	346	365	383	401	420	438	457
237	475	493	511	530	548	566	585	603	621	639
238	658	676	694	712	731	749	767	785	803	822
239	840	858	876	894	912	931	949	967	985	38 003
240	38 021	38 039	38 057	38 075	38 093	38 112	38 130	38 148	38 166	38 184
241	202	220	238	256	274	292	310	328	346	364
242	382	399	417	435	453	471	489	507	525	543
243	561	578	596	614	632	650	668	686	703	721
244	739	757	775	792	810	828	846	863	881	899
245	38 917	38 934	38 952	38 970	38 987	39 005	39 023	39 041	39 058	39 076
246	39 094	39 111	39 129	39 146	39 164	182	199	217	235	252
247	270	287	305	322	340	358	375	393	410	428
248	445	463	480	498	515	533	550	568	585	602
249	620	637	655	672	690	707	724	742	759	777
250	39 794	39 811	39 829	39 846	39 863	39 881	39 898	39 915	39 933	39 950
N	0	1	2	3	4	5	6	7	8	9

250–300

N	0	1	2	3	4	5	6	7	8	9
250	39 794	39 811	39 829	39 846	39 863	39 881	39 898	39 915	39 933	39 950
251	967	985	40 002	40 019	40 037	40 054	40 071	40 088	40 106	40 123
252	40 140	40 157	175	192	209	226	243	261	278	295
253	312	329	346	364	381	398	415	432	449	466
254	483	500	518	535	552	569	586	603	620	637
255	40 654	40 671	40 688	40 705	40 722	40 739	40 756	40 773	40 790	40 807
256	824	841	858	875	892	909	926	943	960	976
257	993	41 010	41 027	41 044	41 061	41 078	41 095	41 111	41 128	41 145
258	41 162	179	196	212	229	246	263	280	296	313
259	330	347	363	380	397	414	430	447	464	481
260	41 497	41 514	41 531	41 547	41 564	41 581	41 597	41 614	41 631	41 647
261	664	681	697	714	731	747	764	780	797	814
262	830	847	863	880	896	913	929	946	963	979
263	996	42 012	42 029	42 045	42 062	42 078	42 095	42 111	42 127	42 144
264	42 160	177	193	210	226	243	259	275	292	308
265	42 325	42 341	42 357	42 374	42 390	42 406	42 423	42 439	42 455	42 472
266	488	504	521	537	553	570	586	602	619	635
267	651	667	684	700	716	732	749	765	781	797
268	813	830	846	862	878	894	911	927	943	959
269	975	991	43 008	43 024	43 040	43 056	43 072	43 088	43 104	43 120
270	43 136	43 152	43 169	43 185	43 201	43 217	43 233	43 249	43 265	43 281
271	297	313	329	345	361	377	393	409	425	441
272	457	473	489	505	521	537	553	569	584	600
273	616	632	648	664	680	696	712	727	743	759
274	775	791	807	823	838	854	870	886	902	917
275	43 933	43 949	43 965	43 981	43 996	44 012	44 028	44 044	44 059	44 075
276	44 091	44 107	44 122	44 138	44 154	170	185	201	217	232
277	248	264	279	295	311	326	342	358	373	389
278	404	420	436	451	467	483	498	514	529	545
279	560	576	592	607	623	638	654	669	685	700
280	44 716	44 731	44 747	44 762	44 778	44 793	44 809	44 824	44 840	44 855
281	871	886	902	917	932	948	963	979	994	45 010
282	45 025	45 040	45 056	45 071	45 086	45 102	45 117	45 133	45 148	163
283	179	194	209	225	240	255	271	286	301	317
284	332	347	362	378	393	408	423	439	454	469
285	45 484	45 500	45 515	45 530	45 545	45 561	45 576	45 591	45 606	45 621
286	637	652	667	682	697	712	728	743	758	773
287	788	803	818	834	849	864	879	894	909	924
288	939	954	969	984	46 000	46 015	46 030	46 045	46 060	46 075
289	46 090	46 105	46 120	46 135	150	165	180	195	210	225
290	46 240	46 255	46 270	46 285	46 300	46 315	46 330	46 345	46 359	46 374
291	389	404	419	434	449	464	479	494	509	523
292	538	553	568	583	598	613	627	642	657	672
293	687	702	716	731	746	761	776	790	805	820
294	835	850	864	879	894	909	923	938	953	967
295	46 982	46 997	47 012	47 026	47 041	47 056	47 070	47 085	47 100	47 114
296	47 129	47 144	159	173	188	202	217	232	246	261
297	276	290	305	319	334	349	363	378	392	407
298	422	436	451	465	480	494	509	524	538	553
299	567	582	596	611	625	640	654	669	683	698
300	47 712	47 727	47 741	47 756	47 770	47 784	47 799	47 813	47 828	47 842
N	0	1	2	3	4	5	6	7	8	9

300-350

N	0	1	2	3	4	5	6	7	8	9
300	47 712	47 727	47 741	47 756	47 770	47 784	47 799	47 813	47 828	47 842
301	857	871	885	900	914	929	943	958	972	986
302	48 001	48 015	48 029	48 044	48 058	48 073	48 087	48 101	48 116	48 130
303	144	159	173	187	202	216	230	244	259	273
304	287	302	316	330	344	359	373	387	401	416
305	48 430	48 444	48 458	48 473	48 487	48 501	48 515	48 530	48 544	48 558
306	572	586	601	615	629	643	657	671	686	700
307	714	728	742	756	770	785	799	813	827	841
308	855	869	883	897	911	926	940	954	968	982
309	996	49 010	49 024	49 038	49 052	49 066	49 080	49 094	49 108	49 122
310	49 136	49 150	49 164	49 178	49 192	49 206	49 220	49 234	49 248	49 262
311	276	290	304	318	332	346	360	374	388	402
312	415	429	443	457	471	485	499	513	527	541
313	554	568	582	596	610	624	638	651	665	679
314	693	707	721	734	748	762	776	790	803	817
315	49 831	49 845	49 859	49 872	49 886	49 900	49 914	49 927	49 941	49 955
316	969	982	996	50 010	50 024	50 037	50 051	50 065	50 079	50 092
317	50 106	50 120	50 133	147	161	174	188	202	215	229
318	243	256	270	284	297	311	325	338	352	365
319	379	393	406	420	433	447	461	474	488	501
320	50 515	50 529	50 542	50 556	50 569	50 583	50 596	50 610	50 623	50 637
321	651	664	678	691	705	718	732	745	759	772
322	786	799	813	826	840	853	866	880	893	907
323	920	934	947	961	974	987	51 001	51 014	51 028	51 041
324	51 055	51 068	51 081	51 095	51 108	51 121	135	148	162	175
325	51 188	51 202	51 215	51 228	51 242	51 255	51 268	51 282	51 295	51 308
326	322	335	348	362	375	388	402	415	428	441
327	455	468	481	495	508	521	534	548	561	574
328	587	601	614	627	640	654	667	680	693	706
329	720	733	746	759	772	786	799	812	825	838
330	51 851	51 865	51 878	51 891	51 904	51 917	51 930	51 943	51 957	51 970
331	983	996	52 009	52 022	52 035	52 048	52 061	52 075	52 088	52 101
332	52 114	52 127	140	153	166	179	192	205	218	231
333	244	257	270	284	297	310	323	336	349	362
334	375	388	401	414	427	440	453	466	479	492
335	52 504	52 517	52 530	52 543	52 556	52 569	52 582	52 595	52 608	52 621
336	634	647	660	673	686	699	711	724	737	750
337	763	776	789	802	815	827	840	853	866	879
338	892	905	917	930	943	956	969	982	994	53 007
339	53 020	53 033	53 046	53 058	53 071	53 084	53 097	53 110	53 122	135
340	53 148	53 161	53 173	53 186	53 199	53 212	53 224	53 237	53 250	53 263
341	275	288	301	314	326	339	352	364	377	390
342	403	415	428	441	453	466	479	491	504	517
343	529	542	555	567	580	593	605	618	631	643
344	656	668	681	694	706	719	732	744	757	769
345	53 782	53 794	53 807	53 820	53 832	53 845	53 857	53 870	53 882	53 895
346	908	920	933	945	958	970	983	995	54 008	54 020
347	54 033	54 045	54 058	54 070	54 083	54 095	54 108	54 120	133	145
348	158	170	183	195	208	220	233	245	258	270
349	283	295	307	320	332	345	357	370	382	394
350	54 407	54 419	54 432	54 444	54 456	54 469	54 481	54 494	54 506	54 518
N	0	1	2	3	4	5	6	7	8	9

350–400

N	0	1	2	3	4	5	6	7	8	9
350	54 407	54 419	54 432	54 444	54 456	54 469	54 481	54 494	54 506	54 518
351	531	543	555	568	580	593	605	617	630	642
352	654	667	679	691	704	716	728	741	753	765
353	777	790	802	814	827	839	851	864	876	888
354	900	913	925	937	949	962	974	986	998	55 011
355	55 023	55 035	55 047	55 060	55 072	55 084	55 096	55 108	55 121	55 133
356	145	157	169	182	194	206	218	230	242	255
357	267	279	291	303	315	328	340	352	364	376
358	388	400	413	425	437	449	461	473	485	497
359	509	522	534	546	558	570	582	594	606	618
360	55 630	55 642	55 654	55 666	55 678	55 691	55 703	55 715	55 727	55 739
361	751	763	775	787	799	811	823	835	847	859
362	871	883	895	907	919	931	943	955	967	979
363	991	56 003	56 015	56 027	56 038	56 050	56 062	56 074	56 086	56 098
364	56 110	122	134	146	158	170	182	194	205	217
365	56 229	56 241	56 253	56 265	56 277	56 289	56 301	56 312	56 324	56 336
366	348	360	372	384	396	407	419	431	443	455
367	467	478	490	502	514	526	538	549	561	573
368	585	597	608	620	632	644	656	667	679	691
369	703	714	726	738	750	761	773	785	797	808
370	56 820	56 832	56 844	56 855	56 867	56 879	56 891	56 902	56 914	56 926
371	937	949	961	972	984	996	57 008	57 019	57 031	57 043
372	57 054	57 066	57 078	57 089	57 101	57 113	124	136	148	159
373	171	183	194	206	217	229	241	252	264	276
374	287	299	310	322	334	345	357	368	380	392
375	57 403	57 415	57 426	57 438	57 449	57 461	57 473	57 484	57 496	57 507
376	519	530	542	553	565	576	588	600	611	623
377	634	646	657	669	680	692	703	715	726	738
378	749	761	772	784	795	807	818	830	841	852
379	864	875	887	898	910	921	933	944	955	967
380	57 978	57 990	58 001	58 013	58 024	58 035	58 047	58 058	58 070	58 081
381	58 092	58 104	115	127	138	149	161	172	184	195
382	206	218	229	240	252	263	274	286	297	309
383	320	331	343	354	365	377	388	399	410	422
384	433	444	456	467	478	490	501	512	524	535
385	58 546	58 557	58 569	58 580	58 591	58 602	58 614	58 625	58 636	58 647
386	659	670	681	692	704	715	726	737	749	760
387	771	782	794	805	816	827	838	850	861	872
388	883	894	906	917	928	939	950	961	973	984
389	995	59 006	59 017	59 028	59 040	59 051	59 062	59 073	59 084	59 095
390	59 106	59 118	59 129	59 140	59 151	59 162	59 173	59 184	59 195	59 207
391	218	229	240	251	262	273	284	295	306	318
392	329	340	351	362	373	384	395	406	417	428
393	439	450	461	472	483	494	506	517	528	539
394	550	561	572	583	594	605	616	627	638	649
395	59 660	59 671	59 682	59 693	59 704	59 715	59 726	59 737	59 748	59 759
396	770	780	791	802	813	824	835	846	857	868
397	879	890	901	912	923	934	945	956	966	977
398	988	999	60 010	60 021	60 032	60 043	60 054	60 065	60 076	60 086
399	60 097	60 108	119	130	141	152	163	173	184	195
400	60 206	60 217	60 228	60 239	60 249	60 260	60 271	60 282	60 293	60 304
N	0	1	2	3	4	5	6	7	8	9

400–450

N	0	1	2	3	4	5	6	7	8	9
400	60 206	60 217	60 228	60 239	60 249	60 260	60 271	60 282	60 293	60 304
401	314	325	336	347	358	369	379	390	401	412
402	423	433	444	455	466	477	487	498	509	520
403	531	541	552	563	574	584	595	606	617	627
404	638	649	660	670	681	692	703	713	724	735
405	60 746	60 756	60 767	60 778	60 788	60 799	60 810	60 821	60 831	60 842
406	853	863	874	885	895	906	917	927	938	949
407	959	970	981	991	61 002	61 013	61 023	61 034	61 045	61 055
408	61 066	61 077	61 087	61 098	109	119	130	140	151	162
409	172	183	194	204	215	225	236	247	257	268
410	61 278	61 289	61 300	61 310	61 321	61 331	61 342	61 352	61 363	61 374
411	384	395	405	416	426	437	448	458	469	479
412	490	500	511	521	532	542	553	563	574	584
413	595	606	616	627	637	648	658	669	679	690
414	700	711	721	731	742	752	763	773	784	794
415	61 805	61 815	61 826	61 836	61 847	61 857	61 868	61 878	61 888	61 899
416	909	920	930	941	951	962	972	982	993	62 003
417	62 014	62 024	62 034	62 045	62 055	62 066	62 076	62 086	62 097	107
418	118	128	138	149	159	170	180	190	201	211
419	221	232	242	252	263	273	284	294	304	315
420	62 325	62 335	62 346	62 356	62 366	62 377	62 387	62 397	62 408	62 418
421	428	439	449	459	469	480	490	500	511	521
422	531	542	552	562	572	583	593	603	613	624
423	634	644	655	665	675	685	696	706	716	726
424	737	747	757	767	778	788	798	808	818	829
425	62 839	62 849	62 859	62 870	62 880	62 890	62 900	62 910	62 921	62 931
426	941	951	961	972	982	992	63 002	63 012	63 022	63 033
427	63 043	63 053	63 063	63 073	63 083	63 094	104	114	124	134
428	144	155	165	175	185	195	205	215	225	236
429	246	256	266	276	286	296	306	317	327	337
430	63 347	63 357	63 367	63 377	63 387	63 397	63 407	63 417	63 428	63 438
431	448	458	468	478	488	498	508	518	528	538
432	548	558	568	579	589	599	609	619	629	639
433	649	659	669	679	689	699	709	719	729	739
434	749	759	769	779	789	799	809	819	829	839
435	63 849	63 859	63 869	63 879	63 889	63 899	63 909	63 919	63 929	63 939
436	949	959	969	979	988	998	64 008	64 018	64 028	64 038
437	64 048	64 058	64 068	64 078	64 088	64 098	108	118	128	137
438	147	157	167	177	187	197	207	217	227	237
439	246	256	266	276	286	296	306	316	326	335
440	64 345	64 355	64 365	64 375	64 385	64 395	64 404	64 414	64 424	64 434
441	444	454	464	473	483	493	503	513	523	532
442	542	552	562	572	582	591	601	611	621	631
443	640	650	660	670	680	689	699	709	719	729
444	738	748	758	768	777	787	797	807	816	826
445	64 836	64 846	64 856	64 865	64 875	64 885	64 895	64 904	64 914	64 924
446	933	943	953	963	972	982	992	65 002	65 011	65 021
447	65 031	65 040	65 050	65 060	65 070	65 079	65 089	099	108	118
448	128	137	147	157	167	176	186	196	205	215
449	225	234	244	254	263	273	283	292	302	312
450	65 321	65 331	65 341	65 350	65 360	65 369	65 379	65 389	65 398	65 408
N	0	1	2	3	4	5	6	7	8	9

450-500

N	0	1	2	3	4	5	6	7	8	9
450	65 321	65 331	65 341	65 350	65 360	65 369	65 379	65 389	65 398	65 408
451	418	427	437	447	456	466	475	485	49_5_	504
452	514	523	533	543	552	562	571	581	591	600
453	610	619	629	639	648	658	667	677	686	696
454	706	715	725	734	744	753	763	772	782	792
455	65 801	65 811	65 820	65 830	65 839	65 849	65 858	65 868	65 877	65 887
456	896	906	916	925	935	944	954	963	973	982
457	992	66 001	66 011	66 020	66 030	66 039	66 049	66 058	66 068	66 077
458	66 087	096	106	11_5_	124	134	143	153	162	172
459	181	191	200	210	219	229	238	247	257	266
460	66 276	66 285	66 295	66 304	66 314	66 323	66 332	66 342	66 351	66 361
461	370	380	389	398	408	417	427	436	445	45_5_
462	464	474	483	492	502	511	521	530	539	549
463	558	567	577	586	596	60_5_	614	624	633	642
464	652	661	671	680	689	699	708	717	727	736
465	66 745	66 75_5_	66 764	66 773	66 783	66 792	66 801	66 811	66 820	66 829
466	839	848	857	867	876	885	894	904	913	922
467	932	941	950	960	969	978	987	997	67 006	67 015
468	67 02_5_	67 034	67 043	67 052	67 062	67 071	67 080	67 089	099	108
469	117	127	136	145	154	164	173	182	191	201
470	67 210	67 219	67 228	67 237	67 247	67 256	67 265	67 274	67 284	67 293
471	302	311	321	330	339	348	357	367	376	38_5_
472	394	403	413	422	431	440	449	459	468	477
473	486	495	504	514	523	532	541	550	560	569
474	578	587	596	605	614	624	633	642	651	660
475	67 669	67 679	67 688	67 697	67 706	67 715	67 724	67 733	67 742	67 752
476	761	770	779	788	797	806	815	82_5_	834	843
477	852	861	870	879	888	897	906	916	92_5_	934
478	943	952	961	970	979	988	997	68 006	68 015	68 024
479	68 034	68 043	68 052	68 061	68 070	68 079	68 088	097	106	115
480	68 124	68 133	68 142	68 151	68 160	68 169	68 178	68 187	68 196	68 205
481	21_5_	224	233	242	251	260	269	278	287	296
482	30_5_	314	323	332	341	3_5_0	359	368	377	386
483	39_5_	404	413	422	431	440	449	458	467	476
484	48_5_	494	502	511	520	529	538	547	556	565
485	68 574	68 583	68 592	68 601	68 610	68 619	68 628	68 637	68 646	68 65_5_
486	664	673	681	690	699	708	717	726	735	744
487	753	762	771	780	789	797	806	815	824	833
488	842	851	860	869	878	886	895	904	913	922
489	931	940	949	958	966	975	984	993	69 002	69 011
490	69 020	69 028	69 037	69 046	69 055	69 064	69 073	69 082	69 090	69 099
491	108	117	126	13_5_	144	152	161	170	179	188
492	197	205	214	223	232	241	249	258	267	276
493	28_5_	294	302	311	320	329	338	346	355	364
494	373	381	390	399	408	417	425	434	443	452
495	69 461	69 469	69 478	69 487	69 496	69 504	69 513	69 522	69 531	69 539
496	548	557	566	574	583	592	601	609	618	627
497	636	644	653	662	671	679	688	697	705	714
498	723	732	740	749	758	767	775	784	793	801
499	810	819	827	836	84_5_	854	862	871	880	888
500	69 897	69 906	69 914	69 923	69 932	69 940	69 949	69 958	69 966	69 975
N	0	1	2	3	4	5	6	7	8	9

500–550

N	0	1	2	3	4	5	6	7	8	9
500	69 897	69 906	69 914	69 923	69 932	69 940	69 949	69 958	69 966	69 975
501	984	992	70 001	70 010	70 018	70 027	70 036	70 044	70 053	70 062
502	70 070	70 079	088	096	105	114	122	131	140	148
503	157	165	174	183	191	200	209	217	226	234
504	243	252	260	269	278	286	295	303	312	321
505	70 329	70 338	70 346	70 355	70 364	70 372	70 381	70 389	70 398	70 406
506	415	424	432	441	449	458	467	475	484	492
507	501	509	518	526	535	544	552	561	569	578
508	586	595	603	612	621	629	638	646	655	663
509	672	680	689	697	706	714	723	731	740	749
510	70 757	70 766	70 774	70 783	70 791	70 800	70 808	70 817	70 825	70 834
511	842	851	859	868	876	885	893	902	910	919
512	927	935	944	952	961	969	978	986	995	71 003
513	71 012	71 020	71 029	71 037	71 046	71 054	71 063	71 071	71 079	088
514	096	105	113	122	130	139	147	155	164	172
515	71 181	71 189	71 198	71 206	71 214	71 223	71 231	71 240	71 248	71 257
516	265	273	282	290	299	307	315	324	332	341
517	349	357	366	374	383	391	399	408	416	425
518	433	441	450	458	466	475	483	492	500	508
519	517	525	533	542	550	559	567	575	584	592
520	71 600	71 609	71 617	71 625	71 634	71 642	71 650	71 659	71 667	71 675
521	684	692	700	709	717	725	734	742	750	759
522	767	775	784	792	800	809	817	825	834	842
523	850	858	867	875	883	892	900	908	917	925
524	933	941	950	958	966	975	983	991	999	72 008
525	72 016	72 024	72 032	72 041	72 049	72 057	72 066	72 074	72 082	72 090
526	099	107	115	123	132	140	148	156	165	173
527	181	189	198	206	214	222	230	239	247	255
528	263	272	280	288	296	304	313	321	329	337
529	346	354	362	370	378	387	395	403	411	419
530	72 428	72 436	72 444	72 452	72 460	72 469	72 477	72 485	72 493	72 501
531	509	518	526	534	542	550	558	567	575	583
532	591	599	607	616	624	632	640	648	656	665
533	673	681	689	697	705	713	722	730	738	746
534	754	762	770	779	787	795	803	811	819	827
535	72 835	72 843	72 852	72 860	72 868	72 876	72 884	72 892	72 900	72 908
536	916	925	933	941	949	957	965	973	981	989
537	997	73 006	73 014	73 022	73 030	73 038	73 046	73 054	73 062	73 070
538	73 078	086	094	102	111	119	127	135	143	151
539	159	167	175	183	191	199	207	215	223	231
540	73 239	73 247	73 255	73 263	73 272	73 280	73 288	73 296	73 304	73 312
541	320	328	336	344	352	360	368	376	384	392
542	400	408	416	424	432	440	448	456	464	472
543	480	488	496	504	512	520	528	536	544	552
544	560	568	576	584	592	600	608	616	624	632
545	73 640	73 648	73 656	73 664	73 672	73 679	73 687	73 695	73 703	73 711
546	719	727	735	743	751	759	767	775	783	791
547	799	807	815	823	830	838	846	854	862	870
548	878	886	894	902	910	918	926	933	941	949
549	957	965	973	981	989	997	74 005	74 013	74 020	74 028
550	74 036	74 044	74 052	74 060	74 068	74 076	74 084	74 092	74 099	74 107
N	0	1	2	3	4	5	6	7	8	9

550–600

N	0	1	2	3	4	5	6	7	8	9
550	74 036	74 044	74 052	74 060	74 068	74 076	74 084	74 092	74 099	74 107
551	115	123	131	139	147	155	162	170	178	186
552	194	202	210	218	225	233	241	249	257	265
553	273	280	288	296	304	312	320	327	335	343
554	351	359	367	374	382	390	398	406	414	421
555	74 429	74 437	74 445	74 453	74 461	74 468	74 476	74 484	74 492	74 500
556	507	515	523	531	539	547	554	562	570	578
557	586	593	601	609	617	624	632	640	648	656
558	663	671	679	687	695	702	710	718	726	733
559	741	749	757	764	772	780	788	796	803	811
560	74 819	74 827	74 834	74 842	74 850	74 858	74 865	74 873	74 881	74 889
561	896	904	912	920	927	935	943	950	958	966
562	974	981	989	997	75 005	75 012	75 020	75 028	75 035	75 043
563	75 051	75 059	75 066	75 074	082	089	097	105	113	120
564	128	136	143	151	159	166	174	182	189	197
565	75 205	75 213	75 220	75 228	75 236	75 243	75 251	75 259	75 266	75 274
566	282	289	297	305	312	320	328	335	343	351
567	358	366	374	381	389	397	404	412	420	427
568	435	442	450	458	465	473	481	488	496	504
569	511	519	526	534	542	549	557	565	572	580
570	75 587	75 595	75 603	75 610	75 618	75 626	75 633	75 641	75 648	75 656
571	664	671	679	686	694	702	709	717	724	732
572	740	747	755	762	770	778	785	793	800	808
573	815	823	831	838	846	853	861	868	876	884
574	891	899	906	914	921	929	937	944	952	959
575	75 967	75 974	75 982	75 989	75 997	76 005	76 012	76 020	76 027	76 035
576	76 042	76 050	76 057	76 065	76 072	080	087	095	103	110
577	118	125	133	140	148	155	163	170	178	185
578	193	200	208	215	223	230	238	245	253	260
579	268	275	283	290	298	305	313	320	328	335
580	76 343	76 350	76 358	76 365	76 373	76 380	76 388	76 395	76 403	76 410
581	418	425	433	440	448	455	462	470	477	485
582	492	500	507	515	522	530	537	545	552	559
583	567	574	582	589	597	604	612	619	626	634
584	641	649	656	664	671	678	686	693	701	708
585	76 716	76 723	76 730	76 738	76 745	76 753	76 760	76 768	76 775	76 782
586	790	797	805	812	819	827	834	842	849	856
587	864	871	879	886	893	901	908	916	923	930
588	938	945	953	960	967	975	982	989	997	77 004
589	77 012	77 019	77 026	77 034	77 041	77 048	77 056	77 063	77 070	078
590	77 085	77 093	77 100	77 107	77 115	77 122	77 129	77 137	77 144	77 151
591	159	166	173	181	188	195	203	210	217	225
592	232	240	247	254	262	269	276	283	291	298
593	305	313	320	327	335	342	349	357	364	371
594	379	386	393	401	408	415	422	430	437	444
595	77 452	77 459	77 466	77 474	77 481	77 488	77 495	77 503	77 510	77 517
596	525	532	539	546	554	561	568	576	583	590
597	597	605	612	619	627	634	641	648	656	663
598	670	677	685	692	699	706	714	721	728	735
599	743	750	757	764	772	779	786	793	801	808
600	77 815	77 822	77 830	77 837	77 844	77 851	77 859	77 866	77 873	77 880
N	0	1	2	3	4	5	6	7	8	9

600–650

N	0	1	2	3	4	5	6	7	8	9
600	77 815	77 822	77 830	77 837	77 844	77 851	77 859	77 866	77 873	77 880
601	887	895	902	909	916	924	931	938	945	952
602	960	967	974	981	988	996	78 003	78 010	78 017	78 025
603	78 032	78 039	78 046	78 053	78 061	78 068	075	082	089	097
604	104	111	118	125	132	140	147	154	161	168
605	78 176	78 183	78 190	78 197	78 204	78 211	78 219	78 226	78 233	78 240
606	247	254	262	269	276	283	290	297	305	312
607	319	326	333	340	347	355	362	369	376	383
608	390	398	405	412	419	426	433	440	447	455
609	462	469	476	483	490	497	504	512	519	526
610	78 533	78 540	78 547	78 554	78 561	78 569	78 576	78 583	78 590	78 597
611	604	611	618	625	633	640	647	654	661	668
612	675	682	689	696	704	711	718	725	732	739
613	746	753	760	767	774	781	789	796	803	810
614	817	824	831	838	845	852	859	866	873	880
615	78 888	78 895	78 902	78 909	78 916	78 923	78 930	78 937	78 944	78 951
616	958	965	972	979	986	993	79 000	79 007	79 014	79 021
617	79 029	79 036	79 043	79 050	79 057	79 064	071	078	085	092
618	099	106	113	120	127	134	141	148	155	162
619	169	176	183	190	197	204	211	218	225	232
620	79 239	79 246	79 253	79 260	79 267	79 274	79 281	79 288	79 295	79 302
621	309	316	323	330	337	344	351	358	365	372
622	379	386	393	400	407	414	421	428	435	442
623	449	456	463	470	477	484	491	498	505	511
624	518	525	532	539	546	553	560	567	574	581
625	79 588	79 595	79 602	79 609	79 616	79 623	79 630	79 637	79 644	79 650
626	657	664	671	678	685	692	699	706	713	720
627	727	734	741	748	754	761	768	775	782	789
628	796	803	810	817	824	831	837	844	851	858
629	865	872	879	886	893	900	906	913	920	927
630	79 934	79 941	79 948	79 955	79 962	79 969	79 975	79 982	79 989	79 996
631	80 003	80 010	80 017	80 024	80 030	80 037	80 044	80 051	80 058	80 065
632	072	079	085	092	099	106	113	120	127	134
633	140	147	154	161	168	175	182	188	195	202
634	209	216	223	229	236	243	250	257	264	271
635	80 277	80 284	80 291	80 298	80 305	80 312	80 318	80 325	80 332	80 339
636	346	353	359	366	373	380	387	393	400	407
637	414	421	428	434	441	448	455	462	468	475
638	482	489	496	502	509	516	523	530	536	543
639	550	557	564	570	577	584	591	598	604	611
640	80 618	80 625	80 632	80 638	80 645	80 652	80 659	80 665	80 672	80 679
641	686	693	699	706	713	720	726	733	740	747
642	754	760	767	774	781	787	794	801	808	814
643	821	828	835	841	848	855	862	868	875	882
644	889	895	902	909	916	922	929	936	943	949
645	80 956	80 963	80 969	80 976	80 983	80 990	80 996	81 003	81 010	81 017
646	81 023	81 030	81 037	81 043	81 050	81 057	81 064	070	077	084
647	090	097	104	111	117	124	131	137	144	151
648	158	164	171	178	184	191	198	204	211	218
649	224	231	238	245	251	258	265	271	278	285
650	81 291	81 298	81 305	81 311	81 318	81 325	81 331	81 338	81 345	81 351
N	0	1	2	3	4	5	6	7	8	9

650–700

N	0	1	2	3	4	5	6	7	8	9
650	81 291	81 298	81 305	81 311	81 318	81 325	81 331	81 338	81 345	81 351
651	358	365	371	378	385	391	398	405	411	418
652	425	431	438	445	451	458	465	471	478	485
653	491	498	505	511	518	525	531	538	544	551
654	558	564	571	578	584	591	598	604	611	617
655	81 624	81 631	81 637	81 644	81 651	81 657	81 664	81 671	81 677	81 684
656	690	697	704	710	717	723	730	737	743	750
657	757	763	770	776	783	790	796	803	809	816
658	823	829	836	842	849	856	862	869	875	882
659	889	895	902	908	915	921	928	935	941	948
660	81 954	81 961	81 968	81 974	81 981	81 987	81 994	82 000	82 007	82 014
661	82 020	82 027	82 033	82 040	82 046	82 053	82 060	066	073	079
662	086	092	099	105	112	119	125	132	138	145
663	151	158	164	171	178	184	191	197	204	210
664	217	223	230	236	243	249	256	263	269	276
665	82 282	82 289	82 295	82 302	82 308	82 315	82 321	82 328	82 334	82 341
666	347	354	360	367	373	380	387	393	400	406
667	413	419	426	432	439	445	452	458	465	471
668	478	484	491	497	504	510	517	523	530	536
669	543	549	556	562	569	575	582	588	595	601
670	82 607	82 614	82 620	82 627	82 633	82 640	82 646	82 653	82 659	82 666
671	672	679	685	692	698	705	711	718	724	730
672	737	743	750	756	763	769	776	782	789	795
673	802	808	814	821	827	834	840	847	853	860
674	866	872	879	885	892	898	905	911	918	924
675	82 930	82 937	82 943	82 950	82 956	82 963	82 969	82 975	82 982	82 988
676	995	83 001	83 008	83 014	83 020	83 027	83 033	83 040	83 046	83 052
677	83 059	065	072	078	085	091	097	104	110	117
678	123	129	136	142	149	155	161	168	174	181
679	187	193	200	206	213	219	225	232	238	245
680	83 251	83 257	83 264	83 270	83 276	83 283	83 289	83 296	83 302	83 308
681	315	321	327	334	340	347	353	359	366	372
682	378	385	391	398	404	410	417	423	429	436
683	442	448	455	461	467	474	480	487	493	499
684	506	512	518	525	531	537	544	550	556	563
685	83 569	83 575	83 582	83 588	83 594	83 601	83 607	83 613	83 620	83 626
686	632	639	645	651	658	664	670	677	683	689
687	696	702	708	715	721	727	734	740	746	753
688	759	765	771	778	784	790	797	803	809	816
689	822	828	835	841	847	853	860	866	872	879
690	83 885	83 891	83 897	83 904	83 910	83 916	83 923	83 929	83 935	83 942
691	948	954	960	967	973	979	985	992	998	84 004
692	84 011	84 017	84 023	84 029	84 036	84 042	84 048	84 055	84 061	067
693	073	080	086	092	098	105	111	117	123	130
694	136	142	148	155	161	167	173	180	186	192
695	84 198	84 205	84 211	84 217	84 223	84 230	84 236	84 242	84 248	84 255
696	261	267	273	280	286	292	298	305	311	317
697	323	330	336	342	348	354	361	367	373	379
698	386	392	398	404	410	417	423	429	435	442
699	448	454	460	466	473	479	485	491	497	504
700	84 510	84 516	84 522	84 528	84 535	84 541	84 547	84 553	84 559	84 566
N	0	1	2	3	4	5	6	7	8	9

700–750

N	0	1	2	3	4	5	6	7	8	9
700	84 510	84 516	84 522	84 528	84 535	84 541	84 547	84 553	84 559	84 566
701	572	578	584	590	597	603	609	615	621	628
702	634	640	646	652	658	665	671	677	683	689
703	696	702	708	714	720	726	733	739	745	751
704	757	763	770	776	782	788	794	800	807	813
705	84 819	84 825	84 831	84 837	84 844	84 850	84 856	84 862	84 868	84 874
706	880	887	893	899	905	911	917	924	930	936
707	942	948	954	960	967	973	979	985	991	997
708	85 003	85 009	85 016	85 022	85 028	85 034	85 040	85 046	85 052	85 058
709	065	071	077	083	089	095	101	107	114	120
710	85 126	85 132	85 138	85 144	85 150	85 156	85 163	85 169	85 175	85 181
711	187	193	199	205	211	217	224	230	236	242
712	248	254	260	266	272	278	285	291	297	303
713	309	315	321	327	333	339	345	352	358	364
714	370	376	382	388	394	400	406	412	418	425
715	85 431	85 437	85 443	85 449	85 455	85 461	85 467	85 473	85 479	85 485
716	491	497	503	509	516	522	528	534	540	546
717	552	558	564	570	576	582	588	594	600	606
718	612	618	625	631	637	643	649	655	661	667
719	673	679	685	691	697	703	709	715	721	727
720	85 733	85 739	85 745	85 751	85 757	85 763	85 769	85 775	85 781	85 788
721	794	800	806	812	818	824	830	836	842	848
722	854	860	866	872	878	884	890	896	902	908
723	914	920	926	932	938	944	950	956	962	968
724	974	980	986	992	998	86 004	86 010	86 016	86 022	86 028
725	86 034	86 040	86 046	86 052	86 058	86 064	86 070	86 076	86 082	86 088
726	094	100	106	112	118	124	130	136	141	147
727	153	159	165	171	177	183	189	195	201	207
728	213	219	225	231	237	243	249	255	261	267
729	273	279	285	291	297	303	308	314	320	326
730	86 332	86 338	86 344	86 350	86 356	86 362	86 368	86 374	86 380	86 386
731	392	398	404	410	415	421	427	433	439	445
732	451	457	463	469	475	481	487	493	499	504
733	510	516	522	528	534	540	546	552	558	564
734	570	576	581	587	593	599	605	611	617	623
735	86 629	86 635	86 641	86 646	86 652	86 658	86 664	86 670	86 676	86 682
736	688	694	700	705	711	717	723	729	735	741
737	747	753	759	764	770	776	782	788	794	800
738	806	812	817	823	829	835	841	847	853	859
739	864	870	876	882	888	894	900	906	911	917
740	86 923	86 929	86 935	86 941	86 947	86 953	86 958	86 964	86 970	86 976
741	982	988	994	999	87 005	87 011	87 017	87 023	87 029	87 035
742	87 040	87 046	87 052	87 058	064	070	075	081	087	093
743	099	105	111	116	122	128	134	140	146	151
744	157	163	169	175	181	186	192	198	204	210
745	87 216	87 221	87 227	87 233	87 239	87 245	87 251	87 256	87 262	87 268
746	274	280	286	291	297	303	309	315	320	326
747	332	338	344	349	355	361	367	373	379	384
748	390	396	402	408	413	419	425	431	437	442
749	448	454	460	466	471	477	483	489	495	500
750	87 506	87 512	87 518	87 523	87 529	87 535	87 541	87 547	87 552	87 558
N	0	1	2	3	4	5	6	7	8	9

750–800

N	0	1	2	3	4	5	6	7	8	9
750	87 506	87 512	87 518	87 523	87 529	87 535	87 541	87 547	87 552	87 558
751	564	570	576	581	587	593	599	604	610	616
752	622	628	633	639	645	651	656	662	668	674
753	679	685	691	697	703	708	714	720	726	731
754	737	743	749	754	760	766	772	777	783	789
755	87 795	87 800	87 806	87 812	87 818	87 823	87 829	87 835	87 841	87 846
756	852	858	864	869	875	881	887	892	898	904
757	910	915	921	927	933	938	944	950	955	961
758	967	973	978	984	990	996	88 001	88 007	88 013	88 018
759	88 024	88 030	88 036	88 041	88 047	88 053	058	064	070	076
760	88 081	88 087	88 093	88 098	88 104	88 110	88 116	88 121	88 127	88 133
761	138	144	150	156	161	167	173	178	184	190
762	195	201	207	213	218	224	230	235	241	247
763	252	258	264	270	275	281	287	292	298	304
764	309	315	321	326	332	338	343	349	355	360
765	88 366	88 372	88 377	88 383	88 389	88 395	88 400	88 406	88 412	88 417
766	423	429	434	440	446	451	457	463	468	474
767	480	485	491	497	502	508	513	519	525	530
768	536	542	547	553	559	564	570	576	581	587
769	593	598	604	610	615	621	627	632	638	643
770	88 649	88 655	88 660	88 666	88 672	88 677	88 683	88 689	88 694	88 700
771	705	711	717	722	728	734	739	745	750	756
772	762	767	773	779	784	790	795	801	807	812
773	818	824	829	835	840	846	852	857	863	868
774	874	880	885	891	897	902	908	913	919	925
775	88 930	88 936	88 941	88 947	88 953	88 958	88 964	88 969	88 975	88 981
776	986	992	997	89 003	89 009	89 014	89 020	89 025	89 031	89 037
777	89 042	89 048	89 053	059	064	070	076	081	087	092
778	098	104	109	115	120	126	131	137	143	148
779	154	159	165	170	176	182	187	193	198	204
780	89 209	89 215	89 221	89 226	89 232	89 237	89 243	89 248	89 254	89 260
781	265	271	276	282	287	293	298	304	310	315
782	321	326	332	337	343	348	354	360	365	371
783	376	382	387	393	398	404	409	415	421	426
784	432	437	443	448	454	459	465	470	476	481
785	89 487	89 492	89 498	89 504	89 509	89 515	89 520	89 526	89 531	89 537
786	542	548	553	559	564	570	575	581	586	592
787	597	603	609	614	620	625	631	636	642	647
788	653	658	664	669	675	680	686	691	697	702
789	708	713	719	724	730	735	741	746	752	757
790	89 763	89 768	89 774	89 779	89 785	89 790	89 796	89 801	89 807	89 812
791	818	823	829	834	840	845	851	856	862	867
792	873	878	883	889	894	900	905	911	916	922
793	927	933	938	944	949	955	960	966	971	977
794	982	988	993	998	90 004	90 009	90 015	90 020	90 026	90 031
795	90 037	90 042	90 048	90 053	90 059	90 064	90 069	90 075	90 080	90 086
796	091	097	102	108	113	119	124	129	135	140
797	146	151	157	162	168	173	179	184	189	195
798	200	206	211	217	222	227	233	238	244	249
799	255	260	266	271	276	282	287	293	298	304
800	90 309	90 314	90 320	90 325	90 331	90 336	90 342	90 347	90 352	90 358
N	0	1	2	3	4	5	6	7	8	9

800-850

N	0	1	2	3	4	5	6	7	8	9
800	90 309	90 314	90 320	90 325	90 331	90 336	90 342	90 347	90 352	90 358
801	363	369	374	380	385	390	396	401	407	412
802	417	423	428	434	439	445	450	455	461	466
803	472	477	482	488	493	499	504	509	515	520
804	526	531	536	542	547	553	558	563	569	574
805	90 580	90 585	90 590	90 596	90 601	90 607	90 612	90 617	90 623	90 628
806	634	639	644	650	655	660	666	671	677	682
807	687	693	698	703	709	714	720	725	730	736
808	741	747	752	757	763	768	773	779	784	789
809	795	800	806	811	816	822	827	832	838	843
810	90 849	90 854	90 859	90 865	90 870	90 875	90 881	90 886	90 891	90 897
811	902	907	913	918	924	929	934	940	945	950
812	956	961	966	972	977	982	988	993	998	91 004
813	91 009	91 014	91 020	91 025	91 030	91 036	91 041	91 046	91 052	057
814	062	068	073	078	084	089	094	100	105	110
815	91 116	91 121	91 126	91 132	91 137	91 142	91 148	91 153	91 158	91 164
816	169	174	180	185	190	196	201	206	212	217
817	222	228	233	238	243	249	254	259	265	270
818	275	281	286	291	297	302	307	312	318	323
819	328	334	339	344	350	355	360	365	371	376
820	91 381	91 387	91 392	91 397	91 403	91 408	91 413	91 418	91 424	91 429
821	434	440	445	450	455	461	466	471	477	482
822	487	492	498	503	508	514	519	524	529	535
823	540	545	551	556	561	566	572	577	582	587
824	593	598	603	609	614	619	624	630	635	640
825	91 645	91 651	91 656	91 661	91 666	91 672	91 677	91 682	91 687	91 693
826	698	703	709	714	719	724	730	735	740	745
827	751	756	761	766	772	777	782	787	793	798
828	803	808	814	819	824	829	834	840	845	850
829	855	861	866	871	876	882	887	892	897	903
830	91 908	91 913	91 918	91 924	91 929	91 934	91 939	91 944	91 950	91 955
831	960	965	971	976	981	986	991	997	92 002	92 007
832	92 012	92 018	92 023	92 028	92 033	92 038	92 044	92 049	054	059
833	065	070	075	080	085	091	096	101	106	111
834	117	122	127	132	137	143	148	153	158	163
835	92 169	92 174	92 179	92 184	92 189	92 195	92 200	92 205	92 210	92 215
836	221	226	231	236	241	247	252	257	262	267
837	273	278	283	288	293	298	304	309	314	319
838	324	330	335	340	345	350	355	361	366	371
839	376	381	387	392	397	402	407	412	418	423
840	92 428	92 433	92 438	92 443	92 449	92 454	92 459	92 464	92 469	92 474
841	480	485	490	495	500	505	511	516	521	526
842	531	536	542	547	552	557	562	567	572	578
843	583	588	593	598	603	609	614	619	624	629
844	634	639	645	650	655	660	665	670	675	681
845	92 686	92 691	92 696	92 701	92 706	92 711	92 716	92 722	92 727	92 732
846	737	742	747	752	758	763	768	773	778	783
847	788	793	799	804	809	814	819	824	829	834
848	840	845	850	855	860	865	870	875	881	886
849	891	896	901	906	911	916	921	927	932	937
850	92 942	92 947	92 952	92 957	92 962	92 967	92 973	92 978	92 983	92 988
N	0	1	2	3	4	5	6	7	8	9

850–900

N	0	1	2	3	4	5	6	7	8	9
850	92 942	92 947	92 952	92 957	92 962	92 967	92 973	92 978	92 983	92 988
851	993	998	93 003	93 008	93 013	93 018	93 024	93 029	93 034	93 039
852	93 044	93 049	054	059	064	069	075	080	085	090
853	095	100	105	110	115	120	125	131	136	141
854	146	151	156	161	166	171	176	181	186	192
855	93 197	93 202	93 207	93 212	93 217	93 222	93 227	93 232	93 237	93 242
856	247	252	258	263	268	273	278	283	288	293
857	298	303	308	313	318	323	328	334	339	344
858	349	354	359	364	369	374	379	384	389	394
859	399	404	409	414	420	425	430	435	440	445
860	93 450	93 455	93 460	93 465	93 470	93 475	93 480	93 485	93 490	93 495
861	500	505	510	515	520	526	531	536	541	546
862	551	556	561	566	571	576	581	586	591	596
863	601	606	611	616	621	626	631	636	641	646
864	651	656	661	666	671	676	682	687	692	697
865	93 702	93 707	93 712	93 717	93 722	93 727	93 732	93 737	93 742	93 747
866	752	757	762	767	772	777	782	787	792	797
867	802	807	812	817	822	827	832	837	842	847
868	852	857	862	867	872	877	882	887	892	897
869	902	907	912	917	922	927	932	937	942	947
870	93 952	93 957	93 962	93 967	93 972	93 977	93 982	93 987	93 992	93 997
871	94 002	94 007	94 012	94 017	94 022	94 027	94 032	94 037	94 042	94 047
872	052	057	062	067	072	077	082	086	091	096
873	101	106	111	116	121	126	131	136	141	146
874	151	156	161	166	171	176	181	186	191	196
875	94 201	94 206	94 211	94 216	94 221	94 226	94 231	94 236	94 240	94 245
876	250	255	260	265	270	275	280	285	290	295
877	300	305	310	315	320	325	330	335	340	345
878	349	354	359	364	369	374	379	384	389	394
879	399	404	409	414	419	424	429	433	438	443
880	94 448	94 453	94 458	94 463	94 468	94 473	94 478	94 483	94 488	94 493
881	498	503	507	512	517	522	527	532	537	542
882	547	552	557	562	567	571	576	581	586	591
883	596	601	606	611	616	621	626	630	635	640
884	645	650	655	660	665	670	675	680	685	689
885	94 694	94 699	94 704	94 709	94 714	94 719	94 724	94 729	94 734	94 738
886	743	748	753	758	763	768	773	778	783	787
887	792	797	802	807	812	817	822	827	832	836
888	841	846	851	856	861	866	871	876	880	885
889	890	895	900	905	910	915	919	924	929	934
890	94 939	94 944	94 949	94 954	94 959	94 963	94 968	94 973	94 978	94 983
891	988	993	998	95 002	95 007	95 012	95 017	95 022	95 027	95 032
892	95 036	95 041	95 046	051	056	061	066	071	075	080
893	085	090	095	100	105	109	114	119	124	129
894	134	139	143	148	153	158	163	168	173	177
895	95 182	95 187	95 192	95 197	95 202	95 207	95 211	95 216	95 221	95 226
896	231	236	240	245	250	255	260	265	270	274
897	279	284	289	294	299	303	308	313	318	323
898	328	332	337	342	347	352	357	361	366	371
899	376	381	386	390	395	400	405	410	415	419
900	95 424	95 429	95 434	95 439	95 444	95 448	95 453	95 458	95 463	95 468
N	0	1	2	3	4	5	6	7	8	9

900–950

N	0	1	2	3	4	5	6	7	8	9
900	95 424	95 429	95 434	95 439	95 444	95 448	95 453	95 458	95 463	95 468
901	472	477	482	487	492	497	501	506	511	516
902	521	525	530	535	540	545	550	554	559	564
903	569	574	578	583	588	593	598	602	607	612
904	617	622	626	631	636	641	646	650	655	660
905	95 665	95 670	95 674	95 679	95 684	95 689	95 694	95 698	95 703	95 708
906	713	718	722	727	732	737	742	746	751	756
907	761	766	770	775	780	785	789	794	799	804
908	809	813	818	823	828	832	837	842	847	852
909	856	861	866	871	875	880	885	890	895	899
910	95 904	95 909	95 914	95 918	95 923	95 928	95 933	95 938	95 942	95 947
911	952	957	961	966	971	976	980	985	990	995
912	999	96 004	96 009	96 014	96 019	96 023	96 028	96 033	96 038	96 042
913	96 047	052	057	061	066	071	076	080	085	090
914	095	099	104	109	114	118	123	128	133	137
915	96 142	96 147	96 152	96 156	96 161	96 166	96 171	96 175	96 180	96 185
916	190	194	199	204	209	213	218	223	227	232
917	237	242	246	251	256	261	265	270	275	280
918	284	289	294	298	303	308	313	317	322	327
919	332	336	341	346	350	355	360	365	369	374
920	96 379	96 384	96 388	96 393	96 398	96 402	96 407	96 412	96 417	96 421
921	426	431	435	440	445	450	454	459	464	468
922	473	478	483	487	492	497	501	506	511	515
923	520	525	530	534	539	544	548	553	558	562
924	567	572	577	581	586	591	595	600	605	609
925	96 614	96 619	96 624	96 628	96 633	96 638	96 642	96 647	96 652	96 656
926	661	666	670	675	680	685	689	694	699	703
927	708	713	717	722	727	731	736	741	745	750
928	755	759	764	769	774	778	783	788	792	797
929	802	806	811	816	820	825	830	834	839	844
930	96 848	96 853	96 858	96 862	96 867	96 872	96 876	96 881	96 886	96 890
931	895	900	904	909	914	918	923	928	932	937
932	942	946	951	956	960	965	970	974	979	984
933	988	993	997	97 002	97 007	97 011	97 016	97 021	97 025	97 030
934	97 035	97 039	97 044	049	053	058	063	067	072	077
935	97 081	97 086	97 090	97 095	97 100	97 104	97 109	97 114	97 118	97 123
936	128	132	137	142	146	151	155	160	165	169
937	174	179	183	188	192	197	202	206	211	216
938	220	225	230	234	239	243	248	253	257	262
939	267	271	276	280	285	290	294	299	304	308
940	97 313	97 317	97 322	97 327	97 331	97 336	97 340	97 345	97 350	97 354
941	359	364	368	373	377	382	387	391	396	400
942	405	410	414	419	424	428	433	437	442	447
943	451	456	460	465	470	474	479	483	488	493
944	497	502	506	511	516	520	525	529	534	539
945	97 543	97 548	97 552	97 557	97 562	97 566	97 571	97 575	97 580	97 585
946	589	594	598	603	607	612	617	621	626	630
947	635	640	644	649	653	658	663	667	672	676
948	681	685	690	695	699	704	708	713	717	722
949	727	731	736	740	745	749	754	759	763	768
950	97 772	97 777	97 782	97 786	97 791	97 795	97 800	97 804	97 809	97 813
N	0	1	2	3	4	5	6	7	8	9

N	0	1	2	3	4	5	6	7	8	9
950	97 772	97 777	97 782	97 786	97 791	97 795	97 800	97 804	97 809	97 813
951	818	823	827	832	836	841	845	850	85_5_	859
952	864	868	873	877	882	886	891	896	900	90_5_
953	909	914	918	923	928	932	937	941	946	950
954	95_5_	959	964	968	973	978	982	987	991	996
955	98 000	98 00_5_	98 009	98 014	98 019	98 023	98 028	98 032	98 037	98 041
956	046	050	05_5_	059	064	068	073	078	082	087
957	091	096	100	10_5_	109	114	118	123	127	132
958	137	141	146	150	15_5_	159	164	168	173	177
959	182	186	191	195	200	204	209	214	218	223
960	98 227	98 232	98 236	98 241	98 245	98 2_5_0	98 254	98 259	98 263	98 268
961	272	277	281	286	290	29_5_	299	304	308	313
962	318	322	327	331	336	340	34_5_	349	354	358
963	363	367	372	376	381	385	390	394	399	403
964	408	412	417	421	426	430	43_5_	439	444	448
965	98 453	98 457	98 462	98 466	98 471	98 475	98 480	98 484	98 489	98 493
966	498	502	507	511	516	520	52_5_	529	534	538
967	543	547	552	556	561	565	570	574	579	583
968	588	592	597	601	605	610	614	619	623	628
969	632	637	641	646	650	65_5_	659	664	668	673
970	98 677	98 682	98 686	98 691	98 695	98 700	98 704	98 709	98 713	98 717
971	722	726	731	735	740	744	749	753	758	762
972	767	771	776	780	784	789	793	798	802	807
973	811	816	820	82_5_	829	834	838	843	847	851
974	856	860	86_5_	869	874	878	883	887	892	896
975	98 900	98 90_5_	98 909	98 914	98 918	98 923	98 927	98 932	98 936	98 941
976	94_5_	949	954	958	963	967	972	976	981	985
977	989	994	998	99 003	99 007	99 012	99 016	99 021	99 025	99 029
978	99 034	99 038	99 043	047	052	056	061	06_5_	069	074
979	078	083	087	092	096	100	10_5_	109	114	118
980	99 123	99 127	99 131	99 136	99 140	99 14_5_	99 149	99 154	99 158	99 162
981	167	171	176	180	18_5_	189	193	198	202	207
982	211	216	220	224	229	233	238	242	247	251
983	255	260	264	269	273	277	282	286	291	295
984	300	304	308	313	317	322	326	330	33_5_	339
985	99 344	99 348	99 352	99 357	99 361	99 366	99 370	99 374	99 379	99 383
986	388	392	396	401	405	410	414	419	423	427
987	432	436	441	44_5_	449	454	458	463	467	471
988	476	480	484	489	493	498	502	506	511	515
989	520	524	528	533	537	542	546	550	55_5_	559
990	99 564	99 568	99 572	99 577	99 581	99 585	99 590	99 594	99 599	99 603
991	607	612	616	621	62_5_	629	634	638	642	647
992	651	656	660	664	669	673	677	682	686	691
993	69_5_	699	704	708	712	717	721	726	730	734
994	739	743	747	752	756	760	76_5_	769	774	778
995	99 782	99 787	99 791	99 795	99 800	99 804	99 808	99 813	99 817	99 822
996	826	830	83_5_	839	843	848	852	856	861	865
997	870	874	878	883	887	891	896	900	904	909
998	913	917	922	926	930	93_5_	939	944	948	952
999	957	961	965	970	974	978	983	987	991	996
1000	00 000	00 004	00 009	00 013	00 017	00 022	00 026	00 030	00 03_5_	00 039
N	0	1	2	3	4	5	6	7	8	9

Number	Log	Number	Log
Circle = 360°	2.55630	$\pi^2 = 9.86960$	0.99430
= 21,600′	4.33445	$\dfrac{1}{\pi^2} = 0.10132$	9.00570 − 10
= 1,296,000″	6.11261		
$\pi = 3.14159$	0.49715	$\sqrt{\pi} = 1.77245$	0.24857
$2\pi = 6.28319$	0.79818	$\dfrac{1}{\sqrt{\pi}} = 0.56419$	9.75143 − 10
$4\pi = 12.56637$	1.09921		
$\dfrac{4\pi}{3} = 4.18879$	0.62209	$\sqrt{\dfrac{4}{\pi}} = 1.12838$	0.05246
$\dfrac{\pi}{4} = 0.78540$	9.89509 − 10	$\sqrt[3]{\pi} = 1.46459$	0.16572
$\dfrac{\pi}{6} = 0.52360$	9.71900 − 10	$\dfrac{1}{\sqrt[3]{\pi}} = 0.68278$	9.83428 − 10
$\dfrac{1}{\pi} = 0.31831$	9.50285 − 10	$\sqrt[3]{\dfrac{3}{4\pi}} = 0.62035$	9.79264 − 10
$\dfrac{1}{2\pi} = 0.15915$	9.20182 − 10	$\sqrt[3]{\dfrac{\pi}{6}} = 0.80600$	9.90633 − 10
$\sqrt{2} = 1.41421$	0.15052	$\sqrt[3]{2} = 1.25992$	0.10034
$\sqrt{3} = 1.73205$	0.23856	$\sqrt[3]{3} = 1.44225$	0.15904
$\sqrt{5} = 2.23606$	0.34949	$\sqrt[3]{5} = 1.70997$	0.23299
$\sqrt{6} = 2.44948$	0.38908	$\sqrt[3]{6} = 1.81712$	0.25938
1 radian = $\dfrac{180°}{\pi}$		$1° = \dfrac{\pi}{180}$ radian	
= 57.2958°	1.75812	1° = 0.01745 radian	8.24188 − 10
= 3437.75′	3.53627	1′ = 0.00029 radian	6.46373 − 10
= 206,264.81″	5.31443	1″ = 0.000005 radian	4.68557 − 10
Base of natural logs., e		$\log_{10} e = \log_{10} 2.71828$	0.43429
$e = 2.71828$	0.43429	$1 : \log_{10} e = 2.302585$	0.36222
1 m. = 39.3708 in.	1.59517	1 naut. mi. = 6080.27 ft.	3.78392
= 1.0936 yd.	0.03886	= 1.1516 mi.	0.06130
= 3.2809 ft.	0.51599	1 lb. Av. = 7000 gr.	3.84510
1 km. = 0.6214 mi.	9.79336 − 10	1 bu. = 2150.42 cu. in.	3.33252
1 mi. = 1.6093 km.	0.20664	1 U.S. gal. = 231 cu. in.	2.36361
1 mi. = 5280 ft.	3.72263	1 Brit. gal. = 277.463 cu. in.	2.44320
1 lb. Av. = 453.5927 g.	2.65666	Earth's radii	
1 acre = 43,560 sq. ft.	4.63909	= 3963 mi.	3.59802
$g = 32.17$ ft./sec.^{2}	1.50745	and 3950 mi.	3.59660
$g = 980.6$ cm./sec.^{2}	2.99149	1 ft.-lb. = 0.1383 kg.-m.	9.14082 − 10

TABLE III 21

LOGARITHMS OF TRIGONOMETRIC FUNCTIONS

0°

′ ″	log sin	log cos	log tan	′ ″	′ ″	log sin	log cos	log tan	′ ″
0 0	—	10.00000	—	**60** 0	**10** 0	7.46373	10.00000	7.46373	**50** 0
10	5.68557	10.00000	5.68557	50	10	7.47090	10.00000	7.47091	50
20	5.98660	10.00000	5.98660	40	20	7.47797	10.00000	7.47797	40
30	6.16270	10.00000	6.16270	30	30	7.48491	10.00000	7.48492	30
40	6.28763	10.00000	6.28763	20	40	7.49175	10.00000	7.49176	20
50	6.38454	10.00000	6.38454	10	50	7.49849	10.00000	7.49849	10
1 0	6.46373	10.00000	6.46373	**59** 0	**11** 0	7.50512	10.00000	7.50512	**49** 0
10	6.53067	10.00000	6.53067	50	10	7.51165	10.00000	7.51165	50
20	6.58866	10.00000	6.58866	40	20	7.51808	10.00000	7.51809	40
30	6.63982	10.00000	6.63982	30	30	7.52442	10.00000	7.52443	30
40	6.68557	10.00000	6.68557	20	40	7.53067	10.00000	7.53067	20
50	6.72697	10.00000	6.72697	10	50	7.53683	10.00000	7.53683	10
2 0	6.76476	10.00000	6.76476	**58** 0	**12** 0	7.54291	10.00000	7.54291	**48** 0
10	6.79952	10.00000	6.79952	50	10	7.54890	10.00000	7.54890	50
20	6.83170	10.00000	6.83170	40	20	7.55481	10.00000	7.55481	40
30	6.86167	10.00000	6.86167	30	30	7.56064	10.00000	7.56064	30
40	6.88969	10.00000	6.88969	20	40	7.56639	10.00000	7.56639	20
50	6.91602	10.00000	6.91602	10	50	7.57206	10.00000	7.57207	10
3 0	6.94085	10.00000	6.94085	**57** 0	**13** 0	7.57767	10.00000	7.57767	**47** 0
10	6.96433	10.00000	6.96433	50	10	7.58320	10.00000	7.58320	50
20	6.98660	10.00000	6.98661	40	20	7.58866	10.00000	7.58867	40
30	7.00779	10.00000	7.00779	30	30	7.59406	10.00000	7.59406	30
40	7.02800	10.00000	7.02800	20	40	7.59939	10.00000	7.59939	20
50	7.04730	10.00000	7.04730	10	50	7.60465	10.00000	7.60466	10
4 0	7.06579	10.00000	7.06579	**56** 0	**14** 0	7.60985	10.00000	7.60986	**46** 0
10	7.08351	10.00000	7.08352	50	10	7.61499	10.00000	7.61500	50
20	7.10055	10.00000	7.10055	40	20	7.62007	10.00000	7.62008	40
30	7.11694	10.00000	7.11694	30	30	7.62509	10.00000	7.62510	30
40	7.13273	10.00000	7.13273	20	40	7.63006	10.00000	7.63006	20
50	7.14797	10.00000	7.14797	10	50	7.63496	10.00000	7.63497	10
5 0	7.16270	10.00000	7.16270	**55** 0	**15** 0	7.63982	10.00000	7.63982	**45** 0
10	7.17694	10.00000	7.17694	50	10	7.64461	10.00000	7.64462	50
20	7.19072	10.00000	7.19073	40	20	7.64936	10.00000	7.64937	40
30	7.20409	10.00000	7.20409	30	30	7.65406	10.00000	7.65406	30
40	7.21705	10.00000	7.21705	20	40	7.65870	10.00000	7.65871	20
50	7.22964	10.00000	7.22964	10	50	7.66330	10.00000	7.66330	10
6 0	7.24188	10.00000	7.24188	**54** 0	**16** 0	7.66784	10.00000	7.66785	**44** 0
10	7.25378	10.00000	7.25378	50	10	7.67235	10.00000	7.67235	50
20	7.26536	10.00000	7.26536	40	20	7.67680	10.00000	7.67680	40
30	7.27664	10.00000	7.27664	30	30	7.68121	10.00000	7.68121	30
40	7.28763	10.00000	7.28764	20	40	7.68557	9.99999	7.68558	20
50	7.29836	10.00000	7.29836	10	50	7.68989	9.99999	7.68990	10
7 0	7.30882	10.00000	7.30882	**53** 0	**17** 0	7.69417	9.99999	7.69418	**43** 0
10	7.31904	10.00000	7.31904	50	10	7.69841	9.99999	7.69842	50
20	7.32903	10.00000	7.32903	40	20	7.70261	9.99999	7.70261	40
30	7.33879	10.00000	7.33879	30	30	7.70676	9.99999	7.70677	30
40	7.34833	10.00000	7.34833	20	40	7.71088	9.99999	7.71088	20
50	7.35767	10.00000	7.35767	10	50	7.71496	9.99999	7.71496	10
8 0	7.36682	10.00000	7.36682	**52** 0	**18** 0	7.71900	9.99999	7.71900	**42** 0
10	7.37577	10.00000	7.37577	50	10	7.72300	9.99999	7.72301	50
20	7.38454	10.00000	7.38455	40	20	7.72697	9.99999	7.72697	40
30	7.39314	10.00000	7.39315	30	30	7.73090	9.99999	7.73090	30
40	7.40158	10.00000	7.40158	20	40	7.73479	9.99999	7.73480	20
50	7.40985	10.00000	7.40985	10	50	7.73865	9.99999	7.73866	10
9 0	7.41797	10.00000	7.41797	**51** 0	**19** 0	7.74248	9.99999	7.74248	**41** 0
10	7.42594	10.00000	7.42594	50	10	7.74627	9.99999	7.74628	50
20	7.43376	10.00000	7.43376	40	20	7.75003	9.99999	7.75004	40
30	7.44145	10.00000	7.44145	30	30	7.75376	9.99999	7.75377	30
40	7.44900	10.00000	7.44900	20	40	7.75745	9.99999	7.75746	20
50	7.45643	10.00000	7.45643	10	50	7.76112	9.99999	7.76113	10
10 0	7.46373	10.00000	7.46373	**50** 0	**20** 0	7.76475	9.99999	7.76476	**40** 0
′ ″	log cos	log sin	log ctn	′ ″	′ ″	log cos	log sin	log ctn	′ ″

0°

′″	log sin	log cos	log tan	′″	′″	log sin	log cos	log tan	′″
20 0	7.76475	9.99999	7.76476	**40** 0	**30** 0	7.94084	9.99998	7.94086	**30** 0
10	7.76836	9.99999	7.76837	50	10	7.94325	9.99998	7.94326	50
20	7.77193	9.99999	7.77194	40	20	7.94564	9.99998	7.94566	40
30	7.77548	9.99999	7.77549	30	30	7.94802	9.99998	7.94804	30
40	7.77899	9.99999	7.77900	20	40	7.95039	9.99998	7.95040	20
50	7.78248	9.99999	7.78249	10	50	7.95274	9.99998	7.95276	10
21 0	7.78594	9.99999	7.78595	**39** 0	**31** 0	7.95508	9.99998	7.95510	**29** 0
10	7.78938	9.99999	7.78938	50	10	7.95741	9.99998	7.95743	50
20	7.79278	9.99999	7.79279	40	20	7.95973	9.99998	7.95974	40
30	7.79616	9.99999	7.79617	30	30	7.96203	9.99998	7.96205	30
40	7.79952	9.99999	7.79952	20	40	7.96432	9.99998	7.96434	20
50	7.80284	9.99999	7.80285	10	50	7.96660	9.99998	7.96662	10
22 0	7.80615	9.99999	7.80615	**38** 0	**32** 0	7.96887	9.99998	7.96889	**28** 0
10	7.80942	9.99999	7.80943	50	10	7.97113	9.99998	7.97114	50
20	7.81268	9.99999	7.81269	40	20	7.97337	9.99998	7.97339	40
30	7.81591	9.99999	7.81591	30	30	7.97560	9.99998	7.97562	30
40	7.81911	9.99999	7.81912	20	40	7.97782	9.99998	7.97784	20
50	7.82229	9.99999	7.82230	10	50	7.98003	9.99998	7.98005	10
23 0	7.82545	9.99999	7.82546	**37** 0	**33** 0	7.98223	9.99998	7.98225	**27** 0
10	7.82859	9.99999	7.82860	50	10	7.98442	9.99998	7.98444	50
20	7.83170	9.99999	7.83171	40	20	7.98660	9.99998	7.98662	40
30	7.83479	9.99999	7.83480	30	30	7.98876	9.99998	7.98878	30
40	7.83786	9.99999	7.83787	20	40	7.99092	9.99998	7.99094	20
50	7.84091	9.99999	7.84092	10	50	7.99306	9.99998	7.99308	10
24 0	7.84393	9.99999	7.84394	**36** 0	**34** 0	7.99520	9.99998	7.99522	**26** 0
10	7.84694	9.99999	7.84695	50	10	7.99732	9.99998	7.99734	50
20	7.84992	9.99999	7.84994	40	20	7.99943	9.99998	7.99946	40
30	7.85289	9.99999	7.85290	30	30	8.00154	9.99998	8.00156	30
40	7.85583	9.99999	7.85584	20	40	8.00363	9.99998	8.00365	20
50	7.85876	9.99999	7.85877	10	50	8.00571	9.99998	8.00574	10
25 0	7.86166	9.99999	7.86167	**35** 0	**35** 0	8.00779	9.99998	8.00781	**25** 0
10	7.86455	9.99999	7.86456	50	10	8.00985	9.99998	8.00987	50
20	7.86741	9.99999	7.86743	40	20	8.01190	9.99998	8.01193	40
30	7.87026	9.99999	7.87027	30	30	8.01395	9.99998	8.01397	30
40	7.87309	9.99999	7.87310	20	40	8.01598	9.99998	8.01600	20
50	7.87591	9.99999	7.87591	10	50	8.01801	9.99998	8.01803	10
26 0	7.87870	9.99999	7.87871	**34** 0	**36** 0	8.02002	9.99998	8.02004	**24** 0
10	7.88147	9.99999	7.88148	50	10	8.02203	9.99998	8.02205	50
20	7.88423	9.99999	7.88424	40	20	8.02402	9.99998	8.02405	40
30	7.88697	9.99999	7.88698	30	30	8.02601	9.99998	8.02604	30
40	7.88969	9.99999	7.88970	20	40	8.02799	9.99998	8.02801	20
50	7.89240	9.99999	7.89241	10	50	8.02996	9.99998	8.02998	10
27 0	7.89509	9.99999	7.89510	**33** 0	**37** 0	8.03192	9.99997	8.03194	**23** 0
10	7.89776	9.99999	7.89777	50	10	8.03387	9.99997	8.03390	50
20	7.90041	9.99999	7.90043	40	20	8.03581	9.99997	8.03584	40
30	7.90305	9.99999	7.90307	30	30	8.03775	9.99997	8.03777	30
40	7.90568	9.99999	7.90569	20	40	8.03967	9.99997	8.03970	20
50	7.90829	9.99999	7.90830	10	50	8.04159	9.99997	8.04162	10
28 0	7.91088	9.99999	7.91089	**32** 0	**38** 0	8.04350	9.99997	8.04353	**22** 0
10	7.91346	9.99999	7.91347	50	10	8.04540	9.99997	8.04543	50
20	7.91602	9.99999	7.91603	40	20	8.04729	9.99997	8.04732	40
30	7.91857	9.99999	7.91858	30	30	8.04918	9.99997	8.04921	30
40	7.92110	9.99998	7.92111	20	40	8.05105	9.99997	8.05108	20
50	7.92362	9.99998	7.92363	10	50	8.05292	9.99997	8.05295	10
29 0	7.92612	9.99998	7.92613	**31** 0	**39** 0	8.05478	9.99997	8.05481	**21** 0
10	7.92861	9.99998	7.92862	50	10	8.05663	9.99997	8.05666	50
20	7.93108	9.99998	7.93110	40	20	8.05848	9.99997	8.05851	40
30	7.93354	9.99998	7.93356	30	30	8.06031	9.99997	8.06034	30
40	7.93599	9.99998	7.93601	20	40	8.06214	9.99997	8.06217	20
50	7.93842	9.99998	7.93844	10	50	8.06396	9.99997	8.06399	10
30 0	7.94084	9.99998	7.94086	**30** 0	**40** 0	8.06578	9.99997	8.06581	**20** 0
′″	log cos	log sin	log ctn	′″	′″	log cos	log sin	log ctn	′″

0°

′ ″	log sin	log cos	log tan	′ ″	′ ″	log sin	log cos	log tan	′ ″
40 0	8. 06 578	9. 99 997	8. 06 581	**20** 0	**50** 0	8. 16 268	9. 99 995	8. 16 273	**10** 0
10	8. 06 758	9. 99 997	8. 06 761	50	10	8. 16 413	9. 99 995	8. 16 417	50
20	8. 06 938	9. 99 997	8. 06 941	40	20	8. 16 557	9. 99 995	8. 16 561	40
30	8. 07 117	9. 99 997	8. 07 120	30	30	8. 16 700	9. 99 995	8. 16 705	30
40	8. 07 295	9. 99 997	8. 07 299	20	40	8. 16 843	9. 99 995	8. 16 848	20
50	8. 07 473	9. 99 997	8. 07 476	10	50	8. 16 986	9. 99 995	8. 16 991	10
41 0	8. 07 650	9. 99 997	8. 07 653	**19** 0	**51** 0	8. 17 128	9. 99 995	8. 17 133	**9** 0
10	8. 07 826	9. 99 997	8. 07 829	50	10	8. 17 270	9. 99 995	8. 17 275	50
20	8. 08 002	9. 99 997	8. 08 005	40	20	8. 17 411	9. 99 995	8. 17 416	40
30	8. 08 176	9. 99 997	8. 08 180	30	30	8. 17 552	9. 99 995	8. 17 557	30
40	8. 08 350	9. 99 997	8. 08 354	20	40	8. 17 692	9. 99 995	8. 17 697	20
50	8. 08 524	9. 99 997	8. 08 527	10	50	8. 17 832	9. 99 995	8. 17 837	10
42 0	8. 08 696	9. 99 997	8. 08 700	**18** 0	**52** 0	8. 17 971	9. 99 995	8. 17 976	**8** 0
10	8. 08 868	9. 99 997	8. 08 872	50	10	8. 18 110	9. 99 995	8. 18 115	50
20	8. 09 040	9. 99 997	8. 09 043	40	20	8. 18 249	9. 99 995	8. 18 254	40
30	8. 09 210	9. 99 997	8. 09 214	30	30	8. 18 387	9. 99 995	8. 18 392	30
40	8. 09 380	9. 99 997	8. 09 384	20	40	8. 18 524	9. 99 995	8. 18 530	20
50	8. 09 550	9. 99 997	8. 09 553	10	50	8. 18 662	9. 99 995	8. 18 667	10
43 0	8. 09 718	9. 99 997	8. 09 722	**17** 0	**53** 0	8. 18 798	9. 99 995	8. 18 804	**7** 0
10	8. 09 886	9. 99 997	8. 09 890	50	10	8. 18 935	9. 99 995	8. 18 940	50
20	8. 10 054	9. 99 997	8. 10 057	40	20	8. 19 071	9. 99 995	8. 19 076	40
30	8. 10 220	9. 99 997	8. 10 224	30	30	8. 19 206	9. 99 995	8. 19 212	30
40	8. 10 386	9. 99 997	8. 10 390	20	40	8. 19 341	9. 99 995	8. 19 347	20
50	8. 10 552	9. 99 996	8. 10 555	10	50	8. 19 476	9. 99 995	8. 19 481	10
44 0	8. 10 717	9. 99 996	8. 10 720	**16** 0	**54** 0	8. 19 610	9. 99 995	8. 19 616	**6** 0
10	8. 10 881	9. 99 996	8. 10 884	50	10	8. 19 744	9. 99 995	8. 19 749	50
20	8. 11 044	9. 99 996	8. 11 048	40	20	8. 19 877	9. 99 995	8. 19 883	40
30	8. 11 207	9. 99 996	8. 11 211	30	30	8. 20 010	9. 99 995	8. 20 016	30
40	8. 11 370	9. 99 996	8. 11 373	20	40	8. 20 143	9. 99 995	8. 20 149	20
50	8. 11 531	9. 99 996	8. 11 535	10	50	8. 20 275	9. 99 994	8. 20 281	10
45 0	8. 11 693	9. 99 996	8. 11 696	**15** 0	**55** 0	8. 20 407	9. 99 994	8. 20 413	**5** 0
10	8. 11 853	9. 99 996	8. 11 857	50	10	8. 20 538	9. 99 994	8. 20 544	50
20	8. 12 013	9. 99 996	8. 12 017	40	20	8. 20 669	9. 99 994	8. 20 675	40
30	8. 12 172	9. 99 996	8. 12 176	30	30	8. 20 800	9. 99 994	8. 20 806	30
40	8. 12 331	9. 99 996	8. 12 335	20	40	8. 20 930	9. 99 994	8. 20 936	20
50	8. 12 489	9. 99 996	8. 12 493	10	50	8. 21 060	9. 99 994	8. 21 066	10
46 0	8. 12 647	9. 99 996	8. 12 651	**14** 0	**56** 0	8. 21 189	9. 99 994	8. 21 195	**4** 0
10	8. 12 804	9. 99 996	8. 12 808	50	10	8. 21 319	9. 99 994	8. 21 324	50
20	8. 12 961	9. 99 996	8. 12 965	40	20	8. 21 447	9. 99 994	8. 21 453	40
30	8. 13 117	9. 99 996	8. 13 121	30	30	8. 21 576	9. 99 994	8. 21 581	30
40	8. 13 272	9. 99 996	8. 13 276	20	40	8. 21 703	9. 99 994	8. 21 709	20
50	8. 13 427	9. 99 996	8. 13 431	10	50	8. 21 831	9. 99 994	8. 21 837	10
47 0	8. 13 581	9. 99 996	8. 13 585	**13** 0	**57** 0	8. 21 958	9. 99 994	8. 21 964	**3** 0
10	8. 13 735	9. 99 996	8. 13 739	50	10	8. 22 085	9. 99 994	8. 22 091	50
20	8. 13 888	9. 99 996	8. 13 892	40	20	8. 22 211	9. 99 994	8. 22 217	40
30	8. 14 041	9. 99 996	8. 14 045	30	30	8. 22 337	9. 99 994	8. 22 343	30
40	8. 14 193	9. 99 996	8. 14 197	20	40	8. 22 463	9. 99 994	8. 22 469	20
50	8. 14 344	9. 99 996	8. 14 348	10	50	8. 22 588	9. 99 994	8. 22 595	10
48 0	8. 14 495	9. 99 996	8. 14 500	**12** 0	**58** 0	8. 22 713	9. 99 994	8. 22 720	**2** 0
10	8. 14 646	9. 99 996	8. 14 650	50	10	8. 22 838	9. 99 994	8. 22 844	50
20	8. 14 796	9. 99 996	8. 14 800	40	20	8. 22 962	9. 99 994	8. 22 968	40
30	8. 14 945	9. 99 996	8. 14 950	30	30	8. 23 086	9. 99 994	8. 23 092	30
40	8. 15 094	9. 99 996	8. 15 099	20	40	8. 23 210	9. 99 994	8. 23 216	20
50	8. 15 243	9. 99 996	8. 15 247	10	50	8. 23 333	9. 99 994	8. 23 339	10
49 0	8. 15 391	9. 99 996	8. 15 395	**11** 0	**59** 0	8. 23 456	9. 99 994	8. 23 462	**1** 0
10	8. 15 538	9. 99 996	8. 15 543	50	10	8. 23 578	9. 99 994	8. 23 585	50
20	8. 15 685	9. 99 996	8. 15 690	40	20	8. 23 700	9. 99 994	8. 23 707	40
30	8. 15 832	9. 99 996	8. 15 836	30	30	8. 23 822	9. 99 993	8. 23 829	30
40	8. 15 978	9. 99 995	8. 15 982	20	40	8. 23 944	9. 99 993	8. 23 950	20
50	8. 16 123	9. 99 995	8. 16 128	10	50	8. 24 065	9. 99 993	8. 24 071	10
50 0	8. 16 268	9. 99 995	8. 16 273	**10** 0	**60** 0	8. 24 186	9. 99 993	8. 24 192	**0** 0
′ ″	log cos	log sin	log ctn	′ ″	′ ″	log cos	log sin	log ctn	′ ″

89°

1°

′ ″	log sin	log cos	log tan	′ ″	′ ″	log sin	log cos	log tan	′ ″
0 0	8. 24 186	9. 99 993	8. 24 192	**60** 0	**10** 0	8. 30 879	9. 99 991	8. 30 888	**50** 0
10	8. 24 306	9. 99 993	8. 24 313	50	10	8. 30 983	9. 99 991	8. 30 992	50
20	8. 24 426	9. 99 993	8. 24 433	40	20	8. 31 086	9. 99 991	8. 31 095	40
30	8. 24 546	9. 99 993	8. 24 553	30	30	8. 31 188	9. 99 991	8. 31 198	30
40	8. 24 665	9. 99 993	8. 24 672	20	40	8. 31 291	9. 99 991	8. 31 300	20
50	8. 24 78<u>5</u>	9. 99 993	8. 24 791	10	50	8. 31 393	9. 99 991	8. 31 403	10
1 0	8. 24 903	9. 99 993	8. 24 910	**59** 0	**11** 0	8. 31 495	9. 99 991	8. 31 505	**49** 0
10	8. 25 022	9. 99 993	8. 25 029	50	10	8. 31 597	9. 99 991	8. 31 606	50
20	8. 25 140	9. 99 993	8. 25 147	40	20	8. 31 699	9. 99 991	8. 31 708	40
30	8. 25 258	9. 99 993	8. 25 26<u>5</u>	30	30	8. 31 800	9. 99 991	8. 31 809	30
40	8. 25 375	9. 99 993	8. 25 382	20	40	8. 31 901	9. 99 991	8. 31 911	20
50	8. 25 493	9. 99 993	8. 25 <u>5</u>00	10	50	8. 32 002	9. 99 991	8. 32 012	10
2 0	8. 25 609	9. 99 993	8. 25 616	**58** 0	**12** 0	8. 32 103	9. 99 990	8. 32 112	**48** 0
10	8. 25 726	9. 99 993	8. 25 733	50	10	8. 32 203	9. 99 990	8. 32 213	50
20	8. 25 842	9. 99 993	8. 25 849	40	20	8. 32 303	9. 99 990	8. 32 313	40
30	8. 25 958	9. 99 993	8. 25 965	30	30	8. 32 403	9. 99 990	8. 32 413	30
40	8. 26 074	9. 99 993	8. 26 081	20	40	8. 32 503	9. 99 990	8. 32 513	20
50	8. 26 189	9. 99 993	8. 26 196	10	50	8. 32 602	9. 99 990	8. 32 612	10
3 0	8. 26 304	9. 99 993	8. 26 312	**57** 0	**13** 0	8. 32 702	9. 99 990	8. 32 711	**47** 0
10	8. 26 419	9. 99 993	8. 26 426	50	10	8. 32 801	9. 99 990	8. 32 811	50
20	8. 26 533	9. 99 993	8. 26 541	40	20	8. 32 899	9. 99 990	8. 32 909	40
30	8. 26 648	9. 99 993	8. 26 65<u>5</u>	30	30	8. 32 998	9. 99 990	8. 33 008	30
40	8. 26 761	9. 99 993	8. 26 769	20	40	8. 33 096	9. 99 990	8. 33 106	20
50	8. 26 87<u>5</u>	9. 99 993	8. 26 882	10	50	8. 33 19<u>5</u>	9. 99 990	8. 33 20<u>5</u>	10
4 0	8. 26 988	9. 99 992	8. 26 996	**56** 0	**14** 0	8. 33 292	9. 99 990	8. 33 302	**46** 0
10	8. 27 101	9. 99 992	8. 27 109	50	10	8. 33 390	9. 99 990	8. 33 400	50
20	8. 27 214	9. 99 992	8. 27 221	40	20	8. 33 488	9. 99 990	8. 33 498	40
30	8. 27 326	9. 99 992	8. 27 334	30	30	8. 33 58<u>5</u>	9. 99 990	8. 33 595	30
40	8. 27 438	9. 99 992	8. 27 446	20	40	8. 33 682	9. 99 990	8. 33 692	20
50	8. 27 5<u>5</u>0	9. 99 992	8. 27 558	10	50	8. 33 779	9. 99 990	8. 33 789	10
5 0	8. 27 661	9. 99 992	8. 27 669	**55** 0	**15** 0	8. 33 875	9. 99 990	8. 33 886	**45** 0
10	8. 27 773	9. 99 992	8. 27 780	50	10	8. 33 972	9. 99 990	8. 33 982	50
20	8. 27 883	9. 99 992	8. 27 891	40	20	8. 34 068	9. 99 990	8. 34 078	40
30	8. 27 994	9. 99 992	8. 28 002	30	30	8. 34 164	9. 99 990	8. 34 174	30
40	8. 28 104	9. 99 992	8. 28 112	20	40	8. 34 260	9. 99 989	8. 34 270	20
50	8. 28 21<u>5</u>	9. 99 992	8. 28 223	10	50	8. 34 355	9. 99 989	8. 34 366	10
6 0	8. 28 324	9. 99 992	8. 28 332	**54** 0	**16** 0	8. 34 450	9. 99 989	8. 34 461	**44** 0
10	8. 28 434	9. 99 992	8. 28 442	50	10	8. 34 546	9. 99 989	8. 34 556	50
20	8. 28 543	9. 99 992	8. 28 551	40	20	8. 34 640	9. 99 989	8. 34 651	40
30	8. 28 652	9. 99 992	8. 28 660	30	30	8. 34 735	9. 99 989	8. 34 746	30
40	8. 28 761	9. 99 992	8. 28 769	20	40	8. 34 830	9. 99 989	8. 34 840	20
50	8. 28 869	9. 99 992	8. 28 877	10	50	8. 34 924	9. 99 989	8. 34 93<u>5</u>	10
7 0	8. 28 977	9. 99 992	8. 28 986	**53** 0	**17** 0	8. 35 018	9. 99 989	8. 35 029	**43** 0
10	8. 29 085	9. 99 992	8. 29 094	50	10	8. 35 112	9. 99 989	8. 35 123	50
20	8. 29 193	9. 99 992	8. 29 201	40	20	8. 35 206	9. 99 989	8. 35 217	40
30	8. 29 300	9. 99 992	8. 29 309	30	30	8. 35 299	9. 99 989	8. 35 310	30
40	8. 29 407	9. 99 992	8. 29 416	20	40	8. 35 392	9. 99 989	8. 35 403	20
50	8. 29 514	9. 99 992	8. 29 523	10	50	8. 35 485	9. 99 989	8. 35 497	10
8 0	8. 29 621	9. 99 991	8. 29 629	**52** 0	**18** 0	8. 35 578	9. 99 989	8. 35 590	**42** 0
10	8. 29 727	9. 99 991	8. 29 736	50	10	8. 35 671	9. 99 989	8. 35 682	50
20	8. 29 833	9. 99 991	8. 29 842	40	20	8. 35 764	9. 99 989	8. 35 77<u>5</u>	40
30	8. 29 939	9. 99 991	8. 29 947	30	30	8. 35 856	9. 99 989	8. 35 867	30
40	8. 30 044	9. 99 991	8. 30 053	20	40	8. 35 948	9. 99 989	8. 35 959	20
50	8. 30 1<u>5</u>0	9. 99 991	8. 30 158	10	50	8. 36 040	9. 99 989	8. 36 051	10
9 0	8. 30 25<u>5</u>	9. 99 991	8. 30 263	**51** 0	**19** 0	8. 36 131	9. 99 989	8. 36 143	**41** 0
10	8. 30 359	9. 99 991	8. 30 368	50	10	8. 36 223	9. 99 988	8. 36 235	50
20	8. 30 464	9. 99 991	8. 30 473	40	20	8. 36 314	9. 99 988	8. 36 326	40
30	8. 30 568	9. 99 991	8. 30 577	30	30	8. 36 405	9. 99 988	8. 36 417	30
40	8. 30 672	9. 99 991	8. 30 681	20	40	8. 36 496	9. 99 988	8. 36 508	20
50	8. 30 776	9. 99 991	8. 30 78<u>5</u>	10	50	8. 36 587	9. 99 988	8. 36 599	10
10 0	8. 30 879	9. 99 991	8. 30 888	**50** 0	**20** 0	8. 36 678	9. 99 988	8. 36 689	**40** 0
′ ″	log cos	log sin	log ctn	′ ″	′ ″	log cos	log sin	log ctn	′ ″

88°

1°

′ ″	log sin	log cos	log tan	′ ″	′ ″	log sin	log cos	log tan	′ ″
20 0	8.36 678	9.99 988	8.36 689	**40** 0	**30** 0	8.41 792	9.99 985	8.41 807	**30** 0
10	8.36 768	9.99 988	8.36 780	50	10	8.41 872	9.99 985	8.41 887	50
20	8.36 858	9.99 988	8.36 870	40	20	8.41 952	9.99 985	8.41 967	40
30	8.36 948	9.99 988	8.36 960	30	30	8.42 032	9.99 985	8.42 048	30
40	8.37 038	9.99 988	8.37 050	20	40	8.42 112	9.99 985	8.42 127	20
50	8.37 128	9.99 988	8.37 140	10	50	8.42 192	9.99 985	8.42 207	10
21 0	8.37 217	9.99 988	8.37 229	**39** 0	**31** 0	8.42 272	9.99 985	8.42 287	**29** 0
10	8.37 306	9.99 988	8.37 318	50	10	8.42 351	9.99 985	8.42 366	50
20	8.37 395	9.99 988	8.37 408	40	20	8.42 430	9.99 985	8.42 446	40
30	8.37 484	9.99 988	8.37 497	30	30	8.42 510	9.99 985	8.42 525	30
40	8.37 573	9.99 988	8.37 585	20	40	8.42 589	9.99 985	8.42 604	20
50	8.37 662	9.99 988	8.37 674	10	50	8.42 667	9.99 985	8.42 683	10
22 0	8.37 750	9.99 988	8.37 762	**38** 0	**32** 0	8.42 746	9.99 984	8.42 762	**28** 0
10	8.37 838	9.99 988	8.37 850	50	10	8.42 825	9.99 984	8.42 840	50
20	8.37 926	9.99 988	8.37 938	40	20	8.42 903	9.99 984	8.42 919	40
30	8.38 014	9.99 987	8.38 026	30	30	8.42 982	9.99 984	8.42 997	30
40	8.38 101	9.99 987	8.38 114	20	40	8.43 060	9.99 984	8.43 075	20
50	8.38 189	9.99 987	8.38 202	10	50	8.43 138	9.99 984	8.43 154	10
23 0	8.38 276	9.99 987	8.38 289	**37** 0	**33** 0	8.43 216	9.99 984	8.43 232	**27** 0
10	8.38 363	9.99 987	8.38 376	50	10	8.43 293	9.99 984	8.43 309	50
20	8.38 450	9.99 987	8.38 463	40	20	8.43 371	9.99 984	8.43 387	40
30	8.38 537	9.99 987	8.38 550	30	30	8.43 448	9.99 984	8.43 464	30
40	8.38 624	9.99 987	8.38 636	20	40	8.43 526	9.99 984	8.43 542	20
50	8.38 710	9.99 987	8.38 723	10	50	8.43 603	9.99 984	8.43 619	10
24 0	8.38 796	9.99 987	8.38 809	**36** 0	**34** 0	8.43 680	9.99 984	8.43 696	**26** 0
10	8.38.882	9.99 987	8.38 895	50	10	8.43 757	9.99 984	8.43 773	50
20	8.38 968	9.99 987	8.38 981	40	20	8.43 834	9.99 984	8.43 850	40
30	8.39 054	9.99 987	8.39 067	30	30	8.43 910	9.99 984	8.43 927	30
40	8.39 139	9.99 987	8.39 153	20	40	8.43 987	9.99 984	8.44 003	20
50	8.39 225	9.99 987	8.39 238	10	50	8.44 063	9.99 983	8.44 080	10
25 0	8.39 310	9.99 987	8.39 323	**35** 0	**35** 0	8.44 139	9.99 983	8.44 156	**25** 0
10	8.39 395	9.99 987	8.39 408	50	10	8.44 216	9.99 983	8.44 232	50
20	8.39 480	9.99 987	8.39 493	40	20	8.44 292	9.99 983	8.44 308	40
30	8.39 565	9.99 987	8.39 578	30	30	8.44 367	9.99 983	8.44 384	30
40	8.39 649	9.99 987	8.39 663	20	40	8.44 443	9.99 983	8.44 460	20
50	8.39 734	9.99 986	8.39 747	10	50	8.44 519	9.99 983	8.44 536	10
26 0	8.39 818	9.99 986	8.39 832	**34** 0	**36** 0	8.44 594	9.99 983	8.44 611	**24** 0
10	8.39 902	9.99 986	8.39 916	50	10	8.44 669	9.99 983	8.44 686	50
20	8.39 986	9.99 986	8.40 000	40	20	8.44 745	9.99 983	8.44 762	40
30	8.40 070	9.99 986	8.40 083	30	30	8.44 820	9.99 983	8.44 837	30
40	8.40 153	9.99 986	8.40 167	20	40	8.44 895	9.99 983	8.44 912	20
50	8.40 237	9.99 986	8.40 251	10	50	8.44 969	9.99 983	8.44 987	10
27 0	8.40 320	9.99 986	8.40 334	**33** 0	**37** 0	8.45 044	9.99 983	8.45 061	**23** 0
10	8.40 403	9.99 986	8.40 417	50	10	8.45 119	9.99 983	8.45 136	50
20	8.40 486	9.99 986	8.40 500	40	20	8.45 193	9.99 983	8.45 210	40
30	8.40 569	9.99 986	8.40 583	30	30	8.45 267	9.99 983	8.45 285	30
40	8.40 651	9.99 986	8.40 665	20	40	8.45 341	9.99 982	8.45 359	20
50	8.40 734	9.99 986	8.40 748	10	50	8.45 415	9.99 982	8.45 433	10
28 0	8.40 816	9.99 986	8.40 830	**32** 0	**38** 0	8.45 489	9.99 982	8.45 507	**22** 0
10	8.40 898	9.99 986	8.40 913	50	10	8.45 563	9.99 982	8.45 581	50
20	8.40 980	9.99 986	8.40 995	40	20	8.45 637	9.99 982	8.45 655	40
30	8.41 062	9.99 986	8.41 077	30	30	8.45 710	9.99 982	8.45 728	30
40	8.41 144	9.99 986	8.41 158	20	40	8.45 784	9.99 982	8.45 802	20
50	8.41 225	9.99 986	8.41 240	10	50	8.45 857	9.99 982	8.45 875	10
29 0	8.41 307	9.99 985	8.41 321	**31** 0	**39** 0	8.45 930	9.99 982	8.45 948	**21** 0
10	8.41 388	9.99 985	8.41 403	50	10	8.46 003	9.99 982	8.46 021	50
20	8.41 469	9.99 985	8.41 484	40	20	8.46 076	9.99 982	8.46 094	40
30	8.41 550	9.99 985	8.41 565	30	30	8.46 149	9.99 982	8.46 167	30
40	8.41 631	9.99 985	8.41 646	20	40	8.46 222	9.99 982	8.46 240	20
50	8.41 711	9.99 985	8.41 726	10	50	8.46 294	9.99 982	8.46 312	10
30 0	8.41 792	9.99 985	8.41 807	**30** 0	**40** 0	8.46 366	9.99 982	8.46 385	**20** 0
′ ″	log cos	log sin	log ctn	′ ″	′ ″	log cos	log sin	log ctn	′ ″

1°

′ ″	log sin	log cos	log tan	′ ″	′ ″	log sin	log cos	log tan	′ ″
40 0	8. 46 366	9. 99 982	8. 46 385	**20** 0	**50** 0	8. 50 504	9. 99 978	8. 50 527	**10** 0
10	8. 46 439	9. 99 982	8. 46 457	50	10	8. 50 570	9. 99 978	8. 50 593	50
20	8. 46 511	9. 99 982	8. 46 529	40	20	8. 50 636	9. 99 978	8. 50 658	40
30	8. 46 583	9. 99 981	8. 46 602	30	30	8. 50 701	9. 99 978	8. 50 724	30
40	8. 46 65<u>5</u>	9. 99 981	8. 46 674	20	40	8. 50 767	9. 99 977	8. 50 789	20
50	8. 46 727	9. 99 981	8. 46 745	10	50	8. 50 832	9. 99 977	8. 50 85<u>5</u>	10
41 0	8. 46 799	9. 99 981	8. 46 817	**19** 0	**51** 0	8. 50 897	9. 99 977	8. 50 920	**9** 0
10	8. 46 870	9. 99 981	8. 46 889	50	10	8. 50 963	9. 99 977	8. 50 985	50
20	8. 46 942	9. 99 981	8. 46 960	40	20	8. 51 028	9. 99 977	8. 51 050	40
30	8. 47 013	9. 99 981	8. 47 032	30	30	8. 51 092	9. 99 977	8. 51 115	30
40	8. 47 084	9. 99 981	8. 47 103	20	40	8. 51 157	9. 99 977	8. 51 180	20
50	8. 47 155	9. 99 981	8. 47 174	10	50	8. 51 222	9. 99 977	8. 51 245	10
42 0	8. 47 226	9. 99 981	8. 47 245	**18** 0	**52** 0	8. 51 287	9. 99 977	8. 51 310	**8** 0
10	8. 47 297	9. 99 981	8. 47 316	50	10	8. 51 351	9. 99 977	8. 51 374	50
20	8. 47 368	9. 99 981	8. 47 387	40	20	8. 51 416	9. 99 977	8. 51 439	40
30	8. 47 439	9. 99 981	8. 47 458	30	30	8. 51 480	9. 99 977	8. 51 503	30
40	8. 47 509	9. 99 981	8. 47 528	20	40	8. 51 544	9. 99 977	8. 51 568	20
50	8. 47 580	9. 99 981	8. 47 599	10	50	8. 51 609	9. 99 977	8. 51 632	10
43 0	8. 47 6<u>5</u>0	9. 99 981	8. 47 669	**17** 0	**53** 0	8. 51 673	9. 99 977	8. 51 696	**7** 0
10	8. 47 720	9. 99 980	8. 47 740	50	10	8. 51 737	9. 99 976	8. 51 760	50
20	8. 47 790	9. 99 980	8. 47 810	40	20	8. 51 801	9. 99 976	8. 51 824	40
30	8. 47 860	9. 99 980	8. 47 880	30	30	8. 51 864	9. 99 976	8. 51 888	30
40	8. 47 930	9. 99 980	8. 47 9<u>5</u>0	20	40	8. 51 928	9. 99 976	8. 51 952	20
50	8. 48 000	9. 99 980	8. 48 020	10	50	8. 51 992	9. 99 976	8. 52 015	10
44 0	8. 48 069	9. 99 980	8. 48 089	**16** 0	**54** 0	8. 52 055	9. 99 976	8. 52 079	**6** 0
10	8. 48 139	9. 99 980	8. 48 159	50	10	8. 52 119	9. 99 976	8. 52 143	50
20	8. 48 208	9. 99 980	8. 48 228	40	20	8. 52 182	9. 99 976	8. 52 206	40
30	8. 48 278	9. 99 980	8. 48 298	30	30	8. 52 245	9. 99 976	8. 52 269	30
40	8. 48 347	9. 99 980	8. 48 367	20	40	8. 52 308	9. 99 976	8. 52 332	20
50	8. 48 416	9. 99 980	8. 48 436	10	50	8. 52 371	9. 99 976	8. 52 396	10
45 0	8. 48 48<u>5</u>	9. 99 980	8. 48 505	**15** 0	**55** 0	8. 52 434	9. 99 976	8. 52 459	**5** 0
10	8. 48 554	9. 99 980	8. 48 574	50	10	8. 52 497	9. 99 976	8. 52 522	50
20	8. 48 622	9. 99 980	8. 48 643	40	20	8. 52 560	9. 99 976	8. 52 584	40
30	8. 48 691	9. 99 980	8. 48 711	30	30	8. 52 623	9. 99 975	8. 52 647	30
40	8. 48 760	9. 99 979	8. 48 780	20	40	8. 52 685	9. 99 975	8. 52 710	20
50	8. 48 828	9. 99 979	8. 48 849	10	50	8. 52 748	9. 99 975	8. 52 772	10
46 0	8. 48 896	9. 99 979	8. 48 917	**14** 0	**56** 0	8. 52 810	9. 99 975	8. 52 83<u>5</u>	**4** 0
10	8. 48 96<u>5</u>	9. 99 979	8. 48 985	50	10	8. 52 872	9. 99 975	8. 52 897	50
20	8. 49 033	9. 99 979	8. 49 053	40	20	8. 52 93<u>5</u>	9. 99 975	8. 52 960	40
30	8. 49 101	9. 99 979	8. 49 121	30	30	8. 52 997	9. 99 975	8. 53 022	30
40	8. 49 169	9. 99 979	8. 49 189	20	40	8. 53 059	9. 99 97<u>5</u>	8. 53 084	20
50	8. 49 236	9. 99 979	8. 49 257	10	50	8. 53 121	9. 99 97<u>5</u>	8. 53 146	10
47 0	8. 49 304	9. 99 979	8. 49 325	**13** 0	**57** 0	8. 53 183	9. 99 97<u>5</u>	8. 53 208	**3** 0
10	8. 49 372	9. 99 979	8. 49 393	50	10	8. 53 24<u>5</u>	9. 99 97<u>5</u>	8. 53 270	50
20	8. 49 439	9. 99 979	8. 49 460	40	20	8. 53 306	9. 99 97<u>5</u>	8. 53 332	40
30	8. 49 506	9. 99 979	8. 49 528	30	30	8. 53 368	9. 99 97<u>5</u>	8. 53 393	30
40	8. 49 574	9. 99 979	8. 49 595	20	40	8. 53 429	9. 99 97<u>5</u>	8. 53 45<u>5</u>	20
50	8. 49 641	9. 99 979	8. 49 662	10	50	8. 53 491	9. 99 974	8. 53 516	10
48 0	8. 49 708	9. 99 979	8. 49 729	**12** 0	**58** 0	8. 53 552	9. 99 974	8. 53 578	**2** 0
10	8. 49 77<u>5</u>	9. 99 979	8. 49 796	50	10	8. 53 614	9. 99 974	8. 53 639	50
20	8. 49 842	9. 99 978	8. 49 863	40	20	8. 53 67<u>5</u>	9. 99 974	8. 53 700	40
30	8. 49 908	9. 99 978	8. 49 930	30	30	8. 53 736	9. 99 974	8. 53 762	30
40	8. 49 975	9. 99 978	8. 49 997	20	40	8. 53 797	9. 99 974	8. 53 823	20
50	8. 50 042	9. 99 978	8. 50 063	10	50	8. 53 858	9. 99 974	8. 53 884	10
49 0	8. 50 108	9. 99 978	8. 50 130	**11** 0	**59** 0	8. 53 919	9. 99 974	8. 53 94<u>5</u>	**1** 0
10	8. 50 174	9. 99 978	8. 50 196	50	10	8. 53 979	9. 99 974	8. 54 005	50
20	8. 50 241	9. 99 978	8. 50 263	40	20	8. 54 040	9. 99 974	8. 54 066	40
30	8. 50 307	9. 99 978	8. 50 329	30	30	8. 54 101	9. 99 974	8. 54 127	30
40	8. 50 373	9. 99 978	8. 50 39<u>5</u>	20	40	8. 54 161	9. 99 974	8. 54 187	20
50	8. 50 439	9. 99 978	8. 50 461	10	50	8. 54 222	9. 99 974	8. 54 248	10
50 0	8. 50 504	9. 99 978	8. 50 527	**10** 0	**60** 0	8. 54 282	9. 99 974	8. 54 308	**0** 0
′ ″	log cos	log sin	log ctn	′ ″	′ ″	log cos	log sin	log ctn	′ ″

88°

1°

′	log sin 8	log cos 9	log tan 8	log ctn 11	′
0	24 186	99 993	24 192	75 808	60
1	24 903	99 993	24 910	75 090	59
2	25 609	99 993	25 616	74 384	58
3	26 304	99 993	26 312	73 688	57
4	26 988	99 992	26 996	73 004	56
5	27 661	99 992	27 669	72 331	55
6	28 324	99 992	28 332	71 668	54
7	28 977	99 992	28 986	71 014	53
8	29 621	99 992	29 629	70 371	52
9	30 255	99 991	30 263	69 737	51
10	30 879	99 991	30 888	69 112	50
11	31 495	99 991	31 505	68 495	49
12	32 103	99 990	32 112	67 888	48
13	32 702	99 990	32 711	67 289	47
14	33 292	99 990	33 302	66 698	46
15	33 875	99 990	33 886	66 114	45
16	34 450	99 989	34 461	65 539	44
17	35 018	99 989	35 029	64 971	43
18	35 578	99 989	35 590	64 410	42
19	36 131	99 989	36 143	63 857	41
20	36 678	99 988	36 689	63 311	40
21	37 217	99 988	37 229	62 771	39
22	37 750	99 988	37 762	62 238	38
23	38 276	99 987	38 289	61 711	37
24	38 796	99 987	38 809	61 191	36
25	39 310	99 987	39 323	60 677	35
26	39 818	99 986	39 832	60 168	34
27	40 320	99 986	40 334	59 666	33
28	40 816	99 986	40 830	59 170	32
29	41 307	99 985	41 321	58 679	31
30	41 792	99 985	41 807	58 193	30
31	42 272	99 985	42 287	57 713	29
32	42 746	99 984	42 762	57 238	28
33	43 216	99 984	43 232	56 768	27
34	43 680	99 984	43 696	56 304	26
35	44 139	99 983	44 156	55 844	25
36	44 594	99 983	44 611	55 389	24
37	45 044	99 983	45 061	54 939	23
38	45 489	99 982	45 507	54 493	22
39	45 930	99 982	45 948	54 052	21
40	46 366	99 982	46 385	53 615	20
41	46 799	99 981	46 817	53 183	19
42	47 226	99 981	47 245	52 755	18
43	47 650	99 981	47 669	52 331	17
44	48 069	99 980	48 089	51 911	16
45	48 485	99 980	48 505	51 495	15
46	48 896	99 979	48 917	51 083	14
47	49 304	99 979	49 325	50 675	13
48	49 708	99 979	49 729	50 271	12
49	50 108	99 978	50 130	49 870	11
50	50 504	99 978	50 527	49 473	10
51	50 897	99 977	50 920	49 080	9
52	51 287	99 977	51 310	48 690	8
53	51 673	99 977	51 696	48 304	7
54	52 055	99 976	52 079	47 921	6
55	52 434	99 976	52 459	47 541	5
56	52 810	99 975	52 835	47 165	4
57	53 183	99 975	53 208	46 792	3
58	53 552	99 974	53 578	46 422	2
59	53 919	99 974	53 945	46 055	1
60	54 282	99 974	54 308	45 692	0
′	log cos 8	log sin 9	log ctn 8	log tan 11	′

88°

2°

′	log sin 8	log cos 9	log tan 8	log ctn 11	′
0	54 282	99 974	54 308	45 692	60
1	54 642	99 973	54 669	45 331	59
2	54 999	99 973	55 027	44 973	58
3	55 354	99 972	55 382	44 618	57
4	55 705	99 972	55 734	44 266	56
5	56 054	99 971	56 083	43 917	55
6	56 400	99 971	56 429	43 571	54
7	56 743	99 970	56 773	43 227	53
8	57 084	99 970	57 114	42 886	52
9	57 421	99 969	57 452	42 548	51
10	57 757	99 969	57 788	42 212	50
11	58 089	99 968	58 121	41 879	49
12	58 419	99 968	58 451	41 549	48
13	58 747	99 967	58 779	41 221	47
14	59 072	99 967	59 105	40 895	46
15	59 395	99 966	59 428	40 572	45
16	59 715	99 966	59 749	40 251	44
17	60 033	99 966	60 068	39 932	43
18	60 349	99 965	60 384	39 616	42
19	60 662	99 964	60 698	39 302	41
20	60 973	99 964	61 009	38 991	40
21	61 282	99 963	61 319	38 681	39
22	61 589	99 963	61 626	38 374	38
23	61 894	99 962	61 931	38 069	37
24	62 196	99 962	62 234	37 766	36
25	62 497	99 961	62 535	37 465	35
26	62 795	99 961	62 834	37 166	34
27	63 091	99 960	63 131	36 869	33
28	63 385	99 960	63 426	36 574	32
29	63 678	99 959	63 718	36 282	31
30	63 968	99 959	64 009	35 991	30
31	64 256	99 958	64 298	35 702	29
32	64 543	99 958	64 585	35 415	28
33	64 827	99 957	64 870	35 130	27
34	65 110	99 956	65 154	34 846	26
35	65 391	99 956	65 435	34 565	25
36	65 670	99 955	65 715	34 285	24
37	65 947	99 955	65 993	34 007	23
38	66 223	99 954	66 269	33 731	22
39	66 497	99 954	66 543	33 457	21
40	66 769	99 953	66 816	33 184	20
41	67 039	99 952	67 087	32 913	19
42	67 308	99 952	67 356	32 644	18
43	67 575	99 951	67 624	32 376	17
44	67 841	99 951	67 890	32 110	16
45	68 104	99 950	68 154	31 846	15
46	68 367	99 949	68 417	31 583	14
47	68 627	99 949	68 678	31 322	13
48	68 886	99 948	68 938	31 062	12
49	69 144	99 948	69 196	30 804	11
50	69 400	99 947	69 453	30 547	10
51	69 654	99 946	69 708	30 292	9
52	69 907	99 946	69 962	30 038	8
53	70 159	99 945	70 214	29 786	7
54	70 409	99 944	70 465	29 535	6
55	70 658	99 944	70 714	29 286	5
56	70 905	99 943	70 962	29 038	4
57	71 151	99 942	71 208	28 792	3
58	71 395	99 942	71 453	28 547	2
59	71 638	99 941	71 697	28 303	1
60	71 880	99 940	71 940	28 060	0
′	log cos 8	log sin 9	log ctn 8	log tan 11	′

87°

3°

′	log sin 8	log cos 9	log tan 8	log ctn 11	′
0	71 880	99 940	71 940	28 060	60
1	72 120	940	72 181	27 819	59
2	359	939	420	580	58
3	597	938	659	341	57
4	72 834	938	72 896	27 104	56
5	73 069	99 937	73 132	26 868	55
6	303	936	366	634	54
7	535	936	600	400	53
8	767	935	73 832	26 168	52
9	73 997	934	74 063	25 937	51
10	74 226	99 934	74 292	25 708	50
11	454	933	521	479	49
12	680	932	748	252	48
13	74 906	932	74 974	25 026	47
14	75 130	931	75 199	24 801	46
15	75 353	99 930	75 423	24 577	45
16	575	929	645	355	44
17	75 795	929	75 867	24 133	43
18	76 015	928	76 087	23 913	42
19	234	927	306	694	41
20	76 451	99 926	76 525	23 475	40
21	667	926	742	258	39
22	76 883	925	76 958	23 042	38
23	77 097	924	77 173	22 827	37
24	310	923	387	613	36
25	77 522	99 923	77 600	22 400	35
26	733	922	77 811	22 189	34
27	77 943	921	78 022	21 978	33
28	78 152	920	232	768	32
29	360	920	441	559	31
30	78 568	99 919	78 649	21 351	30
31	774	918	78 855	21 145	29
32	78 979	917	79 061	20 939	28
33	79 183	917	266	734	27
34	386	916	470	530	26
35	79 588	99 915	79 673	20 327	25
36	789	914	79 875	20 125	24
37	79 990	913	80 076	19 924	23
38	80 189	913	277	723	22
39	388	912	476	524	21
40	80 585	99 911	80 674	19 326	20
41	782	910	80 872	19 128	19
42	80 978	909	81 068	18 932	18
43	81 173	909	264	736	17
44	367	908	459	541	16
45	81 560	99 907	81 653	18 347	15
46	752	906	81 846	18 154	14
47	81 944	905	82 038	17 962	13
48	82 134	904	230	770	12
49	324	904	420	580	11
50	82 513	99 903	82 610	17 390	10
51	701	902	799	201	9
52	82 888	901	82 987	17 013	8
53	83 075	900	83 175	16 825	7
54	261	899	361	639	6
55	83 446	99 898	83 547	16 453	5
56	630	898	732	268	4
57	813	897	83 916	16 084	3
58	83 996	896	84 100	15 900	2
59	84 177	895	282	718	1
60	84 358	99 894	84 464	15 536	0
′	log cos 8	log sin 9	log ctn 8	log tan 11	′

86°

4°

′	log sin 8	log cos 9	log tan 8	log ctn 11	′
0	84 358	99 894	84 464	15 536	60
1	539	893	646	354	59
2	718	892	84 826	15 174	58
3	84 897	891	85 006	14 994	57
4	85 075	891	185	815	56
5	85 252	99 890	85 363	14 637	55
6	429	889	540	460	54
7	605	888	717	283	53
8	780	887	85 893	14 107	52
9	85 955	886	86 069	13 931	51
10	86 128	99 885	86 243	13 757	50
11	301	884	417	583	49
12	474	883	591	409	48
13	645	882	763	237	47
14	816	881	86 935	13 065	46
15	86 987	99 880	87 106	12 894	45
16	87 156	879	277	723	44
17	325	879	447	553	43
18	494	878	616	384	42
19	661	877	785	215	41
20	87 829	99 876	87 953	12 047	40
21	87 995	875	88 120	11 880	39
22	88 161	874	287	713	38
23	326	873	453	547	37
24	490	872	618	382	36
25	88 654	99 871	88 783	11 217	35
26	817	870	88 948	11 052	34
27	88 980	869	89 111	10 889	33
28	89 142	868	274	726	32
29	304	867	437	563	31
30	89 464	99 866	89 598	10 402	30
31	625	865	760	240	29
32	784	864	89 920	10 080	28
33	89 943	863	90 080	09 920	27
34	90 102	862	240	760	26
35	90 260	99 861	90 399	09 601	25
36	417	860	557	443	24
37	574	859	715	285	23
38	730	858	90 872	09 128	22
39	90 885	857	91 029	08 971	21
40	91 040	99 856	91 185	08 815	20
41	195	855	340	660	19
42	349	854	495	505	18
43	502	853	650	350	17
44	655	852	803	197	16
45	91 807	99 851	91 957	08 043	15
46	91 959	850	92 110	07 890	14
47	92 110	848	262	738	13
48	261	847	414	586	12
49	411	846	565	435	11
50	92 561	99 845	92 716	07 284	10
51	710	844	92 866	07 134	9
52	92 859	843	93 016	06 984	8
53	93 007	842	165	835	7
54	154	841	313	687	6
55	93 301	99 840	93 462	06 538	5
56	448	839	609	391	4
57	594	838	756	244	3
58	740	837	93 903	06 097	2
59	93 885	836	94 049	05 951	1
60	94 030	99 834	94 195	05 805	0
′	log cos 8	log sin 9	log ctn 8	log tan 11	′

85°

5°

′	log sin	log cos	log tan	log ctn	′
	8	9	8	11	
0	94 030	99 834	94 195	05 805	60
1	174	833	340	660	59
2	317	832	485	515	58
3	461	831	630	370	57
4	603	830	773	227	56
5	94 746	99 829	94 917	05 083	55
6	94 887	828	95 060	04 940	54
7	95 029	827	202	798	53
8	170	825	344	656	52
9	310	824	486	514	51
10	95 450	99 823	95 627	04 373	50
11	589	822	767	233	49
12	728	821	95 908	04 092	48
13	95 867	820	96 047	03 953	47
14	96 005	819	187	813	46
15	96 143	99 817	96 325	03 675	45
16	280	816	464	536	44
17	417	815	602	398	43
18	553	814	739	261	42
19	689	813	96 877	03 123	41
20	96 825	99 812	97 013	02 987	40
21	96 960	810	150	850	39
22	97 095	809	285	715	38
23	229	808	421	579	37
24	363	807	556	444	36
25	97 496	99 806	97 691	02 309	35
26	629	804	825	175	34
27	762	803	97 959	02 041	33
28	97 894	802	98 092	01 908	32
29	98 026	801	225	775	31
30	98 157	99 800	98 358	01 642	30
31	288	798	490	510	29
32	419	797	622	378	28
33	549	796	753	247	27
34	679	795	98 884	01 116	26
35	98 808	99 793	99 015	00 985	25
36	98 937	792	145	855	24
37	99 066	791	275	725	23
38	194	790	405	595	22
39	322	788	534	466	21
40	99 450	99 787	99 662	00 338	20
41	577	786	791	209	19
42	704	785	99 919	00 081	18
43	830	783	00 046	99 954	17
44	99 956	782	174	826	16
45	00 082	99 781	00 301	99 699	15
46	207	780	427	573	14
47	332	778	553	447	13
48	456	777	679	321	12
49	581	776	805	195	11
50	00 704	99 775	00 930	99 070	10
51	828	773	01 055	98 945	9
52	00 951	772	179	821	8
53	01 074	771	303	697	7
54	196	769	427	573	6
55	01 318	99 768	01 550	98 450	5
56	440	767	673	327	4
57	561	765	796	204	3
58	682	764	01 918	98 082	2
59	803	763	02 040	97 960	1
60	01 923	99 761	02 162	97 838	0
	9	9	9	10	
′	log cos	log sin	log ctn	log tan	′

84°

6°

′	log sin	log cos	log tan	log ctn	′
	9	9	9	10	
0	01 923	99 761	02 162	97 838	60
1	02 043	760	283	717	59
2	163	759	404	596	58
3	283	757	525	475	57
4	402	756	645	355	56
5	02 520	99 755	02 766	97 234	55
6	639	753	02 885	97 115	54
7	757	752	03 005	96 995	53
8	874	751	124	876	52
9	02 992	749	242	758	51
10	03 109	99 748	03 361	96 639	50
11	226	747	479	521	49
12	342	745	597	403	48
13	458	744	714	286	47
14	574	742	832	168	46
15	03 690	99 741	03 948	96 052	45
16	805	740	04 065	95 935	44
17	03 920	738	181	819	43
18	04 034	737	297	703	42
19	149	736	413	587	41
20	04 262	99 734	04 528	95 472	40
21	376	733	643	357	39
22	490	731	758	242	38
23	603	730	873	127	37
24	715	728	04 987	95 013	36
25	04 828	99 727	05 101	94 899	35
26	04 940	726	214	786	34
27	05 052	724	328	672	33
28	164	723	441	559	32
29	275	721	553	447	31
30	05 386	99 720	05 666	94 334	30
31	497	718	778	222	29
32	607	717	05 890	94 110	28
33	717	716	06 002	93 998	27
34	827	714	113	887	26
35	05 937	99 713	06 224	93 776	25
36	06 046	711	335	665	24
37	155	710	445	555	23
38	264	708	556	444	22
39	372	707	666	334	21
40	06 481	99 705	06 775	93 225	20
41	589	704	885	115	19
42	696	702	06 994	93 006	18
43	804	701	07 103	92 897	17
44	06 911	699	211	789	16
45	07 018	99 698	07 320	92 680	15
46	124	696	428	572	14
47	231	695	536	464	13
48	337	693	643	357	12
49	442	692	751	249	11
50	07 548	99 690	07 858	92 142	10
51	653	689	07 964	92 036	9
52	758	687	08 071	91 929	8
53	863	686	177	823	7
54	07 968	684	283	717	6
55	08 072	99 683	08 389	91 611	5
56	176	681	495	505	4
57	280	680	600	400	3
58	383	678	705	295	2
59	486	677	810	190	1
60	08 589	99 675	08 914	91 086	0
	9	9	9	10	
′	log cos	log sin	log ctn	log tan	′

83°

7°

′	log sin 9	log cos 9	log tan 9	log ctn 10	′
0	08 589	99 675	08 914	91 086	60
1	692	674	09 019	90 981	59
2	795	672	123	877	58
3	897	670	227	773	57
4	08 999	669	330	670	56
5	09 101	99 667	09 434	90 566	55
6	202	666	537	463	54
7	304	664	640	360	53
8	405	663	742	258	52
9	506	661	845	155	51
10	09 606	99 659	09 947	90 053	50
11	707	658	10 049	89 951	49
12	807	656	150	850	48
13	09 907	655	252	748	47
14	10 006	653	353	647	46
15	10 106	99 651	10 454	89 546	45
16	205	650	555	445	44
17	304	648	656	344	43
18	402	647	756	244	42
19	501	645	856	144	41
20	10 599	99 643	10 956	89 044	40
21	697	642	11 056	88 944	39
22	795	640	155	845	38
23	893	638	254	746	37
24	10 990	637	353	647	36
25	11 087	99 635	11 452	88 548	35
26	184	633	551	449	34
27	281	632	649	351	33
28	377	630	747	253	32
29	474	629	845	155	31
30	11 570	99 627	11 943	88 057	30
31	666	625	12 040	87 960	29
32	761	624	138	862	28
33	857	622	235	765	27
34	11 952	620	332	668	26
35	12 047	99 618	12 428	87 572	25
36	142	617	525	475	24
37	236	615	621	379	23
38	331	613	717	283	22
39	425	612	813	187	21
40	12 519	99 610	12 909	87 091	20
41	612	608	13 004	86 996	19
42	706	607	099	901	18
43	799	605	194	806	17
44	892	603	289	711	16
45	12 985	99 601	13 384	86 616	15
46	13 078	600	478	522	14
47	171	598	573	427	13
48	263	596	667	333	12
49	355	595	761	239	11
50	13 447	99 593	13 854	86 146	10
51	539	591	13 948	86 052	9
52	630	589	14 041	85 959	8
53	722	588	134	866	7
54	813	586	227	773	6
55	13 904	99 584	14 320	85 680	5
56	13 994	582	412	588	4
57	14 085	581	504	496	3
58	175	579	597	403	2
59	266	577	688	312	1
60	14 356	99 575	14 780	85 220	0
′	9 log cos	9 log sin	9 log ctn	10 log tan	′

8°

′	log sin 9	log cos 9	log tan 9	log ctn 10	′
0	14 356	99 575	14 780	85 220	60
1	445	574	872	128	59
2	535	572	14 963	85 037	58
3	624	570	15 054	84 946	57
4	714	568	145	855	56
5	14 803	99 566	15 236	84 764	55
6	891	565	327	673	54
7	14 980	563	417	583	53
8	15 069	561	508	492	52
9	157	559	598	402	51
10	15 245	99 557	15 688	84 312	50
11	333	556	777	223	49
12	421	554	867	133	48
13	508	552	15 956	84 044	47
14	596	550	16 046	83 954	46
15	15 683	99 548	16 135	83 865	45
16	770	546	224	776	44
17	857	545	312	688	43
18	15 944	543	401	599	42
19	16 030	541	489	511	41
20	16 116	99 539	16 577	83 423	40
21	203	537	665	335	39
22	289	535	753	247	38
23	374	533	841	159	37
24	460	532	16 928	83 072	36
25	16 545	99 530	17 016	82 984	35
26	631	528	103	897	34
27	716	526	190	810	33
28	801	524	277	723	32
29	886	522	363	637	31
30	16 970	99 520	17 450	82 550	30
31	17 055	518	536	464	29
32	139	517	622	378	28
33	223	515	708	292	27
34	307	513	794	206	26
35	17 391	99 511	17 880	82 120	25
36	474	509	17 965	82 035	24
37	558	507	18 051	81 949	23
38	641	505	136	864	22
39	724	503	221	779	21
40	17 807	99 501	18 306	81 694	20
41	890	499	391	609	19
42	17 973	497	475	525	18
43	18 055	495	560	440	17
44	137	494	644	356	16
45	18 220	99 492	18 728	81 272	15
46	302	490	812	188	14
47	383	488	896	104	13
48	465	486	18 979	81 021	12
49	547	484	19 063	80 937	11
50	18 628	99 482	19 146	80 854	10
51	709	480	229	771	9
52	790	478	312	688	8
53	871	476	395	605	7
54	18 952	474	478	522	6
55	19 033	99 472	19 561	80 439	5
56	113	470	643	357	4
57	193	468	725	275	3
58	273	466	807	193	2
59	353	464	889	111	1
60	19 433	99 462	19 971	80 029	0
′	9 log cos	9 log sin	9 log ctn	10 log tan	′

82°   81°

9°

′	log sin 9	log cos 9	log tan 9	log ctn 10	′
0	19 433	99 462	19 971	80 029	**60**
1	513	460	20 053	79 947	59
2	592	458	134	866	58
3	672	456	216	784	57
4	751	454	297	703	56
5	19 830	99 452	20 378	79 622	**55**
6	909	450	459	541	54
7	19 988	448	540	460	53
8	20 067	446	621	379	52
9	145	444	701	299	51
10	20 223	99 442	20 782	79 218	**50**
11	302	440	862	138	49
12	380	438	20 942	79 058	48
13	458	436	21 022	78 978	47
14	535	434	102	898	46
15	20 613	99 432	21 182	78 818	**45**
16	691	429	261	739	44
17	768	427	341	659	43
18	845	425	420	580	42
19	922	423	499	501	41
20	20 999	99 421	21 578	78 422	**40**
21	21 076	419	657	343	39
22	153	417	736	264	38
23	229	415	814	186	37
24	306	413	893	107	36
25	21 382	99 411	21 971	78 029	**35**
26	458	409	22 049	77 951	34
27	534	407	127	873	33
28	610	404	205	795	32
29	685	402	283	717	31
30	21 761	99 400	22 361	77 639	**30**
31	836	398	438	562	29
32	912	396	516	484	28
33	21 987	394	593	407	27
34	22 062	392	670	330	26
35	22 137	99 390	22 747	77 253	**25**
36	211	388	824	176	24
37	286	385	901	099	23
38	361	383	22 977	77 023	22
39	435	381	23 054	76 946	21
40	22 509	99 379	23 130	76 870	**20**
41	583	377	206	794	19
42	657	375	283	717	18
43	731	372	359	641	17
44	805	370	435	565	16
45	22 878	99 368	23 510	76 490	**15**
46	22 952	366	586	414	14
47	23 025	364	661	339	13
48	098	362	737	263	12
49	171	359	812	188	11
50	23 244	99 357	23 887	76 113	**10**
51	317	355	23 962	76 038	9
52	390	353	24 037	75 963	8
53	462	351	112	888	7
54	535	348	186	814	6
55	23 607	99 346	24 261	75 739	**5**
56	679	344	335	665	4
57	752	342	410	590	3
58	823	340	484	516	2
59	895	337	558	442	1
60	23 967	99 335	24 632	75 368	**0**
	log cos 9	log sin 9	log ctn 9	log tan 10	′

80°

10°

′	log sin 9	log cos 9	log tan 9	log ctn 10	′
0	23 967	99 335	24 632	75 368	**60**
1	24 039	333	706	294	59
2	110	331	779	221	58
3	181	328	853	147	57
4	253	326	24 926	074	56
5	24 324	99 324	25 000	75 000	**55**
6	395	322	073	74 927	54
7	466	319	146	854	53
8	536	317	219	781	52
9	607	315	292	708	51
10	24 677	99 313	25 365	74 635	**50**
11	748	310	437	563	49
12	818	308	510	490	48
13	888	306	582	418	47
14	24 958	304	655	345	46
15	25 028	99 301	25 727	74 273	**45**
16	098	299	799	201	44
17	168	297	871	129	43
18	237	294	25 943	74 057	42
19	307	292	26 015	73 985	41
20	25 376	99 290	26 086	73 914	**40**
21	445	288	158	842	39
22	514	285	229	771	38
23	583	283	301	699	37
24	652	281	372	628	36
25	25 721	99 278	26 443	73 557	**35**
26	790	276	514	486	34
27	858	274	585	415	33
28	927	271	655	345	32
29	25 995	269	726	274	31
30	26 063	99 267	26 797	73 203	**30**
31	131	264	867	133	29
32	199	262	26 937	73 063	28
33	267	260	27 008	72 992	27
34	335	257	078	922	26
35	26 403	99 255	27 148	72 852	**25**
36	470	252	218	782	24
37	538	250	288	712	23
38	605	248	357	643	22
39	672	245	427	573	21
40	26 739	99 243	27 496	72 504	**20**
41	806	241	566	434	19
42	873	238	635	365	18
43	26 940	236	704	296	17
44	27 007	233	773	227	16
45	27 073	99 231	27 842	72 158	**15**
46	140	229	911	089	14
47	206	226	27 980	72 020	13
48	273	224	28 049	71 951	12
49	339	221	117	883	11
50	27 405	99 219	28 186	71 814	**10**
51	471	217	254	746	9
52	537	214	323	677	8
53	602	212	391	609	7
54	668	209	459	541	6
55	27 734	99 207	28 527	71 473	**5**
56	799	204	595	405	4
57	864	202	662	338	3
58	930	200	730	270	2
59	27 995	197	798	202	1
60	28 060	99 195	28 865	71 135	**0**
	log cos 9	log sin 9	log ctn 9	log tan 10	′

79°

11°

′	log sin 9	log cos 9	log tan 9	log ctn 10	′
0	28 060	99 195	28 865	71 135	60
1	125	192	28 933	067	59
2	190	190	29 000	71 000	58
3	254	187	067	70 933	57
4	319	185	134	866	56
5	28 384	99 182	29 201	70 799	55
6	448	180	268	732	54
7	512	177	335	665	53
8	577	175	402	598	52
9	641	172	468	532	51
10	28 705	99 170	29 535	70 465	50
11	769	167	601	399	49
12	833	165	668	332	48
13	896	162	734	266	47
14	28 960	160	800	200	46
15	29 024	99 157	29 866	70 134	45
·16	087	155	932	068	44
17	150	152	29 998	70 002	43
18	214	150	30 064	69 936	42
19	277	147	130	870	41
20	29 340	99 145	30 195	69 805	40
21	403	142	261	739	39
22	466	140	326	674	38
23	529	137	391	609	37
24	591	135	457	543	36
25	29 654	99 132	30 522	69 478	35
26	716	130	587	413	34
27	779	127	652	348	33
28	841	124	717	283	32
29	903	122	782	218	31
30	29 966	99 119	30 846	69 154	30
31	30 028	117	911	089	29
32	090	114	30 975	69 025	28
33	151	112	31 040	68 960	27
34	213	109	104	896	26
35	30 275	99 106	31 168	68 832	25
36	336	104	233	767	24
37	398	101	297	703	23
38	459	099	361	639	22
39	521	096	425	575	21
40	30 582	99 093	31 489	68 511	20
41	643	091	552	448	19
42	704	088	616	384	18
43	765	086	679	321	17
44	826	083	743	257	16
45	30 887	99 080	31 806	68 194	15
46	30 947	078	870	130	14
47	31 008	075	933	067	13
48	068	072	31 996	68 004	12
49	129	070	32 059	67 941	11
50	31 189	99 067	32 122	67 878	10
51	250	064	185	815	9
52	310	062	248	752	8
53	370	059	311	689	7
54	430	056	373	627	6
55	31 490	99 054	32 436	67 564	5
56	549	051	498	502	4
57	609	048	561	439	3
58	669	046	623	377	2
59	728	043	685	315	1
60	31 788	99 040	32 747	67 253	0
′	log cos 9	log sin 9	log ctn 9	log tan 10	′

12°

′	log sin 9	log cos 9	log tan 9	log ctn 10	′
0	31 788	99 040	32 747	67 253	60
1	847	038	810	190	59
2	907	035	872	128	58
3	31 966	032	933	067	57
4	32 025	030	32 995	67 005	56
5	32 084	99 027	33 057	66 943	55
6	143	024	119	881	54
7	202	022	180	820	53
8	261	019	242	758	52
9	319	016	303	697	51
10	32 378	99 013	33 365	66 635	50
11	437	011	426	574	49
12	495	008	487	513	48
13	553	005	548	452	47
14	612	002	609	391	46
15	32 670	99 000	33 670	66 330	45
16	728	98 997	731	269	44
17	786	994	792	208	43
18	844	991	853	147	42
19	902	989	913	087	41
20	32 960	98 986	33 974	66 026	40
21	33 018	983	34 034	65 966	39
22	075	980	095	905	38
23	133	978	155	845	37
24	190	975	215	785	36
25	33 248	98 972	34 276	65 724	35
26	305	969	336	664	34
27	362	967	396	604	33
28	420	964	456	544	32
29	477	961	516	484	31
30	33 534	98 958	34 576	65 424	30
31	591	955	635	365	29
32	647	953	695	305	28
33	704	950	755	245	27
34	761	947	814	186	26
35	33 818	98 944	34 874	65 126	25
36	874	941	933	067	24
37	931	938	34 992	65 008	23
38	33 987	936	35 051	64 949	22
39	34 043	933	111	889	21
40	34 100	98 930	35 170	64 830	20
41	156	927	229	771	19
42	212	924	288	712	18
43	268	921	347	653	17
44	324	919	405	595	16
45	34 380	98 916	35 464	64 536	15
46	436	913	523	477	14
47	491	910	581	419	13
48	547	907	640	360	12
49	602	904	698	302	11
50	34 658	98 901	35 757	64 243	10
51	713	898	815	185	9
52	769	896	873	127	8
53	824	893	931	069	7
54	879	890	35 989	64 011	6
55	34 934	98 887	36 047	63 953	5
56	34 989	884	105	895	4
57	35 044	881	163	837	3
58	099	878	221	779	2
59	154	875	279	721	1
60	35 209	98 872	36 336	63 664	0
′	log cos 9	log sin 9	log ctn 9	log tan 10	′

13°

′	log sin	log cos	log tan	log ctn	′
	9	9	9	10	
0	35 209	98 872	36 336	63 664	60
1	263	869	394	606	59
2	318	867	452	548	58
3	373	864	509	491	57
4	427	861	566	434	56
5	35 481	98 858	36 624	63 376	55
6	536	855	681	319	54
7	590	852	738	262	53
8	644	849	795	205	52
9	698	846	852	148	51
10	35 752	98 843	36 909	63 091	50
11	806	840	36 966	63 034	49
12	860	837	37 023	62 977	48
13	914	834	080	920	47
14	35 968	831	137	863	46
15	36 022	98 828	37 193	62 807	45
16	075	825	250	750	44
17	129	822	306	694	43
18	182	819	363	637	42
19	236	816	419	581	41
20	36 289	98 813	37 476	62 524	40
21	342	810	532	468	39
22	395	807	588	412	38
23	449	804	644	356	37
24	502	801	700	300	36
25	36 555	98 798	37 756	62 244	35
26	608	795	812	188	34
27	660	792	868	132	33
28	713	789	924	076	32
29	766	786	37 980	62 020	31
30	36 819	98 783	38 035	61 965	30
31	871	780	091	909	29
32	924	777	147	853	28
33	36 976	774	202	798	27
34	37 028	771	257	743	26
35	37 081	98 768	38 313	61 687	25
36	133	765	368	632	24
37	185	762	423	577	23
38	237	759	479	521	22
39	289	756	534	466	21
40	37 341	98 753	38 589	61 411	20
41	393	750	644	356	19
42	445	746	699	301	18
43	497	743	754	246	17
44	549	740	808	192	16
45	37 600	98 737	38 863	61 137	15
46	652	734	918	082	14
47	703	731	38 972	61 028	13
48	755	728	39 027	60 973	12
49	806	725	082	918	11
50	37 858	98 722	39 136	60 864	10
51	909	719	190	810	9
52	37 960	715	245	755	8
53	38 011	712	299	701	7
54	062	709	353	647	6
55	38 113	98 706	39 407	60 593	5
56	164	703	461	539	4
57	215	700	515	485	3
58	266	697	569	431	2
59	317	694	623	377	1
60	38 368	98 690	39 677	60 323	0
	9	9	9	10	
′	log cos	log sin	log ctn	log tan	′

76°

14°

′	log sin	log cos	log tan	log ctn	′
	9	9	9	10	
0	38 368	98 690	39 677	60 323	60
1	418	687	731	269	59
2	469	684	785	215	58
3	519	681	838	162	57
4	570	678	892	108	56
5	38 620	98 675	39 945	60 055	55
6	670	671	39 999	60 001	54
7	721	668	40 052	59 948	53
8	771	665	106	894	52
9	821	662	159	841	51
10	38 871	98 659	40 212	59 788	50
11	921	656	266	734	49
12	38 971	652	319	681	48
13	39 021	649	372	628	47
14	071	646	425	575	46
15	39 121	98 643	40 478	59 522	45
16	170	640	531	469	44
17	220	636	584	416	43
18	270	633	636	364	42
19	319	630	689	311	41
20	39 369	98 627	40 742	59 258	40
21	418	623	795	205	39
22	467	620	847	153	38
23	517	617	900	100	37
24	566	614	40 952	59 048	36
25	39 615	98 610	41 005	58 995	35
26	664	607	057	943	34
27	713	604	109	891	33
28	762	601	161	839	32
29	811	597	214	786	31
30	39 860	98 594	41 266	58 734	30
31	909	591	318	682	29
32	39 958	588	370	630	28
33	40 006	584	422	578	27
34	055	581	474	526	26
35	40 103	98 578	41 526	58 474	25
36	152	574	578	422	24
37	200	571	629	371	23
38	249	568	681	319	22
39	297	565	733	267	21
40	40 346	98 561	41 784	58 216	20
41	394	558	836	164	19
42	442	555	887	113	18
43	490	551	939	061	17
44	538	548	41 990	58 010	16
45	40 586	98 545	42 041	57 959	15
46	634	541	093	907	14
47	682	538	144	856	13
48	730	535	195	805	12
49	778	531	246	754	11
50	40 825	98 528	42 297	57 703	10
51	873	525	348	652	9
52	921	521	399	601	8
53	40 968	518	450	550	7
54	41 016	515	501	499	6
55	41 063	98 511	42 552	57 448	5
56	111	508	603	397	4
57	158	505	653	347	3
58	205	501	704	296	2
59	252	498	755	245	1
60	41 300	98 494	42 805	57 195	0
	9	9	9	10	
′	log cos	log sin	log ctn	log tan	′

75°

15°

′	log sin	log cos	log tan	log ctn	′
	9	9	9	10	
0	41 300	98 494	42 805	57 195	60
1	347	491	856	144	59
2	394	488	906	094	58
3	441	484	42 957	57 043	57
4	488	481	43 007	56 993	56
5	41 535	98 477	43 057	56 943	55
6	582	474	108	892	54
7	628	471	158	842	53
8	675	467	208	792	52
9	722	464	258	742	51
10	41 768	98 460	43 308	56 692	50
11	815	457	358	642	49
12	861	453	408	592	48
13	908	450	458	542	47
14	41 954	447	508	492	46
15	42 001	98 443	43 558	56 442	45
16	047	440	607	393	44
17	093	436	657	343	43
18	140	433	707	293	42
19	186	429	756	244	41
20	42 232	98 426	43 806	56 194	40
21	278	422	855	145	39
22	324	419	905	095	38
23	370	415	43 954	56 046	37
24	416	412	44 004	55 996	36
25	42 461	98 409	44 053	55 947	35
26	507	405	102	898	34
27	553	402	151	849	33
28	599	398	201	799	32
29	644	395	250	750	31
30	42 690	98 391	44 299	55 701	30
31	735	388	348	652	29
32	781	384	397	603	28
33	826	381	446	554	27
34	872	377	495	505	26
35	42 917	98 373	44 544	55 456	25
36	42 962	370	592	408	24
37	43 008	366	641	359	23
38	053	363	690	310	22
39	098	359	738	262	21
40	43 143	98 356	44 787	55 213	20
41	188	352	836	164	19
42	233	349	884	116	18
43	278	345	933	067	17
44	323	342	44 981	55 019	16
45	43 367	98 338	45 029	54 971	15
46	412	334	078	922	14
47	457	331	126	874	13
48	502	327	174	826	12
49	546	324	222	778	11
50	43 591	98 320	45 271	54 729	10
51	635	317	319	681	9
52	680	313	367	633	8
53	724	309	415	585	7
54	769	306	463	537	6
55	43 813	98 302	45 511	54 489	5
56	857	299	559	441	4
57	901	295	606	394	3
58	946	291	654	346	2
59	43 990	288	702	298	1
60	44 034	98 284	45 750	54 250	0
	9	9	9	10	
	log cos	log sin	log ctn	log tan	′

16°

′	log sin	log cos	log tan	log ctn	′
	9	9	9	10	
0	44 034	98 284	45 750	54 250	60
1	078	281	797	203	59
2	122	277	845	155	58
3	166	273	892	108	57
4	210	270	940	060	56
5	44 253	98 266	45 987	54 013	55
6	297	262	46 035	53 965	54
7	341	259	082	918	53
8	385	255	130	870	52
9	428	251	177	823	51
10	44 472	98 248	46 224	53 776	50
11	516	244	271	729	49
12	559	240	319	681	48
13	602	237	366	634	47
14	646	233	413	587	46
15	44 689	98 229	46 460	53 540	45
16	733	226	507	493	44
17	776	222	554	446	43
18	819	218	601	399	42
19	862	215	648	352	41
20	44 905	98 211	46 694	53 306	40
21	948	207	741	259	39
22	44 992	204	788	212	38
23	45 035	200	835	165	37
24	077	196	881	119	36
25	45 120	98 192	46 928	53 072	35
26	163	189	46 975	53 025	34
27	206	185	47 021	52 979	33
28	249	181	068	932	32
29	292	177	114	886	31
30	45 334	98 174	47 160	52 840	30
31	377	170	207	793	29
32	419	166	253	747	28
33	462	162	299	701	27
34	504	159	346	654	26
35	45 547	98 155	47 392	52 608	25
36	589	151	438	562	24
37	632	147	484	516	23
38	674	144	530	470	22
39	716	140	576	424	21
40	45 758	98 136	47 622	52 378	20
41	801	132	668	332	19
42	843	129	714	286	18
43	885	125	760	240	17
44	927	121	806	194	16
45	45 969	98 117	47 852	52 148	15
46	46 011	113	897	103	14
47	053	110	943	057	13
48	095	106	47 989	52 011	12
49	136	102	48 035	51 965	11
50	46 178	98 098	48 080	51 920	10
51	220	094	126	874	9
52	262	090	171	829	8
53	303	087	217	783	7
54	345	083	262	738	6
55	46 386	98 079	48 307	51 693	5
56	428	075	353	647	4
57	469	071	398	602	3
58	511	067	443	557	2
59	552	063	489	511	1
60	46 594	98 060	48 534	51 466	0
	9	9	9	10	
	log cos	log sin	log ctn	log tan	′

17°

′	log sin 9	log cos 9	log tan 9	log ctn 10	′
0	46 594	98 060	48 534	51 466	60
1	635	056	579	421	59
2	676	052	624	376	58
3	717	048	669	331	57
4	758	044	714	286	56
5	46 800	98 040	48 759	51 241	55
6	841	036	804	196	54
7	882	032	849	151	53
8	923	029	894	106	52
9	46 964	025	939	061	51
10	47 005	98 021	48 984	51 016	50
11	045	017	49 029	50 971	49
12	086	013	073	927	48
13	127	009	118	882	47
14	168	005	163	837	46
15	47 209	98 001	49 207	50 793	45
16	249	97 997	252	748	44
17	290	993	296	704	43
18	330	989	341	659	42
19	371	986	385	615	41
20	47 411	97 982	49 430	50 570	40
21	452	978	474	526	39
22	492	974	519	481	38
23	533	970	563	437	37
24	573	966	607	393	36
25	47 613	97 962	49 652	50 348	35
26	654	958	696	304	34
27	694	954	740	260	33
28	734	950	784	216	32
29	774	946	828	172	31
30	47 814	97 942	49 872	50 128	30
31	854	938	916	084	29
32	894	934	49 960	50 040	28
33	934	930	50 004	49 996	27
34	47 974	926	048	952	26
35	48 014	97 922	50 092	49 908	25
36	054	918	136	864	24
37	094	914	180	820	23
38	133	910	223	777	22
39	173	906	267	733	21
40	48 213	97 902	50 311	49 689	20
41	252	898	355	645	19
42	292	894	398	602	18
43	332	890	442	558	17
44	371	886	485	515	16
45	48 411	97 882	50 529	49 471	15
46	450	878	572	428	14
47	490	874	616	384	13
48	529	870	659	341	12
49	568	866	703	297	11
50	48 607	97 861	50 746	49 254	10
51	647	857	789	211	9
52	686	853	833	167	8
53	725	849	876	124	7
54	764	845	919	081	6
55	48 803	97 841	50 962	49 038	5
56	842	837	51 005	48 995	4
57	881	833	048	952	3
58	920	829	092	908	2
59	959	825	135	865	1
60	48 998	97 821	51 178	48 822	0
′	log cos 9	log sin 9	log ctn 9	log tan 10	′

72°

18°

′	log sin 9	log cos 9	log tan 9	log ctn 10	′
0	48 998	97 821	51 178	48 822	60
1	49 037	817	221	779	59
2	076	812	264	736	58
3	115	808	306	694	57
4	153	804	349	651	56
5	49 192	97 800	51 392	48 608	55
6	231	796	435	565	54
7	269	792	478	522	53
8	308	788	520	480	52
9	347	784	563	437	51
10	49 385	97 779	51 606	48 394	50
11	424	775	648	352	49
12	462	771	691	309	48
13	500	767	734	266	47
14	539	763	776	224	46
15	49 577	97 759	51 819	48 181	45
16	615	754	861	139	44
17	654	750	903	097	43
18	692	746	946	054	42
19	730	742	51 988	48 012	41
20	49 768	97 738	52 031	47 969	40
21	806	734	073	927	39
22	844	729	115	885	38
23	882	725	157	843	37
24	920	721	200	800	36
25	49 958	97 717	52 242	47 758	35
26	49 996	713	284	716	34
27	50 034	708	326	674	33
28	072	704	368	632	32
29	110	700	410	590	31
30	50 148	97 696	52 452	47 548	30
31	185	691	494	506	29
32	223	687	536	464	28
33	261	683	578	422	27
34	298	679	620	380	26
35	50 336	97 674	52 661	47 339	25
36	374	670	703	297	24
37	411	666	745	255	23
38	449	662	787	213	22
39	486	657	829	171	21
40	50 523	97 653	52 870	47 130	20
41	561	649	912	088	19
42	598	645	953	047	18
43	635	640	52 995	47 005	17
44	673	636	53 037	46 963	16
45	50 710	97 632	53 078	46 922	15
46	747	628	120	880	14
47	784	623	161	839	13
48	821	619	202	798	12
49	858	615	244	756	11
50	50 896	97 610	53 285	46 715	10
51	933	606	327	673	9
52	50 970	602	368	632	8
53	51 007	597	409	591	7
54	043	593	450	550	6
55	51 080	97 589	53 492	46 508	5
56	117	584	533	467	4
57	154	580	574	426	3
58	191	576	615	385	2
59	227	571	656	344	1
60	51 264	97 567	53 697	46 303	0
′	log cos 9	log sin 9	log ctn 9	log tan 10	′

71°

19°　　　　　　　　　　　　　20°

′	log sin	log cos	log tan	log ctn	′	′	log sin	log cos	log tan	log ctn	′
	9	**9**	**9**	**10**			**9**	**9**	**9**	**10**	
0	51 264	97 567	53 697	46 303	**60**	**0**	53 405	97 299	56 107	43 893	**60**
1	301	563	738	262	59	1	440	294	146	854	59
2	338	558	779	221	58	2	475	289	185	815	58
3	374	554	820	180	57	3	509	285	224	776	57
4	411	550	861	139	56	4	544	280	264	736	56
5	51 447	97 545	53 902	46 098	**55**	**5**	53 578	97 276	56 303	43 697	**55**
6	484	541	943	057	54	6	613	271	342	658	54
7	520	536	53 984	46 016	53	7	647	266	381	619	53
8	557	532	54 025	45 975	52	8	682	262	420	580	52
9	593	528	065	935	51	9	716	257	459	541	51
10	51 629	97 523	54 106	45 894	**50**	**10**	53 751	97 252	56 498	43 502	**50**
11	666	519	147	853	49	11	785	248	537	463	49
12	702	515	187	813	48	12	819	243	576	424	48
13	738	510	228	772	47	13	854	238	615	385	47
14	774	506	269	731	46	14	888	234	654	346	46
15	51 811	97 501	54 309	45 691	**45**	**15**	53 922	97 229	56 693	43 307	**45**
16	847	497	350	650	44	16	957	224	732	268	44
17	883	492	390	610	43	17	53 991	220	771	229	43
18	919	488	431	569	42	18	54 025	215	810	190	42
19	955	484	471	529	41	19	059	210	849	151	41
20	51 991	97 479	54 512	45 488	**40**	**20**	54 093	97 206	56 887	43 113	**40**
21	52 027	475	552	448	39	21	127	201	926	074	39
22	063	470	593	407	38	22	161	196	56 965	43 035	38
23	099	466	633	367	37	23	195	192	57 004	42 996	37
24	135	461	673	327	36	24	229	187	042	958	36
25	52 171	97 457	54 714	45 286	**35**	**25**	54 263	97 182	57 081	42 919	**35**
26	207	453	754	246	34	26	297	178	120	880	34
27	242	448	794	206	33	27	331	173	158	842	33
28	278	444	835	165	32	28	365	168	197	803	32
29	314	439	875	125	31	29	399	163	235	765	31
30	52 350	97 435	54 915	45 085	**30**	**30**	54 433	97 159	57 274	42 726	**30**
31	385	430	955	045	29	31	466	154	312	688	29
32	421	426	54 995	45 005	28	32	500	149	351	649	28
33	456	421	55 035	44 965	27	33	534	145	389	611	27
34	492	417	075	925	26	34	567	140	428	572	26
35	52 527	97 412	55 115	44 885	**25**	**35**	54 601	97 135	57 466	42 534	**25**
36	563	408	155	845	24	36	635	130	504	496	24
37	598	403	195	805	23	37	668	126	543	457	23
38	634	399	235	765	22	38	702	121	581	419	22
39	669	394	275	725	21	39	735	116	619	381	21
40	52 705	97 390	55 315	44 685	**20**	**40**	54 769	97 111	57 658	42 342	**20**
41	740	385	355	645	19	41	802	107	696	304	19
42	775	381	395	605	18	42	836	102	734	266	18
43	811	376	434	566	17	43	869	097	772	228	17
44	846	372	474	526	16	44	903	092	810	190	16
45	52 881	97 367	55 514	44 486	**15**	**45**	54 936	97 087	57 849	42 151	**15**
46	916	363	554	446	14	46	54 969	083	887	113	14
47	951	358	593	407	13	47	55 003	078	925	075	13
48	52 986	353	633	367	12	48	036	073	57 963	42 037	12
49	53 021	349	673	327	11	49	069	068	58 001	41 999	11
50	53 056	97 344	55 712	44 288	**10**	**50**	55 102	97 063	58 039	41 961	**10**
51	092	340	752	248	9	51	136	059	077	923	9
52	126	335	791	209	8	52	169	054	115	885	8
53	161	331	831	169	7	53	202	049	153	847	7
54	196	326	870	130	6	54	235	044	191	809	6
55	53 231	97 322	55 910	44 090	**5**	**55**	55 268	97 039	58 229	41 771	**5**
56	266	317	949	051	4	56	301	035	267	733	4
57	301	312	55 989	44 011	3	57	334	030	304	696	3
58	336	308	56 028	43 972	2	58	367	025	342	658	2
59	370	303	067	933	1	59	400	020	380	620	1
60	53 405	97 299	56 107	43 893	**0**	**60**	55 433	97 015	58 418	41 582	**0**
	9	**9**	**9**	**10**			**9**	**9**	**9**	**10**	
′	log cos	log sin	log ctn	log tan	′	′	log cos	log sin	log ctn	log tan	′

70°　　　　　　　　　　　　　**69°**

21°

′	log sin	log cos	log tan	log ctn	′
	9	**9**	**9**	**10**	
0	55 433	97 015	58 418	41 582	**60**
1	466	010	455	545	59
2	499	005	493	507	58
3	532	97 001	531	469	57
4	564	96 996	569	431	56
5	55 597	96 991	58 606	41 394	**55**
6	630	986	644	356	54
7	663	981	681	319	53
8	695	976	719	281	52
9	728	971	757	243	51
10	55 761	96 966	58 794	41 206	**50**
11	793	962	832	168	49
12	826	957	869	131	48
13	858	952	907	093	47
14	891	947	944	056	46
15	55 923	96 942	58 981	41 019	**45**
16	956	937	59 019	40 981	44
17	55 988	932	056	944	43
18	56 021	927	094	906	42
19	053	922	131	869	41
20	56 085	96 917	59 168	40 832	**40**
21	118	912	205	795	39
22	150	907	243	757	38
23	182	903	280	720	37
24	215	898	317	683	36
25	56 247	96 893	59 354	40 646	**35**
26	279	888	391	609	34
27	311	883	429	571	33
28	343	878	466	534	32
29	375	873	503	497	31
30	56 408	96 868	59 540	40 460	**30**
31	440	863	577	423	29
32	472	858	614	386	28
33	504	853	651	349	27
34	536	848	688	312	26
35	56 568	96 843	59 725	40 275	**25**
36	599	838	762	238	24
37	631	833	799	201	23
38	663	828	835	165	22
39	695	823	872	128	21
40	56 727	96 818	59 909	40 091	**20**
41	759	813	946	054	19
42	790	808	59 983	40 017	18
43	822	803	60 019	39 981	17
44	854	798	056	944	16
45	56 886	96 793	60 093	39 907	**15**
46	917	788	130	870	14
47	949	783	166	834	13
48	56 980	778	203	797	12
49	57 012	772	240	760	11
50	57 044	96 767	60 276	39 724	**10**
51	075	762	313	687	9
52	107	757	349	651	8
53	138	752	386	614	7
54	169	747	422	578	6
55	57 201	96 742	60 459	39 541	**5**
56	232	737	495	505	4
57	264	732	532	468	3
58	295	727	568	432	2
59	326	722	605	395	1
60	57 358	96 717	60 641	39 359	**0**
	9	**9**	**9**	**10**	
′	log cos	log sin	log ctn	log tan	′

22°

′	log sin	log cos	log tan	log ctn	′
	9	**9**	**9**	**10**	
0	57 358	96 717	60 641	39 359	**60**
1	389	711	677	323	59
2	420	706	714	286	58
3	451	701	750	250	57
4	482	696	786	214	56
5	57 514	96 691	60 823	39 177	**55**
6	545	686	859	141	54
7	576	681	895	105	53
8	607	676	931	069	52
9	638	670	60 967	39 033	51
10	57 669	96 665	61 004	38 996	**50**
11	700	660	040	960	49
12	731	655	076	924	48
13	762	650	112	888	47
14	793	645	148	852	46
15	57 824	96 640	61 184	38 816	**45**
16	855	634	220	780	44
17	885	629	256	744	43
18	916	624	292	708	42
19	947	619	328	672	41
20	57 978	96 614	61 364	38 636	**40**
21	58 008	608	400	600	39
22	039	603	436	564	38
23	070	598	472	528	37
24	101	593	508	492	36
25	58 131	96 588	61 544	38 456	**35**
26	162	582	579	421	34
27	192	577	615	385	33
28	223	572	651	349	32
29	253	567	687	313	31
30	58 284	96 562	61 722	38 278	**30**
31	314	556	758	242	29
32	345	551	794	206	28
33	375	546	830	170	27
34	406	541	865	135	26
35	58 436	96 535	61 901	38 099	**25**
36	467	530	936	064	24
37	497	525	61 972	38 028	23
38	527	520	62 008	37 992	22
39	557	514	043	957	21
40	58 588	96 509	62 079	37 921	**20**
41	618	504	114	886	19
42	648	498	150	850	18
43	678	493	185	815	17
44	709	488	221	779	16
45	58 739	96 483	62 256	37 744	**15**
46	769	477	292	708	14
47	799	472	327	673	13
48	829	467	362	638	12
49	859	461	398	602	11
50	58 889	96 456	62 433	37 567	**10**
51	919	451	468	532	9
52	949	445	504	496	8
53	58 979	440	539	461	7
54	59 009	435	574	426	6
55	59 039	96 429	62 609	37 391	**5**
56	069	424	645	355	4
57	098	419	680	320	3
58	128	413	715	285	2
59	158	408	750	250	1
60	59 188	96 403	62 785	37 215	**0**
	9	**9**	**9**	**10**	
′	log cos	log sin	log ctn	log tan	′

68°   **67°**

23°

′	log sin 9	log cos 9	log tan 9	log ctn 10	′
0	59 188	96 403	62 785	37 21<u>5</u>	60
1	218	397	820	180	59
2	247	392	855	14<u>5</u>	58
3	277	387	890	110	57
4	307	381	926	074	56
5	59 336	96 376	62 961	37 039	55
6	366	370	62 996	37 004	54
7	396	36<u>5</u>	63 031	36 969	53
8	425	360	066	934	52
9	45<u>5</u>	354	101	899	51
10	59 484	96 349	63 135	36 86<u>5</u>	50
11	514	343	170	830	49
12	543	338	205	79<u>5</u>	48
13	573	333	240	760	47
14	602	327	275	72<u>5</u>	46
15	59 632	96 322	63 310	36 690	45
16	661	316	34<u>5</u>	655	44
17	690	311	379	621	43
18	720	305	414	586	42
19	749	300	449	551	41
20	59 778	96 294	63 484	36 516	40
21	808	289	519	481	39
22	837	284	553	447	38
23	866	278	588	412	37
24	895	273	623	377	36
25	59 924	96 267	63 657	36 343	35
26	954	262	692	308	34
27	59 983	256	726	274	33
28	60 012	251	761	239	32
29	041	245	796	204	31
30	60 070	96 240	63 830	36 170	30
31	099	234	86<u>5</u>	135	29
32	128	229	899	101	28
33	157	223	934	066	27
34	186	218	63 968	36 032	26
35	60 21<u>5</u>	96 212	64 003	35 997	25
36	244	207	037	963	24
37	273	201	072	928	23
38	302	196	106	894	22
39	331	190	140	860	21
40	60 359	96 18<u>5</u>	64 17<u>5</u>	35 825	20
41	388	179	209	791	19
42	417	174	243	757	18
43	446	168	278	722	17
44	474	162	312	688	16
45	60 503	96 157	64 346	35 654	15
46	532	151	381	619	14
47	561	146	41<u>5</u>	585	13
48	589	140	449	551	12
49	618	13<u>5</u>	483	517	11
50	60 646	96 129	64 517	35 483	10
51	675	123	552	448	9
52	704	118	586	414	8
53	732	112	620	380	7
54	761	107	654	346	6
55	60 789	96 101	64 688	35 312	5
56	818	095	722	278	4
57	846	090	756	244	3
58	87<u>5</u>	084	790	210	2
59	903	079	824	176	1
60	60 931	96 073	64 858	35 142	0
	9	9	9	10	
′	log cos	log sin	log ctn	log tan.	′

66°

24°

′	log sin 9	log cos 9	log tan 9	log ctn 10	′
0	60 931	96 073	64 858	35 142	60
1	960	067	892	108	59
2	60 988	062	926	074	58
3	61 016	056	960	040	57
4	04<u>5</u>	050	64 994	35 006	56
5	61 073	96 04<u>5</u>	65 028	34 972	55
6	101	039	062	938	54
7	129	034	096	904	53
8	158	028	130	870	52
9	186	022	164	836	51
10	61 214	96 017	65 197	34 803	50
11	242	011	231	769	49
12	270	005	265	73<u>5</u>	48
13	298	96 000	299	701	47
14	326	95 994	333	667	46
15	61 354	95 988	65 366	34 634	45
16	382	982	400	600	44
17	411	977	434	566	43
18	438	971	467	533	42
19	466	965	501	499	41
20	61 494	95 960	65 53<u>5</u>	34 465	40
21	522	954	568	432	39
22	550	948	602	398	38
23	578	942	636	364	37
24	606	937	669	331	36
25	61 634	95 931	65 703	34 297	35
26	662	925	736	264	34
27	689	920	770	230	33
28	717	914	803	197	32
29	74<u>5</u>	908	837	163	31
30	61 773	95 902	65 870	34 130	30
31	800	897	904	096	29
32	828	891	937	063	28
33	856	88<u>5</u>	65 971	34 029	27
34	883	879	66 004	33 996	26
35	61 911	95 873	66 038	33 962	25
36	939	868	071	929	24
37	966	862	104	896	23
38	61 994	856	138	862	22
39	62 021	850	171	829	21
40	62 049	95 844	66 204	33 796	20
41	076	839	238	762	19
42	104	833	271	729	18
43	131	827	304	696	17
44	159	821	337	663	16
45	62 186	95 815	66 371	33 629	15
46	214	810	404	596	14
47	241	804	437	563	13
48	268	798	470	530	12
49	296	792	503	497	11
50	62 323	95 786	66 537	33 463	10
51	350	780	570	430	9
52	377	77<u>5</u>	603	397	8
53	40<u>5</u>	769	636	364	7
54	432	763	669	331	6
55	62 459	95 757	66 702	33 298	5
56	486	751	735	26<u>5</u>	4
57	513	745	768	232	3
58	541	739	801	199	2
59	568	733	834	166	1
60	62 595	95 728	66 867	33 133	0
	9	9	9	10	
′	log cos	log sin	log ctn	log tan	′

65°

25°

′	log sin	log cos	log tan	log ctn	′
	9	9	9	10	
0	62 595	95 728	66 867	33 133	60
1	622	722	900	100	59
2	649	716	933	067	58
3	676	710	966	034	57
4	703	704	66 999	33 001	56
5	62 730	95 698	67 032	32 968	55
6	757	692	065	935	54
7	784	686	098	902	53
8	811	680	131	869	52
9	838	674	163	837	51
10	62 865	95 668	67 196	32 804	50
11	892	663	229	771	49
12	918	657	262	738	48
13	945	651	295	705	47
14	972	645	327	673	46
15	62 999	95 639	67 360	32 640	45
16	63 026	633	393	607	44
17	052	627	426	574	43
18	079	621	458	542	42
19	106	615	491	509	41
20	63 133	95 609	67 524	32 476	40
21	159	603	556	444	39
22	186	597	589	411	38
23	213	591	622	378	37
24	239	585	654	346	36
25	63 266	95 579	67 687	32 313	35
26	292	573	719	281	34
27	319	567	752	248	33
28	345	561	785	215	32
29	372	555	817	183	31
30	63 398	95 549	67 850	32 150	30
31	425	543	882	118	29
32	451	537	915	085	28
33	478	531	947	053	27
34	504	525	67 980	32 020	26
35	63 531	95 519	68 012	31 988	25
36	557	513	044	956	24
37	583	507	077	923	23
38	610	500	109	891	22
39	636	494	142	858	21
40	63 662	95 488	68 174	31 826	20
41	689	482	206	794	19
42	715	476	239	761	18
43	741	470	271	729	17
44	767	464	303	697	16
45	63 794	95 458	68 336	31 664	15
46	820	452	368	632	14
47	846	446	400	600	13
48	872	440	432	568	12
49	898	434	465	535	11
50	63 924	95 427	68 497	31 503	10
51	950	421	529	471	9
52	63 976	415	561	439	8
53	64 002	409	593	407	7
54	028	403	626	374	6
55	64 054	95 397	68 658	31 342	5
56	080	391	690	310	4
57	106	384	722	278	3
58	132	378	754	246	2
59	158	372	786	214	1
60	64 184	95 366	68 818	31 182	0
	9	9	9	10	
′	log cos	log sin	log ctn	log tan	′

64°

26°

′	log sin	log cos	log tan	log ctn	′
	9	9	9	10	
0	64 184	95 366	68 818	31 182	60
1	210	360	850	150	59
2	236	354	882	118	58
3	262	348	914	086	57
4	288	341	946	054	56
5	64 313	95 335	68 978	31 022	55
6	339	329	69 010	30 990	54
7	365	323	042	958	53
8	391	317	074	926	52
9	417	310	106	894	51
10	64 442	95 304	69 138	30 862	50
11	468	298	170	830	49
12	494	292	202	798	48
13	519	286	234	766	47
14	545	279	266	734	46
15	64 571	95 273	69 298	30 702	45
16	596	267	329	671	44
17	622	261	361	639	43
18	647	254	393	607	42
19	673	248	425	575	41
20	64 698	95 242	69 457	30 543	40
21	724	236	488	512	39
22	749	229	520	480	38
23	775	223	552	448	37
24	800	217	584	416	36
25	64 826	95 211	69 615	30 385	35
26	851	204	647	353	34
27	877	198	679	321	33
28	902	192	710	290	32
29	927	185	742	258	31
30	64 953	95 179	69 774	30 226	30
31	64 978	173	805	195	29
32	65 003	167	837	163	28
33	029	160	868	132	27
34	054	154	900	100	26
35	65 079	95 148	69 932	30 068	25
36	104	141	963	037	24
37	130	135	69 995	30 005	23
38	155	129	70 026	29 974	22
39	180	122	058	942	21
40	65 205	95 116	70 089	29 911	20
41	230	110	121	879	19
42	255	103	152	848	18
43	281	097	184	816	17
44	306	090	215	785	16
45	65 331	95 084	70 247	29 753	15
46	356	078	278	722	14
47	381	071	309	691	13
48	406	065	341	659	12
49	431	059	372	628	11
50	65 456	95 052	70 404	29 596	10
51	481	046	435	565	9
52	506	039	466	534	8
53	531	033	498	502	7
54	556	027	529	471	6
55	65 580	95 020	70 560	29 440	5
56	605	014	592	408	4
57	630	007	623	377	3
58	655	95 001	654	346	2
59	680	94 995	685	315	1
60	65 705	94 988	70 717	29 283	0
	9	9	9	10	
′	log cos	log sin	log ctn	log tan	′

63°

27°

′	log sin 9	log cos 9	log tan 9	log ctn 10	′
0	65 705	94 988	70 717	29 283	60
1	729	982	748	252	59
2	754	975	779	221	58
3	779	969	810	190	57
4	804	962	841	159	56
5	65 828	94 956	70 873	29 127	55
6	853	949	904	096	54
7	878	943	935	065	53
8	902	936	966	034	52
9	927	930	70 997	29 003	51
10	65 952	94 923	71 028	28 972	50
11	65 976	917	059	941	49
12	66 001	911	090	910	48
13	025	904	121	879	47
14	050	898	153	847	46
15	66 075	94 891	71 184	28 816	45
16	099	885	215	785	44
17	124	878	246	754	43
18	148	871	277	723	42
19	173	865	308	692	41
20	66 197	94 858	71 339	28 661	40
21	221	852	370	630	39
22	246	845	401	599	38
23	270	839	431	569	37
24	295	832	462	538	36
25	66 319	94 826	71 493	28 507	35
26	343	819	524	476	34
27	368	813	555	445	33
28	392	806	586	414	32
29	416	799	617	383	31
30	66 441	94 793	71 648	28 352	30
31	465	786	679	321	29
32	489	780	709	291	28
33	513	773	740	260	27
34	537	767	771	229	26
35	66 562	94 760	71 802	28 198	25
36	586	753	833	167	24
37	610	747	863	137	23
38	634	740	894	106	22
39	658	734	925	075	21
40	66 682	94 727	71 955	28 045	20
41	706	720	71 986	28 014	19
42	731	714	72 017	27 983	18
43	755	707	048	952	17
44	779	700	078	922	16
45	66 803	94 694	72 109	27 891	15
46	827	687	140	860	14
47	851	680	170	830	13
48	875	674	201	799	12
49	899	667	231	769	11
50	66 922	94 660	72 262	27 738	10
51	946	654	293	707	9
52	970	647	323	677	8
53	66 994	640	354	646	7
54	67 018	634	384	616	6
55	67 042	94 627	72 415	27 585	5
56	066	620	445	555	4
57	090	614	476	524	3
58	113	607	506	494	2
59	137	600	537	463	1
60	67 161	94 593	72 567	27 433	0
′	log cos 9	log sin 9	log ctn 9	log tan 10	′

28°

′	log sin 9	log cos 9	log tan 9	log ctn 10	′
0	67 161	94 593	72 567	27 433	60
1	185	587	598	402	59
2	208	580	628	372	58
3	232	573	659	341	57
4	256	567	689	311	56
5	67 280	94 560	72 720	27 280	55
6	303	553	750	250	54
7	327	546	780	220	53
8	350	540	811	189	52
9	374	533	841	159	51
10	67 398	94 526	72 872	27 128	50
11	421	519	902	098	49
12	445	513	932	068	48
13	468	506	963	037	47
14	492	499	72 993	27 007	46
15	67 515	94 492	73 023	26 977	45
16	539	485	054	946	44
17	562	479	084	916	43
18	586	472	114	886	42
19	609	465	144	856	41
20	67 633	94 458	73 175	26 825	40
21	656	451	205	795	39
22	680	445	235	765	38
23	703	438	265	735	37
24	726	431	295	705	36
25	67 750	94 424	73 326	26 674	35
26	773	417	356	644	34
27	796	410	386	614	33
28	820	404	416	584	32
29	843	397	446	554	31
30	67 866	94 390	73 476	26 524	30
31	890	383	507	493	29
32	913	376	537	463	28
33	936	369	567	433	27
34	959	362	597	403	26
35	67 982	94 355	73 627	26 373	25
36	68 006	349	657	343	24
37	029	342	687	313	23
38	052	335	717	283	22
39	075	328	747	253	21
40	68 098	94 321	73 777	26 223	20
41	121	314	807	193	19
42	144	307	837	163	18
43	167	300	867	133	17
44	190	293	897	103	16
45	68 213	94 286	73 927	26 073	15
46	237	279	957	043	14
47	260	273	73 987	26 013	13
48	283	266	74 017	25 983	12
49	305	259	047	953	11
50	68 328	94 252	74 077	25 923	10
51	351	245	107	893	9
52	374	238	137	863	8
53	397	231	166	834	7
54	420	224	196	804	6
55	68 443	94 217	74 226	25 774	5
56	466	210	256	744	4
57	489	203	286	714	3
58	512	196	316	684	2
59	534	189	345	655	1
60	68 557	94 182	74 375	25 625	0
′	log cos 9	log sin 9	log ctn 9	log tan 10	′

29°

′	log sin	log cos	log tan	log ctn	′
	9	9	9	10	
0	68 557	94 182	74 375	25 625	60
1	580	175	405	595	59
2	603	168	435	565	58
3	625	161	465	535	57
4	648	154	494	506	56
5	68 671	94 147	74 524	25 476	55
6	694	140	554	446	54
7	716	133	583	417	53
8	739	126	613	387	52
9	762	119	643	357	51
10	68 784	94 112	74 673	25 327	50
11	807	105	702	298	49
12	829	098	732	268	48
13	852	090	762	238	47
14	875	083	791	209	46
15	68 897	94 076	74 821	25 179	45
16	920	069	851	149	44
17	942	062	880	120	43
18	965	055	910	090	42
19	68 987	048	939	061	41
20	69 010	94 041	74 969	25 031	40
21	032	034	74 998	25 002	39
22	055	027	75 028	24 972	38
23	077	020	058	942	37
24	100	012	087	913	36
25	69 122	94 005	75 117	24 883	35
26	144	93 998	146	854	34
27	167	991	176	824	33
28	189	984	205	795	32
29	212	977	235	765	31
30	69 234	93 970	75 264	24 736	30
31	256	963	294	706	29
32	279	955	323	677	28
33	301	948	353	647	27
34	323	941	382	618	26
35	69 345	93 934	75 411	24 589	25
36	368	927	441	559	24
37	390	920	470	530	23
38	412	912	500	500	22
39	434	905	529	471	21
40	69 456	93 898	75 558	24 442	20
41	479	891	588	412	19
42	501	884	617	383	18
43	523	876	647	353	17
44	545	869	676	324	16
45	69 567	93 862	75 705	24 295	15
46	589	855	735	265	14
47	611	847	764	236	13
48	633	840	793	207	12
49	655	833	822	178	11
50	69 677	93 826	75 852	24 148	10
51	699	819	881	119	9
52	721	811	910	090	8
53	743	804	939	061	7
54	765	797	969	031	6
55	69 787	93 789	75 998	24 002	5
56	809	782	76 027	23 973	4
57	831	775	056	944	3
58	853	768	086	914	2
59	875	760	115	885	1
60	69 897	93 753	76 144	23 856	0
	9	9	9	10	
′	log cos	log sin	log ctn	log tan	′

60°

30°

′	log sin	log cos	log tan	log ctn	′
	9	9	9	10	
0	69 897	93 753	76 144	23 856	60
1	919	746	173	827	59
2	941	738	202	798	58
3	963	731	231	769	57
4	69 984	724	261	739	56
5	70 006	93 717	76 290	23 710	55
6	028	709	319	681	54
7	050	702	348	652	53
8	072	695	377	623	52
9	093	687	406	594	51
10	70 115	93 680	76 435	23 565	50
11	137	673	464	536	49
12	159	665	493	507	48
13	180	658	522	478	47
14	202	650	551	449	46
15	70 224	93 643	76 580	23 420	45
16	245	636	609	391	44
17	267	628	639	361	43
18	288	621	668	332	42
19	310	614	697	303	41
20	70 332	93 606	76 725	23 275	40
21	353	599	754	246	39
22	375	591	783	217	38
23	396	584	812	188	37
24	418	577	841	159	36
25	70 439	93 569	76 870	23 130	35
26	461	562	899	101	34
27	482	554	928	072	33
28	504	547	957	043	32
29	525	539	76 986	23 014	31
30	70 547	93 532	77 015	22 985	30
31	568	525	044	956	29
32	590	517	073	927	28
33	611	510	101	899	27
34	633	502	130	870	26
35	70 654	93 495	77 159	22 841	25
36	675	487	188	812	24
37	697	480	217	783	23
38	718	472	246	754	22
39	739	465	274	726	21
40	70 761	93 457	77 303	22 697	20
41	782	450	332	668	19
42	803	442	361	639	18
43	824	435	390	610	17
44	846	427	418	582	16
45	70 867	93 420	77 447	22 553	15
46	888	412	476	524	14
47	909	405	505	495	13
48	931	397	533	467	12
49	952	390	562	438	11
50	70 973	93 382	77 591	22 409	10
51	70 994	375	619	381	9
52	71 015	367	648	352	8
53	036	360	677	323	7
54	058	352	706	294	6
55	71 079	93 344	77 734	22 266	5
56	100	337	763	237	4
57	121	329	791	209	3
58	142	322	820	180	2
59	163	314	849	151	1
60	71 184	93 307	77 877	22 123	0
	9	9	9	10	
′	log cos	log sin	log ctn	log tan	′

59°

31°

′	log sin 9	log cos 9	log tan 9	log ctn 10	′
0	71 184	93 307	77 877	22 123	60
1	205	299	906	094	59
2	226	291	935	065	58
3	247	284	963	037	57
4	268	276	77 992	22 008	56
5	71 289	93 269	78 020	21 980	55
6	310	261	049	951	54
7	331	253	077	923	53
8	352	246	106	894	52
9	373	238	135	865	51
10	71 393	93 230	78 163	21 837	50
11	414	223	192	808	49
12	435	215	220	780	48
13	456	207	249	751	47
14	477	200	277	723	46
15	71 498	93 192	78 306	21 694	45
16	519	184	334	666	44
17	539	177	363	637	43
18	560	169	391	609	42
19	581	161	419	581	41
20	71 602	93 154	78 448	21 552	40
21	622	146	476	524	39
22	643	138	505	495	38
23	664	131	533	467	37
24	685	123	562	438	36
25	71 705	93 115	78 590	21 410	35
26	726	108	618	382	34
27	747	100	647	353	33
28	767	092	675	325	32
29	788	084	704	296	31
30	71 809	93 077	78 732	21 268	30
31	829	069	760	240	29
32	850	061	789	211	28
33	870	053	817	183	27
34	891	046	845	155	26
35	71 911	93 038	78 874	21 126	25
36	932	030	902	098	24
37	952	022	930	070	23
38	973	014	959	041	22
39	71 994	93 007	78 987	21 013	21
40	72 014	92 999	79 015	20 985	20
41	034	991	043	957	19
42	055	983	072	928	18
43	075	976	100	900	17
44	096	968	128	872	16
45	72 116	92 960	79 156	20 844	15
46	137	952	185	815	14
47	157	944	213	787	13
48	177	936	241	759	12
49	198	929	269	731	11
50	72 218	92 921	79 297	20 703	10
51	238	913	326	674	9
52	259	905	354	646	8
53	279	897	382	618	7
54	299	889	410	590	6
55	72 320	92 881	79 438	20 562	5
56	340	874	466	534	4
57	360	866	495	505	3
58	381	858	523	477	2
59	401	850	551	449	1
60	72 421	92 842	79 579	20 421	0
′	9 log cos	9 log sin	9 log ctn	10 log tan	′

32°

′	log sin 9	log cos 9	log tan 9	log ctn 10	′
0	72 421	92 842	79 579	20 421	60
1	441	834	607	393	59
2	461	826	635	365	58
3	482	818	663	337	57
4	502	810	691	309	56
5	72 522	92 803	79 719	20 281	55
6	542	795	747	253	54
7	562	787	776	224	53
8	582	779	804	196	52
9	602	771	832	168	51
10	72 622	92 763	79 860	20 140	50
11	643	755	888	112	49
12	663	747	916	084	48
13	683	739	944	056	47
14	703	731	79 972	20 028	46
15	72 723	92 723	80 000	20 000	45
16	743	715	028	19 972	44
17	763	707	056	944	43
18	783	699	084	916	42
19	803	691	112	888	41
20	72 823	92 683	80 140	19 860	40
21	843	675	168	832	39
22	863	667	195	805	38
23	883	659	223	777	37
24	902	651	251	749	36
25	72 922	92 643	80 279	19 721	35
26	942	635	307	693	34
27	962	627	335	665	33
28	72 982	619	363	637	32
29	73 002	611	391	609	31
30	73 022	92 603	80 419	19 581	30
31	041	595	447	553	29
32	061	587	474	526	28
33	081	579	502	498	27
34	101	571	530	470	26
35	73 121	92 563	80 558	19 442	25
36	140	555	586	414	24
37	160	546	614	386	23
38	180	538	642	358	22
39	200	530	669	331	21
40	73 219	92 522	80 697	19 303	20
41	239	514	725	275	19
42	259	506	753	247	18
43	278	498	781	219	17
44	298	490	808	192	16
45	73 318	92 482	80 836	19 164	15
46	337	473	864	136	14
47	357	465	892	108	13
48	377	457	919	081	12
49	396	449	947	053	11
50	73 416	92 441	80 975	19 025	10
51	435	433	81 003	18 997	9
52	455	425	030	970	8
53	474	416	058	942	7
54	494	408	086	914	6
55	73 513	92 400	81 113	18 887	5
56	533	392	141	859	4
57	552	384	169	831	3
58	572	376	196	804	2
59	591	367	224	776	1
60	73 611	92 359	81 252	18 748	0
′	9 log cos	9 log sin	9 log ctn	10 log tan	′

33°

′	log sin	log cos	log tan	log ctn	′
	9	9	9	10	
0	73 611	92 359	81 252	18 748	60
1	630	351	279	721	59
2	650	343	307	693	58
3	669	335	335	665	57
4	689	326	362	638	56
5	73 708	92 318	81 390	18 610	55
6	727	310	418	582	54
7	747	302	445	555	53
8	766	293	473	527	52
9	785	285	500	500	51
10	73 805	92 277	81 528	18 472	50
11	824	269	556	444	49
12	843	260	583	417	48
13	863	252	611	389	47
14	882	244	638	362	46
15	73 901	92 235	81 666	18 334	45
16	921	227	693	307	44
17	940	219	721	279	43
18	959	211	748	252	42
19	978	202	776	224	41
20	73 997	92 194	81 803	18 197	40
21	74 017	186	831	169	39
22	036	177	858	142	38
23	055	169	886	114	37
24	074	161	913	087	36
25	74 093	92 152	81 941	18 059	35
26	113	144	968	032	34
27	132	136	81 996	18 004	33
28	151	127	82 023	17 977	32
29	170	119	051	949	31
30	74 189	92 111	82 078	17 922	30
31	208	102	106	894	29
32	227	094	133	867	28
33	246	086	161	839	27
34	265	077	188	812	26
35	74 284	92 069	82 215	17 785	25
36	303	060	243	757	24
37	322	052	270	730	23
38	341	044	298	702	22
39	360	035	325	675	21
40	74 379	92 027	82 352	17 648	20
41	398	018	380	620	19
42	417	010	407	593	18
43	436	92 002	435	565	17
44	455	91 993	462	538	16
45	74 474	91 985	82 489	17 511	15
46	493	976	517	483	14
47	512	968	544	456	13
48	531	959	571	429	12
49	549	951	599	401	11
50	74 568	91 942	82 626	17 374	10
51	587	934	653	347	9
52	606	925	681	319	8
53	625	917	708	292	7
54	644	908	735	265	6
55	74 662	91 900	82 762	17 238	5
56	681	891	790	210	4
57	700	883	817	183	3
58	719	874	844	156	2
59	737	866	871	129	1
60	74 756	91 857	82 899	17 101	0
	9	9	9	10	
′	log cos	log sin	log ctn	log tan	′

56°

34°

′	log sin	log cos	log tan	log ctn	′
	9	9	9	10	
0	74 756	91 857	82 899	17 101	60
1	775	849	926	074	59
2	794	840	953	047	58
3	812	832	82 980	17 020	57
4	831	823	83 008	16 992	56
5	74 850	91 815	83 035	16 965	55
6	868	806	062	938	54
7	887	798	089	911	53
8	906	789	117	883	52
9	924	781	144	856	51
10	74 943	91 772	83 171	16 829	50
11	961	763	198	802	49
12	980	755	225	775	48
13	74 999	746	252	748	47
14	75 017	738	280	720	46
15	75 036	91 729	83 307	16 693	45
16	054	720	334	666	44
17	073	712	361	639	43
18	091	703	388	612	42
19	110	695	415	585	41
20	75 128	91 686	83 442	16 558	40
21	147	677	470	530	39
22	165	669	497	503	38
23	184	660	524	476	37
24	202	651	551	449	36
25	75 221	91 643	83 578	16 422	35
26	239	634	605	395	34
27	258	625	632	368	33
28	276	617	659	341	32
29	294	608	686	314	31
30	75 313	91 599	83 713	16 287	30
31	331	591	740	260	29
32	350	582	768	232	28
33	368	573	795	205	27
34	386	565	822	178	26
35	75 405	91 556	83 849	16 151	25
36	423	547	876	124	24
37	441	538	903	097	23
38	459	530	930	070	22
39	478	521	957	043	21
40	75 496	91 512	83 984	16 016	20
41	514	504	84 011	15 989	19
42	533	495	038	962	18
43	551	486	065	935	17
44	569	477	092	908	16
45	75 587	91 469	84 119	15 881	15
46	605	460	146	854	14
47	624	451	173	827	13
48	642	442	200	800	12
49	660	433	227	773	11
50	75 678	91 425	84 254	15 746	10
51	696	416	280	720	9
52	714	407	307	693	8
53	733	398	334	666	7
54	751	389	361	639	6
55	75 769	91 381	84 388	15 612	5
56	787	372	415	585	4
57	805	363	442	558	3
58	823	354	469	531	2
59	841	345	496	504	1
60	75 859	91 336	84 523	15 477	0
	9	9	9	10	
′	log cos	log sin	log ctn	log tan	′

55°

35°

′	log sin 9	log cos 9	log tan 9	log ctn 10	′
0	75 859	91 336	84 523	15 477	60
1	877	328	55̲0	450	59
2	895	319	576	424	58
3	913	310	603	397	57
4	931	301	630	370	56
5	75 949	91 292	84 657	15 343	55
6	967	283	684	316	54
7	75 985	274	711	289	53
8	76 003	266	738	262	52
9	021	257	764	236	51
10	76 039	91 248	84 791	15 209	50
11	057	239	818	182	49
12	07̲5	230	84̲5	155	48
13	093	221	872	128	47
14	111	212	899	101	46
15	76 129	91 203	84 925	15 075	45
16	146	194	952	048	44
17	164	185	84 979	15 021	43
18	182	176	85 006	14 994	42
19	200	167	033	967	41
20	76 218	91 158	85 059	14 941	40
21	236	149	086	914	39
22	253	141	113	887	38
23	271	132	140	860	37
24	289	123	166	834	36
25	76 307	91 114	85 193	14 807	35
26	324	10̲5	220	780	34
27	342	096	247	753	33
28	360	087	273	727	32
29	378	078	300	700	31
30	76 395	91 069	85 327	14 673	30
31	413	060	354	646	29
32	431	051	380	620	28
33	448	042	407	593	27
34	466	033	434	566	26
35	76 484	91 023	85 460	14 540	25
36	501	014	487	513	24
37	519	91 005	514	486	23
38	537	90 996	540	460	22
39	554	987	567	433	21
40	76 572	90 978	85 594	14 406	20
41	590	969	620	380	19
42	607	960	647	353	18
43	62̲5	951	674	326	17
44	642	942	700	300	16
45	76 660	90 933	85 727	14 273	15
46	677	924	754	246	14
47	69̲5	915	780	220	13
48	712	906	807	193	12
49	730	896	834	166	11
50	76 747	90 887	85 860	14 140	10
51	76̲5	878	887	113	9
52	782	869	913	087	8
53	800	860	940	060	7
54	817	851	967	033	6
55	76 83̲5	90 84̲2	85 993	14 007	5
56	852	832	86 020	13 980	4
57	870	823	046	954	3
58	887	814	073	927	2
59	904	80̲5	100	900	1
60	76 922	90 796	86 126	13 874	0
′	9 log cos	9 log sin	9 log ctn	10 log tan	′

36°

′	log sin 9	log cos 9	log tan 9	log ctn 10	′
0	76 922	90 796	86 126	13 874	60
1	939	787	153	847	59
2	957	777	179	821	58
3	974	768	206	794	57
4	76 991	759	232	768	56
5	77 009	90 750	86 259	13 741	55
6	026	741	285	71̲5	54
7	043	731	312	688	53
8	061	722	338	662	52
9	078	713	365	63̲5	51
10	77 095	90 704	86 392	13 608	50
11	112	694	418	582	49
12	130	685	44̲5	555	48
13	147	676	471	529	47
14	164	667	498	502	46
15	77 181	90 657	86 524	13 476	45
16	199	648	551	449	44
17	216	639	577	423	43
18	233	630	603	397	42
19	250	620	630	370	41
20	77 268	90 611	86 656	13 344	40
21	285	602	683	317	39
22	302	592	709	291	38
23	319	583	736	264	37
24	336	574	762	238	36
25	77 353	90 565	86 789	13 211	35
26	370	555	815	18̲5	34
27	387	546	842	158	33
28	40̲5	537	868	132	32
29	422	527	894	106	31
30	77 439	90 518	86 921	13 079	30
31	456	509	947	053	29
32	473	499	86 974	026	28
33	490	490	87 000	13 000	27
34	507	480	027	12 973	26
35	77 524	90 471	87 053	12 947	25
36	541	462	079	921	24
37	558	452	106	894	23
38	575	443	132	868	22
39	592	434	158	842	21
40	77 609	90 424	87 185	12 815	20
41	626	41̲5	211	789	19
42	643	40̲5	238	762	18
43	660	396	264	736	17
44	677	386	290	710	16
45	77 694	90 377	87 317	12 683	15
46	711	368	343	657	14
47	728	358	369	631	13
48	744	349	396	604	12
49	761	339	422	578	11
50	77 778	90 330	87 448	12 552	10
51	795	320	47̲5	525	9
52	812	311	501	499	8
53	829	301	527	473	7
54	846	292	554	446	6
55	77 862	90 282	87 580	12 420	5
56	879	273	606	394	4
57	896	263	633	367	3
58	913	254	659	341	2
59	930	244	685	31̲5	1
60	77 946	90 23̲5	87 711	12 289	0
′	9 log cos	9 log sin	9 log ctn	10 log tan	′

37°

′	log sin 9	log cos 9	log tan 9	log ctn 10	′
0	77 946	90 235	87 711	12 289	60
1	963	225	738	262	59
2	980	216	764	236	58
3	77 997	206	790	210	57
4	78 013	197	817	183	56
5	78 030	90 187	87 843	12 157	55
6	047	178	869	131	54
7	063	168	895	105	53
8	080	159	922	078	52
9	097	149	948	052	51
10	78 113	90 139	87 974	12 026	50
11	130	130	88 000	12 000	49
12	147	120	027	11 973	48
13	163	111	053	947	47
14	180	101	079	921	46
15	78 197	90 091	88 105	11 895	45
16	213	082	131	869	44
17	230	072	158	842	43
18	246	063	184	816	42
19	263	053	210	790	41
20	78 280	90 043	88 236	11 764	40
21	296	034	262	738	39
22	313	024	289	711	38
23	329	014	315	685	37
24	346	90 005	341	659	36
25	78 362	89 995	88 367	11 633	35
26	379	985	393	607	34
27	395	976	420	580	33
28	412	966	446	554	32
29	428	956	472	528	31
30	78 445	89 947	88 498	11 502	30
31	461	937	524	476	29
32	478	927	550	450	28
33	494	918	577	423	27
34	510	908	603	397	26
35	78 527	89 898	88 629	11 371	25
36	543	888	655	345	24
37	560	879	681	319	23
38	576	869	707	293	22
39	592	859	733	267	21
40	78 609	89 849	88 759	11 241	20
41	625	840	786	214	19
42	642	830	812	188	18
43	658	820	838	162	17
44	674	810	864	136	16
45	78 691	89 801	88 890	11 110	15
46	707	791	916	084	14
47	723	781	942	058	13
48	739	771	968	032	12
49	756	761	88 994	11 006	11
50	78 772	89 752	89 020	10 980	10
51	788	742	046	954	9
52	805	732	073	927	8
53	821	722	099	901	7
54	837	712	125	875	6
55	78 853	89 702	89 151	10 849	5
56	869	693	177	823	4
57	886	683	203	797	3
58	902	673	229	771	2
59	918	663	255	745	1
60	78 934	89 653	89 281	10 719	0
′	9 log cos	9 log sin	9 log ctn	10 log tan	′

52°

38°

′	log sin 9	log cos 9	log tan 9	log ctn 10	′
0	78 934	89 653	89 281	10 719	60
1	950	643	307	693	59
2	967	633	333	667	58
3	983	624	359	641	57
4	78 999	614	385	615	56
5	79 015	89 604	89 411	10 589	55
6	031	594	437	563	54
7	047	584	463	537	53
8	063	574	489	511	52
9	079	564	515	485	51
10	79 095	89 554	89 541	10 459	50
11	111	544	567	433	49
12	128	534	593	407	48
13	144	524	619	381	47
14	160	514	645	355	46
15	79 176	89 504	89 671	10 329	45
16	192	495	697	303	44
17	208	485	723	277	43
18	224	475	749	251	42
19	240	465	775	225	41
20	79 256	89 455	89 801	10 199	40
21	272	445	827	173	39
22	288	435	853	147	38
23	304	425	879	121	37
24	319	415	905	095	36
25	79 335	89 405	89 931	10 069	35
26	351	395	957	043	34
27	367	385	89 983	10 017	33
28	383	375	90 009	09 991	32
29	399	364	035	965	31
30	79 415	89 354	90 061	09 939	30
31	431	344	086	914	29
32	447	334	112	888	28
33	463	324	138	862	27
34	478	314	164	836	26
35	79 494	89 304	90 190	09 810	25
36	510	294	216	784	24
37	526	284	242	758	23
38	542	274	268	732	22
39	558	264	294	706	21
40	79 573	89 254	90 320	09 680	20
41	589	244	346	654	19
42	605	233	371	629	18
43	621	223	397	603	17
44	636	213	423	577	16
45	79 652	89 203	90 449	09 551	15
46	668	193	475	525	14
47	684	183	501	499	13
48	699	173	527	473	12
49	715	162	553	447	11
50	79 731	89 152	90 578	09 422	10
51	746	142	604	396	9
52	762	132	630	370	8
53	778	122	656	344	7
54	793	112	682	318	6
55	79 809	89 101	90 708	09 292	5
56	825	091	734	266	4
57	840	081	759	241	3
58	856	071	785	215	2
59	872	060	811	189	1
60	79 887	89 050	90 837	09 163	0
′	9 log cos	9 log sin	9 log ctn	10 log tan	′

51°

39°

'	log sin	log cos	log tan	log ctn	'
	9	9	9	10	
0	79 887	89 050	90 837	09 163	60
1	903	040	863	137	59
2	918	030	889	111	58
3	934	020	914	086	57
4	950	89 009	940	060	56
5	79 965	88 999	90 966	09 034	55
6	981	989	90 992	09 008	54
7	79 996	978	91 018	08 982	53
8	80 012	968	043	957	52
9	027	958	069	931	51
10	80 043	88 948	91 095	08 905	50
11	058	937	121	879	49
12	074	927	147	853	48
13	089	917	172	828	47
14	105	906	198	802	46
15	80 120	88 896	91 224	08 776	45
16	136	886	250	750	44
17	151	875	276	724	43
18	166	865	301	699	42
19	182	855	327	673	41
20	80 197	88 844	91 353	08 647	40
21	213	834	379	621	39
22	228	824	404	596	38
23	244	813	430	570	37
24	259	803	456	544	36
25	80 274	88 793	91 482	08 518	35
26	290	782	507	493	34
27	305	772	533	467	33
28	320	761	559	441	32
29	336	751	585	415	31
30	80 351	88 741	91 610	08 390	30
31	366	730	636	364	29
32	382	720	662	338	28
33	397	709	688	312	27
34	412	699	713	287	26
35	80 428	88 688	91 739	08 261	25
36	443	678	765	235	24
37	458	668	791	209	23
38	473	657	816	184	22
39	489	647	842	158	21
40	80 504	88 636	91 868	08 132	20
41	519	626	893	107	19
42	534	615	919	081	18
43	550	605	945	055	17
44	565	594	971	029	16
45	80 580	88 584	91 996	08 004	15
46	595	573	92 022	07 978	14
47	610	563	048	952	13
48	625	552	073	927	12
49	641	542	099	901	11
50	80 656	88 531	92 125	07 875	10
51	671	521	150	850	9
52	686	510	176	824	8
53	701	499	202	798	7
54	716	489	227	773	6
55	80 731	88 478	92 253	07 747	5
56	746	468	279	721	4
57	762	457	304	696	3
58	777	447	330	670	2
59	792	436	356	644	1
60	80 807	88 425	92 381	07 619	0
	9	9	9	10	
'	log cos	log sin	log ctn	log tan	'

40°

'	log sin	log cos	log tan	log ctn	'
	9	9	9	10	
0	80 807	88 425	92 381	07 619	60
1	822	415	407	593	59
2	837	404	433	567	58
3	852	394	458	542	57
4	867	383	484	516	56
5	80 882	88 372	92 510	07 490	55
6	897	362	535	465	54
7	912	351	561	439	53
8	927	340	587	413	52
9	942	330	612	388	51
10	80 957	88 319	92 638	07 362	50
11	972	308	663	337	49
12	80 987	298	689	311	48
13	81 002	287	715	285	47
14	017	276	740	260	46
15	81 032	88 266	92 766	07 234	45
16	047	255	792	208	44
17	061	244	817	183	43
18	076	234	843	157	42
19	091	223	868	132	41
20	81 106	88 212	92 894	07 106	40
21	121	201	920	080	39
22	136	191	945	055	38
23	151	180	971	029	37
24	166	169	92 996	07 004	36
25	81 180	88 158	93 022	06 978	35
26	195	148	048	952	34
27	210	137	073	927	33
28	225	126	099	901	32
29	240	115	124	876	31
30	81 254	88 105	93 150	06 850	30
31	269	094	175	825	29
32	284	083	201	799	28
33	299	072	227	773	27
34	314	061	252	748	26
35	81 328	88 051	93 278	06 722	25
36	343	040	303	697	24
37	358	029	329	671	23
38	372	018	354	646	22
39	387	88 007	380	620	21
40	81 402	87 996	93 406	06 594	20
41	417	985	431	569	19
42	431	975	457	543	18
43	446	964	482	518	17
44	461	953	508	492	16
45	81 475	87 942	93 533	06 467	15
46	490	931	559	441	14
47	505	920	584	416	13
48	519	909	610	390	12
49	534	898	636	364	11
50	81 549	87 887	93 661	06 339	10
51	563	877	687	313	9
52	578	866	712	288	8
53	592	855	738	262	7
54	607	844	763	237	6
55	81 622	87 833	93 789	06 211	5
56	636	822	814	186	4
57	651	811	840	160	3
58	665	800	865	135	2
59	680	789	891	109	1
60	81 694	87 778	93 916	06 084	0
	9	9	9	10	
'	log cos	log sin	log ctn	log tan	'

50°   **49°**

41°

′	log sin	log cos	log tan	log ctn	′
	9	9	9	10	
0	81 694	87 778	93 916	06 084	60
1	709	767	942	058	59
2	723	756	967	033	58
3	738	745	93 993	06 007	57
4	752	734	94 018	05 982	56
5	81 767	87 723	94 044	05 956	55
6	781	712	069	931	54
7	796	701	095	905	53
8	810	690	120	880	52
9	825	679	146	854	51
10	81 839	87 668	94 171	05 829	50
11	854	657	197	803	49
12	868	646	222	778	48
13	882	635	248	752	47
14	897	624	273	727	46
15	81 911	87 613	94 299	05 701	45
16	926	601	324	676	44
17	940	590	350	650	43
18	955	579	375	625	42
19	969	568	401	599	41
20	81 983	87 557	94 426	05 574	40
21	81 998	546	452	548	39
22	82 012	535	477	523	38
23	026	524	503	497	37
24	041	513	528	472	36
25	82 055	87 501	94 554	05 446	35
26	069	490	579	421	34
27	084	479	604	396	33
28	098	468	630	370	32
29	112	457	655	345	31
30	82 126	87 446	94 681	05 319	30
31	141	434	706	294	29
32	155	423	732	268	28
33	169	412	757	243	27
34	184	401	783	217	26
35	82 198	87 390	94 808	05 192	25
36	212	378	834	166	24
37	226	367	859	141	23
38	240	356	884	116	22
39	255	345	910	090	21
40	82 269	87 334	94 935	05 065	20
41	283	322	961	039	19
42	297	311	94 986	05 014	18
43	311	300	95 012	04 988	17
44	326	288	037	963	16
45	82 340	87 277	95 062	04 938	15
46	354	266	088	912	14
47	368	255	113	887	13
48	382	243	139	861	12
49	396	232	164	836	11
50	82 410	87 221	95 190	04 810	10
51	424	209	215	785	9
52	439	198	240	760	8
53	453	187	266	734	7
54	467	175	291	709	6
55	82 481	87 164	95 317	04 683	5
56	495	153	342	658	4
57	509	141	368	632	3
58	523	130	393	607	2
59	537	119	418	582	1
60	82 551	87 107	95 444	04 556	0
	9	9	9	10	
′	log cos	log sin	log ctn	log tan	′

48°

42°

′	log sin	log cos	log tan	log ctn	′
	9	9	9	10	
0	82 551	87 107	95 444	04 556	60
1	565	096	469	531	59
2	579	085	495	505	58
3	593	073	520	480	57
4	607	062	545	455	56
5	82 621	87 050	95 571	04 429	55
6	635	039	596	404	54
7	649	028	622	378	53
8	663	016	647	353	52
9	677	87 005	672	328	51
10	82 691	86 993	95 698	04 302	50
11	705	982	723	277	49
12	719	970	748	252	48
13	733	959	774	226	47
14	747	947	799	201	46
15	82 761	86 936	95 825	04 175	45
16	775	924	850	150	44
17	788	913	875	125	43
18	802	902	901	099	42
19	816	890	926	074	41
20	82 830	86 879	95 952	04 048	40
21	844	867	95 977	04 023	39
22	858	855	96 002	03 998	38
23	872	844	028	972	37
24	885	832	053	947	36
25	82 899	86 821	96 078	03 922	35
26	913	809	104	896	34
27	927	798	129	871	33
28	941	786	155	845	32
29	955	775	180	820	31
30	82 968	86 763	96 205	03 795	30
31	982	752	231	769	29
32	82 996	740	256	744	28
33	83 010	728	281	719	27
34	023	717	307	693	26
35	83 037	86 705	96 332	03 668	25
36	051	694	357	643	24
37	065	682	383	617	23
38	078	670	408	592	22
39	092	659	433	567	21
40	83 106	86 647	96 459	03 541	20
41	120	635	484	516	19
42	133	624	510	490	18
43	147	612	535	465	17
44	161	600	560	440	16
45	83 174	86 589	96 586	03 414	15
46	188	577	611	389	14
47	202	565	636	364	13
48	215	554	662	338	12
49	229	542	687	313	11
50	83 242	86 530	96 712	03 288	10
51	256	518	738	262	9
52	270	507	763	237	8
53	283	495	788	212	7
54	297	483	814	186	6
55	83 310	86 472	96 839	03 161	5
56	324	460	864	136	4
57	338	448	890	110	3
58	351	436	915	085	2
59	365	425	940	060	1
60	83 378	86 413	96 966	03 034	0
	9	9	9	10	
′	log cos	log sin	log ctn	log tan	′

47°

43°

′	log sin 9	log cos 9	log tan 9	log ctn 10	′
0	83 378	86 413	96 966	03 034	60
1	392	401	96 991	03 009	59
2	405	389	97 016	02 984	58
3	419	377	042	958	57
4	432	366	067	933	56
5	83 446	86 354	97 092	02 908	55
6	459	342	118	882	54
7	473	330	143	857	53
8	486	318	168	832	52
9	500	306	193	807	51
10	83 513	86 295	97 219	02 781	50
11	527	283	244	756	49
12	540	271	269	731	48
13	554	259	295	705	47
14	567	247	320	680	46
15	83 581	86 235	97 345	02 655	45
16	594	223	371	629	44
17	608	211	396	604	43
18	621	200	421	579	42
19	634	188	447	553	41
20	83 648	86 176	97 472	02 528	40
21	661	164	497	503	39
22	674	152	523	477	38
23	688	140	548	452	37
24	701	128	573	427	36
25	83 715	86 116	97 598	02 402	35
26	728	104	624	376	34
27	741	092	649	351	33
28	755	080	674	326	32
29	768	068	700	300	31
30	83 781	86 056	97 725	02 275	30
31	795	044	750	250	29
32	808	032	776	224	28
33	821	020	801	199	27
34	834	86 008	826	174	26
35	83 848	85 996	97 851	02 149	25
36	861	984	877	123	24
37	874	972	902	098	23
38	887	960	927	073	22
39	901	948	953	047	21
40	83 914	85 936	97 978	02 022	20
41	927	924	98 003	01 997	19
42	940	912	029	971	18
43	954	900	054	946	17
44	967	888	079	921	16
45	83 980	85 876	98 104	01 896	15
46	83 993	864	130	870	14
47	84 006	851	155	845	13
48	020	839	180	820	12
49	033	827	206	794	11
50	84 046	85 815	98 231	01 769	10
51	059	803	256	744	9
52	072	791	281	719	8
53	085	779	307	693	7
54	098	766	332	668	6
55	84 112	85 754	98 357	01 643	5
56	125	742	383	617	4
57	138	730	408	592	3
58	151	718	433	567	2
59	164	706	458	542	1
60	84 177	85 693	98 484	01 516	0
′	log cos 9	log sin 9	log ctn 9	log tan 10	′

44°

′	log sin 9	log cos 9	log tan 9	log ctn 10	′
0	84 177	85 693	98 484	01 516	60
1	190	681	509	491	59
2	203	669	534	466	58
3	216	657	560	440	57
4	229	645	585	415	56
5	84 242	85 632	98 610	01 390	55
6	255	620	635	365	54
7	269	608	661	339	53
8	282	596	686	314	52
9	295	583	711	289	51
10	84 308	85 571	98 737	01 263	50
11	321	559	762	238	49
12	334	547	787	213	48
13	347	534	812	188	47
14	360	522	838	162	46
15	84 373	85 510	98 863	01 137	45
16	385	497	888	112	44
17	398	485	913	087	43
18	411	473	939	061	42
19	424	460	964	036	41
20	84 437	85 448	98 989	01 011	40
21	450	436	99 015	00 985	39
22	463	423	040	960	38
23	476	411	065	935	37
24	489	399	090	910	36
25	84 502	85 386	99 116	00 884	35
26	515	374	141	859	34
27	528	361	166	834	33
28	540	349	191	809	32
29	553	337	217	783	31
30	84 566	85 324	99 242	00 758	30
31	579	312	267	733	29
32	592	299	293	707	28
33	605	287	318	682	27
34	618	274	343	657	26
35	84 630	85 262	99 368	00 632	25
36	643	250	394	606	24
37	656	237	419	581	23
38	669	225	444	556	22
39	682	212	469	531	21
40	84 694	85 200	99 495	00 505	20
41	707	187	520	480	19
42	720	175	545	455	18
43	733	162	570	430	17
44	745	150	596	404	16
45	84 758	85 137	99 621	00 379	15
46	771	125	646	354	14
47	784	112	672	328	13
48	796	100	697	303	12
49	809	087	722	278	11
50	84 822	85 074	99 747	00 253	10
51	835	062	773	227	9
52	847	049	798	202	8
53	860	037	823	177	7
54	873	024	848	152	6
55	84 885	85 012	99 874	00 126	5
56	898	84 999	899	101	4
57	911	986	924	076	3
58	923	974	949	051	2
59	936	961	975	025	1
60	84 949	84 949	00 000	00 000	0
′	log cos 9	log sin 9	log ctn 10	log tan 10	′

TABLE IV.   DEGREES AND RADIANS   49

1. To Change Degrees, Minutes, and Seconds into Radians

o	Radians	'	Radians	''	Radians
1	0.01745 33	1	0.00029 09	1	0.00000 48
2	0.03490 66	2	0.00058 18	2	0.00000 97
3	0.05235 99	3	0.00087 27	3	0.00001 45
4	0.06981 32	4	0.00116 36	4	0.00001 94
5	0.08726 65	5	0.00145 44	5	0.00002 42
6	0.10471 98	6	0.00174 53	6	0.00002 91
7	0.12217 30	7	0.00203 62	7	0.00003 39
8	0.13962 63	8	0.00232 71	8	0.00003 88
9	0.15707 96	9	0.00261 80	9	0.00004 36
10	0.17453 29	10	0.00290 89	10	0.00004 85
20	0.34906 59	20	0.00581 78	20	0.00009 70
30	0.52359 88	30	0.00872 66	30	0.00014 54
40	0.69813 17	40	0.01163 55	40	0.00019 39
50	0.87266 46	50	0.01454 44	50	0.00024 24
60	1.04719 76	60	0.01745 33	60	0.00029 09

2. To Change Radians to Degrees, Minutes, and Seconds

Rad.	Radians			Tenths			Hundredths			Thousandths			Ten-Thousandths	
	o	'	''	o	'	''	o	'	''	o	'	''	'	''
1	57	17	45	5	43	46	0	34	23	0	3	26	0	21
2	114	35	30	11	27	33	1	8	45	0	6	53	0	41
3	171	53	14	17	11	19	1	43	8	0	10	19	1	2
4	229	10	59	22	55	6	2	17	31	0	13	45	1	22
5	286	28	44	28	38	52	2	51	53	0	17	11	1	43
6	343	46	29	34	22	39	3	26	16	0	20	38	2	4
7	401	4	14	40	6	25	4	0	38	0	24	4	2	24
8	458	21	58	45	50	12	4	35	1	0	27	30	2	45
9	515	39	43	51	33	58	5	9	24	0	30	56	3	6

3. To Change Minutes and Seconds into Decimal Parts of a Degree

From Minutes		From Seconds	
1' = 0.0167°	8' = 0.1333°	1'' = 0.00 028°	8'' = 0.00 222°
2' = 0.0333°	9' = 0.1500°	2'' = 0.00 056°	9'' = 0.00 250°
3' = 0.0500°	10' = 0.1667°	3'' = 0.00 083°	10'' = 0.00 278°
4' = 0.0667°	20' = 0.3333°	4'' = 0.00 111°	20'' = 0.00 556°
5' = 0.0833°	30' = 0.5000°	5'' = 0.00 139°	30'' = 0.00 833°
6' = 0.1000°	40' = 0.6667°	6'' = 0 00 167°	40'' = 0.01 111°
7' = 0.1167°	50' = 0.8333°	7'' = 0.00 194°	50'' = 0.01 389°

x	e^x	e^{-x}	$\sinh x$	$\cosh x$	x	e^x	e^{-x}	$\sinh x$	$\cosh x$
0.00	1.0000	1.0000	0.0000	1.0000	**0.50**	1.6487	.60 653	0.5211	1.1276
0.01	1.0101	.99 005	0.0100	1.0001	0.51	1.6653	.60 050	0.5324	1.1329
0.02	1.0202	.98 020	0.0200	1.0002	0.52	1.6820	.59 452	0.5438	1.1383
0.03	1.0305	.97 045	0.0300	1.0005	0.53	1.6989	.58 860	0.5552	1.1438
0.04	1.0408	.96 079	0.0400	1.0008	0.54	1.7160	.58 275	0.5666	1.1494
0.05	1.0513	.95 123	0.0500	1.0013	0.55	1.7333	.57 695	0.5782	1.1551
0.06	1.0618	.94 176	0.0600	1.0018	0.56	1.7507	.57 121	0.5897	1.1609
0.07	1.0725	.93 239	0.0701	1.0025	0.57	1.7683	.56 553	0.6014	1.1669
0.08	1.0833	.92 312	0.0801	1.0032	0.58	1.7860	.55 990	0.6131	1.1730
0.09	1.0942	.91 393	0.0901	1.0041	0.59	1.8040	.55 433	0.6248	1.1792
0.10	1.1052	.90 484	0.1002	1.0050	**0.60**	1.8221	.54 881	0.6367	1.1855
0.11	1.1163	.89 583	0.1102	1.0061	0.61	1.8404	.54 335	0.6485	1.1919
0.12	1.1275	.88 692	0.1203	1.0072	0.62	1.8589	.53 794	0.6605	1.1984
0.13	1.1388	.87 809	0.1304	1.0085	0.63	1.8776	.53 259	0.6725	1.2051
0.14	1.1503	.86 936	0.1405	1.0098	0.64	1.8965	.52 729	0.6846	1.2119
0.15	1.1618	.86 071	0.1506	1.0113	0.65	1.9155	.52 205	0.6967	1.2188
0.16	1.1735	.85 214	0.1607	1.0128	0.66	1.9348	.51 685	0.7090	1.2258
0.17	1.1853	.84 366	0.1708	1.0145	0.67	1.9542	.51 171	0.7213	1.2330
0.18	1.1972	.83 527	0.1810	1.0162	0.68	1.9739	.50 662	0.7336	1.2402
0.19	1.2092	.82 696	0.1911	1.0181	0.69	1.9937	.50 158	0.7461	1.2476
0.20	1.2214	.81 873	0.2013	1.0201	**0.70**	2.0138	.49 659	0.7586	1.2552
0.21	1.2337	.81 058	0.2115	1.0221	0.71	2.0340	.49 164	0.7712	1.2628
0.22	1.2461	.80 252	0.2218	1.0243	0.72	2.0544	.48 675	0.7838	1.2706
0.23	1.2586	.79 453	0.2320	1.0266	0.73	2.0751	.48 191	0.7966	1.2785
0.24	1.2712	.78 663	0.2423	1.0289	0.74	2.0959	.47 711	0.8094	1.2865
0.25	1.2840	.77 880	0.2526	1.0314	0.75	2.1170	.47 237	0.8223	1.2947
0.26	1.2969	.77 105	0.2629	1.0340	0.76	2.1383	.46 767	0.8353	1.3030
0.27	1.3100	.76 338	0.2733	1.0367	0.77	2.1598	.46 301	0.8484	1.3114
0.28	1.3231	.75 578	0.2837	1.0395	0.78	2.1815	.45 841	0.8615	1.3199
0.29	1.3364	.74 826	0.2941	1.0423	0.79	2.2034	.45 384	0.8748	1.3286
0.30	1.3499	.74 082	0.3045	1.0453	**0.80**	2.2255	.44 933	0.8881	1.3374
0.31	1.3634	.73 345	0.3150	1.0484	0.81	2.2479	.44 486	0.9015	1.3464
0.32	1.3771	.72 615	0.3255	1.0516	0.82	2.2705	.44 043	0.9150	1.3555
0.33	1.3910	.71 892	0.3360	1.0549	0.83	2.2933	.43 605	0.9286	1.3647
0.34	1.4049	.71 177	0.3466	1.0584	0.84	2.3164	.43 171	0.9423	1.3740
0.35	1.4191	.70 469	0.3572	1.0619	0.85	2.3396	.42 741	0.9561	1.3835
0.36	1.4333	.69 768	0.3678	1.0655	0.86	2.3632	.42 316	0.9700	1.3932
0.37	1.4477	.69 073	0.3785	1.0692	0.87	2.3869	.41 895	0.9840	1.4029
0.38	1.4623	.68 386	0.3892	1.0731	0.88	2.4109	.41 478	0.9981	1.4128
0.39	1.4770	.67 706	0.4000	1.0770	0.89	2.4351	.41 066	1.0122	1.4229
0.40	1.4918	.67 032	0.4108	1.0811	**0.90**	2.4596	.40 657	1.0265	1.4331
0.41	1.5068	.66 365	0.4216	1.0852	0.91	2.4843	.40 252	1.0409	1.4434
0.42	1.5220	.65 705	0.4325	1.0895	0.92	2.5093	.39 852	1.0554	1.4539
0.43	1.5373	.65 051	0.4434	1.0939	0.93	2.5345	.39 455	1.0700	1.4645
0.44	1.5527	.64 404	0.4543	1.0984	0.94	2.5600	.39 063	1.0847	1.4753
0.45	1.5683	.63 763	0.4653	1.1030	0.95	2.5857	.38 674	1.0995	1.4862
0.46	1.5841	.63 128	0.4764	1.1077	0.96	2.6117	.38 289	1.1144	1.4973
0.47	1.6000	.62 500	0.4875	1.1125	0.97	2.6379	.37 908	1.1294	1.5085
0.48	1.6161	.61 878	0.4986	1.1174	0.98	2.6645	.37 531	1.1446	1.5199
0.49	1.6323	.61 263	0.5098	1.1225	0.99	2.6912	.37 158	1.1598	1.5314
0.50	1.6487	.60 653	0.5211	1.1276	**1.00**	2.7183	.36 788	1.1752	1.5431
x	e^x	e^{-x}	$\sinh x$	$\cosh x$	x	e^x	e^{-x}	$\sinh x$	$\cosh x$

TABLE VI 51

NATURAL LOGARITHMS

0.19–9

N	$\log_e$	N	$\log_e$	N	$\log_e$	N	$\log_e$	N	$\log_e$
0	$-\infty$	2.0	0.69 315	4.0	1.38 629	6.0	1.79 176	8.0	2.07 944
0.1	7.697 − 10	2.1	0.74 194	4.1	1.41 099	6.1	1.80 829	8.1	2.09 186
0.2	8.391 − 10	2.2	0.78 846	4.2	1.43 508	6.2	1.82 455	8.2	2.10 413
0.3	8.796 − 10	2.3	0.83 291	4.3	1.45 862	6.3	1.84 055	8.3	2.11 626
0.4	9.084 − 10	2.4	0.87 547	4.4	1.48 160	6.4	1.85 630	8.4	2.12 823
0.5	9.307 − 10	2.5	0.91 629	4.5	1.50 408	6.5	1.87 180	8.5	2.14 007
0.6	9.489 − 10	2.6	0.95 551	4.6	1.52 606	6.6	1.88 707	8.6	2.15 176
0.7	9.643 − 10	2.7	0.99 325	4.7	1.54 756	6.7	1.90 211	8.7	2.16 332
0.8	9.777 − 10	2.8	1.02 962	4.8	1.56 862	6.8	1.91 692	8.8	2.17 475
0.9	9.895 − 10	2.9	1.06 471	4.9	1.58 924	6.9	1.93 152	8.9	2.18 605
1.0	0.00 000	3.0	1.09 861	5.0	1.60 944	7.0	1.94 591	9.0	2.19 722
1.1	0.09 531	3.1	1.13 140	5.1	1.62 924	7.1	1.96 009	9.1	2.20 827
1.2	0.18 232	3.2	1.16 315	5.2	1.64 866	7.2	1.97 408	9.2	2.21 920
1.3	0.26 236	3.3	1.19 392	5.3	1.66 771	7.3	1.98 787	9.3	2.23 001
1.4	0.33 647	3.4	1.22 378	5.4	1.68 640	7.4	2.00 148	9.4	2.24 071
1.5	0.40 547	3.5	1.25 276	5.5	1.70 475	7.5	2.01 490	9.5	2.25 129
1.6	0.47 000	3.6	1.28 093	5.6	1.72 277	7.6	2.02 815	9.6	2.26 176
1.7	0.53 063	3.7	1.30 833	5.7	1.74 047	7.7	2.04 122	9.7	2.27 213
1.8	0.58 779	3.8	1.33 500	5.8	1.75 786	7.8	2.05 412	9.8	2.28 238
1.9	0.64 185	3.9	1.36 098	5.9	1.77 495	7.9	2.06 686	9.9	2.29 253

1–250

N	$\log_e$	N	$\log_e$	N	$\log_e$	N	$\log_e$	N	$\log_e$
0	$-\infty$	50	3.91 202	100	4.60 517	150	5.01 064	200	5.29 832
1	0.00 000	51	3.93 183	101	4.61 512	151	5.01 728	201	5.30 330
2	0.69 315	52	3.95 124	102	4.62 497	152	5.02 388	202	5.30 827
3	1.09 861	53	3.97 029	103	4.63 473	153	5.03 044	203	5.31 321
4	1.38 629	54	3.98 898	104	4.64 439	154	5.03 695	204	5.31 812
5	1.60 944	55	4.00 733	105	4.65 396	155	5.04 343	205	5.32 301
6	1.79 176	56	4.02 535	106	4.66 344	156	5.04 986	206	5.32 788
7	1.94 591	57	4.04 305	107	4.67 283	157	5.05 625	207	5.33 272
8	2.07 944	58	4.06 044	108	4.68 213	158	5.06 260	208	5.33 754
9	2.19 722	59	4.07 754	109	4.69 135	159	5.06 890	209	5.34 233
10	2.30 259	60	4.09 434	110	4.70 048	160	5.07 517	210	5.34 711
11	2.39 790	61	4.11 087	111	4.70 953	161	5.08 140	211	5.35 186
12	2.48 491	62	4.12 713	112	4.71 850	162	5.08 760	212	5.35 659
13	2.56 495	63	4.14 313	113	4.72 739	163	5.09 375	213	5.36 129
14	2.63 906	64	4.15 888	114	4.73 620	164	5.09 987	214	5.36 598
15	2.70 805	65	4.17 439	115	4.74 493	165	5.10 595	215	5.37 064
16	2.77 259	66	4.18 965	116	4.75 359	166	5.11 199	216	5.37 528
17	2.83 321	67	4.20 469	117	4.76 217	167	5.11 799	217	5.37 990
18	2.89 037	68	4.21 951	118	4.77 068	168	5.12 396	218	5.38 450
19	2.94 444	69	4.23 411	119	4.77 912	169	5.12 990	219	5.38 907
20	2.99 573	70	4.24 850	120	4.78 749	170	5.13 580	220	5.39 363
21	3.04 452	71	4.26 268	121	4.79 579	171	5.14 166	221	5.39 816
22	3.09 104	72	4.27 667	122	4.80 402	172	5.14 749	222	5.40 268
23	3.13 549	73	4.29 046	123	4.81 218	173	5.15 329	223	5.40 717
24	3.17 805	74	4.30 407	124	4.82 028	174	5.15 906	224	5.41 165
25	3.21 888	75	4.31 749	125	4.82 831	175	5.16 479	225	5.41 610
26	3.25 810	76	4.33 073	126	4.83 628	176	5.17 048	226	5.42 053
27	3.29 584	77	4.34 381	127	4.84 419	177	5.17 615	227	5.42 495
28	3.33 220	78	4.35 671	128	4.85 203	178	5.18 178	228	5.42 935
29	3.36 730	79	4.36 945	129	4.85 981	179	5.18 739	229	5.43 372
30	3.40 120	80	4.38 203	130	4.86 753	180	5.19 296	230	5.43 808
31	3.43 399	81	4.39 445	131	4.87 520	181	5.19 850	231	5.44 242
32	3.46 574	82	4.40 672	132	4.88 280	182	5.20 401	232	5.44 674
33	3.49 651	83	4.41 884	133	4.89 035	183	5.20 949	233	5.45 104
34	3.52 636	84	4.43 082	134	4.89 784	184	5.21 494	234	5.45 532
35	3.55 535	85	4.44 265	135	4.90 527	185	5.22 036	235	5.45 959
36	3.58 352	86	4.45 435	136	4.91 265	186	5.22 575	236	5.46 383
37	3.61 092	87	4.46 591	137	4.91 998	187	5.23 111	237	5.46 806
38	3.63 759	88	4.47 734	138	4.92 725	188	5.23 644	238	5.47 227
39	3.66 356	89	4.48 864	139	4.93 447	189	5.24 175	239	5.47 646
40	3.68 888	90	4.49 981	140	4.94 164	190	5.24 702	240	5.48 064
41	3.71 357	91	4.51 086	141	4.94 876	191	5.25 227	241	5.48 480
42	3.73 767	92	4.52 179	142	4.95 583	192	5.25 750	242	5.48 894
43	3.76 120	93	4.53 260	143	4.96 284	193	5.26 269	243	5.49 306
44	3.78 419	94	4.54 329	144	4.96 981	194	5.26 786	244	5.49 717
45	3.80 666	95	4.55 388	145	4.97 673	195	5.27 300	245	5.50 126
46	3.82 864	96	4.56 435	146	4.98 361	196	5.27 811	246	5.50 533
47	3.85 015	97	4.57 471	147	4.99 043	197	5.28 320	247	5.50 939
48	3.87 120	98	4.58 497	148	4.99 721	198	5.28 827	248	5.51 343
49	3.89 182	99	4.59 512	149	5.00 395	199	5.29 330	249	5.51 745
50	3.91 202	100	4.60 517	150	5.01 064	200	5.29 832	250	5.52 146
N	$\log_e$	N	$\log_e$	N	$\log_e$	N	$\log_e$	N	$\log_e$

TABLE VII   53

SQUARES, SQUARE ROOTS, RECIPROCALS

n	n^2	$\sqrt{n}$	$\sqrt{10\,n}$	$1/n$	n	n^2	$\sqrt{n}$	$\sqrt{10\,n}$	$1/n$
1.00	1.0000	1.00 000	3.16 228	1.00 000	1.50	2.2500	1.22 474	3.87 298	.666 667
1.01	1.0201	1.00 499	3.17 805	.990 099	1.51	2.2801	1.22 882	3.88 587	.662 252
1.02	1.0404	1.00 995	3.19 374	.980 392	1.52	2.3104	1.23 288	3.89 872	.657 895
1.03	1.0609	1.01 489	3.20 936	.970 874	1.53	2.3409	1.23 693	3.91 152	.653 595
1.04	1.0816	1.01 980	3.22 490	.961 538	1.54	2.3716	1.24 097	3.92 428	.649 351
1.05	1.1025	1.02 470	3.24 037	.952 381	1.55	2.4025	1.24 499	3.93 700	.645 161
1.06	1.1236	1.02 956	3.25 576	.943 396	1.56	2.4336	1.24 900	3.94 968	.641 026
1.07	1.1449	1.03 441	3.27 109	.934 579	1.57	2.4649	1.25 300	3.96 232	.636 943
1.08	1.1664	1.03 923	3.28 634	.925 926	1.58	2.4964	1.25 698	3.97 492	.632 911
1.09	1.1881	1.04 403	3.30 151	.917 431	1.59	2.5281	1.26 095	3.98 748	.628 931
1.10	1.2100	1.04 881	3.31 662	.909 091	1.60	2.5600	1.26 491	4.00 000	.625 000
1.11	1.2321	1.05 357	3.33 167	.900 901	1.61	2.5921	1.26 886	4.01 248	.621 118
1.12	1.2544	1.05 830	3.34 664	.892 857	1.62	2.6244	1.27 279	4.02 492	.617 284
1.13	1.2769	1.06 301	3.36 155	.884 956	1.63	2.6569	1.27 671	4.03 733	.613 497
1.14	1.2996	1.06 771	3.37 639	.877 193	1.64	2.6896	1.28 062	4.04 969	.609 756
1.15	1.3225	1.07 238	3.39 116	.869 565	1.65	2.7225	1.28 452	4.06 202	.606 061
1.16	1.3456	1.07 703	3.40 588	.862 069	1.66	2.7556	1.28 841	4.07 431	.602 410
1.17	1.3689	1.08 167	3.42 053	.854 701	1.67	2.7889	1.29 228	4.08 656	.598 802
1.18	1.3924	1.08 628	3.43 511	.847 458	1.68	2.8224	1.29 615	4.09 878	.595 238
1.19	1.4161	1.09 087	3.44 964	.840 336	1.69	2.8561	1.30 000	4.11 096	.591 716
1.20	1.4400	1.09 545	3.46 410	.833 333	1.70	2.8900	1.30 384	4.12 311	.588 235
1.21	1.4641	1.10 000	3.47 851	.826 446	1.71	2.9241	1.30 767	4.13 521	.584 795
1.22	1.4884	1.10 454	3.49 285	.819 672	1.72	2.9584	1.31 149	4.14 729	.581 395
1.23	1.5129	1.10 905	3.50 714	.813 008	1.73	2.9929	1.31 529	4.15 933	.578 035
1.24	1.5376	1.11 355	3.52 136	.806 452	1.74	3.0276	1.31 909	4.17 133	.574 713
1.25	1.5625	1.11 803	3.53 553	.800 000	1.75	3.0625	1.32 288	4.18 330	.571 429
1.26	1.5876	1.12 250	3.54 965	.793 651	1.76	3.0976	1.32 665	4.19 524	.568 182
1.27	1.6129	1.12 694	3.56 371	.787 402	1.77	3.1329	1.33 041	4.20 714	.564 972
1.28	1.6384	1.13 137	3.57 771	.781 250	1.78	3.1684	1.33 417	4.21 900	.561 798
1.29	1.6641	1.13 578	3.59 166	.775 194	1.79	3.2041	1.33 791	4.23 084	.558 659
1.30	1.6900	1.14 018	3.60 555	.769 231	1.80	3.2400	1.34 164	4.24 264	.555 556
1.31	1.7161	1.14 455	3.61 939	.763 359	1.81	3.2761	1.34 536	4.25 441	.552 486
1.32	1.7424	1.14 891	3.63 318	.757 576	1.82	3.3124	1.34 907	4.26 615	.549 451
1.33	1.7689	1.15 326	3.64 692	.751 880	1.83	3.3489	1.35 277	4.27 785	.546 448
1.34	1.7956	1.15 758	3.66 060	.746 269	1.84	3.3856	1.35 647	4.28 952	.543 478
1.35	1.8225	1.16 190	3.67 423	.740 741	1.85	3.4225	1.36 015	4.30 116	.540 541
1.36	1.8496	1.16 619	3.68 782	.735 294	1.86	3.4596	1.36 382	4.31 277	.537 634
1.37	1.8769	1.17 047	3.70 135	.729 927	1.87	3.4969	1.36 748	4.32 435	.534 759
1.38	1.9044	1.17 473	3.71 484	.724 638	1.88	3.5344	1.37 113	4.33 590	.531 915
1.39	1.9321	1.17 898	3.72 827	.719 424	1.89	3.5721	1.37 477	4.34 741	.529 101
1.40	1.9600	1.18 322	3.74 166	.714 286	1.90	3.6100	1.37 840	4.35 890	.526 316
1.41	1.9881	1.18 743	3.75 500	.709 220	1.91	3.6481	1.38 203	4.37 035	.523 560
1.42	2.0164	1.19 164	3.76 829	.704 225	1.92	3.6864	1.38 564	4.38 178	.520 833
1.43	2.0449	1.19 583	3.78 153	.699 301	1.93	3.7249	1.38 924	4.39 318	.518 135
1.44	2.0736	1.20 000	3.79 473	.694 444	1.94	3.7636	1.39 284	4.40 454	.515 464
1.45	2.1025	1.20 416	3.80 789	.689 655	1.95	3.8025	1.39 642	4.41 588	.512 821
1.46	2.1316	1.20 830	3.82 099	.684 932	1.96	3.8416	1.40 000	4.42 719	.510 204
1.47	2.1609	1.21 244	3.83 406	.680 272	1.97	3.8809	1.40 357	4.43 847	.507 614
1.48	2.1904	1.21 655	3.84 708	.675 676	1.98	3.9204	1.40 712	4.44 972	.505 051
1.49	2.2201	1.22 066	3.86 005	.671 141	1.99	3.9601	1.41 067	4.46 094	.502 513
1.50	2.2500	1.22 474	3.87 298	.666 667	2.00	4.0000	1.41 421	4.47 214	.500 000
n	n^2	$\sqrt{n}$	$\sqrt{10\,n}$	$1/n$	n	n^2	$\sqrt{n}$	$\sqrt{10\,n}$	$1/n$

n	n^2	$\sqrt{n}$	$\sqrt{10\,n}$	$1/n$	n	n^2	$\sqrt{n}$	$\sqrt{10\,n}$	$1/n$
2.00	4.0000	1.41 421	4.47 214	.500 000	2.50	6.2500	1.58 114	5.00 000	.400 000
2.01	4.0401	1.41 774	4.48 330	.497 512	2.51	6.3001	1.58 430	5.00 999	.398 406
2.02	4.0804	1.42 127	4.49 444	.495 050	2.52	6.3504	1.58 745	5.01 996	.396 825
2.03	4.1209	1.42 478	4.50 555	.492 611	2.53	6.4009	1.59 060	5.02 991	.395 257
2.04	4.1616	1.42 829	4.51 664	.490 196	2.54	6.4516	1.59 374	5.03 984	.393 701
2.05	4.2025	1.43 178	4.52 769	.487 805	2.55	6.5025	1.59 687	5.04 975	.392 157
2.06	4.2436	1.43 527	4.53 872	.485 437	2.56	6.5536	1.60 000	5.05 964	.390 625
2.07	4.2849	1.43 875	4.54 973	.483 092	2.57	6.6049	1.60 312	5.06 952	.389 105
2.08	4.3264	1.44 222	4.56 070	.480 769	2.58	6.6564	1.60 624	5.07 937	.387 597
2.09	4.3681	1.44 568	4.57 165	.478 469	2.59	6.7081	1.60 935	5.08 920	.386 100
2.10	4.4100	1.44 914	4.58 258	.476 190	2.60	6.7600	1.61 245	5.09 902	.384 615
2.11	4.4521	1.45 258	4.59 347	.473 934	2.61	6.8121	1.61 555	5.10 882	.383 142
2.12	4.4944	1.45 602	4.60 435	.471 698	2.62	6.8644	1.61 864	5.11 859	.381 679
2.13	4.5369	1.45 945	4.61 519	.469 434	2.63	6.9169	1.62 173	5.12 835	.380 228
2.14	4.5796	1.46 287	4.62 601	.467 290	2.64	6.9696	1.62 481	5.13 809	.378 788
2.15	4.6225	1.46 629	4.63 681	.465 116	2.65	7.0225	1.62 788	5.14 782	.377 358
2.16	4.6656	1.46 969	4.64 758	.462 963	2.66	7.0756	1.63 095	5.15 752	.375 940
2.17	4.7089	1.47 309	4.65 833	.460 829	2.67	7.1289	1.63 401	5.16 720	.374 532
2.18	4.7524	1.47 648	4.66 905	.458 716	2.68	7.1824	1.63 707	5.17 687	.373 134
2.19	4.7961	1.47 986	4.67 974	.456 621	2.69	7.2361	1.64 012	5.18 652	.371 747
2.20	4.8400	1.48 324	4.69 042	.454 545	2.70	7.2900	1.64 317	5.19 615	.370 370
2.21	4.8841	1.48 661	4.70 106	.452 489	2.71	7.3441	1.64 621	5.20 577	.369 004
2.22	4.9284	1.48 997	4.71 169	.450 450	2.72	7.3984	1.64 924	5.21 536	.367 647
2.23	4.9729	1.49 332	4.72 229	.448 430	2.73	7.4529	1.65 227	5.22 494	.366 300
2.24	5.0176	1.49 666	4.73 286	.446 429	2.74	7.5076	1.65 529	5.23 450	.364 964
2.25	5.0625	1.50 000	4.74 342	.444 444	2.75	7.5625	1.65 831	5.24 404	.363 636
2.26	5.1076	1.50 333	4.75 395	.442 478	2.76	7.6176	1.66 132	5.25 357	.362 319
2.27	5.1529	1.50 665	4.76 445	.440 529	2.77	7.6729	1.66 433	5.26 308	.361 011
2.28	5.1984	1.50 997	4.77 493	.438 596	2.78	7.7284	1.66 733	5.27 257	.359 712
2.29	5.2441	1.51 327	4.78 539	.436 681	2.79	7.7841	1.67 033	5.28 205	.358 423
2.30	5.2900	1.51 658	4.79 583	.434 783	2.80	7.8400	1.67 332	5.29 150	.357 143
2.31	5.3361	1.51 987	4.80 625	.432 900	2.81	7.8961	1.67 631	5.30 094	.355 872
2.32	5.3824	1.52 315	4.81 664	.431 034	2.82	7.9524	1.67 929	5.31 037	.354 610
2.33	5.4289	1.52 643	4.82 701	.429 185	2.83	8.0089	1.68 226	5.31 977	.353 357
2.34	5.4756	1.52 971	4.83 735	.427 350	2.84	8.0656	1.68 523	5.32 917	.352 113
2.35	5.5225	1.53 297	4.84 768	.425 532	2.85	8.1225	1.68 819	5.33 854	.350 877
2.36	5.5696	1.53 623	4.85 798	.423 729	2.86	8.1796	1.69 115	5.34 790	.349 650
2.37	5.6169	1.53 948	4.86 826	.421 941	2.87	8.2369	1.69 411	5.35 724	.348 432
2.38	5.6644	1.54 272	4.87 852	.420 168	2.88	8.2944	1.69 706	5.36 656	.347 222
2.39	5.7121	1.54 596	4.88 876	.418 410	2.89	8.3521	1.70 000	5.37 587	.346 021
2.40	5.7600	1.54 919	4.89 898	.416 667	2.90	8.4100	1.70 294	5.38 516	.344 828
2.41	5.8081	1.55 242	4.90 918	.414 938	2.91	8.4681	1.70 587	5.39 444	.343 643
2.42	5.8564	1.55 563	4.91 935	.413 223	2.92	8.5264	1.70 880	5.40 370	.342 466
2.43	5.9049	1.55 885	4.92 950	.411 523	2.93	8.5849	1.71 172	5.41 295	.341 297
2.44	5.9536	1.56 205	4.93 964	.409 836	2.94	8.6436	1.71 464	5.42 218	.340 136
2.45	6.0025	1.56 525	4.94 975	.408 163	2.95	8.7025	1.71 756	5.43 139	.338 983
2.46	6.0516	1.56 844	4.95 984	.406 504	2.96	8.7616	1.72 047	5.44 059	.337 838
2.47	6.1009	1.57 162	4.96 991	.404 858	2.97	8.8209	1.72 337	5.44 977	.336 700
2.48	6.1504	1.57 480	4.97 996	.403 226	2.98	8.8804	1.72 627	5.45 894	.335 570
2.49	6.2001	1.57 797	4.98 999	.401 606	2.99	8.9401	1.72 916	5.46 809	.334 448
2.50	6.2500	1.58 114	5.00 000	.400 000	3.00	9.0000	1.73 205	5.47 723	.333 333
n	n^2	$\sqrt{n}$	$\sqrt{10\,n}$	$1/n$	n	n^2	$\sqrt{n}$	$\sqrt{10\,n}$	$1/n$

n	n^2	$\sqrt{n}$	$\sqrt{10\,n}$	$1/n$	n	n^2	$\sqrt{n}$	$\sqrt{10\,n}$	$1/n$
3.00	9.0000	1.73 205	5.47 723	.333 333	**3.50**	12.2500	1.87 083	5.91 608	.285 714
3.01	9.0601	1.73 494	5.48 635	.332 226	3.51	12.3201	1.87 350	5.92 453	.284 900
3.02	9.1204	1.73 781	5.49 545	.331 126	3.52	12.3904	1.87 617	5.93 296	.284 091
3.03	9.1809	1.74 069	5.50 454	.330 033	3.53	12.4609	1.87 883	5.94 138	.283 286
3.04	9.2416	1.74 356	5.51 362	.328 947	3.54	12.5316	1.88 149	5.94 979	.282 486
3.05	9.3025	1.74 642	5.52 268	.327 869	3.55	12.6025	1.88 414	5.95 819	.281 690
3.06	9.3636	1.74 929	5.53 173	.326 797	3.56	12.6736	1.88 680	5.96 657	.280 899
3.07	9.4249	1.75 214	5.54 076	.325 733	3.57	12.7449	1.88 944	5.97 495	.280 112
3.08	9.4864	1.75 499	5.54 977	.324 675	3.58	12.8164	1.89 209	5.98 331	.279 330
3.09	9.5481	1.75 784	5.55 878	.323 625	3.59	12.8881	1.89 473	5.99 166	.278 552
3.10	9.6100	1.76 068	5.56 776	.322 581	**3.60**	12.9600	1.89 737	6.00 000	.277 778
3.11	9.6721	1.76 352	5.57 674	.321 543	3.61	13.0321	1.90 000	6.00 833	.277 008
3.12	9.7344	1.76 635	5.58 570	.320 513	3.62	13.1044	1.90 263	6.01 664	.276 243
3.13	9.7969	1.76 918	5.59 464	.319 489	3.63	13.1769	1.90 526	6.02 495	.275 482
3.14	9.8596	1.77 200	5.60 357	.318 471	3.64	13.2496	1.90 788	6.03 324	.274 725
3.15	9.9225	1.77 482	5.61 249	.317 460	3.65	13.3225	1.91 050	6.04 152	.273 973
3.16	9.9856	1.77 764	5.62 139	.316 456	3.66	13.3956	1.91 311	6.04 979	.273 224
3.17	10.0489	1.78 045	5.63 028	.315 457	3.67	13.4689	1.91 572	6.05 805	.272 480
3.18	10.1124	1.78 326	5.63 915	.314 465	3.68	13.5424	1.91 833	6.06 630	.271 739
3.19	10.1761	1.78 606	5.64 801	.313 480	3.69	13.6161	1.92 094	6.07 454	.271 003
3.20	10.2400	1.78 885	5.65 685	.312 500	**3.70**	13.6900	1.92 354	6.08 276	.270 270
3.21	10.3041	1.79 165	5.66 569	.311 526	3.71	13.7641	1.92 614	6.09 098	.269 542
3.22	10.3684	1.79 444	5.67 450	.310 559	3.72	13.8384	1.92 873	6.09 918	.268 817
3.23	10.4329	1.79 722	5.68 331	.309 598	3.73	13.9129	1.93 132	6.10 737	.268 097
3.24	10.4976	1.80 000	5.69 210	.308 642	3.74	13.9876	1.93 391	6.11 555	.267 380
3.25	10.5625	1.80 278	5.70 088	.307 692	3.75	14.0625	1.93 649	6.12 372	.266 667
3.26	10.6276	1.80 555	5.70 964	.306 748	3.76	14.1376	1.93 907	6.13 188	.265 957
3.27	10.6929	1.80 831	5.71 839	.305 810	3.77	14.2129	1.94 165	6.14 003	.265 252
3.28	10.7584	1.81 108	5.72 713	.304 878	3.78	14.2884	1.94 422	6.14 817	.264 550
3.29	10.8241	1.81 384	5.73 585	.303 951	3.79	14.3641	1.94 679	6.15 630	.263 852
3.30	10.8900	1.81 659	5.74 456	.303 030	**3.80**	14.4400	1.94 936	6.16 441	.263 158
3.31	10.9561	1.81 934	5.75 326	.302 115	3.81	14.5161	1.95 192	6.17 252	.262 467
3.32	11.0224	1.82 209	5.76 194	.301 205	3.82	14.5924	1.95 448	6.18 061	.261 780
3.33	11.0889	1.82 483	5.77 062	.300 300	3.83	14.6689	1.95 704	6.18 870	.261 097
3.34	11.1556	1.82 757	5.77 927	.299 401	3.84	14.7456	1.95 959	6.19 677	.260 417
3.35	11.2225	1.83 030	5.78 792	.298 507	3.85	14.8225	1.96 214	6.20 484	.259 740
3.36	11.2896	1.83 303	5.79 655	.297 619	3.86	14.8996	1.96 469	6.21 289	.259 067
3.37	11.3569	1.83 576	5.80 517	.296 736	3.87	14.9769	1.96 723	6.22 093	.258 398
3.38	11.4244	1.83 848	5.81 378	.295 858	3.88	15.0544	1.96 977	6.22 896	.257 732
3.39	11.4921	1.84 120	5.82 237	.294 985	3.89	15.1321	1.97 231	6.23 699	.257 069
3.40	11.5600	1.84 391	5.83 095	.294 118	**3.90**	15.2100	1.97 484	6.24 500	.256 410
3.41	11.6281	1.84 662	5.83 952	.293 255	3.91	15.2881	1.97 737	6.25 300	.255 754
3.42	11.6964	1.84 932	5.84 808	.292 398	3.92	15.3664	1.97 990	6.26 099	.255 102
3.43	11.7649	1.85 203	5.85 662	.291 545	3.93	15.4449	1.98 242	6.26 897	.254 453
3.44	11.8336	1.85 472	5.86 515	.290 698	3.94	15.5236	1.98 494	6.27 694	.253 807
3.45	11.9025	1.85 742	5.87 367	.289 855	3.95	15.6025	1.98 746	6.28 490	.253 165
3.46	11.9716	1.86 011	5.88 218	.289 017	3.96	15.6816	1.98 997	6.29 285	.252 525
3.47	12.0409	1.86 279	5.89 067	.288 184	3.97	15.7609	1.99 249	6.30 079	.251 889
3.48	12.1104	1.86 548	5.89 915	.287 356	3.98	15.8404	1.99 499	6.30 872	.251 256
3.49	12.1801	1.86 815	5.90 762	.286 533	3.99	15.9201	1.99 750	6.31 664	.250 627
3.50	12.2500	1.87 083	5.91 608	.285 714	**4.00**	16.0000	2.00 000	6.32 456	.250 000
n	n^2	$\sqrt{n}$	$\sqrt{10\,n}$	$1/n$	n	n^2	$\sqrt{n}$	$\sqrt{10\,n}$	$1/n$

n	n^2	$\sqrt{n}$	$\sqrt{10\,n}$	$1/n$	n	n^2	$\sqrt{n}$	$\sqrt{10\,n}$	$1/n$
4.00	16.0000	2.00 000	6.32 456	.250 000	**4.50**	20.2500	2.12 132	6.70 820	.222 222
4.01	16.0801	2.00 250	6.33 246	.249 377'	4.51	20.3401	2.12 368	6.71 565	.221 729
4.02	16.1604	2.00 499	6.34 035	.248 756	4.52	20.4304	2.12 603	6.72 309	.221 239
4.03	16.2409	2.00 749	6.34 823	.248 139	4.53	20.5209	2.12 838	6.73 053	.220 751
4.04	16.3216	2.00 998	6.35 610	.247 525	4.54	20.6116	2.13 073	6.73 795	.220 264
4.05	16.4025	2.01 246	6.36 396	.246 914	4.55	20.7025	2.13 307	6.74 537	.219 780
4.06	16.4836	2.01 494	6.37 181	.246 305	4.56	20.7936	2.13 542	6.75 278	.219 298
4.07	16.5649	2.01 742	6.37 966	.245 700	4.57	20.8849	2.13 776	6.76 018	.218 818
4.08	16.6464	2.01 990	6.38 749	.245 098	4.58	20.9764	2.14 009	6.76 757	.218 341
4.09	16.7281	2.02 237	6.39 531	.244 499	4.59	21.0681	2.14 243	6.77 495	.217 865
4.10	16.8100	2.02 485	6.40 312	.243 902	**4.60**	21.1600	2.14 476	6.78 233	.217 391
4.11	16.8921	2.02 731	6.41 093	.243 309	4.61	21.2521	2.14 709	6.78 970	.216 920
4.12	16.9744	2.02 978	6.41 872	.242 718	4.62	21.3444	2.14 942	6.79 706	.216 450
4.13	17.0569	2.03 224	6.42 651	.242 131	4.63	21.4369	2.15 174	6.80 441	.215 983
4.14	17.1396	2.03 470	6.43 428	.241 546	4.64	21.5296	2.15 407	6.81 175	.215 517
4.15	17.2225	2.03 715	6.44 205	.240 964	4.65	21.6225	2.15 639	6.81 909	.215 054
4.16	17.3056	2.03 961	6.44 981	.240 385	4.66	21.7156	2.15 870	6.82 642	.214 592
4.17	17.3889	2.04 206	6.45 755	.239 808	4.67	21.8089	2.16 102	6.83 374	.214 133
4.18	17.4724	2.04 450	6.46 529	.239 234	4.68	21.9024	2.16 333	6.84 105	.213 675
4.19	17.5561	2.04 695	6.47 302	.238 663	4.69	21.9961	2.16 564	6.84 836	.213 220
4.20	17.6400	2.04 939	6.48 074	.238 095	**4.70**	22.0900	2.16 795	6.85 565	.212 766
4.21	17.7241	2.05 183	6.48 845	.237 530	4.71	22.1841	2.17 025	6.86 294	.212 314
4.22	17.8084	2.05 426	6.49 615	.236 967	4.72	22.2784	2.17 256	6.87 023	.211 864
4.23	17.8929	2.05 670	6.50 384	.236 407	4.73	22.3729	2.17 486	6.87 750	.211 416
4.24	17.9776	2.05 913	6.51 153	.235 849	4.74	22.4676	2.17 715	6.88 477	.210 970
4.25	18.0625	2.06 155	6.51 920	.235 294	4.75	22.5625	2.17 945	6.89 202	.210 526
4.26	18.1476	2.06 398	6.52 687	.234 742	4.76	22.6576	2.18 174	6.89 928	.210 084
4.27	18.2329	2.06 640	6.53 452	.234 192	4.77	22.7529	2.18 403	6.90 652	.209 644
4.28	18.3184	2.06 882	6.54 217	.233 645	4.78	22.8484	2.18 632	6.91 375	.209 205
4.29	18.4041	2.07 123	6.54 981	.233 100	4.79	22.9441	2.18 861	6.92 098	.208 768
4.30	18.4900	2.07 364	6.55 744	.232 558	**4.80**	23.0400	2.19 089	6.92 820	.208 333
4.31	18.5761	2.07 605	6.56 506	.232 019	4.81	23.1361	2.19 317	6.93 542	.207 900
4.32	18.6624	2.07 846	6.57 267	.231 481	4.82	23.2324	2.19 545	6.94 262	.207 469
4.33	18.7489	2.08 087	6.58 027	.230 947	4.83	23.3289	2.19 773	6.94 982	.207 039
4.34	18.8356	2.08 327	6.58 787	.230 415	4.84	23.4256	2.20 000	6.95 701	.206 612
4.35	18.9225	2.08 567	6.59 545	.229 885	4.85	23.5225	2.20 227	6.96 419	.206 186
4.36	19.0096	2.08 806	6.60 303	.229 358	4.86	23.6196	2.20 454	6.97 137	.205 761
4.37	19.0969	2.09 045	6.61 060	.228 833	4.87	23.7169	2.20 681	6.97 854	.205 339
4.38	19.1844	2.09 284	6.61 816	.228 311	4.88	23.8144	2.20 907	6.98 570	.204 918
4.39	19.2721	2.09 523	6.62 571	.227 790	4.89	23.9121	2.21 133	6.99 285	.204 499
4.40	19.3600	2.09 762	6.63 325	.227 273	**4.90**	24.0100	2.21 359	7.00 000	.204 082
4.41	19.4481	2.10 000	6.64 078	.226 757	4.91	24.1081	2.21 585	7.00 714	.203 666
4.42	19.5364	2.10 238	6.64 831	.226 244	4.92	24.2064	2.21 811	7.01 427	.203 252
4.43	19.6249	2.10 476	6.65 582	.225 734	4.93	24.3049	2.22 036	7.02 140	.202 840
4.44	19.7136	2.10 713	6.66 333	.225 225	4.94	24.4036	2.22 261	7.02 851	.202 429
4.45	19.8025	2.10 950	6.67 083	.224 719	4.95	24.5025	2.22 486	7.03 562	.202 020
4.46	19.8916	2.11 187	6.67 832	.224 215	4.96	24.6016	2.22 711	7.04 273	.201 613
4.47	19.9809	2.11 424	6.68 581	.223 714	4.97	24.7009	2.22 935	7.04 982	.201 207
4.48	20.0704	2.11 660	6.69 328	.223 214	4.98	24.8004	2.23 159	7.05 691	.200 803
4.49	20.1601	2.11 896	6.70 075	.222 717	4.99	24.9001	2.23 383	7.06 399	.200 401
4.50	20.2500	2.12 132	6.70 820	.222 222	**5.00**	25.0000	2.23 607	7.07 107	.200 000
n	n^2	$\sqrt{n}$	$\sqrt{10\,n}$	$1/n$	n	n^2	$\sqrt{n}$	$\sqrt{10\,n}$	$1/n$

n	n^2	$\sqrt{n}$	$\sqrt{10n}$	$1/n$	n	n^2	$\sqrt{n}$	$\sqrt{10n}$	$1/n$
5.00	25.0000	2.23 607	7.07 107	.200 000	**5.50**	30.2500	2.34 521	7.41 620	.181 818
5.01	25.1001	2.23 830	7.07 814	.199 601	5.51	30.3601	2.34 734	7.42 294	.181 488
5.02	25.2004	2.24 054	7.08 520	.199 203	5.52	30.4704	2.34 947	7.42 967	.181 159
5.03	25.3009	2.24 277	7.09 225	.198 807	5.53	30.5809	2.35 160	7.43 640	.180 832
5.04	25.4016	2.24 499	7.09 930	.198 413	5.54	30.6916	2.35 372	7.44 312	.180 505
5.05	25.5025	2.24 722	7.10 634	.198 020	5.55	30.8025	2.35 584	7.44 983	.180 180
5.06	25.6036	2.24 944	7.11 337	.197 628	5.56	30.9136	2.35 797	7.45 654	.179 856
5.07	25.7049	2.25 167	7.12 039	.197 239	5.57	31.0249	2.36 008	7.46 324	.179 533
5.08	25.8064	2.25 389	7.12 741	.196 850	5.58	31.1364	2.36 220	7.46 994	.179 211
5.09	25.9081	2.25 610	7.13 442	.196 464	5.59	31.2481	2.36 432	7.47 663	.178 891
5.10	26.0100	2.25 832	7.14 143	.196 078	**5.60**	31.3600	2.36 643	7.48 331	.178 571
5.11	26.1121	2.26 053	7.14 843	.195 695	5.61	31.4721	2.36 854	7.48 999	.178 253
5.12	26.2144	2.26 274	7.15 542	.195 312	5.62	31.5844	2.37 065	7.49 667	.177 936
5.13	26.3169	2.26 495	7.16 240	.194 932	5.63	31.6969	2.37 276	7.50 333	.177 620
5.14	26.4196	2.26 716	7.16 938	.194 553	5.64	31.8096	2.37 487	7.50 999	.177 305
5.15	26.5225	2.26 936	7.17 635	.194 175	5.65	31.9225	2.37 697	7.51 665	.176 991
5.16	26.6256	2.27 156	7.18 331	.193 798	5.66	32.0356	2.37 908	7.52 330	.176 678
5.17	26.7289	2.27 376	7.19 027	.193 424	5.67	32.1489	2.38 118	7.52 994	.176 367
5.18	26.8324	2.27 596	7.19 722	.193 050	5.68	32.2624	2.38 328	7.53 658	.176 056
5.19	26.9361	2.27 816	7.20 417	.192 678	5.69	32.3761	2.38 537	7.54 321	.175 747
5.20	27.0400	2.28 035	7.21 110	.192 308	**5.70**	32.4900	2.38 747	7.54 983	.175 439
5.21	27.1441	2.28 254	7.21 803	.191 939	5.71	32.6041	2.38 956	7.55 645	.175 131
5.22	27.2484	2.28 473	7.22 496	.191 571	5.72	32.7184	2.39 165	7.56 307	.174 825
5.23	27.3529	2.28 692	7.23 187	.191 205	5.73	32.8329	2.39 374	7.56 968	.174 520
5.24	27.4576	2.28 910	7.23 878	.190 840	5.74	32.9476	2.39 583	7.57 628	.174 216
5.25	27.5625	2.29 129	7.24 569	.190 476	5.75	33.0625	2.39 792	7.58 288	.173 913
5.26	27.6676	2.29 347	7.25 259	.190 114	5.76	33.1776	2.40 000	7.58 947	.173 611
5.27	27.7729	2.29 565	7.25 948	.189 753	5.77	33.2929	2.40 208	7.59 605	.173 310
5.28	27.8784	2.29 783	7.26 636	.189 394	5.78	33.4084	2.40 416	7.60 263	.173 010
5.29	27.9841	2.30 000	7.27 324	.189 036	5.79	33.5241	2.40 624	7.60 920	.172 712
5.30	28.0900	2.30 217	7.28 011	.188 679	**5.80**	33.6400	2.40 832	7.61 577	.172 414
5.31	28.1961	2.30 434	7.28 697	.188 324	5.81	33.7561	2.41 039	7.62 234	.172 117
5.32	28.3024	2.30 651	7.29 383	.187 970	5.82	33.8724	2.41 247	7.62 889	.171 821
5.33	28.4089	2.30 868	7.30 068	.187 617	5.83	33.9889	2.41 454	7.63 544	.171 527
5.34	28.5156	2.31 084	7.30 753	.187 266	5.84	34.1056	2.41 661	7.64 199	.171 233
5.35	28.6225	2.31 301	7.31 437	.186 916	5.85	34.2225	2.41 868	7.64 853	.170 940
5.36	28.7296	2.31 517	7.32 120	.186 567	5.86	34.3396	2.42 074	7.65 506	.170 649
5.37	28.8369	2.31 733	7.32 803	.186 220	5.87	34.4569	2.42 281	7.66 159	.170 358
5.38	28.9444	2.31 948	7.33 485	.185 874	5.88	34.5744	2.42 487	7.66 812	.170 068
5.39	29.0521	2.32 164	7.34 166	.185 529	5.89	34.6921	2.42 693	7.67 463	.169 779
5.40	29.1600	2.32 379	7.34 847	.185 185	**5.90**	34.8100	2.42 899	7.68 115	.169 492
5.41	29.2681	2.32 594	7.35 527	.184 843	5.91	34.9281	2.43 105	7.68 765	.169 205
5.42	29.3764	2.32 809	7.36 206	.184 502	5.92	35.0464	2.43 311	7.69 415	.168 919
5.43	29.4849	2.33 024	7.36 885	.184 162	5.93	35.1649	2.43 516	7.70 065	.168 634
5.44	29.5936	2.33 238	7.37 564	.183 824	5.94	35.2836	2.43 721	7.70 714	.168 350
5.45	29.7025	2.33 452	7.38 241	.183 486	5.95	35.4025	2.43 926	7.71 362	.168 067
5.46	29.8116	2.33 666	7.38 918	.183 150	5.96	35.5216	2.44 131	7.72 010	.167 785
5.47	29.9209	2.33 880	7.39 594	.182 815	5.97	35.6409	2.44 336	7.72 658	.167 504
5.48	30.0304	2.34 094	7.40 270	.182 482	5.98	35.7604	2.44 540	7.73 305	.167 224
5.49	30.1401	2.34 307	7.40 945	.182 149	5.99	35.8801	2.44 745	7.73 951	.166 945
5.50	30.2500	2.34 521	7.41 620	.181 818	**6.00**	36.0000	2.44 949	7.74 597	.166 667
n	n^2	$\sqrt{n}$	$\sqrt{10n}$	$1/n$	n	n^2	$\sqrt{n}$	$\sqrt{10n}$	$1/n$

n	n^2	$\sqrt{n}$	$\sqrt{10n}$	$1/n$	n	n^2	$\sqrt{n}$	$\sqrt{10n}$	$1/n$
6.00	36.0000	2.44 949	7.74 597	.166 667	**6.50**	42.2500	2.54 951	8.06 226	.153 846
6.01	36.1201	2.45 153	7.75 242	.166 389	6.51	42.3801	2.55 147	8.06 846	.153 610
6.02	36.2404	2.45 357	7.75 887	.166 113	6.52	42.5104	2.55 343	8 07 465	.153 374
6.03	36.3609	2.45 561	7.76 531	.165 837	6.53	42.6409	2.55 539	8.08 084	.153 139
6.04	36.4816	2.45 764	7.77 174	.165 563	6.54	42.7716	2.55 734	8.08 703	.152 905
6.05	36.6025	2.45 967	7.77 817	.165 289	6.55	42.9025	2.55 930	8.09 321	.152 672
6.06	36.7236	2.46 171	7.78 460	.165 017	6.56	43.0336	2.56 125	8.09 938	.152 439
6.07	36.8449	2.46 374	7.79 102	.164 745	6.57	43.1649	2.56 320	8.10 555	.152 207
6.08	36.9664	2.46 577	7.79 744	.164 474	6.58	43.2964	2.56 515	8.11 172	.151 976
6.09	37.0881	2.46 779	7.80 385	.164 204	6.59	43.4281	2.56 710	8.11 788	.151 745
6.10	37.2100	2.46 982	7.81 025	.163 934	**6.60**	43.5600	2.56 905	8.12 404	.151 515
6.11	37.3321	2.47 184	7.81 665	.163 666	6.61	43.6921	2.57 099	8.13 019	.151 286
6.12	37.4544	2.47 386	7.82 304	.163 399	6.62	43.8244	2.57 294	8.13 634	.151 057
6.13	37.5769	2.47 588	7.82 943	.163 132	6.63	43.9569	2.57 488	8.14 248	.150 830
6.14	37.6996	2.47 790	7.83 582	.162 866	6.64	44.0896	2.57 682	8.14 862	.150 602
6.15	37.8225	2.47 992	7.84 219	.162 602	6.65	44.2225	2.57 876	8.15 475	.150 376
6.16	37.9456	2.48 193	7.84 857	.162 338	6.66	44.3556	2.58 070	8.16 088	.150 150
6.17	38.0689	2.48 395	7.85 493	.162 075	6.67	44.4889	2.58 263	8.16 701	.149 925
6.18	38.1924	2.48 596	7.86 130	.161 812	6.68	44.6224	2.58 457	8.17 313	.149 701
6.19	38.3161	2.48 797	7.86 766	.161 551	6.69	44.7561	2.58 650	8.17 924	.149 477
6.20	38.4400	2.48 998	7.87 401	.161 290	**6.70**	44.8900	2.58 844	8.18 535	.149 254
6.21	38.5641	2.49 199	7.88 036	.161 031	6.71	45.0241	2.59 037	8.19 146	.149 031
6.22	38.6884	2.49 399	7.88 670	.160 772	6.72	45.1584	2.59 230	8.19 756	.148 810
6.23	38.8129	2.49 600	7.89 303	.160 514	6.73	45.2929	2.59 422	8.20 366	.148 588
6.24	38.9376	2.49 800	7.89 937	.160 256	6.74	45.4276	2.59 615	8.20 975	.148 368
6.25	39.0625	2.50 000	7.90 569	.160 000	6.75	45.5625	2.59 808	8.21 584	.148 148
6.26	39.1876	2.50 200	7.91 202	.159 744	6.76	45.6976	2.60 000	8.22 192	.147 929
6.27	39.3129	2.50 400	7.91 833	.159 490	6.77	45.8329	2.60 192	8.22 800	.147 710
6.28	39.4384	2.50 599	7.92 465	.159 236	6.78	45.9684	2.60 384	8.23 408	.147 493
6.29	39.5641	2.50 799	7.93 095	.158 983	6.79	46.1041	2.60 576	8.24 015	.147 275
6.30	39.6900	2.50 998	7.93 725	.158 730	**6.80**	46.2400	2.60 768	8.24 621	.147 059
6.31	39.8161	2.51 197	7.94 355	.158 479	6.81	46.3761	2.60 960	8.25 227	.146 843
6.32	39.9424	2.51 396	7.94 984	.158 228	6.82	46.5124	2.61 151	8.25 833	.146 628
6.33	40.0689	2.51 595	7.95 613	.157 978	6.83	46.6489	2.61 343	8.26 438	.146 413
6.34	40.1956	2.51 794	7.96 241	.157 729	6.84	46.7856	2.61 534	8.27 043	.146 199
6.35	40.3225	2.51 992	7.96 869	.157 480	6.85	46.9225	2.61 725	8.27 647	.145 985
6.36	40.4496	2.52 190	7.97 496	.157 233	6.86	47.0596	2.61 916	8.28 251	.145 773
6.37	40.5769	2.52 389	7.98 123	.156 986	6.87	47.1969	2.62 107	8.28 855	.145 560
6.38	40.7044	2.52 587	7.98 749	.156 740	6.88	47.3344	2.62 298	8.29 458	.145 349
6.39	40.8321	2.52 784	7.99 375	.156 495	6.89	47.4721	2.62 488	8.30 060	.145 138
6.40	40.9600	2.52 982	8.00 000	.156 250	**6.90**	47.6100	2.62 679	8.30 662	.144 928
6.41	41.0881	2.53 180	8.00 625	.156 006	6.91	47.7481	2.62 869	8.31 264	.144 718
6.42	41.2164	2.53 377	8.01 249	.155 763	6.92	47.8864	2.63 059	8.31 865	.144 509
6.43	41.3449	2.53 574	8.01 873	.155 521	6.93	48.0249	2.63 249	8.32 466	.144 300
6.44	41.4736	2.53 772	8.02 496	.155 280	6.94	48.1636	2.63 439	8.33 067	.144 092
6.45	41.6025	2.53 969	8.03 119	.155 039	6.95	48.3025	2.63 629	8.33 667	.143 885
6.46	41.7316	2.54 165	8.03 741	.154 799	6.96	48.4416	2.63 818	8.34 266	.143 678
6.47	41.8609	2.54 362	8.04 363	.154 560	6.97	48.5809	2.64 008	8.34 865	.143 472
6.48	41.9904	2.54 558	8.04 984	.154 321	6.98	48.7204	2.64 197	8.35 464	.143 266
6.49	42.1201	2.54 755	8.05 605	.154 083	6.99	48.8601	2.64 386	8.36 062	.143 062
6.50	42.2500	2.54 951	8.06 226	.153 846	**7.00**	49.0000	2.64 575	8.36 660	.142 857
n	n^2	$\sqrt{n}$	$\sqrt{10n}$	$1/n$	n	n^2	$\sqrt{n}$	$\sqrt{10n}$	$1/n$

n	n^2	$\sqrt{n}$	$\sqrt{10n}$	$1/n$	n	n^2	$\sqrt{n}$	$\sqrt{10n}$	$1/n$
7.00	49.0000	2.64 575	8.36 660	.142 857	7.50	56.2500	2.73 861	8.66 025	.133 333
7.01	49.1401	2.64 764	8.37 257	.142 653	7.51	56.4001	2.74 044	8.66 603	.133 156
7.02	49.2804	2.64 953	8.37 854	.142 450	7.52	56.5504	2.74 226	8.67 179	.132 979
7.03	49.4209	2.65 141	8.38 451	.142 248	7.53	56.7009	2.74 408	8.67 756	.132 802
7.04	49.5616	2.65 330	8.39 047	.142 045	7.54	56.8516	2.74 591	8.68 332	.132 626
7.05	49.7025	2.65 518	8.39 643	.141 844	7.55	57.0025	2.74 773	8.68 907	.132 450
7.06	49.8436	2.65 707	8.40 238	.141 643	7.56	57.1536	2.74 955	8.69 483	.132 275
7.07	49.9849	2.65 895	8.40 833	.141 443	7.57	57.3049	2.75 136	8.70 057	.132 100
7.08	50.1264	2.66 083	8.41 427	.141 243	7.58	57.4564	2.75 318	8.70 632	.131 926
7.09	50.2681	2.66 271	8.42 021	.141 044	7.59	57.6081	2.75 500	8.71 206	.131 752
7.10	50.4100	2.66 458	8.42 615	.140 845	7.60	57.7600	2.75 681	8.71 780	.131 579
7.11	50.5521	2.66 646	8.43 208	.140 647	7.61	57.9121	2.75 862	8.72 353	.131 406
7.12	50.6944	2.66 833	8.43 801	.140 449	7.62	58.0644	2.76 043	8.72 926	.131 234
7.13	50.8369	2.67 021	8.44 393	.140 252	7.63	58.2169	2.76 225	8.73 499	.131 062
7.14	50.9796	2.67 208	8.44 985	.140 056	7.64	58.3696	2.76 405	8.74 071	.130 890
7.15	51.1225	2.67 395	8.45 577	.139 860	7.65	58.5225	2.76 586	8.74 643	.130 719
7.16	51.2656	2.67 582	8.46 168	.139 665	7.66	58.6756	2.76 767	8.75 214	.130 548
7.17	51.4089	2.67 769	8.46 759	.139 470	7.67	58.8289	2.76 948	8.75 785	.130 378
7.18	51.5524	2.67 955	8.47 349	.139 276	7.68	58.9824	2.77 128	8.76 356	.130 208
7.19	51.6961	2.68 142	8.47 939	.139 082	7.69	59.1361	2.77 308	8.76 926	.130 039
7.20	51.8400	2.68 328	8.48 528	.138 889	7.70	59.2900	2.77 489	8.77 496	.129 870
7.21	51.9841	2.68 514	8.49 117	.138 696	7.71	59.4441	2.77 669	8.78 066	.129 702
7.22	52.1284	2.68 701	8.49 706	.138 504	7.72	59.5984	2.77 849	8.78 635	.129 534
7.23	52.2729	2.68 887	8.50 294	.138 313	7.73	59.7529	2.78 029	8.79 204	.129 366
7.24	52.4176	2.69 072	8.50 882	.138 122	7.74	59.9076	2.78 209	8.79 773	.129 199
7.25	52.5625	2.69 258	8.51 469	.137 931	7.75	60.0625	2.78 388	8.80 341	.129 032
7.26	52.7076	2.69 444	8.52 056	.137 741	7.76	60.2176	2.78 568	8.80 909	.128 866
7.27	52.8529	2.69 629	8.52 643	.137 552	7.77	60.3729	2.78 747	8.81 476	.128 700
7.28	52.9984	2.69 815	8.53 229	.137 363	7.78	60.5284	2.78 927	8.82 043	.128 535
7.29	53.1441	2.70 000	8.53 815	.137 174	7.79	60.6841	2.79 106	8.82 610	.128 370
7.30	53.2900	2.70 185	8.54 400	.136 986	7.80	60.8400	2.79 285	8.83 176	.128 205
7.31	53.4361	2.70 370	8.54 985	.136 799	7.81	60.9961	2.79 464	8.83 742	.128 041
7.32	53.5824	2.70 555	8.55 570	.136 612	7.82	61.1524	2.79 643	8.84 308	.127 877
7.33	53.7289	2.70 740	8.56 154	.136 426	7.83	61.3089	2.79 821	8.84 873	.127 714
7.34	53.8756	2.70 924	8.56 738	.136 240	7.84	61.4656	2.80 000	8.85 438	.127 551
7.35	54.0225	2.71 109	8.57 321	.136 054	7.85	61.6225	2.80 179	8.86 002	.127 389
7.36	54.1696	2.71 293	8.57 904	.135 870	7.86	61.7796	2.80 357	8.86 566	.127 226
7.37	54.3169	2.71 477	8.58 487	.135 685	7.87	61.9369	2.80 535	8.87 130	.127 065
7.38	54.4644	2.71 662	8.59 069	.135 501	7.88	62.0944	2.80 713	8.87 694	.126 904
7.39	54.6121	2.71 846	8.59 651	.135 318	7.89	62.2521	2.80 891	8.88 257	.126 743
7.40	54.7600	2.72 029	8.60 233	.135 135	7.90	62.4100	2.81 069	8.88 819	.126 582
7.41	54.9081	2.72 213	8.60 814	.134 953	7.91	62.5681	2.81 247	8.89 382	.126 422
7.42	55.0564	2.72 397	8.61 394	.134 771	7.92	62.7264	2.81 425	8.89 944	.126 263
7.43	55.2049	2.72 580	8.61 974	.134 590	7.93	62.8849	2.81 603	8.90 505	.126 103
7.44	55.3536	2.72 764	8.62 554	.134 409	7.94	63.0436	2.81 780	8.91 067	.125 945
7.45	55.5025	2.72 947	8.63 134	.134 228	7.95	63.2025	2.81 957	8.91 628	.125 786
7.46	55.6516	2.73 130	8.63 713	.134 048	7.96	63.3616	2.82 135	8.92 188	.125 628
7.47	55.8009	2.73 313	8.64 292	.133 869	7.97	63.5209	2.82 312	8.92 749	.125 471
7.48	55.9504	2.73 496	8.64 870	.133 690	7.98	63.6804	2.82 489	8.93 308	.125 313
7.49	56.1001	2.73 679	8.65 448	.133 511	7.99	63.8401	2.82 666	8.93 868	.125 156
7.50	56.2500	2.73 861	8.66 025	.133 333	8.00	64.0000	2.82 843	8.94 427	.125 000
n	n^2	$\sqrt{n}$	$\sqrt{10n}$	$1/n$	n	n^2	$\sqrt{n}$	$\sqrt{10n}$	$1/n$

n	n^2	$\sqrt{n}$	$\sqrt{10\,n}$	$1/n$	n	n^2	$\sqrt{n}$	$\sqrt{10\,n}$	$1/n$
8.00	64.0000	2.82 843	8.94 427	.125 000	8.50	72.2500	2.91 548	9.21 954	.117 647
8.01	64.1601	2.83 019	8.94 986	.124 844	8.51	72.4201	2.91 719	9.22 497	.117 509
8.02	64.3204	2.83 196	8.95 545	.124 688	8.52	72.5904	2.91 890	9.23 038	.117 371
8.03	64.4809	2.83 373	8.96 103	.124 533	8.53	72.7609	2.92 062	9.23 580	.117 233
8.04	64.6416	2.83 549	8.96 660	.124 378	8.54	72.9316	2.92 233	9.24 121	.117 096
8.05	64.8025	2.83 725	8.97 218	.124 224	8.55	73.1025	2.92 404	9.24 662	.116 959
8.06	64.9636	2.83 901	8.97 775	.124 069	8.56	73.2736	2.92 575	9.25 203	.116 822
8.07	65.1249	2.84 077	8.98 332	.123 916	8.57	73.4449	2.92 746	9.25 743	.116 686
8.08	65.2864	2.84 253	8.98 888	.123 762	8.58	73.6164	2.92 916	9.26 283	.116 550
8.09	65.4481	2.84 429	8.99 444	.123 609	8.59	73.7881	2.93 087	9.26 823	.116 414
8.10	65.6100	2.84 605	9.00 000	.123 457	8.60	73.9600	2.93 258	9.27 362	.116 279
8.11	65.7721	2.84 781	9.00 555	.123 305	8.61	74.1321	2.93 428	9.27 901	.116 144
8.12	65.9344	2.84 956	9.01 110	.123 153	8.62	74.3044	2.93 598	9.28 440	.116 009
8.13	66.0969	2.85 132	9.01 665	.123 001	8.63	74.4769	2.93 769	9.28 978	.115 875
8.14	66.2596	2.85 307	9.02 219	.122 850	8.64	74.6496	2.93 939	9.29 516	.115 741
8.15	66.4225	2.85 482	9.02 774	.122 699	8.65	74.8225	2.94 109	9.30 054	.115 607
8.16	66.5856	2.85 657	9.03 327	.122 549	8.66	74.9956	2.94 279	9.30 591	.115 473
8.17	66.7489	2.85 832	9.03 881	.122 399	8.67	75.1689	2.94 449	9.31 128	.115 340
8.18	66.9124	2.86 007	9.04 434	.122 249	8.68	75.3424	2.94 618	9.31 665	.115 207
8.19	67.0761	2.86 182	9.04 986	.122 100	8.69	75.5161	2.94 788	9.32 202	.115 075
8.20	67.2400	2.86 356	9.05 539	.121 951	8.70	75.6900	2.94 958	9.32 738	.114 943
8.21	67.4041	2.86 531	9.06 091	.121 803	8.71	75.8641	2.95 127	9.33 274	.114 811
8.22	67.5684	2.86 705	9.06 642	.121 655	8.72	76.0384	2.95 296	9.33 809	.114 679
8.23	67.7329	2.86 880	9.07 193	.121 507	8.73	76.2129	2.95 466	9.34 345	.114 548
8.24	67.8976	2.87 054	9.07 744	.121 359	8.74	76.3876	2.95 635	9.34 880	.114 416
8.25	68.0625	2.87 228	9.08 295	.121 212	8.75	76.5625	2.95 804	9.35 414	.114 286
8.26	68.2276	2.87 402	9.08 845	.121 065	8.76	76.7376	2.95 973	9.35 949	.114 155
8.27	68.3929	2.87 576	9.09 395	.120 919	8.77	76.9129	2.96 142	9.36 483	.114 025
8.28	68.5584	2.87 750	9.09 945	.120 773	8.78	77.0884	2.96 311	9.37 017	.113 895
8.29	68.7241	2.87 924	9.10 494	.120 627	8.79	77.2641	2.96 479	9.37 550	.113 766
8.30	68.8900	2.88 097	9.11 043	.120 482	8.80	77.4400	2.96 648	9.38 083	.113 636
8.31	69.0561	2.88 271	9.11 592	.120 337	8.81	77.6161	2.96 816	9.38 616	.113 507
8.32	69.2224	2.88 444	9.12 140	.120 192	8.82	77.7924	2.96 985	9.39 149	.113 379
8.33	69.3889	2.88 617	9.12 688	.120 048	8.83	77.9689	2.97 153	9.39 681	.113 250
8.34	69.5556	2.88 791	9.13 236	.119 904	8.84	78.1456	2.97 321	9.40 213	.113 122
8.35	69.7225	2.88 964	9.13 783	.119 760	8.85	78.3225	2.97 489	9.40 744	.112 994
8.36	69.8896	2.89 137	9.14 330	.119 617	8.86	78.4996	2.97 658	9.41 276	.112 867
8.37	70.0569	2.89 310	9.14 877	.119 474	8.87	78.6769	2.97 825	9.41 807	.112 740
8.38	70.2244	2.89 482	9.15 423	.119 332	8.88	78.8544	2.97 993	9.42 338	.112 613
8.39	70.3921	2.89 655	9.15 969	.119 190	8.89	79.0321	2.98 161	9.42 868	.112 486
8.40	70.5600	2.89 828	9.16 515	.119 048	8.90	79.2100	2.98 329	9.43 398	.112 360
8.41	70.7281	2.90 000	9.17 061	.118 906	8.91	79.3881	2.98 496	9.43 928	.112 233
8.42	70.8964	2.90 172	9.17 606	.118 765	8.92	79.5664	2.98 664	9.44 458	.112 108
8.43	71.0649	2.90 345	9.18 150	.118 624	8.93	79.7449	2.98 831	9.44 987	.111 982
8.44	71.2336	2.90 517	9.18 695	.118 483	8.94	79.9236	2.98 998	9.45 516	.111 857
8.45	71.4025	2.90 689	9.19 239	.118 343	8.95	80.1025	2.99 166	9.46 044	.111 732
8.46	71.5716	2.90 861	9.19 783	.118 203	8.96	80.2816	2.99 333	9.46 573	.111 607
8.47	71.7409	2.91 033	9.20 326	.118 064	8.97	80.4609	2.99 500	9.47 101	.111 483
8.48	71.9104	2.91 204	9.20 869	.117 925	8.98	80.6404	2.99 666	9.47 629	.111 359
8.49	72.0801	2.91 376	9.21 412	.117 786	8.99	80.8201	2.99 833	9.48 156	.111 235
8.50	72.2500	2.91 548	9.21 954	.117 647	9.00	81.0000	3.00 000	9.48 683	.111 111
n	n^2	$\sqrt{n}$	$\sqrt{10\,n}$	$1/n$	n	n^2	$\sqrt{n}$	$\sqrt{10\,n}$	$1/n$

n	n^2	$\sqrt{n}$	$\sqrt{10n}$	$1/n$	n	n^2	$\sqrt{n}$	$\sqrt{10n}$	$1/n$
9.00	81.0000	3.00 000	9.48 683	.111 111	**9.50**	90.2500	3.08 221	9.74 679	.105 263
9.01	81.1801	3.00 167	9.49 210	.110 988	9.51	90.4401	3.08 383	9.75 192	.105 152
9.02	81.3604	3.00 333	9.49 737	.110 865	9.52	90.6304	3.08 545	9.75 705	.105 042
9.03	81.5409	3.00 500	9.50 263	.110 742	9.53	90.8209	3.08 707	9.76 217	.104 932
9.04	81.7216	3.00 666	9.50 789	.110 619	9.54	91.0116	3.08 869	9.76 729	.104 822
9.05	81.9025	3.00 832	9.51 315	.110 497	9.55	91.2025	3.09 031	9.77 241	.104 712
9 06	82.0836	3.00 998	9.51 840	.110 375	9.56	91.3936	3.09 192	9.77 753	.104 603
9.07	82.2649	3.01 164	9.52 365	.110 254	9.57	91.5849	3.09 354	9.78 264	.104 493
9.08	82.4464	3.01 330	9.52 890	.110 132	9.58	91.7764	3.09 516	9.78 775	.104 384
9.09	82.6281	3.01 496	9.53 415	.110 011	9.59	91.9681	3.09 677	9.79 285	.104 275
9.10	82.8100	3.01 662	9.53 939	.109 890	**9.60**	92.1600	3.09 839	9.79 796	.104 167
9.11	82.9921	3.01 828	9.54 463	.109 769	9.61	92.3521	3.10 000	9.80 306	.104 058
9.12	83.1744	3.01 993	9.54 987	.109 649	9.62	92.5444	3.10 161	9.80 816	.103 950
9.13	83.3569	3.02 159	9.55 510	.109 529	9.63	92.7369	3.10 322	9.81 326	.103 842
9.14	83.5396	3.02 324	9.56 033	.109 409	9.64	92.9296	3.10 483	9.81 835	.103 734
9.15	83.7225	3.02 490	9.56 556	.109 290	9.65	93.1225	3.10 644	9.82 344	.103 627
9.16	83.9056	3.02 655	9.57 079	.109 170	9.66	93.3156	3.10 805	9.82 853	.103 520
9.17	84.0889	3.02 820	9.57 601	.109 051	9.67	93.5089	3.10 966	9.83 362	.103 413
9.18	84.2724	3.02 985	9.58 123	.108 932	9.68	93.7024	3.11 127	9.83 870	.103 306
9.19	84.4561	3.03 150	9.58 645	.108 814	9.69	93.8961	3.11 288	9.84 378	.103 199
9.20	84.6400	3.03 315	9.59 166	.108 696	**9.70**	94.0900	3.11 448	9.84 886	.103 093
9.21	84.8241	3.03 480	9.59 687	.108 578	9.71	94.2841	3.11 609	9.85 393	.102 987
9.22	85.0084	3.03 645	9.60 208	.108 460	9.72	94.4784	3.11 769	9.85 901	.102 881
9.23	85.1929	3.03 809	9.60 729	.108 342	9.73	94.6729	3.11 929	9.86 408	.102 775
9.24	85.3776	3.03 974	9.61 249	.108 225	9.74	94.8676	3.12 090	9.86 914	.102 669
9.25	85.5625	3.04 138	9.61 769	.108 108	9.75	95.0625	3.12 250	9.87 421	.102 564
9.26	85.7476	3.04 302	9.62 289	.107 991	9.76	95.2576	3.12 410	9.87 927	.102 459
9.27	85.9329	3.04 467	9.62 808	.107 875	9.77	95.4529	3.12 570	9.88 433	.102 354
9.28	86.1184	3.04 631	9.63 328	.107 759	9.78	95.6484	3.12 730	9.88 939	.102 249
9.29	86.3041	3.04 795	9.63 846	.107 643	9.79	95.8441	3.12 890	9.89 444	.102 145
9.30	86.4900	3.04 959	9.64 365	.107 527	**9.80**	96.0400	3.13 050	9.89 949	.102 041
9.31	86.6761	3.05 123	9.64 883	.107 411	9.81	96.2361	3.13 209	9.90 454	.101 937
9.32	86.8624	3.05 287	9.65 401	.107 296	9.82	96.4324	3.13 369	9.90 959	.101 833
9.33	87.0489	3.05 450	9.65 919	.107 181	9.83	96.6289	3.13 528	9.91 464	.101 729
9.34	87.2356	3.05 614	9.66 437	.107 066	9.84	96.8256	3.13 688	9.91 968	.101 626
9.35	87.4225	3.05 778	9.66 954	.106 952	9.85	97.0225	3.13 847	9.92 472	.101 523
9.36	87.6096	3.05 941	9.67 471	.106 838	9.86	97.2196	3.14 006	9.92 975	.101 420
9.37	87.7969	3.06 105	9.67 988	.106 724	9.87	97.4169	3.14 166	9.93 479	.101 317
9.38	87.9844	3.06 268	9.68 504	.106 610	9.88	97.6144	3.14 325	9.93 982	.101 215
9.39	88.1721	3.06 431	9.69 020	.106 496	9.89	97.8121	3.14 484	9.94 485	.101 112
9.40	88.3600	3.06 594	9.69 536	.106 383	**9.90**	98.0100	3.14 643	9.94 987	.101 010
9.41	88.5481	3.06 757	9.70 052	.106 270	9.91	98.2081	3.14 802	9.95 490	.100 908
9.42	88.7364	3.06 920	9.70 567	.106 157	9.92	98.4064	3.14 960	9.95 992	.100 806
9.43	88.9249	3.07 083	9.71 082	.106 045	9.93	98.6049	3.15 119	9.96 494	.100 705
9.44	89.1136	3.07 246	9.71 597	.105 932	9.94	98.8036	3.15 278	9.96 995	.100 604
9.45	89.3025	3.07 409	9.72 111	.105 820	9.95	99.0025	3.15 436	9.97 497	.100 503
9.46	89.4916	3.07 571	9.72 625	.105 708	9.96	99.2016	3.15 595	9.97 998	.100 402
9.47	89.6809	3.07 734	9.73 139	.105 597	9.97	99.4009	3.15 753	9.98 499	.100 301
9.48	89.8704	3.07 896	9.73 653	.105 485	9.98	99.6004	3.15 911	9.98 999	.100 200
9.49	90.0601	3.08 058	9.74 166	.105 374	9.99	99.8001	3.16 070	9.99 500	.100 100
9.50	90.2500	3.08 221	9.74 679	.105 263	**10.00**	100.000	3.16 228	10.0000	.100 000

n	n^2	$\sqrt{n}$	$\sqrt{10n}$	$1/n$	n	n^2	$\sqrt{n}$	$\sqrt{10n}$	$1/n$

FOUR-PLACE LOGARITHMS OF NUMBERS
100–500

Each mantissa should be preceded by a decimal point, and the proper characteristic should be written.

On account of the great differences between the successive mantissas in the first ten rows, interpolation should not be employed in that part of the table. Table I should be used in this case. In general, an error of one unit may appear in the last figure of any interpolated value.

N	0	1	2	3	4	5	6	7	8	9
10	0000	0043	0086	0128	0170	0212	0253	0294	0334	0374
11	0414	0453	0492	0531	0569	0607	0645	0682	0719	0755
12	0792	0828	0864	0899	0934	0969	1004	1038	1072	1106
13	1139	1173	1206	1239	1271	1303	1335	1367	1399	1430
14	1461	1492	1523	1553	1584	1614	1644	1673	1703	1732
15	1761	1790	1818	1847	1875	1903	1931	1959	1987	2014
16	2041	2068	2095	2122	2148	2175	2201	2227	2253	2279
17	2304	2330	2355	2380	2405	2430	2455	2480	2504	2529
18	2553	2577	2601	2625	2648	2672	2695	2718	2742	2765
19	2788	2810	2833	2856	2878	2900	2923	2945	2967	2989
20	3010	3032	3054	3075	3096	3118	3139	3160	3181	3201
21	3222	3243	3263	3284	3304	3324	3345	3365	3385	3404
22	3424	3444	3464	3483	3502	3522	3541	3560	3579	3598
23	3617	3636	3655	3674	3692	3711	3729	3747	3766	3784
24	3802	3820	3838	3856	3874	3892	3909	3927	3945	3962
25	3979	3997	4014	4031	4048	4065	4082	4099	4116	4133
26	4150	4166	4183	4200	4216	4232	4249	4265	4281	4298
27	4314	4330	4346	4362	4378	4393	4409	4425	4440	4456
28	4472	4487	4502	4518	4533	4548	4564	4579	4594	4609
29	4624	4639	4654	4669	4683	4698	4713	4728	4742	4757
30	4771	4786	4800	4814	4829	4843	4857	4871	4886	4900
31	4914	4928	4942	4955	4969	4983	4997	5011	5024	5038
32	5051	5065	5079	5092	5105	5119	5132	5145	5159	5172
33	5185	5198	5211	5224	5237	5250	5263	5276	5289	5302
34	5315	5328	5340	5353	5366	5378	5391	5403	5416	5428
35	5441	5453	5465	5478	5490	5502	5514	5527	5539	5551
36	5563	5575	5587	5599	5611	5623	5635	5647	5658	5670
37	5682	5694	5705	5717	5729	5740	5752	5763	5775	5786
38	5798	5809	5821	5832	5843	5855	5866	5877	5888	5899
39	5911	5922	5933	5944	5955	5966	5977	5988	5999	6010
40	6021	6031	6042	6053	6064	6075	6085	6096	6107	6117
41	6128	6138	6149	6160	6170	6180	6191	6201	6212	6222
42	6232	6243	6253	6263	6274	6284	6294	6304	6314	6325
43	6335	6345	6355	6365	6375	6385	6395	6405	6415	6425
44	6435	6444	6454	6464	6474	6484	6493	6503	6513	6522
45	6532	6542	6551	6561	6571	6580	6590	6599	6609	6618
46	6628	6637	6646	6656	6665	6675	6684	6693	6702	6712
47	6721	6730	6739	6749	6758	6767	6776	6785	6794	6803
48	6812	6821	6830	6839	6848	6857	6866	6875	6884	6893
49	6902	6911	6920	6928	6937	6946	6955	6964	6972	6981
50	6990	6998	7007	7016	7024	7033	7042	7050	7059	7067
N	0	1	2	3	4	5	6	7	8	9

100–500

500–1000

N	0	1	2	3	4	5	6	7	8	9
50	6990	6998	7007	7016	7024	7033	7042	7050	7059	7067
51	7076	7084	7093	7101	7110	7118	7126	7135	7143	7152
52	7160	7168	7177	7185	7193	7202	7210	7218	7226	7235
53	7243	7251	7259	7267	7275	7284	7292	7300	7308	7316
54	7324	7332	7340	7348	7356	7364	7372	7380	7388	7396
55	7404	7412	7419	7427	7435	7443	7451	7459	7466	7474
56	7482	7490	7497	7505	7513	7520	7528	7536	7543	7551
57	7559	7566	7574	7582	7589	7597	7604	7612	7619	7627
58	7634	7642	7649	7657	7664	7672	7679	7686	7694	7701
59	7709	7716	7723	7731	7738	7745	7752	7760	7767	7774
60	7782	7789	7796	7803	7810	7818	7825	7832	7839	7846
61	7853	7860	7868	7875	7882	7889	7896	7903	7910	7917
62	7924	7931	7938	7945	7952	7959	7966	7973	7980	7987
63	7993	8000	8007	8014	8021	8028	8035	8041	8048	8055
64	8062	8069	8075	8082	8089	8096	8102	8109	8116	8122
65	8129	8136	8142	8149	8156	8162	8169	8176	8182	8189
66	8195	8202	8209	8215	8222	8228	8235	8241	8248	8254
67	8261	8267	8274	8280	8287	8293	8299	8306	8312	8319
68	8325	8331	8338	8344	8351	8357	8363	8370	8376	8382
69	8388	8395	8401	8407	8414	8420	8426	8432	8439	8445
70	8451	8457	8463	8470	8476	8482	8488	8494	8500	8506
71	8513	8519	8525	8531	8537	8543	8549	8555	8561	8567
72	8573	8579	8585	8591	8597	8603	8609	8615	8621	8627
73	8633	8639	8645	8651	8657	8663	8669	8675	8681	8686
74	8692	8698	8704	8710	8716	8722	8727	8733	8739	8745
75	8751	8756	8762	8768	8774	8779	8785	8791	8797	8802
76	8808	8814	8820	8825	8831	8837	8842	8848	8854	8859
77	8865	8871	8876	8882	8887	8893	8899	8904	8910	8915
78	8921	8927	8932	8938	8943	8949	8954	8960	8965	8971
79	8976	8982	8987	8993	8998	9004	9009	9015	9020	9025
80	9031	9036	9042	9047	9053	9058	9063	9069	9074	9079
81	9085	9090	9096	9101	9106	9112	9117	9122	9128	9133
82	9138	9143	9149	9154	9159	9165	9170	9175	9180	9186
83	9191	9196	9201	9206	9212	9217	9222	9227	9232	9238
84	9243	9248	9253	9258	9263	9269	9274	9279	9284	9289
85	9294	9299	9304	9309	9315	9320	9325	9330	9335	9340
86	9345	9350	9355	9360	9365	9370	9375	9380	9385	9390
87	9395	9400	9405	9410	9415	9420	9425	9430	9435	9440
88	9445	9450	9455	9460	9465	9469	9474	9479	9484	9489
89	9494	9499	9504	9509	9513	9518	9523	9528	9533	9538
90	9542	9547	9552	9557	9562	9566	9571	9576	9581	9586
91	9590	9595	9600	9605	9609	9614	9619	9624	9628	9633
92	9638	9643	9647	9652	9657	9661	9666	9671	9675	9680
93	9685	9689	9694	9699	9703	9708	9713	9717	9722	9727
94	9731	9736	9741	9745	9750	9754	9759	9763	9768	9773
95	9777	9782	9786	9791	9795	9800	9805	9809	9814	9818
96	9823	9827	9832	9836	9841	9845	9850	9854	9859	9863
97	9868	9872	9877	9881	9886	9890	9894	9899	9903	9908
98	9912	9917	9921	9926	9930	9934	9939	9943	9948	9952
99	9956	9961	9965	9969	9974	9978	9983	9987	9991	9996
100	0000	0004	0009	0013	0017	0022	0026	0030	0035	0039
N	**0**	**1**	**2**	**3**	**4**	**5**	**6**	**7**	**8**	**9**

TABLE IX

FOUR-PLACE LOGARITHMS OF FUNCTIONS

Degrees	log sin	log cos	log tan	log ctn	Degrees
0° 00′	− ∞	0.0000	− ∞	∞	90° 00′
10	7.4637	.0000	7.4637	2.5363	50
20	.7648	.0000	.7648	.2352	40
30	.9408	.0000	.9409	.0591	30
40	8.0658	.0000	8.0658	1.9342	20
50	.1627	.0000	.1627	.8373	10
1° 00′	8.2419	9.9999	8.2419	1.7581	89° 00′
10	.3088	.9999	.3089	.6911	50
20	.3668	.9999	.3669	.6331	40
30	.4179	.9999	.4181	.5819	30
40	.4637	.9998	.4638	.5362	20
50	.5050	.9998	.5053	.4947	10
2° 00′	8.5428	9.9997	8.5431	1.4569	88° 00′
10	.5776	.9997	.5779	.4221	50
20	.6097	.9996	.6101	.3899	40
30	.6397	.9996	.6401	.3599	30
40	.6677	.9995	6682	.3318	20
50	.6940	.9995	.6945	.3055	10
3° 00′	8.7188	9.9994	8.7194	1.2806	87° 00′
10	.7423	.9993	.7429	.2571	50
20	.7645	.9993	.7652	.2348	40
30	.7857	.9992	.7865	.2135	30
40	.8059	.9991	.8067	.1933	20
50	.8251	.9990	.8261	.1739	10
4° 00′	8.8436	9.9989	8.8446	1.1554	86° 00′
10	.8613	.9989	.8624	.1376	50
20	.8783	.9988	.8795	.1205	40
30	.8946	.9987	.8960	.1040	30
40	.9104	.9986	.9118	.0882	20
50	.9256	.9985	.9272	.0728	10
5° 00′	8.9403	9.9983	8.9420	1.0580	85° 00′
10	.9545	.9982	.9563	.0437	50
20	.9682	.9981	.9701	.0299	40
30	.9816	.9980	9836	.0164	30
40	.9945	.9979	.9966	.0034	20
50	9.0070	.9977	9.0093	0.9907	10
6° 00′	9.0192	9.9976	9.0216	0.9784	84° 00′
10	.0311	.9975	.0336	.9664	50
20	.0426	.9973	.0453	.9547	40
30	.0539	.9972	.0567	.9433	30
40	.0648	.9971	.0678	.9322	20
50	.0755	.9969	.0786	.9214	10
7° 00′	9.0859	9.9968	9.0891	0.9109	83° 00′
10	.0961	.9966	.0995	.9005	50
20	.1060	.9964	.1096	.8904	40
30	.1157	.9963	.1194	.8806	30
40	.1252	.9961	.1291	.8709	20
50	.1345	.9959	.1385	.8615	10
8° 00′	9.1436	9.9958	9.1478	0.8522	82° 00′
10	.1525	.9956	.1569	.8431	50
20	.1612	.9954	.1658	.8342	40
30	.1697	.9952	.1745	.8255	30
40	.1781	.9950	.1831	.8169	20
50	.1863	.9948	.1915	.8085	10
9° 00′	9.1943	9.9946	9.1997	0.8003	81° 00′
Degrees	log cos	log sin	log ctn	log tan	Degrees

Degrees	log sin	log cos	log tan	log ctn	Degrees
9° 00′	9.1943	9.9946	9.1997	0.8003	81° 00′
10	.2022	.9944	.2078	.7922	50
20	.2100	.9942	.2158	.7842	40
30	.2176	.9940	.2236	.7764	30
40	.2251	.9938	.2313	.7687	20
50	.2324	.9936	.2389	.7611	10
10° 00′	9.2397	9.9934	9.2463	0.7537	80° 00′
10	.2468	.9931	.2536	.7464	50
20	.2538	.9929	.2609	.7391	40
30	.2606	.9927	.2680	.7320	30
40	.2674	.9924	.2750	.7250	20
50	.2740	.9922	.2819	.7181	10
11° 00′	9.2806	9.9919	9.2887	0.7113	79° 00′
10	.2870	.9917	.2953	.7047	50
20	.2934	.9914	.3020	.6980	40
30	.2997	.9912	.3085	.6915	30
40	.3058	.9909	.3149	.6851	20
50	.3119	.9907	.3212	.6788	10
12° 00′	9.3179	9.9904	9.3275	0.6725	78° 00′
10	.3238	.9901	.3336	.6664	50
20	.3296	.9899	.3397	.6603	40
30	.3353	.9896	.3458	.6542	30
40	.3410	.9893	.3517	.6483	20
50	.3466	.9890	.3576	.6424	10
13° 00′	9.3521	9.9887	9.3634	0.6366	77° 00′
10	.3575	.9884	.3691	.6309	50
20	.3629	.9881	.3748	.6252	40
30	.3682	.9878	.3804	.6196	30
40	.3734	.9875	.3859	.6141	20
50	.3786	.9872	.3914	.6086	10
14° 00′	9.3837	9.9869	9.3968	0.6032	76° 00′
10	.3887	.9866	.4021	.5979	50
20	.3937	.9863	.4074	.5926	40
30	.3986	.9859	.4127	.5873	30
40	.4035	.9856	.4178	.5822	20
50	.4083	.9853	.4230	.5770	10
15° 00′	9.4130	9.9849	9.4281	0.5719	75° 00′
10	.4177	.9846	.4331	.5669	50
20	.4223	.9843	.4381	.5619	40
30	.4269	.9839	.4430	.5570	30
40	.4314	.9836	.4479	.5521	20
50	.4359	.9832	.4527	.5473	10
16° 00′	9.4403	9.9828	9.4575	0.5425	74° 00′
10	.4447	.9825	.4622	.5378	50
20	.4491	.9821	.4669	.5331	40
30	.4533	.9817	.4716	.5284	30
40	.4576	.9814	.4762	.5238	20
50	.4618	.9810	.4808	.5192	10
17° 00′	9.4659	9.9806	9.4853	0.5147	73° 00′
10	.4700	.9802	.4898	.5102	50
20	.4741	.9798	.4943	.5057	40
30	.4781	.9794	.4987	.5013	30
40	.4821	.9790	.5031	.4969	20
50	.4861	.9786	.5075	.4925	10
18° 00′	9.4900	9.9782	9.5118	0.4882	72° 00′
Degrees	log cos	log sin	log ctn	log tan	Degrees

Degrees	log sin	log cos	log tan	log ctn	Degrees
18° 00′	9.4900	9.9782	9.5118	0.4882	72° 00′
10	.4939	.9778	.5161	.4839	50
20	.4977	.9774	.5203	.4797	40
30	.5015	.9770	.5245	.4755	30
40	.5052	.9765	.5287	.4713	20
50	.5090	.9761	.5329	.4671	10
19° 00′	9.5126	9.9757	9.5370	0.4630	71° 00′
10	.5163	.9752	.5411	.4589	50
20	.5199	.9748	.5451	.4549	40
30	.5235	.9743	.5491	.4509	30
40	.5270	.9739	.5531	.4469	20
50	.5306	.9734	.5571	.4429	10
20° 00′	9.5341	9.9730	9.5611	0.4389	70° 00′
10	.5375	.9725	.5650	.4350	50
20	.5409	.9721	.5689	.4311	40
30	.5443	.9716	.5727	.4273	30
40	.5477	.9711	.5766	.4234	20
50	.5510	.9706	.5804	.4196	10
21° 00′	9.5543	9.9702	9.5842	0.4158	69° 00′
10	.5576	.9697	.5879	.4121	50
20	.5609	.9692	.5917	.4083	40
30	.5641	.9687	.5954	.4046	30
40	.5673	.9682	.5991	.4009	20
50	.5704	.9677	.6028	.3972	10
22° 00′	9.5736	9.9672	9.6064	0.3936	68° 00′
10	.5767	.9667	.6100	.3900	50
20	.5798	.9661	.6136	.3864	40
30	.5828	.9656	.6172	.3828	30
40	.5859	.9651	.6208	.3792	20
50	.5889	.9646	.6243	.3757	10
23° 00′	9.5919	9.9640	9.6279	0.3721	67° 00′
10	.5948	.9635	.6314	.3686	50
20	.5978	.9629	.6348	3652	40
30	.6007	.9624	.6383	3617	30
40	.6036	.9618	.6417	3583	20
50	.6065	.9613	.6452	.3548	10
24° 00′	9.6093	9.9607	9.6486	0.3514	66° 00′
10	.6121	.9602	.6520	.3480	50
20	.6149	.9596	.6553	.3447	40
30	.6177	.9590	.6587	.3413	30
40	.6205	.9584	.6620	.3380	20
50	.6232	.9579	.6654	.3346	10
25° 00′	9.6259	9.9573	9.6687	0.3313	65° 00′
10	.6286	.9567	.6720	.3280	50
20	.6313	.9561	.6752	.3248	40
30	.6340	.9555	.6785	.3215	30
40	.6366	.9549	.6817	.3183	20
50	.6392	.9543	.6850	.3150	10
26° 00′	9.6418	9.9537	9.6882	0.3118	64° 00′
10	.6444	.9530	.6914	.3086	50
20	.6470	.9524	.6946	.3054	40
30	.6495	.9518	.6977	.3023	30
40	.6521	.9512	.7009	.2991	20
50	.6546	.9505	.7040	.2960	10
27° 00′	9.6570	9.9499	9.7072	0.2928	63° 00′
Degrees	log cos	log sin	log ctn	log tan	Degrees

Degrees	log sin	log cos	log tan	log ctn	Degrees
27° 00′	9.6570	9.9499	9.7072	0.2928	63° 00′
10	.6595	.9492	.7103	.2897	50
20	.6620	.9486	.7134	.2866	40
30	.6644	.9479	.7165	.2835	30
40	.6668	.9473	.7196	.2804	20
50	.6692	.9466	.7226	.2774	10
28° 00′	9.6716	9.9459	9.7257	0.2743	62° 00′
10	.6740	.9453	.7287	.2713	50
20	.6763	.9446	.7317	.2683	40
30	.6787	.9439	.7348	.2652	30
40	.6810	.9432	.7378	.2622	20
50	.6833	.9425	.7408	.2592	10
29° 00′	9.6856	9.9418	9.7438	0.2562	61° 00′
10	.6878	.9411	.7467	.2533	50
20	.6901	.9404	.7497	.2503	40
30	.6923	.9397	.7526	.2474	30
40	.6946	.9390	.7556	.2444	20
50	.6968	.9383	.7585	.2415	10
30° 00′	9.6990	9.9375	9.7614	0.2386	60° 00′
10	.7012	.9368	.7644	.2356	50
20	.7033	.9361	.7673	.2327	40
30	.7055	.9353	.7701	.2299	30
40	.7076	.9346	.7730	.2270	20
50	.7097	.9338	.7759	.2241	10
31° 00′	9.7118	9.9331	9.7788	0.2212	59° 00′
10	.7139	.9323	.7816	.2184	50
20	.7160	.9315	.7845	.2155	40
30	.7181	.9308	.7873	.2127	30
40	.7201	.9300	7902	.2098	20
50	.7222	.9292	.7930	2070	10
32° 00′	9.7242	9.9284	9.7958	0.2042	58° 00′
10	.7262	.9276	.7986	.2014	50
20	.7282	.9268	.8014	.1986	40
30	.7302	.9260	.8042	.1958	30
40	.7322	.9252	.8070	.1930	20
50	.7342	.9244	.8097	.1903	10
33° 00′	9.7361	9.9236	9.8125	0.1875	57° 00′
10	.7380	.9228	.8153	.1847	50
20	.7400	.9219	.8180	.1820	40
30	.7419	.9211	.8208	.1792	30
40	.7438	.9203	.8235	.1765	20
50	.7457	.9194	.8263	.1737	10
34° 00′	9.7476	9.9186	9.8290	0.1710	56° 00′
10	.7494	.9177	.8317	.1683	50
20	.7513	.9169	.8344	.1656	40
30	.7531	.9160	.8371	.1629	30
40	.7550	.9151	.8398	.1602	20
50	.7568	.9142	.8425	.1575	10
35° 00′	9.7586	9.9134	9.8452	0.1548	55° 00′
10	.7604	.9125	.8479	.1521	50
20	.7622	.9116	.8506	.1494	40
30	.7640	.9107	.8533	.1467	30
40	.7657	.9098	.8559	.1441	20
50	.7675	.9089	.8586	.1414	10
36° 00′	9.7692	9.9080	9.8613	0.1387	54° 00′
Degrees	log cos	log sin	log ctn	log tan	Degrees

Degrees	log sin	log cos	log tan	log ctn	Degrees
36° 00'	9.7692	9.9080	9.8613	0.1387	**54° 00'**
10	.7710	.9070	.8639	.1361	50
20	.7727	.9061	.8666	.1334	40
30	.7744	.9052	.8692	.1308	30
40	.7761	.9042	.8718	.1282	20
50	.7778	.9033	.8745	.1255	10
37° 00'	9.7795	9.9023	9.8771	0.1229	**53° 00'**
10	.7811	.9014	.8797	.1203	50
20	.7828	.9004	.8824	.1176	40
30	.7844	.8995	.8850	.1150	30
40	.7861	.8985	.8876	.1124	20
50	.7877	.8975	.8902	.1098	10
38° 00'	9.7893	9.8965	9.8928	0.1072	**52° 00'**
10	.7910	.8955	.8954	.1046	50
20	.7926	.8945	.8980	.1020	40
30	.7941	.8935	.9006	.0994	30
40	.7957	.8925	.9032	.0968	20
50	.7973	.8915	.9058	.0942	10
39° 00'	9.7989	9.8905	9.9084	0.0916	**51° 00'**
10	.8004	.8895	.9110	.0890	50
20	.8020	.8884	.9135	.0865	40
30	.8035	.8874	.9161	.0839	30
40	.8050	.8864	.9187	.0813	20
50	.8066	.8853	.9212	.0788	10
40° 00'	9.8081	9.8843	9.9238	0.0762	**50° 00'**
10	.8096	.8832	.9264	.0736	50
20	.8111	.8821	.9289	.0711	40
30	.8125	.8810	.9315	.0685	30
40	.8140	.8800	.9341	.0659	20
50	.8155	.8789	.9366	.0634	10
41° 00'	9.8169	9.8778	9.9392	0.0608	**49° 00'**
10	.8184	.8767	.9417	.0583	50
20	.8198	.8756	.9443	.0557	40
30	.8213	.8745	.9468	.0532	30
40	.8227	.8733	.9494	.0506	20
50	.8241	.8722	.9519	.0481	10
42° 00'	9.8255	9.8711	9.9544	0.0456	**48° 00'**
10	.8269	.8699	.9570	.0430	50
20	.8283	.8688	.9595	.0405	40
30	.8297	.8676	.9621	.0379	30
40	.8311	.8665	.9646	.0354	20
50	.8324	.8653	.9671	.0329	10
43° 00'	9.8338	9.8641	9.9697	0.0303	**47° 00'**
10	.8351	.8629	.9722	.0278	50
20	.8365	.8618	.9747	.0253	40
30	.8378	.8606	.9772	.0228	30
40	.8391	.8594	.9798	.0202	20
50	.8405	.8582	.9823	.0177	10
44° 00'	9.8418	9.8569	9.9848	0.0152	**46° 00'**
10	.8431	.8557	.9874	.0126	50
20	.8444	.8545	.9899	.0101	40
30	.8457	.8532	.9924	.0076	30
40	.8469	.8520	.9949	.0051	20
50	.8482	.8507	.9975	.0025	10
45° 00'	9.8495	9.8495	0.0000	0.0000	**45° 00'**
Degrees	log cos	log sin	log ctn	log tan	**Degrees**

TABLE X 69

NATURAL FUNCTIONS AND RADIANS

Angle	Radians	Sin	Csc	Tan	Ctn	Sec	Cos		
0° 00'	.0000	.0000	-----	.0000	-----	1.000	1.0000	1.5708	90° 00'
10'	029	.0029	343.8	.0029	343.8	1.000	1.0000	679	50'
20'	058	.0058	171.9	.0058	171.9	1.000	1.0000	650	40'
30'	.0087	.0087	114.6	.0087	114.6	1.000	1.0000	1.5621	30'
40'	116	.0116	85.95	.0116	85.94	1.000	0.9999	592	20'
50'	145	.0145	68.76	.0145	68.75	1.000	0.9999	563	10'
1° 00'	.0175	.0175	57.30	.0175	57.29	1.000	0.9998	1.5533	89° 00'
10'	204	.0204	49.11	.0204	49.10	1.000	.9998	504	50'
20'	233	.0233	42.98	.0233	42.96	1.000	.9997	475	40'
30'	.0262	.0262	38.20	.0262	38.19	1.000	.9997	1.5446	30'
40'	291	.0291	34.38	.0291	34.37	1.000	.9996	417	20'
50'	320	.0320	31.26	.0320	31.24	1.001	.9995	388	10'
2° 00'	.0349	.0349	28.65	.0349	28.64	1.001	.9994	1.5359	88° 00'
10'	378	.0378	26.45	.0378	26.43	1.001	.9993	330	50'
20'	407	.0407	24.56	.0407	24.54	1.001	.9992	301	40'
30'	.0436	.0436	22.93	.0437	22.90	1.001	.9990	1.5272	30'
40'	465	.0465	21.49	.0466	21.47	1.001	.9989	243	20'
50'	495	.0494	20.23	.0495	20.21	1.001	.9988	213	10'
3° 00'	.0524	.0523	19.11	.0524	19.08	1.001	.9986	1.5184	87° 00'
10'	553	.0552	18.10	.0553	18.07	1.002	.9985	155	50'
20'	582	.0581	17.20	.0582	17.17	1.002	.9983	126	40'
30'	.0611	.0610	16.38	.0612	16.35	1.002	.9981	1.5097	30'
40'	640	.0640	15.64	.0641	15.60	1.002	.9980	068	20'
50'	669	.0669	14.96	.0670	14.92	1.002	.9978	039	10'
4° 00'	.0698	.0698	14.34	.0699	14.30	1.002	.9976	1.5010	86° 00'
10'	727	.0727	13.76	.0729	13.73	1.003	.9974	1.4981	50'
20'	756	.0756	13.23	.0758	13.20	1.003	.9971	952	40'
30'	.0785	.0785	12.75	.0787	12.71	1.003	.9969	1.4923	30'
40'	814	.0814	12.29	.0816	12.25	1.003	.9967	893	20'
50'	844	.0843	11.87	.0846	11.83	1.004	.9964	864	10'
5° 00'	.0873	.0872	11.47	.0875	11.43	1.004	.9962	1.4835	85° 00'
10'	902	.0901	11.10	.0904	11.06	1.004	.9959	806	50'
20'	931	.0929	10.76	.0934	10.71	1.004	.9957	777	40'
30'	.0960	.0958	10.43	.0963	10.39	1.005	.9954	1.4748	30'
40'	989	.0987	10.13	.0992	10.08	1.005	.9951	719	20'
50'	.1018	.1016	9.839	.1022	9.788	1.005	.9948	690	10'
6° 00'	.1047	.1045	9.567	.1051	9.514	1.006	.9945	1.4661	84° 00'
10'	076	.1074	9.309	.1080	9.255	1.006	.9942	632	50'
20'	105	.1103	9.065	.1110	9.010	1.006	.9939	603	40'
30'	.1134	.1132	8.834	.1139	8.777	1.006	.9936	1.4573	30'
40'	164	.1161	8.614	.1169	8.556	1.007	.9932	544	20'
50'	193	.1190	8.405	.1198	8.345	1.007	.9929	515	10'
7° 00'	.1222	.1219	8.206	.1228	8.144	1.008	.9925	1.4486	83° 00'
10'	251	.1248	8.016	.1257	7.953	1.008	.9922	457	50'
20'	280	.1276	7.834	.1287	7.770	1.008	.9918	428	40'
30'	.1309	.1305	7.661	.1317	7.596	1.009	.9914	1.4399	30'
40'	338	.1334	7.496	.1346	7.429	1.009	.9911	370	20'
50'	367	.1363	7.337	.1376	7.269	1.009	.9907	341	10'
8° 00'	.1396	.1392	7.185	.1405	7.115	1.010	.9903	1.4312	82° 00'
10'	425	.1421	7.040	.1435	6.968	1.010	.9899	283	50'
20'	454	.1449	6.900	.1465	6.827	1.011	.9894	254	40'
30'	.1484	.1478	6.765	.1495	6.691	1.011	.9890	1.4224	30'
40'	513	.1507	6.636	.1524	6.561	1.012	.9886	195	20'
50'	542	.1536	6.512	.1554	6.435	1.012	.9881	166	10'
9° 00'	.1571	.1564	6.392	.1584	6.314	1.012	.9877	1.4137	81° 00'
		Cos	Sec	Ctn	Tan	Csc	Sin	Radians	Angle

Angle	Radians	Sin	Csc	Tan	Ctn	Sec	Cos		
9° 00'	.1571	.1564	6.392	.1584	6.314	1.012	.9877	1.4137	81° 00'
10'	600	.1593	6.277	.1614	6.197	1.013	.9872	108	50'
20'	629	.1622	6.166	.1644	6.084	1.013	.9868	079	40'
30'	.1658	.1650	6.059	.1673	5.976	1.014	.9863	1.4050	30'
40'	687	.1679	5.955	.1703	5.871	1.014	.9858	1.4021	20'
50'	716	.1708	5.855	.1733	5.769	1.015	.9853	1.3992	10'
10° 00'	.1745	.1736	5.759	.1763	5.671	1.015	.9848	1.3963	80° 00'
10'	774	.1765	5.665	.1793	5.576	1.016	.9843	934	50'
20'	804	.1794	5.575	.1823	5.485	1.016	.9838	904	40'
30'	.1833	.1822	5.487	.1853	5.396	1.017	.9833	1.3875	30'
40'	862	.1851	5.403	.1883	5.309	1.018	.9827	846	20'
50'	891	.1880	5.320	.1914	5.226	1.018	.9822	817	10'
11° 00'	.1920	.1908	5.241	.1944	5.145	1.019	.9816	1.3788	79° 00'
10'	949	.1937	5.164	.1974	5.066	1.019	.9811	759	50'
20'	978	.1965	5.089	.2004	4.989	1.020	.9805	730	40'
30'	.2007	.1994	5.016	.2035	4.915	1.020	.9799	1.3701	30'
40'	036	.2022	4.945	.2065	4.843	1.021	.9793	672	20'
50'	065	.2051	4.876	.2095	4.773	1.022	.9787	643	10'
12° 00'	.2094	.2079	4.810	.2126	4.705	1.022	.9781	1.3614	78° 00'
10'	123	.2108	4.745	.2156	4.638	1.023	.9775	584	50'
20'	153	.2136	4.682	.2186	4.574	1.024	.9769	555	40'
30'	.2182	.2164	4.620	.2217	4.511	1.024	.9763	1.3526	30'
40'	211	.2193	4.560	.2247	4.449	1.025	.9757	497	20'
50'	240	.2221	4.502	.2278	4.390	1.026	.9750	468	10'
13° 00'	.2269	.2250	4.445	.2309	4.331	1.026	.9744	1.3439	77° 00'
10'	298	.2278	4.390	.2339	4.275	1.027	.9737	410	50'
20'	327	.2306	4.336	.2370	4.219	1.028	.9730	381	40'
30'	.2356	.2334	4.284	.2401	4.165	1.028	.9724	1.3352	30'
40'	385	.2363	4.232	.2432	4.113	1.029	.9717	323	20'
50'	414	.2391	4.182	.2462	4.061	1.030	.9710	294	10'
14° 00'	.2443	.2419	4.134	.2493	4.011	1.031	.9703	1.3265	76° 00'
10'	473	.2447	4.086	.2524	3.962	1.031	.9696	235	50'
20'	502	.2476	4.039	.2555	3.914	1.032	.9689	206	40'
30'	.2531	.2504	3.994	.2586	3.867	1.033	.9681	1.3177	30'
40'	560	.2532	3.950	.2617	3.821	1.034	.9674	148	20'
50'	589	.2560	3.906	.2648	3.776	1.034	.9667	119	10'
15° 00'	.2618	.2588	3.864	.2679	3.732	1.035	.9659	1.3090	75° 00'
10'	647	.2616	3.822	.2711	3.689	1.036	.9652	061	50'
20'	676	.2644	3.782	.2742	3.647	1.037	.9644	032	40'
30'	.2705	.2672	3.742	.2773	3.606	1.038	.9636	1.3003	30'
40'	734	.2700	3.703	.2805	3.566	1.039	.9628	1.2974	20'
50'	763	.2728	3.665	.2836	3.526	1.039	.9621	945	10'
16° 00'	.2793	.2756	3.628	.2867	3.487	1.040	.9613	1.2915	74° 00'
10'	822	.2784	3.592	.2899	3.450	1.041	.9605	886	50'
20'	851	.2812	3.556	.2931	3.412	1.042	.9596	857	40'
30'	.2880	.2840	3.521	.2962	3.376	1.043	.9588	1.2828	30'
40'	909	.2868	3.487	.2994	3.340	1.044	.9580	799	20'
50'	938	.2896	3.453	.3026	3.305	1.045	.9572	770	10'
17° 00'	.2967	.2924	3.420	.3057	3.271	1.046	.9563	1.2741	73° 00'
10'	996	.2952	3.388	.3089	3.237	1.047	.9555	712	50'
20'	.3025	.2979	3.357	.3121	3.204	1.048	.9546	683	40'
30'	.3054	.3007	3.326	.3153	3.172	1.048	.9537	1.2654	30'
40'	083	.3035	3.295	.3185	3.140	1.049	.9528	625	20'
50'	113	.3062	3.265	.3217	3.108	1.050	.9520	595	10'
18° 00'	.3142	.3090	3.236	.3249	3.078	1.051	.9511	1.2566	72° 00'
		Cos	Sec	Ctn	Tan	Csc	Sin	Radians	Angle

Angle	Radians	Sin	Csc	Tan	Ctn	Sec	Cos		
18° 00'	.3142	.3090	3.236	.3249	3.078	1.051	.9511	1.2566	72° 00'
10'	171	.3118	3.207	.3281	3.047	1.052	.9502	537	50'
20'	200	.3145	3.179	.3314	3.018	1.053	.9492	508	40'
30'	.3229	.3173	3.152	.3346	2.989	1.054	.9483	1.2479	30'
40'	258	.3201	3.124	.3378	2.960	1.056	.9474	450	20'
50'	287	.3228	3.098	.3411	2.932	1.057	.9465	421	10'
19° 00'	.3316	.3256	3.072	.3443	2.904	1.058	.9455	1.2392	71° 00'
10'	345	.3283	3.046	.3476	2.877	1.059	.9446	363	50'
20'	374	.3311	3.021	.3508	2.850	1.060	.9436	334	40'
30'	.3403	.3338	2.996	.3541	2.824	1.061	.9426	1.2305	30'
40'	432	.3365	2.971	.3574	2.798	1.062	.9417	275	20'
50'	462	.3393	2.947	.3607	2.773	1.063	.9407	246	10'
20° 00'	.3491	.3420	2.924	.3640	2.747	1.064	.9397	1.2217	70° 00'
10'	520	.3448	2.901	.3673	2.723	1.065	.9387	188	50'
20'	549	.3475	2.878	.3706	2.699	1.066	.9377	159	40'
30'	.3578	.3502	2.855	.3739	2.675	1.068	.9367	1.2130	30'
40'	607	.3529	2.833	.3772	2.651	1.069	.9356	101	20'
50'	636	.3557	2.812	.3805	2.628	1.070	.9346	072	10'
21° 00'	.3665	.3584	2.790	.3839	2.605	1.071	.9336	1.2043	69° 00'
10'	694	.3611	2.769	.3872	2.583	1.072	.9325	1.2014	50'
20'	723	.3638	2.749	.3906	2.560	1.074	.9315	1.1985	40'
30'	.3752	.3665	2.729	.3939	2.539	1.075	.9304	1.1956	30'
40'	782	.3692	2.709	.3973	2.517	1.076	.9293	926	20'
50'	811	.3719	2.689	.4006	2.496	1.077	.9283	897	10'
22° 00'	.3840	.3746	2.669	.4040	2.475	1.079	.9272	1.1868	68° 00'
10'	869	.3773	2.650	.4074	2.455	1.080	.9261	839	50'
20'	898	.3800	2.632	.4108	2.434	1.081	.9250	810	40'
30'	.3927	.3827	2.613	.4142	2.414	1.082	.9239	1.1781	30'
40'	956	.3854	2.595	.4176	2.394	1.084	.9228	752	20'
50'	985	.3881	2.577	.4210	2.375	1.085	.9216	723	10'
23° 00'	.4014	.3907	2.559	.4245	2.356	1.086	.9205	1.1694	67° 00'
10'	043	.3934	2.542	.4279	2.337	1.088	.9194	665	50'
20'	072	.3961	2.525	.4314	2.318	1.089	.9182	636	40'
30'	.4102	.3987	2.508	.4348	2.300	1.090	.9171	1.1606	30'
40'	131	.4014	2.491	.4383	2.282	1.092	.9159	577	20'
50'	160	.4041	2.475	.4417	2.264	1.093	.9147	548	10'
24° 00'	.4189	.4067	2.459	.4452	2.246	1.095	.9135	1.1519	66° 00'
10'	218	.4094	2.443	.4487	2.229	1.096	.9124	490	50'
20'	247	.4120	2.427	.4522	2.211	1.097	.9112	461	40'
30'	.4276	.4147	2.411	.4557	2.194	1.099	.9100	1.1432	30'
40'	305	.4173	2.396	.4592	2.177	1.100	.9088	403	20'
50'	334	.4200	2.381	.4628	2.161	1.102	.9075	374	10'
25° 00'	.4363	.4226	2.366	.4663	2.145	1.103	.9063	1.1345	65° 00'
10'	392	.4253	2.352	.4699	2.128	1.105	.9051	316	50'
20'	422	.4279	2.337	.4734	2.112	1.106	.9038	286	40'
30'	.4451	.4305	2.323	.4770	2.097	1.108	.9026	1.1257	30'
40'	480	.4331	2.309	.4806	2.081	1.109	.9013	228	20'
50'	509	.4358	2.295	.4841	2.066	1.111	.9001	199	10'
26° 00'	.4538	.4384	2.281	.4877	2.050	1.113	.8988	1.1170	64° 00'
10'	567	.4410	2.268	.4913	2.035	1.114	.8975	141	50'
20'	596	.4436	2.254	.4950	2.020	1.116	.8962	112	40'
30'	.4625	.4462	2.241	.4986	2.006	1.117	.8949	1.1083	30'
40'	654	.4488	2.228	.5022	1.991	1.119	.8936	054	20'
50'	683	.4514	2.215	.5059	1.977	1.121	.8923	1.1025	10'
27° 00'	.4712	.4540	2.203	.5095	1.963	1.122	.8910	1.0996	63° 00'
		Cos	Sec	Ctn	Tan	Csc	Sin	Radians	Angle

Angle	Radians	Sin	Csc	Tan	Ctn	Sec	Cos		Angle
27° 00'	.4712	.4540	2.203	.5095	1.963	1.122	.8910	1.0996	63° 00'
10'	741	.4566	2.190	.5132	1.949	1.124	.8897	966	50'
20'	771	.4592	2.178	.5169	1.935	1.126	.8884	937	40'
30'	.4800	.4617	2.166	.5206	1.921	1.127	.8870	1.0908	30'
40'	829	.4643	2.154	.5243	1.907	1.129	.8857	879	20'
50'	858	.4669	2.142	.5280	1.894	1.131	.8843	850	10'
28° 00'	.4887	.4695	2.130	.5317	1.881	1.133	.8829	1.0821	62° 00'
10'	916	.4720	2.118	.5354	1.868	1.134	.8816	792	50'
20'	945	.4746	2.107	.5392	1.855	1.136	.8802	763	40'
30'	.4974	.4772	2.096	.5430	1.842	1.138	.8788	1.0734	30'
40'	.5003	.4797	2.085	.5467	1.829	1.140	.8774	705	20'
50'	032	.4823	2.074	.5505	1.816	1.142	.8760	676	10'
29° 00'	.5061	.4848	2.063	.5543	1.804	1.143	.8746	1.0647	61° 00'
10'	091	.4874	2.052	.5581	1.792	1.145	.8732	617	50'
20'	120	.4899	2.041	.5619	1.780	1.147	.8718	588	40'
30'	.5149	.4924	2.031	.5658	1.767	1.149	.8704	1.0559	30'
40'	178	.4950	2.020	.5696	1.756	1.151	.8689	530	20'
50'	207	.4975	2.010	.5735	1.744	1.153	.8675	501	10'
30° 00'	.5236	.5000	2.000	.5774	1.732	1.155	.8660	1.0472	60° 00'
10'	265	.5025	1.990	.5812	1.720	1.157	.8646	443	50'
20'	294	.5050	1.980	.5851	1.709	1.159	.8631	414	40'
30'	.5323	.5075	1.970	.5890	1.698	1.161	.8616	1.0385	30'
40'	352	.5100	1.961	.5930	1.686	1.163	.8601	356	20'
50'	381	.5125	1.951	.5969	1.675	1.165	.8587	327	10'
31° 00'	.5411	.5150	1.942	.6009	1.664	1.167	.8572	1.0297	59° 00'
10'	440	.5175	1.932	.6048	1.653	1.169	.8557	268	50'
20'	469	.5200	1.923	.6088	1.643	1.171	.8542	239	40'
30'	.5498	.5225	1.914	.6128	1.632	1.173	.8526	1.0210	30'
40'	527	.5250	1.905	.6168	1.621	1.175	.8511	181	20'
50'	556	.5275	1.896	.6208	1.611	1.177	.8496	152	10'
32° 00'	.5585	.5299	1.887	.6249	1.600	1.179	.8480	1.0123	58° 00'
10'	614	.5324	1.878	.6289	1.590	1.181	.8465	094	50'
20'	643	.5348	1.870	.6330	1.580	1.184	.8450	065	40'
30'	.5672	.5373	1.861	.6371	1.570	1.186	.8434	1.0036	30'
40'	701	.5398	1.853	.6412	1.560	1.188	.8418	1.0007	20'
50'	730	.5422	1.844	.6453	1.550	1.190	.8403	.9977	10'
33° 00'	.5760	.5446	1.836	.6494	1.540	1.192	.8387	.9948	57° 00'
10'	789	.5471	1.828	.6536	1.530	1.195	.8371	919	50'
20'	818	.5495	1.820	.6577	1.520	1.197	.8355	890	40'
30'	.5847	.5519	1.812	.6619	1.511	1.199	.8339	.9861	30'
40'	876	.5544	1.804	.6661	1.501	1.202	.8323	832	20'
50'	905	.5568	1.796	.6703	1.492	1.204	.8307	803	10'
34° 00'	.5934	.5592	1.788	.6745	1.483	1.206	.8290	.9774	56° 00'
10'	963	.5616	1.781	.6787	1.473	1.209	.8274	745	50'
20'	992	.5640	1.773	.6830	1.464	1.211	.8258	716	40'
30'	.6021	.5664	1.766	.6873	1.455	1.213	.8241	.9687	30'
40'	050	.5688	1.758	.6916	1.446	1.216	.8225	657	20'
50'	080	.5712	1.751	.6959	1.437	1.218	.8208	628	10'
35° 00'	.6109	.5736	1.743	.7002	1.428	1.221	.8192	.9599	55° 00'
10'	138	.5760	1.736	.7046	1.419	1.223	.8175	570	50'
20'	167	.5783	1.729	.7089	1.411	1.226	.8158	541	40'
30'	.6196	.5807	1.722	.7133	1.402	1.228	.8141	.9512	30'
40'	225	.5831	1.715	.7177	1.393	1.231	.8124	483	20'
50'	254	.5854	1.708	.7221	1.385	1.233	.8107	454	10'
36° 00'	.6283	.5878	1.701	.7265	1.376	1.236	.8090	.9425	54° 00'
		Cos	Sec	Ctn	Tan	Csc	Sin	Radians	Angle

Angle	Radians	Sin	Csc	Tan	Ctn	Sec	Cos		
36° 00'	.6283	.5878	1.701	.7265	1.376	1.236	.8090	.9425	54° 00'
10'	312	.5901	1.695	.7310	1.368	1.239	.8073	396	50'
20'	341	.5925	1.688	.7355	1.360	1.241	.8056	367	40'
30'	.6370	.5948	1.681	.7400	1.351	1.244	.8039	.9338	30'
40'	400	.5972	1.675	.7445	1.343	1.247	.8021	308	20'
50'	429	.5995	1.668	.7490	1.335	1.249	.8004	279	10'
37° 00'	.6458	.6018	1.662	.7536	1.327	1.252	.7986	.9250	53° 00'
10'	487	.6041	1.655	.7581	1.319	1.255	.7969	221	50'
20'	516	.6065	1.649	.7627	1.311	1.258	.7951	192	40'
30'	.6545	.6088	1.643	.7673	1.303	1.260	.7934	.9163	30'
40'	574	.6111	1.636	.7720	1.295	1.263	.7916	134	20'
50'	603	.6134	1.630	.7766	1.288	1.266	.7898	105	10'
38° 00'	.6632	.6157	1.624	.7813	1.280	1.269	.7880	.9076	52° 00'
10'	661	.6180	1.618	.7860	1.272	1.272	.7862	047	50'
20'	690	.6202	1.612	.7907	1.265	1.275	.7844	.9018	40'
30'	.6720	.6225	1.606	.7954	1.257	1.278	.7826	.8988	30'
40'	749	.6248	1.601	.8002	1.250	1.281	.7808	959	20'
50'	778	.6271	1.595	.8050	1.242	1.284	.7790	930	10'
39° 00'	.6807	.6293	1.589	.8098	1.235	1.287	.7771	.8901	51° 00'
10'	836	.6316	1.583	.8146	1.228	1.290	.7753	872	50'
20'	865	.6338	1.578	.8195	1.220	1.293	.7735	843	40'
30'	.6894	.6361	1.572	.8243	1.213	1.296	.7716	.8814	30'
40'	923	.6383	1.567	.8292	1.206	1.299	.7698	785	20'
50'	952	.6406	1.561	.8342	1.199	1.302	.7679	756	10'
40° 00'	.6981	.6428	1.556	.8391	1.192	1.305	.7660	.8727	50° 00'
10'	.7010	.6450	1.550	.8441	1.185	1.309	.7642	698	50'
20'	039	.6472	1.545	.8491	1.178	1.312	.7623	668	40'
30'	.7069	.6494	1.540	.8541	1.171	1.315	.7604	.8639	30'
40'	098	.6517	1.535	.8591	1.164	1.318	.7585	610	20'
50'	127	.6539	1.529	.8642	1.157	1.322	.7566	581	10'
41° 00'	.7156	.6561	1.524	.8693	1.150	1.325	.7547	.8552	49° 00'
10'	185	.6583	1.519	.8744	1.144	1.328	.7528	523	50'
20'	214	.6604	1.514	.8796	1.137	1.332	.7509	494	40'
30'	.7243	.6626	1.509	.8847	1.130	1.335	.7490	.8465	30'
40'	272	.6648	1.504	.8899	1.124	1.339	.7470	436	20'
50'	301	.6670	1.499	.8952	1.117	1.342	.7451	407	10'
42° 00'	.7330	.6691	1.494	.9004	1.111	1.346	.7431	.8378	48° 00'
10'	359	.6713	1.490	.9057	1.104	1.349	.7412	348	50'
20'	389	.6734	1.485	.9110	1.098	1.353	.7392	319	40'
30'	.7418	.6756	1.480	.9163	1.091	1.356	.7373	.8290	30'
40'	447	.6777	1.476	.9217	1.085	1.360	.7353	261	20'
50'	476	.6799	1.471	.9271	1.079	1.364	.7333	232	10'
43° 00'	.7505	.6820	1.466	.9325	1.072	1.367	.7314	.8203	47° 00'
10'	534	.6841	1.462	.9380	1.066	1.371	.7294	174	50'
20'	563	.6862	1.457	.9435	1.060	1.375	.7274	145	40'
30'	.7592	.6884	1.453	.9490	1.054	1.379	.7254	.8116	30'
40'	621	.6905	1.448	.9545	1.048	1.382	.7234	087	20'
50'	650	.6926	1.444	.9601	1.042	1.386	.7214	058	10'
44° 00'	.7679	.6947	1.440	.9657	1.036	1.390	.7193	.8029	46° 00'
10'	709	.6967	1.435	.9713	1.030	1.394	.7173	.7999	50'
20'	738	.6988	1.431	.9770	1.024	1.398	.7153	970	40'
30'	.7767	.7009	1.427	.9827	1.018	1.402	.7133	.7941	30'
40'	796	.7030	1.423	.9884	1.012	1.406	.7112	912	20'
50'	825	.7050	1.418	.9942	1.006	1.410	.7092	883	10'
45° 00'	.7854	.7071	1.414	1.000	1.000	1.414	.7071	.7854	45° 00'
		Cos	Sec	Ctn	Tan	Csc	Sin	Radians	Angle

TABLE XI

PROPORTIONAL PARTS OF DIFFERENCES

D	1	2	3	4	5	6	7	8	9
1	0.1	0.2	0.3	0.4	0.5	0.6	0.7	0.8	0.9
2	0.2	0.4	0.6	0.8	1.0	1.2	1.4	1.6	1.8
3	0.3	0.6	0.9	1.2	1.5	1.8	2.1	2.4	2.7
4	0.4	0.8	1.2	1.6	2.0	2.4	2.8	3.2	3.6
5	0.5	1.0	1.5	2.0	2.5	3.0	3.5	4.0	4.5
6	0.6	1.2	1.8	2.4	3.0	3.6	4.2	4.8	5.4
7	0.7	1.4	2.1	2.8	3.5	4.2	4.9	5.6	6.3
8	0.8	1.6	2.4	3.2	4.0	4.8	5.6	6.4	7.2
9	0.9	1.8	2.7	3.6	4.5	5.4	6.3	7.2	8.1
10	1.0	2.0	3.0	4.0	5.0	6.0	7.0	8.0	9.0
11	1.1	2.2	3.3	4.4	5.5	6.6	7.7	8.8	9.9
12	1.2	2.4	3.6	4.8	6.0	7.2	8.4	9.6	10.8
13	1.3	2.6	3.9	5.2	6.5	7.8	9.1	10.4	11.7
14	1.4	2.8	4.2	5.6	7.0	8.4	9.8	11.2	12.6
15	1.5	3.0	4.5	6.0	7.5	9.0	10.5	12.0	13.5
16	1.6	3.2	4.8	6.4	8.0	9.6	11.2	12.8	14.4
17	1.7	3.4	5.1	6.8	8.5	10.2	11.9	13.6	15.3
18	1.8	3.6	5.4	7.2	9.0	10.8	12.6	14.4	16.2
19	1.9	3.8	5.7	7.6	9.5	11.4	13.3	15.2	17.1
20	2.0	4.0	6.0	8.0	10.0	12.0	14.0	16.0	18.0
21	2.1	4.2	6.3	8.4	10.5	12.6	14.7	16.8	18.9
22	2.2	4.4	6.6	8.8	11.0	13.2	15.4	17.6	19.8
23	2.3	4.6	6.9	9.2	11.5	13.8	16.1	18.4	20.7
24	2.4	4.8	7.2	9.6	12.0	14.4	16.8	19.2	21.6
25	2.5	5.0	7.5	10.0	12.5	15.0	17.5	20.0	22.5
26	2.6	5.2	7.8	10.4	13.0	15.6	18.2	20.8	23.4
27	2.7	5.4	8.1	10.8	13.5	16.2	18.9	21.6	24.3
28	2.8	5.6	8.4	11.2	14.0	16.8	19.6	22.4	25.2
29	2.9	5.8	8.7	11.6	14.5	17.4	20.3	23.2	26.1
30	3.0	6.0	9.0	12.0	15.0	18.0	21.0	24.0	27.0
31	3.1	6.2	9.3	12.4	15.5	18.6	21.7	24.8	27.9
32	3.2	6.4	9.6	12.8	16.0	19.2	22.4	25.6	28.8
33	3.3	6.6	9.9	13.2	16.5	19.8	23.1	26.4	29.7
34	3.4	6.8	10.2	13.6	17.0	20.4	23.8	27.2	30.6
35	3.5	7.0	10.5	14.0	17.5	21.0	24.5	28.0	31.5
36	3.6	7.2	10.8	14.4	18.0	21.6	25.2	28.8	32.4
37	3.7	7.4	11.1	14.8	18.5	22.2	25.9	29.6	33.3
38	3.8	7.6	11.4	15.2	19.0	22.8	26.6	30.4	34.2
39	3.9	7.8	11.7	15.6	19.5	23.4	27.3	31.2	35.1
40	4.0	8.0	12.0	16.0	20.0	24.0	28.0	32.0	36.0
41	4.1	8.2	12.3	16.4	20.5	24.6	28.7	32.8	36.9
42	4.2	8.4	12.6	16.8	21.0	25.2	29.4	33.6	37.8
43	4.3	8.6	12.9	17.2	21.5	25.8	30.1	34.4	38.7
44	4.4	8.8	13.2	17.6	22.0	26.4	30.8	35.2	39.6
45	4.5	9.0	13.5	18.0	22.5	27.0	31.5	36.0	40.5
46	4.6	9.2	13.8	18.4	23.0	27.6	32.2	36.8	41.4
47	4.7	9.4	14.1	18.8	23.5	28.2	32.9	37.6	42.3
48	4.8	9.6	14.4	19.2	24.0	28.8	33.6	38.4	43.2
49	4.9	9.8	14.7	19.6	24.5	29.4	34.3	39.2	44.1
50	5.0	10.0	15.0	20.0	25.0	30.0	35.0	40.0	45.0
	1	**2**	**3**	**4**	**5**	**6**	**7**	**8**	**9**

This table contains the proportional parts of differences from 1 to 100. For example, if the difference between two numbers is 73, 0.7 of this difference is 51.1.

D	1	2	3	4	5	6	7	8	9
51	5.1	10.2	15.3	20.4	25.5	30.6	35.7	40.8	45.9
52	5.2	10.4	15.6	20.8	26.0	31.2	36.4	41.6	46.8
53	5.3	10.6	15.9	21.2	26.5	31.8	37.1	42.4	47.7
54	5.4	10.8	16.2	21.6	27.0	32.4	37.8	43.2	48.6
55	5.5	11.0	16.5	22.0	27.5	33.0	38.5	44.0	49.5
56	5.6	11.2	16.8	22.4	28.0	33.6	39.2	44.8	50.4
57	5.7	11.4	17.1	22.8	28.5	34.2	39.9	45.6	51.3
58	5.8	11.6	17.4	23.2	29.0	34.8	40.6	46.4	52.2
59	5.9	11.8	17.7	23.6	29.5	35.4	41.3	47.2	53.1
60	6.0	12.0	18.0	24.0	30.0	36.0	42.0	48.0	54.0
61	6.1	12.2	18.3	24.4	30.5	36.6	42.7	48.8	54.9
62	6.2	12.4	18.6	24.8	31.0	37.2	43.4	49.6	55.8
63	6.3	12.6	18.9	25.2	31.5	37.8	44.1	50.4	56.7
64	6.4	12.8	19.2	25.6	32.0	38.4	44.8	51.2	57.6
65	6.5	13.0	19.5	26.0	32.5	39.0	45.5	52.0	58.5
66	6.6	13.2	19.8	26.4	33.0	39.6	46.2	52.8	59.4
67	6.7	13.4	20.1	26.8	33.5	40.2	46.9	53.6	60.3
68	6.8	13.6	20 4	27.2	34.0	40.8	47.6	54.4	61.2
69	6.9	13.8	20.7	27.6	34.5	41.4	48.3	55.2	62.1
70	7.0	14.0	21.0	28.0	35.0	42.0	49.0	56.0	63.0
71	7.1	14.2	21.3	28.4	35.5	42.6	49.7	56.8	63.9
72	7.2	14.4	21.6	28.8	36.0	43.2	50.4	57.6	64.8
73	7.3	14.6	21.9	29.2	36.5	43.8	51.1	58.4	65.7
74	7.4	14.8	22.2	29.6	37.0	44.4	51.8	59.2	66.6
75	7.5	15.0	22.5	30.0	37.5	45.0	52.5	60.0	67.5
76	7.6	15.2	22.8	30.4	38.0	45.6	53.2	60.8	68.4
77	7.7	15.4	23.1	30.8	38.5	46.2	53.9	61.6	69.3
78	7.8	15.6	23.4	31.2	39.0	46.8	54.6	62.4	70.2
79	7.9	15.8	23.7	31.6	39.5	47.4	55.3	63.2	71.1
80	8.0	16.0	24.0	32.0	40.0	48.0	56.0	64.0	72.0
81	8.1	16.2	24.3	32.4	40.5	48.6	56.7	64.8	72.9
82	8.2	16.4	24.6	32.8	41.0	49.2	57.4	65.6	73.8
83	8.3	16.6	24.9	33.2	41.5	49.8	58.1	66.4	74.7
84	8.4	16.8	25.2	33.6	42.0	50.4	58.8	67.2	75.6
85	8.5	17.0	25.5	34.0	42.5	51.0	59.5	68.0	76.5
86	8.6	17.2	25.8	34.4	43.0	51.6	60.2	68.8	77.4
87	8.7	17.4	26.1	34.8	43.5	52.2	60.9	69.6	78.3
88	8.8	17.6	26.4	35.2	44.0	52.8	61.6	70.4	79.2
89	8.9	17.8	26.7	35.6	44.5	53.4	62.3	71.2	80.1
90	9.0	18.0	27.0	36.0	45.0	54.0	63.0	72.0	81.0
91	9.1	18.2	27.3	36.4	45.5	54.6	63.7	72.8	81.9
92	9.2	18.4	27.6	36.8	46.0	55.2	64.4	73.6	82.8
93	9.3	18.6	27.9	37.2	46.5	55.8	65.1	74.4	83.7
94	9.4	18.8	28.2	37.6	47.0	56.4	65.8	75.2	84.6
95	9.5	19.0	28.5	38.0	47.5	57.0	66.5	76.0	85.5
96	9.6	19.2	28.8	38.4	48.0	57.6	67.2	76.8	86.4
97	9.7	19.4	29.1	38.8	48.5	58.2	67.9	77.6	87.3
98	9.8	19.6	29.4	39.2	49.0	58.8	68.6	78.4	88.2
99	9.9	19.8	29.7	39.6	49.5	59.4	69.3	79.2	89.1
100	10.0	20.0	30.0	40.0	50.0	60.0	70.0	80.0	90.0
	1	2	3	4	5	6	7	8	9

INDEX

Δ

ANSWERS
TO ODD-NUMBERED PROBLEMS

ANSWERS
TO ODD-NUMBERED PROBLEMS

PAGE 9

<u>3</u>. 62.4 ft.   <u>5</u>. 96°; 162 ft; 100 ft.

PAGES 20-21

<u>1</u>. 0.6; 0.8; 0.5; 0.9; 0.5; 0.8; 0.9
<u>3</u>. 0.8; 1.3; 0.5; 2; 0.6; 1.7; 1.9
<u>5</u>. 1.2; 1.7; 1.1; 2.2; 1.2; 2; 2.1
<u>7</u>. 0.4; 0.4; 0.7; 0.7; 0.6; 0.6
<u>9</u>. 0.8; 1.5; 0.7; 0.6; 1.7; 0.5; 0.9

<u>11</u>. <u>a</u>. $\sin A = \dfrac{DC}{AC}$ <u>b</u>. $\sin A = \dfrac{BC}{AB}$ <u>c</u>. $\sin B = \dfrac{CD}{BC}$

$\cos A = \dfrac{AD}{AC}$ $\cos A = \dfrac{AC}{AB}$ $\cos B = \dfrac{DB}{BC}$

$\tan A = \dfrac{CD}{AD}$ $\tan A = \dfrac{BC}{AC}$ $\tan B = \dfrac{CD}{DB}$

$\csc A = \dfrac{AC}{DC}$ $\csc A = \dfrac{AB}{BC}$ $\csc B = \dfrac{BC}{CD}$

$\sec A = \dfrac{AC}{AD}$ $\sec A = \dfrac{AB}{AC}$ $\sec B = \dfrac{BC}{DB}$

$\operatorname{ctn} A = \dfrac{AD}{CD}$ $\operatorname{ctn} A = \dfrac{AC}{BC}$ $\operatorname{ctn} B = \dfrac{DB}{CD}$

Page 24

		sin	cos	tan	csc	sec	ctn
<u>1</u>.	30°	0.50	0.87	0.58	2.0	1.1	1.7
<u>3</u>.	60°	0.87	0.50	1.7	1.2	2.0	0.58
<u>5</u>.	20°	0.34	0.94	0.36	2.9	1.1	2.7
<u>7</u>.	50°	0.77	0.64	1.2	1.3	1.6	0.84

<u>9</u>. 42°   <u>11</u>. 52°   <u>13</u>. 40°

Pages 24-25

<u>1</u>. cos A = .87; tan A = .58; ctn A = 1.7; sec A = 1.2; csc A = 2

<u>3</u>. sin 60° = 0.87; tan 60° = 1.7; sec 60° = 2.0; cos 60° = 0.50; ctn 60° = 0.58; csc 60° = 1.2

<u>7</u>. sin 18° = 0.32   sin 72° = .95

cos 18° = 0.95   cos 72° = .32

tan 18° = 0.33   tan 72° = 3.0

ctn 18° = 3.0   ctn 72° = 0.33

sec 18° = 1.1   sec 72° = 3.2

csc 18° = 3.2   csc 72° = 1.1

<u>9</u>. a = 16 in., b = 12 in.; ∠A = 53°; ∠B = 37°

Pages 27-28

<u>1</u>. cos 61°   <u>3</u>. ctn 16°   <u>5</u>. csc 10°   <u>7</u>. sec 55°
<u>9</u>. sin 45°   <u>11</u>. ctn 55°   <u>13</u>. ctn 2°   <u>15</u>. sin 13°   <u>17</u>. csc 42°
<u>19</u>. cos 2°54'   <u>21</u>. $\frac{2}{5}$ <u>23</u>. All false   <u>25</u>. 18°   <u>27</u>. 18°
<u>29</u>. 18°   <u>31</u>. $\frac{4}{7}$

Page 31

<u>1</u>. 1.000   <u>9</u>. 1.040   <u>17</u>. 0.9407   <u>25</u>. 72°10'
<u>3</u>. 0.2756   <u>11</u>. 0.3145   <u>19</u>. 4.989   <u>27</u>. 46°0'
<u>5</u>. 3.078   <u>13</u>. 3.647   <u>21</u>. 36°50'   <u>29</u>. 84°50'
<u>7</u>. 0.1564   <u>15</u>. 1.844   <u>23</u>. 61°20'   <u>31</u>. 38°0'

Page 32

<u>1</u>. .3132   <u>3</u>. .6051   <u>5</u>. .9692   <u>7</u>. 3.066   <u>9</u>. .9583
<u>11</u>. .4363

Page 33

<u>1</u>. 20°4'   <u>3</u>. 47°32'   <u>5</u>. 22°47'   <u>7</u>. 33°0'   <u>9</u>. 80°5'
<u>11</u>. 42°45'

Page 35

<u>5</u>. 33°40'

Page 37

<u>1</u>. sin, csc   <u>3</u>. sin, csc   <u>5</u>. cos, sec   <u>7</u>. 20.84, or 21
<u>9</u>. 5.732, or 5.7   <u>11</u>. 59.12 or 59   <u>13</u>. 59°22'   <u>15</u>. 168.9 ft.,
or 169 ft.   <u>17</u>. 439.4 ft.   <u>19</u>. 73°44', or 73°40'   <u>21</u>. 12.9 in.
<u>25</u>. 89.4, or 90   <u>27</u>. 4619 ft., or 4600 ft.

Pages 41-43

<u>1</u>. A = 47°50'; b = 13.3; c = 19.8
<u>3</u>. B = 24°45'; b = 38.87; c = 92.84

<u>5</u>. A = 60°26';   B = 29°34';   c = 877.2

<u>7</u>. A = 21°14';   B = 68°46';   b = 402.1

<u>9</u>. 8 in.   <u>11</u>. 23°5'   <u>13</u>. 11°6'   <u>15</u>. 469 ft.

<u>17</u>. $111.74   <u>19</u>. 32.92 in.   <u>21</u>. 86.3 in.   <u>23</u>. 1056 ft.

<u>25</u>. 18 ft. 4 in.; 39 ft. 4 in.   <u>27</u>. 94.8 ft.

Page 44

<u>1</u>. True   <u>3</u>. False   <u>5</u>. True   <u>7</u>. 1.   <u>9</u>. 30°

<u>11</u>. $\cos A = \frac{12}{13}$; $\operatorname{ctn} A = \frac{12}{5}$; $\csc A = \frac{13}{5}$; $\tan A = \frac{5}{12}$;

$\sec A = \frac{13}{12}$.   <u>13</u>. sin A = .7183;   cos A = .6957;   tan A = 1.033;

ctn A = .9685;   csc A = 1.392.   <u>15</u>. <u>a</u>. b   <u>b</u>. b csc A   <u>c</u>. ctn

<u>d</u>. csc   <u>e</u>. ctn   <u>17</u>. .0016

Page 47

<u>1</u>. $\frac{1}{30}$; $\frac{1}{3000}$ <u>5</u>. 45.4   <u>9</u>. 78.6   <u>13</u>. 23.15

<u>3</u>. 4.8   <u>7</u>. 19.0   <u>11</u>. 4.79   <u>15</u>. 7.28

<u>17</u>. 4.20

Page 49

<u>1</u>. 4   <u>3</u>. 4   <u>5</u>. 4   <u>7</u>. 2   <u>9</u>. 1 (if rounded to tens)

<u>11</u>. 2 (if rounded to ten-thousands)   <u>13</u>. 8420   <u>15</u>. 47.6

<u>17</u>. .0417   <u>19</u>. .0242   <u>21</u>. 71,850   <u>23</u>. 3218   <u>25</u>. 480.8

<u>27</u>. 749,100

Pages 50-51

<u>1</u>. .05 sec.;   .005 in.;   .00005 in.;   500 mi.;   5000 mi.

<u>3</u>. 18.13 in.;   equally accurate

Page 53

<u>1</u>. 7.0   <u>3</u>. 508.2   <u>5</u>. 4.3   <u>7</u>. 3.91   <u>9</u>. 11.1

Pages 54-55

<u>1</u>. 3.   <u>3</u>. 1   <u>5</u>. 3   <u>7</u>. 3   <u>9</u>. 203; 18.3

Pages 55-56

<u>1</u>. 1.62×10^3 <u>3</u>. 4.6×10 <u>5</u>. 2.1300×10^{-1} <u>7</u>. 5×10^{-2}

<u>9</u>. 6.5×10^{-2} <u>11</u>. 9.3×10^7 <u>13</u>. 5×10^{-5} cm.   <u>15</u>. 1.55×10^8 mi.

<u>17</u>. .0000003 sec.   <u>19</u>. 400,000

Pages 58–59

$\underline{1}$. $\log_4 16 = 2$ $\underline{3}$. $\log_{10} 100 = 2$ $\underline{5}$. $\log_2 16 = 4$
$\underline{7}$. $\log_{10} 10,000 = 4$ $\underline{9}$. $\log_5 625 = 4$ $\underline{11}$. $\log_7 343 = 3$
$\underline{13}$. $\log_{10} 1 = 0$ $\underline{15}$. $\log_4 \frac{1}{16} = -2$ $\underline{17}$. $\log_{10} .001 = -3$
$\underline{19}$. $\log_8 1 = 0$ $\underline{21}$. $\log_5 .04 = -2$ $\underline{23}$. $4^1 = 4$ or $4 = 4$
$\underline{25}$. $10^0 = 1$ $\underline{27}$. $7^2 = 49$ $\underline{29}$. $10^{.602} = 4$ $\underline{31}$. $4^4 = 256$
$\underline{33}$. $10^{.69} = 4.9$ $\underline{35}$. 2 $\underline{37}$. 1 $\underline{39}$. 3 $\underline{41}$. 0 $\underline{43}$. 1
$\underline{45}$. 2

Page 61

$\underline{1}$. $\log 7.476 = 0.87367$ $7.476 = 10^{0.87367}$
$\underline{3}$. $\log 5.214 = 0.71717$ $5.214 = 10^{0.71717}$
$\underline{5}$. $\log 2.81 = 0.44871$ $2.81 = 10^{0.44871}$
$\underline{7}$. $\log 4.49 = 0.65225$ $4.49 = 10^{0.65225}$
$\underline{9}$. $\log 8 = 0.90309$ $8 = 10^{0.90309}$
$\underline{11}$. $\log 1.428 = 0.15473$ $1.428 = 10^{0.15473}$
$\underline{13}$. $\log 2.9 = 0.46240$ $2.9 = 10^{0.46240}$
$\underline{15}$. $\log 7.368 = 0.86735$ $7.368 = 10^{0.86735}$

Page 62

$\underline{1}$. 5.805 $\underline{5}$. 5.485 $\underline{9}$. 1.241 $\underline{13}$. 1.605
$\underline{3}$. 1.152 $\underline{7}$. 1.806, approx. $\underline{11}$. 9.245 $\underline{15}$. 1.877, approx.

Pages 63–64

$\underline{1}$. $\underline{a}$. 3.25792 $\underline{3}$. $\underline{a}$. 3.87633 $\underline{5}$. $\underline{a}$. 0.76582
   $\underline{b}$. 1.25792 $\underline{b}$. 4.87633 $\underline{b}$. 1.76582
   $\underline{c}$. 2.25792 $\underline{c}$. 1.87633 $\underline{c}$. 3.76582
   $\underline{d}$. 4.25792 $\underline{d}$. 2.87633 $\underline{d}$. 4.76582

$\underline{7}$. Their mantissa. $\underline{9}$. $\log 0.2789 = 0.44545-1$

Page 65

$\underline{1}$. 3.92752 $\underline{5}$. 2.71433 $\underline{9}$. 0.90309 $\underline{13}$. 3.96914
$\underline{3}$. 0.66577 $\underline{7}$. 0.68215 $\underline{11}$. 2.34025 $\underline{15}$. 3.84547

Page 66

$\underline{1}$. $10^{9.92941-10}$ $\underline{5}$. $10^{5.4284-10}$ $\underline{9}$. $9.2173-10$
$\underline{3}$. $10^{6.23070-10}$ $\underline{7}$. $7.64171-10$ $\underline{11}$. $5.4632-10$

Page 67

1. 9.67742-10   5. 9.50705-10   9. 9.05115-10   13. 8.66577-10
3. 7.89209-10   7. 9.72616-10   11. 7.67210-10   15. 6.90309-10

Page 68 (top)

1. 7001   3. 58.06   5. .03288   7. 393.6   9. 291.1
11. .002226

Page 68 (bottom)

1. 0; 1.0   3. Increases

Page 72

To 4 significant figures: 1. 1,152,000   3. 10.97   5. 20.88
7. 808,000,000   9. 467,700   11. .002649   13. 1.718
15. .8812   17. .002000

Page 73

1. Negative; positive   5. 1.13787   7. 5.88874-10
3. 7.78675-10   9. 1.79778

Page 75

1. 1.62476   5. 7.85652   9. 9.66415-10
3. 3.71996   7. 3.28199   11. 0.96428

Page 76

1. 58.355   5. 20.063   9. 6257
3. .009306   7. .00031623   11. 115.23

Page 77

1. 387,950   5. 53.314   9. 60.18
3. 514.14   7. -9.773   11. 1.3638

Page 78

1. 48.879   5. .76342   9. 444.6
3. 348.87   7. 16.199   11. .15385

Pages 78-80

1. 1.55630; 2.33445; 2.77815; 0.38908.   3. 2.4771; 1.0458

<u>5</u>. 9.1549-10;   2.5353   <u>7</u>. 43 sq.in.;   43.32 sq.in.   *<u>9</u>. 22.8
sq.in. (22.795)   <u>11</u>. 3.3 (3.3238)   <u>13</u>. 397 H.P. (397.31)
<u>15</u>. 41,600 (41,560)   <u>17</u>. 400 bu. (433.92)   <u>19</u>. $90 (85.916)

Pages 80-81

<u>1</u>. 3   <u>5</u>. 3   <u>9</u>. -3   <u>13</u>. 76.442   <u>17</u>. 2.9%
<u>3</u>. 4   <u>7</u>. 5   <u>11</u>. 3.3219   <u>15</u>. 8.0856

Page 82

<u>1</u>. 1.6610   <u>3</u>. 3.1610   <u>5</u>. 1.5   <u>7</u>. 4.1134   <u>9</u>. 1

Pages 84-85

<u>1</u>. 9.26063-10   <u>3</u>. 9.87557-10   <u>5</u>. 0.12683   <u>7</u>. 9.15245-10
<u>9</u>. 9.76167-10   <u>11</u>. 0   <u>13</u>. 0.64786   <u>15</u>. 9.92181-10
<u>17</u>. 0.11831   <u>19</u>. 0.02085   <u>21</u>. 0.57642   <u>23</u>. 7.76764-10
<u>25</u>. 9.99992-10   <u>27</u>. 8.16417-10   <u>29</u>. 7.90307-10   <u>31</u>. 9.99974-10
<u>33</u>. 8.26598-10

Page 86

<u>1</u>. 26°46'   <u>5</u>. 16°30'8"   <u>9</u>. 61°24'10"
<u>3</u>. 43°50'   <u>7</u>. 10°26'30"   <u>11</u>. 28°27'50"

Pages 86-87

<u>1</u>. 7.26 x 10^4 <u>3</u>. 1.6 x 10^{-3} <u>5</u>. 2.4 x 10^5 <u>7</u>. <u>a</u>. 1760
<u>b</u>. 8140   <u>c</u>. 84.6   <u>d</u>. 7.93   <u>e</u>. 42.6   <u>f</u>. 184   <u>9</u>. 2.753 (2.7526)
<u>11</u>. 110 (113.6)   <u>13</u>. 11.7   <u>15</u>. 0   <u>17</u>. 2   <u>19</u>. 1   <u>21</u>. -1
<u>23</u>. 4   <u>25</u>. 2   <u>27</u>. 248.3 (248.34)   <u>29</u>. 16,347   <u>31</u>. 51,580
(51,579)   <u>33</u>. 3.7974   <u>35</u>. .834 (.83443)   <u>37</u>. 2.38 (2.3751)
<u>39</u>. -1.70 (-1.7040)   <u>41</u>. 0.30103; 1.20412; 9.39794-10
<u>43</u>. .5148; .1287   <u>45</u>. 4   <u>47</u>. .53565   <u>49</u>. 3   <u>51</u>. mantissa;
characteristic   <u>53</u>. a + b; a - b; 2a - b; a - 2b
<u>55</u>. 9.50037-10   <u>57</u>. 9.27543-10

Page 94**

<u>1</u>. 14   <u>3</u>. 200   <u>5</u>. 736   <u>7</u>. 972   <u>9</u>. 210,000   <u>11</u>. 6680

*Double answers are given as an aid in checking computation. The first one
has been rounded; the second contains the number of significant figures in the
table.
**Results in this chapter are given to 3 significant figures.

Page 95

1. 16   3. 4   5. 39   7. .549   9. .222   11. 164

Page 96

1. 81   5. 4100   9. 25   13. 45   17. 11.2
3. 49   7. 858   11. 13   15. 3.16   19. 2.12

Page 97

1. 4.80   3. 259   5. 40.2   7. 17.5   9. 18.8

Page 98

1. 11.5   3. 1300   5. 168   7. 4.58   9. 6.21

Page 100 (top)

1. .951   5. .264   9. .342   13. .219
3. .267   7. .645   11. .951   15. .709

Page 100 (foot)

1. 3.09   3. 14.7   5. 13.7

Page 101

1. .445   3. .271   5. .135   7. 1.00   9. .0699   11. .0929

Page 102 (top)

1. 11.4   3. 1.19   5. 5.88   7. 1.11

Page 102 (foot)

1. 30.4   3. 4.02   5. 5.36   7. 56

Page 103

1. Yes   3. D   5. Mantissa   7. .470   9. .268   11. .906
13. 5.94   15. 81.5   17. 2400   19. 21.7   21. 40.2
23. 16.7

Pages 109-110

1. A = 55°50'; b = 287.11, or 287; c = 511.23, or 511.
3. A = 31°28'; a = 1025.2, or 1025; b = 1675.2, or 1675.

5. A = 35°11'49", or 35°12'; B = 54°48'11", or 54°48'; c = 54.199, or 54.20

7. A = 30°0'; B = 60°0'; b = 29.947, or 29.95

9. B = 69°27'15"; a = 331.24; b = 883.78

11. B = 64°46'42", or 64°46'40"; a = .82526; b = 1.7521

13. 11.542, or 11.5 in.

15. 3.7344, or 3.73 in.

17. 35°50'30", or 35°50'

19. 3.103 in.

21. 98.362, or 98.4 ft.

23. 33°41'24"
    56°18'36"

25. 13.866 in.

Pages 111-112

1. 1293.4, or 1293   3. 475.94   5. 393,890, or 393,900

7. 2702.7, or 2703   9. 16.524   11. 4481.13, or 4500 sq.ft.

Page 113

1. B = A; C = 180° - 2A; b = $\frac{\frac{1}{2}c}{\cos A}$; a = b; h = $\frac{1}{2}c \tan A$.

3. A = B; C = 180° - 2B; b = a; c = 2a cos B; h = a sin B.

5. A = B = $\frac{1}{2}$(180° - C); b = $\frac{\frac{1}{2}c}{\cos A}$; a = b; h = $\frac{1}{2}c \tan B$.

7. B = A; C = 180° - 2A; a = b; h = b sin A; c = 2b cos A.

9. C = 102°36'; c = 18.418, or 18.42; h = 7.3778, or 7.378.

11. C = 70°56'; c = 250.92, or 250.9; a = b = 216.22, or 261.2.

13. A = B = 62°36'30", or 62°36'; a = b = 7842.4, or 7842; h = 6963.2, or 6963.

15. 281.03, or 280 sq.ft.   17. 4326.4, or 4300 sq.in.

Page 115

1. 117.56, or 120 in.

3. 9.2376, or 9.2 ft.

5. r = 19.754, or 20 in.;
    s = 6.2572, or 6.3 in.

7. 554.39, or 550 sq.in.

Pages 119-122

1. a. 0°; b. 90°; c. 60°; d. 30°.   3. 5.0344, or 5.034 in.; 6.2168, or 6.217 in.   5. 590.32, or 590 sq.ft.   7. 8.7296, or 8.7 knots south; 9.3614, or 9.4 knots east.   9. Zero.

11. 1687.3, or 1700 ft. north; 751.24 or 750 ft. east.

13. S86°W; N54°W.   15. 3°15'26", or 3°   17. 561.55, or 560 ft.

19. 198°12'49", or 200°.   21. 22.452, or 22 m.p.h.   23. 700.07, or 700 ft. south; 637.75, or 638 ft. east.

Pages 136-137

<u>1-11</u>. See table on p. 136 of the text.　<u>13</u>. -2.　<u>15</u>. 2.

Pages 137-138

<u>1</u>. -sin 25°　<u>3</u>. -tan 20°　<u>5</u>. -sec 29°　<u>7</u>. -cos 10°
<u>9</u>. sin 57°　<u>11</u>. csc 78°　<u>13</u>. sin 65°　<u>15</u>. sec 12°
<u>17</u>. -1$\frac{1}{2}$　<u>19</u>. 2

Pages 140-141

<u>1</u>. <u>a</u>. cos 72°　　<u>g</u>. sin 25°　　<u>m</u>. tan 87°　　<u>s</u>. -csc 68°
　　<u>b</u>. cos 5°　　<u>h</u>. sin 80°　　<u>n</u>. -tan 30°　　<u>t</u>. csc 74°
　　<u>c</u>. -cos 58°　<u>i</u>. ctn 78°　　<u>o</u>. tan 20°　　<u>u</u>. -sec 83°
　　<u>d</u>. -cos 50°　<u>j</u>. -ctn 70°　<u>p</u>. -tan 25°　<u>v</u>. -sec 20°
　　<u>e</u>. sin 20°　　<u>k</u>. ctn 80°　　<u>q</u>. csc 68°　　<u>w</u>. sec 8°
　　<u>f</u>. -sin 40°　<u>l</u>. -ctn 60°　<u>r</u>. -csc 70°　<u>x</u>. -sec 30°

　　<u>3</u>. <u>a</u>. sin θ;　<u>b</u>. tan (80° + θ);　<u>c</u>. -sec θ;　<u>d</u>. sin θ;
<u>e</u>. ctn θ;　<u>f</u>. csc (40° + θ).

Page 141

<u>1</u>. (Values are given in the order: sin, cos, tan, ctn, sec, csc.)

<u>a</u>. I: $\frac{2}{3}$, $\frac{\sqrt{5}}{3}$; $\frac{2\sqrt{5}}{5}$; $\frac{\sqrt{5}}{2}$; $\frac{3\sqrt{5}}{5}$; $\frac{3}{2}$.

　　II: $\frac{2}{3}$; $-\frac{\sqrt{5}}{3}$; $-\frac{2\sqrt{5}}{5}$; $-\frac{\sqrt{5}}{2}$; $-\frac{3\sqrt{5}}{5}$; $\frac{3}{2}$.

<u>b</u>. II: $\frac{\sqrt{2}}{2}$; $-\frac{\sqrt{2}}{2}$; -1; -1; $-\sqrt{2}$; $\sqrt{2}$.

　　III: $-\frac{\sqrt{2}}{2}$; $-\frac{\sqrt{2}}{2}$; 1; 1; $-\sqrt{2}$; $-\sqrt{2}$.

<u>c</u>. I: $\frac{3}{5}$; $\frac{4}{5}$; $\frac{3}{4}$; $\frac{4}{3}$; $\frac{5}{4}$; $\frac{5}{3}$.

　　III: $-\frac{3}{5}$; $-\frac{4}{5}$; $\frac{3}{4}$; $\frac{4}{3}$; $-\frac{5}{4}$; $-\frac{5}{3}$.

<u>d</u>. II: $\frac{3\sqrt{10}}{10}$; $-\frac{\sqrt{10}}{10}$; -3; $-\frac{1}{3}$; $-\sqrt{10}$; $\frac{\sqrt{10}}{3}$.

　　IV: $-\frac{3\sqrt{10}}{10}$; $\frac{\sqrt{10}}{10}$; -3; $-\frac{1}{3}$; $\sqrt{10}$; $-\frac{\sqrt{10}}{3}$.

<u>e</u>. I: $\frac{12}{13}$; $\frac{5}{13}$; $\frac{12}{5}$; $\frac{5}{12}$; $\frac{13}{5}$; $\frac{13}{12}$.

　　IV: $-\frac{12}{13}$; $\frac{5}{13}$; $-\frac{12}{5}$; $-\frac{5}{12}$; $\frac{13}{5}$; $-\frac{13}{12}$.

<u>f</u>. II: $\frac{4\sqrt{65}}{65}$; $-\frac{7\sqrt{65}}{65}$; $-\frac{4}{7}$; $-\frac{7}{4}$; $-\frac{\sqrt{65}}{7}$; $\frac{\sqrt{65}}{4}$.

　　IV: $-\frac{4\sqrt{65}}{65}$; $\frac{7\sqrt{65}}{65}$; $-\frac{4}{7}$; $-\frac{7}{4}$; $\frac{\sqrt{65}}{7}$; $-\frac{\sqrt{65}}{4}$.

g. III: $-\frac{\sqrt{2}}{2}$; $-\frac{\sqrt{2}}{2}$; 1; 1; $-\sqrt{2}$; $-\sqrt{2}$.

   IV: $-\frac{\sqrt{2}}{2}$; $\frac{\sqrt{2}}{2}$; -1; -1; $\sqrt{2}$; $-\sqrt{2}$.

h. III: $-\frac{1}{5}$; $-\frac{2\sqrt{6}}{5}$; $\frac{\sqrt{6}}{12}$; $2\sqrt{6}$; $-\frac{5\sqrt{6}}{12}$; -5.

   IV: $-\frac{1}{5}$; $\frac{2\sqrt{6}}{5}$; $-\frac{\sqrt{6}}{12}$; $-2\sqrt{6}$; $\frac{5\sqrt{6}}{12}$; -5.

i. I: $\frac{3\sqrt{5}}{7}$; $\frac{2}{7}$; $\frac{3\sqrt{5}}{2}$; $\frac{2\sqrt{5}}{15}$; $\frac{7}{2}$; $\frac{7\sqrt{5}}{15}$.

   IV: $-\frac{3\sqrt{5}}{7}$; $\frac{2}{7}$; $-\frac{3\sqrt{5}}{2}$; $-\frac{2\sqrt{5}}{15}$; $\frac{7}{2}$; $-\frac{7\sqrt{5}}{15}$.

3. a. sin θ (cos θ + sin θ)   d. sin θ (cos θ + 1) − ctn θ
   b. sin θ (cos θ − 1) − ctn θ   e. 2 cos θ − $\frac{\sqrt{3}}{2}$ tan θ
   c. −sin θ cos²θ

5. sin C = .9397   cos C = −.3420   tan C = −2.747
   ctn C = −.3640   sec C = −2.924   csc C = 1.064

Pages 145-146

   Ex. 1-15 and 29-33 are in radians.   1. $\frac{\pi}{10}$.   3. π.   5. $\frac{\pi}{6}$.

7. $\frac{\pi}{12}$.   9. $\frac{2\pi}{3}$.   11. $\frac{3\pi}{2}$.   13. $\frac{\pi}{8}$.   15. $\frac{5\pi}{3}$.   17. 180°   19. 90°

21. 45°   23. 120°   25. 9°   27. 225°   29. .87266

31. .08727   33. .14148   35. .79279   37. 132°21'11"

39. 33°13'53"   41. 125°28'39"   43. 0°20'38"   45. 8.8462,

or 8.8 in.   47. sin θ   49. tan θ   51. −sin θ   53. ctn θ

55. sin θ   57. −sin θ   59. −cos θ   61. −ctn θ

Pages 147-148

1. 18.84, or 19   9. .138, or .14 radians, approx. 8°
3. 7.8305, or 7.83   11. 720 revolutions.
5. 2.7 radians   13. 48.823, or 48.82 miles
7. 37°14'32", or 37°

Pages 149-150

1. 600π radians per minute   7. 225 ft. per second
3. 480π radians per minute   9. 25.893, or 26 in.
5. 1500 revolutions per minute

Pages 151-152

1. $39\frac{1}{16}\pi$, or 39π sq.in.   3. 108.27, or 110 sq.in.

<u>5</u>. 29.43, or 29 sq.in.   <u>9</u>. 567.46, or 570 gallons

<u>7</u>. 5.8248, or 5.825 sq.in.   <u>11</u>. 138.68, or 140 sq.in.

Pages 154–155

<u>1</u>. <u>a</u>. $71\frac{1}{9}$ mils.   <u>b</u>. $355\frac{5}{9}$ mils.   <u>c</u>. $213\frac{1}{3}$ mils.   <u>d</u>. $1\frac{5}{27}$ mils.

<u>3</u>. <u>a</u>. 31 radians.   <u>b</u>. 1 radian.   <u>c</u>. 2 radians.

<u>5</u>. A radian.   <u>7</u>. 6 mils.   <u>9</u>. 5,000 ft.

Pages 155–156

<u>1</u>. Radian; degree.   <u>3</u>. <u>a</u>. $\frac{3\pi}{20}$. <u>b</u>. π. <u>c</u>. $\frac{\pi}{2}$. <u>d</u>. $\frac{\pi}{4}$.

<u>5</u>. <u>a</u>. $14\frac{2}{3}$, or 15. <u>b</u>. 578.05, or 578. <u>c</u>. 3.768, or 3.8.

<u>7</u>. $\frac{1}{4}$ unit.   <u>9</u>. <u>a</u>. 25.12, or 25 in. <u>b</u>. 16.75, or 17 in. <u>c</u>. 6.70, or 6.7 in.   <u>11</u>. 50.756, or 51 in.   <u>15</u>. 25 radians per second, approx.   <u>17</u>. 8.9586, or 9.0 sq.in.

Page 161

<u>1</u>. Quadrants I-IV in order: OB, + − − +; OC, + − − +; OE, + + − −; OD, + + + +.   <u>3</u>. Secant and cosecant.   <u>5</u>. sine. <u>7</u>. cosine.   <u>9</u>. sine and cosine.   <u>11</u>. tangent and cotangent; or secant and cosecant.

Pages 165–166

<u>3</u>. sine and cosine, −1 to +1; tangent and cotangent, −∞ to +∞; secant and cosecant, +1 to +∞ and −1 to −∞.   <u>5</u>. <u>a</u>. 210°, 300°, 350°. <u>b</u>. 40°, 300°, 80°, 350°. <u>c</u>. 40°, 210°, 80°. <u>11</u>. <u>a</u>. IV. <u>b</u>. I and IV. <u>c</u>. II and III. <u>d</u>. None.   <u>13</u>. <u>a</u>. tan θ is greater. <u>b</u>. Neither is greater.

Page 168

<u>1</u>. 0 to 1; +1 to −1; −1 to 0.   <u>3</u>. repeats.   <u>5</u>. .7, −1.

Page 169

<u>1</u>. It repeats itself.   <u>3</u>. Decreases from 1 to −1; increases from −1 to 1.   <u>5</u>. 1; −1.   <u>7</u>. Yes.

Page 170

<u>1</u>. 0 to 1.   <u>3</u>. +∞ to −∞.   <u>5</u>. 180°.   <u>7</u>. .25; −1.

Page 172

<u>1</u>. 360° or 2π;   360° or 2π.

<u>3</u>. They have the same absolute value but are of opposite sign.
One is slightly less than +∞, and the other slightly more than −∞.

Page 174

<u>1</u>. −5.5, −2.4, .8, 3.9, and 7.1 radians, approx.

<u>3</u>. −π and 0 radians, π and 2π radians;   −2π and −π radians,
0 and π radians.   <u>5</u>. Conclusion: The value of the cosine of any
angle is the slope of the sine function at that angle.

Page 179

<u>1</u>. $\frac{2\pi}{3}$, 1.   <u>3</u>. π, 3.   <u>5</u>. π, ∞.   <u>9</u>. At point P, the in-
crease in the function is equal to the increase in X.   <u>11</u>. 180°.
<u>15</u>. 1591.9, or 1590 kilocycles per second.

Page 180

<u>1</u>. <u>a</u>. True. <u>b</u>. False. <u>c</u>. True. <u>d</u>. True.   <u>3</u>. As x increases
from 0° to 90°, tan x increases from 0 to ∞;   from 90° to 180°,
tan x increases from −∞ to 0;   from 180° to 270°, tan x increases
from 0 to ∞;   from 270° to 360°, tan x increases from −∞ to 0.
<u>5</u>. sine and cosecant;   tangent and cotangent;   cosine and secant.
<u>7</u>. sine and cosine.   <u>9</u>. tangent, cotangent, secant, and cosecant.
<u>11</u>. Horizontal line segments are positive to the right of the
y-axis and negative to its left. Vertical line segments are positive above the x-axis and negative below it. The terminal side of
the angle is positive.   <u>13</u>. Negative.   <u>15</u>. All quadrants;   all
quadrants.   <u>17</u>. 30°, 274°, −40°.   <u>21</u>. $\frac{3}{5}$;   180° or π.

Page 187

<u>1</u>. $\sin \phi = \pm\sqrt{1 - \cos^2\phi}$

$\tan \phi = \pm\dfrac{\sqrt{1 - \cos^2\phi}}{\cos \phi}$

$\operatorname{ctn} \phi = \pm\dfrac{\cos \phi}{\sqrt{1 - \cos^2\phi}}$

$\sec \phi = \dfrac{1}{\cos \phi}$

$\csc \phi = \pm\dfrac{1}{\sqrt{1 - \cos^2\phi}}$

<u>3</u>. $\sin \phi = \pm\dfrac{1}{\sqrt{1 + \operatorname{ctn}^2\phi}}$

$\cos \phi = \pm\dfrac{\operatorname{ctn} \phi}{\sqrt{\operatorname{ctn}^2\phi + 1}}$

$\tan \phi = \dfrac{1}{\operatorname{ctn} \phi}$

$\sec \phi = \pm\dfrac{\sqrt{\operatorname{ctn}^2\phi + 1}}{\operatorname{ctn} \phi}$

$\csc \phi = \pm\sqrt{1 + \operatorname{ctn}^2\phi}$

5. $\sin \phi = \dfrac{1}{\csc \phi}$ $\operatorname{ctn} \phi = \pm\sqrt{\csc^2\phi - 1}$

 $\cos \phi = \pm \dfrac{\sqrt{\csc^2\phi - 1}}{\csc \phi}$ $\sec \phi = \pm \dfrac{\csc \phi}{\sqrt{\csc^2\phi - 1}}$

 $\tan \phi = \pm \dfrac{1}{\sqrt{\csc^2\phi - 1}}$

7. $\cos^2\phi$ 9. 2   11. 2 sin 20°

Pages 188–189

1. sin θ   3. sec x   5. csc θ   7. $\dfrac{\sin x - 1}{\cos x}$

9. $\dfrac{\cos^3\theta + \cos^2\theta - 1}{\sin \theta \cos \theta}$ 11. $\sin^2 y$ 13. $\csc^2\beta$ 15. 1

17. $\tan^2 A$ 19. $2 \cos^2\theta - 1$ 21. 1   23. cos A − sin A

25. $\sin^2\phi$

Pages 196–197

1. 120°, 240°   3. 30°, 150°, 210°, 330°   5. 90°, 270°

7. 30°, 210°   9. 45°, 135°, 225°, 315°   11. 120°, 300°

13. 30°, 90°, 150°, 210°, 270°, 330°   15. 63°26', 116°34',
243°26', 296°34'*   17. 45°, 225°   19. 60°, 120°, 240°, 360°

21. 45°, 135°, 225°, 270°, 315°   23. 26°34', 153°26', 206°34',
333°26'   25. 90°, 199°28', 340°32'   27. 70°32', 289°28'

29. 0°, 180°   31. 240°, 300°   33. 201°28', 338°32'   35. 30°,
150°, 210°, 330°   37. 90°, 180°   39. 90°, 330°   41. 45°, 90°,
135°, 225°, 270°, 315°   43. 67°30', 247°30', 157°29', 337°29'

45. 60°, 180°, 300°   47. 32°13', 212°13'

Page 198 (top)

1. r = 0, θ = 0°, and 180°; r = $\sqrt{3}$, θ = 60°; r = $-\sqrt{3}$,
θ = 300°.   3. r = .8944, θ = 26°34'; r = −.8944, θ = 206°34'.
5. r = 2, θ = 60°, and 300°; r = −2, θ = 120°, and 240°.

Page 198

1. .45, approx.   3. ±.82, approx.   5. 2.7, approx.

Pages 198–199

1. a. sin 84°   c. tan 32°   e. −sin 36°   g. cos 27°
   b. −cos 78°   d. ctn 46°   f. −csc 5°   h. −sec 80°

*Results which have been read from Table **X** are given to the nearest minute.

<u>3</u>. <u>a</u>. 30°   <u>c</u>. 120°   <u>e</u>. 157°30'   <u>g</u>. -120°   <u>i</u>. -45°
   <u>b</u>. 135°   <u>d</u>. 150°   <u>f</u>. 900°   <u>h</u>. 210°   <u>j</u>. 114°36'

<u>5</u>. <u>a</u>. sin θ   <u>c</u>. -ctn θ   <u>e</u>. -cos θ   <u>g</u>. -csc θ   <u>i</u>. -cos θ
   <u>b</u>. -cos θ   <u>d</u>. tan θ   <u>f</u>. -csc θ   <u>h</u>. -cos θ

<u>7</u>. 2210.56, or 2000 ft. per minute.   <u>9</u>. 1.0986, approx.
<u>11</u>. 2.   <u>13</u>. ±1.3170, approx.   <u>15</u>. B = 56°43'; a = 41.817, or
41.8 ft.; c = 76.20, or 76.2 ft.

Pages 204-205

<u>1</u>. $\frac{1}{4}(\sqrt{6} + \sqrt{2})$, $\frac{1}{4}(\sqrt{2} - \sqrt{6})$, $-2 - \sqrt{3}$.   <u>5</u>. <u>a</u>. $-\frac{21}{221}$, $\frac{220}{221}$, $-\frac{21}{220}$

<u>b</u>. $\frac{171}{221}$, $\frac{140}{221}$, $\frac{171}{140}$ <u>c</u>. $\frac{5}{13}$, $\frac{12}{13}$, $\frac{5}{12}$ <u>d</u>. $\frac{8}{17}$, $\frac{15}{17}$, $\frac{8}{15}$ <u>7</u>. <u>a</u>. $-\frac{4}{5}$.

<u>b</u>. $\frac{3}{5}$ <u>c</u>. $\frac{44}{117}$ <u>d</u>. $= \frac{44}{125}$.   <u>13</u>. <u>a</u>. sin θ   <u>b</u>. cos α   <u>15</u>. 1.

Pages 208-209

<u>1</u>. sin 15° = $\frac{1}{2}\sqrt{2 - \sqrt{3}}$; cos 15° = $\frac{1}{2}\sqrt{2 + \sqrt{3}}$; tan 15° = $2 - \sqrt{3}$.

<u>3</u>. <u>a</u>. sin 2θ = $\frac{24}{25}$; cos 2θ = $-\frac{7}{25}$; tan 2θ = $-\frac{24}{7}$.

   <u>b</u>. sin $\frac{1}{2}$θ = $\frac{1}{5}\sqrt{5}$; cos $\frac{1}{2}$θ = $\frac{2}{5}\sqrt{5}$; tan $\frac{1}{2}$θ = $\frac{1}{2}$.

<u>5</u>. <u>a</u>. sin $22\frac{1}{2}°$ = $\frac{1}{2}\sqrt{2 - \sqrt{2}}$ <u>c</u>. sin $67\frac{1}{2}°$ = $\frac{1}{2}\sqrt{2 + \sqrt{2}}$

   cos $22\frac{1}{2}°$ = $\frac{1}{2}\sqrt{2 + \sqrt{2}}$ cos $67\frac{1}{2}°$ = $\frac{1}{2}\sqrt{2 - \sqrt{2}}$

   tan $22\frac{1}{2}°$ = $\sqrt{2} - 1$ tan $67\frac{1}{2}°$ = $\sqrt{2} + 1$

   <u>b</u>. sin 105° = $\frac{1}{2}\sqrt{2 + \sqrt{3}}$ <u>d</u>. sin 150° = $\frac{1}{2}$

   cos 105° = $-\frac{1}{2}\sqrt{2 - \sqrt{3}}$ cos 150° = $-\frac{1}{2}\sqrt{3}$

   tan 105° = $-2 - \sqrt{3}$ tan 150° = $-\frac{1}{3}\sqrt{3}$

<u>9</u>. <u>a</u>. sin 2θ = $-\frac{240}{289}$ <u>11</u>. <u>a</u>. $3 \sin θ - 4 \sin^3 θ$

   <u>b</u>. tan 2θ = $\frac{240}{161}$ <u>b</u>. $4 \cos^3 θ - 3 \cos θ$

   <u>c</u>. tan $\frac{1}{2}$θ = $\frac{5}{3}$ <u>c</u>. $\frac{\tan θ (3 - \tan^2 θ)}{1 - 3 \tan^2 θ}$

   <u>d</u>. sin $\frac{1}{2}$θ = $\frac{5}{34}\sqrt{34}$ <u>d</u>. $4\sqrt{1 - \sin^2 θ}(\sin θ - 2 \sin^3 θ)$

   <u>e</u>. cos $\frac{1}{2}$θ = $\frac{3}{34}\sqrt{34}$

Page 211

1. $\sin 8A - \sin 4A$ 3. $\cos \phi - \cos 5\phi$ 5. $\frac{1}{2}(\sin 6\beta + \sin 2\beta)$
7. $\frac{1}{2}(\sin \frac{3}{2}\theta - \sin \frac{1}{2}\theta)$ 9. $\frac{1}{2}(\cos 2z - \cos 6z)$ 11. $-2 \sin 4\theta$
$\sin \theta$ 13. $2 \cos 2\alpha \cos \alpha$ 15. $-2 \sin \phi \sin \frac{1}{2}\phi$ 17. $2 \sin 3\theta$
$\cos 2\theta$ 19. $\frac{1}{2}\sqrt{6}$ 21. $-\frac{1}{2}\sqrt{2}$

Pages 216-217

1. $x = 0°, 180°$ 3. $\beta = 60°, 300°$ 5. $\theta = 26°34', 90°, 206°34',$
$270°$ 7. $y = 0°, 45°, 135°, 180°, 225°, 315°$ 9. $\phi = 30°, 150°,$
$210°, 330°$ 11. $x = 36°52', 143°8', 216°52', 323°8'$ 13. $A = 0°,$
$30°, 150°, 180°$ 15. $\alpha = 30°, 150°, 210°, 330°$ 17. $x = 30°, 90°,$
$150°, 210°, 270°, 330°$ 19. $\phi = 0°, 15°, 75°, 90°, 105°, 165°, 180°,$
$195°, 255°, 270°, 285°, 345°$ 21. $\theta = 30°, 60°, 120°, 150°, 210°,$
$240°, 300°, 330°$ 23. $\theta = 135°, 315°$ 25. $A = 0°, 60°, 120°, 180°,$
$240°, 300°$ 27. $\phi = 90°, 270°$ 29. $y = 0°, 60°, 120°, 180°,$
$240°, 300°$ 31. $\alpha = 0°, 60°, 90°, 120°, 180°, 240°, 270°, 300°$
33. $y = 0°, 60°, 120°, 135°, 180°, 240°, 300°, 315°$ 35. No
solution   37. $\phi = 60°, 90°, 300°$ 39. $x = 90°, 270°$

Page 224

1. $A = 61°45'$; $b = 30.510$, or 30.51; $c = 23.433$, or 23.43
3. $C = 58°00'$; $a = 1.1617$, or 1.162; $c = 1.2814$, or 1.281
5. $B = 75°10'55"$; $a = 7.2583$; $c = 5.3846$
7. $A = 65°55'$; $a = 937.88$, or 937.9; $b = 235.46$, or 235.5
9. $C = 67°54'$; $b = 4.7673$, or 4.767; $c = 7.9472$, or 7.947

Pages 229-231

1. Case IIA. One solution   9. Case IIB (2). One solution
3. Case IIC (1). No solution   11. $B = 37°18'25"$, or $37°18'$
5. Case IIC (2). Two solutions $C = 98°16'35"$, or $98°17'$
7. Case IIC (2). One solution $c = 5.9188$, or 5.919

13. (Two solutions.)
  $B = 35°9'57"$, or $35°10'$ $B' = 144°50'3"$, or $144°50'$
  $C = 123°7'3"$, or $123°7'$ $C' = 13°26'57"$, or $13°27'$
  $c = 76.260$, or 76.26 $c' = 21.176$, or 21.18

15. $A = 36°48'15"$, or $36°48'$; $C = 32°29'0"$, or $32°29'$;
$a = 10.978$, or 10.98.   17. 5.0049, or 5.00 in.   19. $239,430$
miles; $239,380$ miles. To four places, they are each $239,400$ miles.
21. 20.026, or 20 miles.

Page 233

1. A = 88°10', or 88°; B = 45°33', or 46°; c = 10.13, or 10.
3. B = 59°34', or 60°; C = 43°37', or 44°; a = 28.23, or 28.
5. B = 93°17', or 93°; C = 41°44', or 42°; a = 21.25 or 21.

Page 234

1. A = 82°49', or 83°; B = 41°25', or 41°; C = 55°46', or 56°.
3. A = 48°11', or 48°; B = 58°25', or 58°; C = 73°24', or 73°.
5. A = 28°5'; B = 61°56', or 62°0'; C = 90°0'.

Page 237

1. A = 46°45'43", or 46°50'
   B = 66°40'17", or 66°40'
   c = 512.59, or 513

3. B = 35°37'26", or 35°37'
   C = 70°55'34", or 70°56'
   a = 76.262, or 76.26

5. A = 25°48'28", or 25°48'
   B = 32°41'32", or 32°42'
   c = 38.738, or 38.74

7. B = 89°51'51", or 89°51'50"
   C = 47°49'29", or 47°49'30"
   a = 48.563

9. A = 37°31'42", or 37°31'40"; C = 48°11'38", or 48°11'40";
b = 45.774.

Page 242

1. A = 73°31'36", or 73°30'
   B = 56°32'0", or 56°30'
   C = 49°56'14", or 50°0'

3. A = 63°57'38", or 63°58'
   B = 43°22'6", or 43°22'
   C = 72°40'14", or 72°40'

5. A = 28°4'50", or 28°5'
   B = 62°14'50", or 62°15'
   C = 89°40'18", or 89°40'

7. A = 103°18", or 103°0'
   B = 44°4'4", or 44°4'
   C = 32°55'42", or 32°56'

9. A = 78°36'50", or 78°37'; B = 61°6'8", or 61°6';
C = 40°17'4", or 40°17'.

Page 243 (top)

1. C = 46°47'; a = 164.27, or 164.3; b = 149.81, or 149.8

3. B = 24°17'16", or 24°17'
   C = 115°27'44", or 115°28'
   c = 33.761, or 33.76

5. A = 52°3'21", or 52°3'20"
   B = 103°37'51", or 103°37'50"
   c = 8.0266

Pages 243-246

1. 14.694, or 14.69 ft.;   8.8646, or 8.865 ft.

5. 74.885, or 75 ft.   13. 101°5'52", or 101°

7. 191.31, or 191 miles   15. 33.230, or 33

9. 7.889, or 7.9 ft.   17. 3067.7, or 3068 ft.

11. 748.27, or 748.3 ft.

Pages 249-251

1. 1112.8, or 1100 sq.units   3. 192.88, or 193 sq.units
5. 2819.1, or 2819 sq.units   7. 14,109, or 14,110 sq.units
9. 2786.3 sq.units   11. 11,735, or 12,000 sq.units   13. 5.2916,
or 5.3   15. 6.5, or 6   17. 1.7537, or 1.754 acres   19. 40
chains   21. 80.59, or 81 sq.ft.   23. 8.99, or 9.0 sq.ft.
25. 133.41, or 133.4 sq.in.   27. 8.294, or 8.3 sq.in.
33. 20,405, or 20,400 sq.ft.

Pages 256-258

1. 12.806, or 10 lb.;   51°20', or 50°;   38°40', or 40°.
3. 670.43, or 670 lb.;   20°2'48", or 20°;   24°57'12", or 25°.
5. 1373.7, or 1400 lb.;   947.3, or 950 lb.   7. 2771.2, or 2800 lb.
9. 26.46, or 26 lb.;   48°36', or 49°   15. 319.24, or 320 lb.;
52°53'59", or 52°50'.

Pages 262-263

1. 3.92, or 3.9 m.p.h.   3. 86°12'9", or 86°;   181.17, or
180 knots.   5. 0°;   335 knots.   7. 3°8'32", or 3°9'.
9. 39.48, or 39 m.p.h.;   185°11'48", or 190°.   11. 13°24'15",
or 13°.   13. 58.304, or 58 m.p.h.

Pages 263-264

1. Case I: two angles and a side
   Case II: two sides and an angle opposite one of them.
   Case III: two sides and their included angle.
   Case IV: three sides.

3. Cases I, II, and III.   5. a. side.   b. angle.   7. $\dfrac{a - b}{c}$
$= \dfrac{\sin \frac{1}{2}(A - B)}{\cos \frac{1}{2}C}$.   9. One.   Case IIC(2)(b).   11. 46°34'6", or 47°.
13. 16.507, or 17 in.   15. 646.36, or 646 sq.in.   17. 9.511,
or 9.5 in.   19. B = 39°54'8", or 40°;   C = 65°53'52", or 66°;

C = 119.53, or 120.   <u>21</u>. A = 52°29'12", or 52°29'; B = 56°31'52", or 56°32'; C = 70°58'54", or 70°59'.   <u>23</u>. 8.5   <u>25</u>. 268.416, or 270 m.p.h.   <u>27</u>. 317°33', or 318°.   <u>29</u>. They will meet. <u>31</u>. 221.27, or 220 lb.

Page 267

<u>1</u>. 45°, 225°   <u>3</u>. 150°, 330°   <u>5</u>. 60°, 300°   <u>7</u>. 180°

<u>9</u>. 45°, 315°   <u>11</u>. 1°, 179°   <u>13</u>. $x = \frac{1}{2}$ arc sin y   <u>15</u>. x = $\frac{1}{2}$ arc sec $\frac{1}{2}$y   <u>17</u>. x = $\frac{1}{5}$ cos y   <u>19</u>. x = $\frac{1}{2}$ ctn $\frac{y}{2}$ <u>21</u>. x = $\frac{1}{5}$ csc $\frac{3}{4}$y

<u>23</u>. θ = arc cos $\frac{\sqrt{x(-x-2)}}{1}$

θ = arc tan $\frac{x+1}{\sqrt{x(-x-2)}}$

θ = arc ctn $\frac{\sqrt{x(-x-2)}}{x+1}$

θ = arc sec $\frac{1}{\sqrt{x(-x-2)}}$

θ = arc csc $\frac{1}{x+1}$

<u>25</u>. θ = arc sin $\sqrt{1-x^2}$

θ = arc cos x

θ = arc ctn $\frac{x}{\sqrt{1-x^2}}$

θ = arc sec $\frac{1}{x}$

θ = arc csc $\frac{1}{\sqrt{1-x^2}}$

<u>27</u>. θ = arc cos $\sqrt{1-e^{2x}}$

θ = arc tan $\frac{e^x}{\sqrt{1-e^{2x}}}$

θ = arc ctn $\frac{\sqrt{1-e^{2x}}}{e^x}$

θ = arc sec $\frac{1}{\sqrt{1-e^{2x}}}$

θ = arc csc $\frac{1}{e^x}$

Pages 268-269

<u>1</u>. 45°   <u>3</u>. -45°   <u>5</u>. -135°   <u>7</u>. -30°   <u>9</u>. -60°   <u>11</u>. 60°

<u>13</u>. 60°   <u>15</u>. -45°   <u>17</u>. 0°   <u>19</u>. 2   <u>21</u>. $\frac{\sqrt{2}}{2}$ <u>23</u>. $\frac{\sqrt{3}}{3}$

Pages 273-274

<u>1</u>. $\frac{1}{6}(2 + \sqrt{15})$ <u>3</u>. 3   19 and 21 are identities   <u>23</u>. x = $\frac{1}{6}$ <u>25</u>. x = $\frac{1}{2}$ <u>27</u>. Impossible   <u>29</u>. x = $\sqrt{3}$ <u>31</u>. x = $\frac{1}{5}$

Pages 279-280

<u>1</u>. 3 - 4i   <u>3</u>. 7 + i$\sqrt{3}$ <u>5</u>. $\sqrt{3}$ - i   <u>7</u>. 4i   <u>9</u>. 2i$\sqrt{2}$

<u>11</u>. 15i   <u>13</u>. 22i$\sqrt{3}$ <u>15</u>. 4i$\sqrt{5}$ <u>17</u>. $-\frac{2}{3}$ <u>19</u>. -13i

<u>21</u>. $\frac{\sqrt{10} - 1 + i(\sqrt{2} + \sqrt{5})}{3}$ <u>23</u>. 7 + 6i$\sqrt{2}$ <u>25</u>. 2 - 11i   <u>27</u>. x = $\sqrt{3}$; y = -3   <u>29</u>. x = 0; y = 4   <u>31</u>. -5 + i$\sqrt{2}$ <u>33</u>. x = ±2i$\sqrt{3}$ <u>35</u>. x = $\frac{-1 \pm i\sqrt{3}}{2}$ <u>37</u>. x = 1; x = $\frac{-1 \pm i\sqrt{3}}{2}$

Page 281

<u>13</u>. 7 + 7i   <u>15</u>. 2 + 6i   <u>17</u>. 1 + 8i

Page 284

<u>1</u>. r cis θ = $\sqrt{2}$ cis 45°   <u>5</u>. r cis θ = $\sqrt{13}$ cis 146°19'

<u>3</u>. r cis θ = $\sqrt{29}$ cis 68°12'   <u>7</u>. r cis θ = 4 cis 180°

<u>9</u>. $3\sqrt{3}$ + 3i   <u>11</u>. −3i   <u>13</u>. $-2\sqrt{3}$ − 2i   <u>15</u>. 2

Page 287

<u>1</u>. −6   <u>3</u>. 3i   <u>5</u>. $4\sqrt{2}$ cis 375°   <u>7</u>. $2\sqrt{2}$ cis 135°, or
−2 + 2i   <u>9</u>. 243 cis 450°, or 243i   <u>11</u>. 64 cis 1980°, or −64
<u>13</u>. $2^{\frac{1}{8}}$ cis 11°15'   <u>15</u>. $2^{\frac{3}{8}}$ cis 33°45'   <u>17</u>. 3 cis 0°;
3 cis 120°; 3 cis 240°   <u>19</u>. 2 cis 0°; 2 cis 120°; 2 cis 240°
<u>21</u>. $(3\sqrt{2})^{\frac{1}{2}}$ cis 80°16'   <u>23</u>. x = 1, .7071 + .7071i, 1, −.7071 +
.7071i, −1, −.7071 − .7071i, −1, .7071 − .7071i.
<u>25</u>. x = $\frac{\sqrt{3}}{2} - \frac{1}{2}i$, $-\frac{\sqrt{3}}{2} - \frac{1}{2}i$, 1.   <u>27</u>. x = .8090 + .5878i,
−.3090 + .9511i, −1, −.3090 − .9511i, .8090 − .5878i.
<u>29</u>. x = $\frac{3}{2} + 1\frac{3\sqrt{3}}{2}$, −3, $\frac{3}{2} - 1\frac{3\sqrt{3}}{2}$.

Pages 290-291

<u>Note</u>: In Ex. 1-5, the first value given is that computed;
the second value is that found in Table X.

<u>1</u>. .8333; .8415   <u>3</u>. 1.522; 1.558   <u>5</u>. .8776; .8775
<u>29</u>. x = 0, 0.69315

Pages 292-293

<u>True</u>: <u>1</u>, <u>3</u>, <u>5</u>, <u>7</u>, <u>13</u>, <u>19</u>.   <u>False</u>: <u>9</u>, <u>11</u>, <u>15</u>, <u>17</u>.   <u>21</u>. 0.55205
<u>23</u>. $10^{4.24206}$ <u>25</u>. 100   <u>27</u>. 1.3010   <u>29</u>. 893.66, or 894
<u>31</u>. x = 5   <u>33</u>. x = 1   <u>35</u>. x = 10   <u>37</u>. B = 57°41'; a = 8.489;
c = 15.88   <u>39</u>. A = 30°51'; B = 59°9'; b = 337.1

Pages 293-295

<u>1-10</u>. <u>True</u>: <u>1</u>, <u>3</u>, <u>7</u>.   <u>False</u>: <u>5</u>, <u>9</u>,

<u>11</u>. sin A = $-\frac{3\sqrt{10}}{10}$;   cos A = $-\frac{\sqrt{10}}{10}$;   tan A = 3;   sec A = $-\sqrt{10}$;
csc A = $-\frac{\sqrt{10}}{3}$.

13. **a.** sin 45°   **d.** −ctn 50°   **g.** −csc 19°48'

    b. −cos 10°   **e.** −sec 30°   **h.** sin 62°47'

    c. −tan 20°   **f.** −cos 68°   **i.** −tan 15°23'

15. 45°   **17.** 9.5554, or 9.555 in.   **19.** −cos θ   **21.** cos θ

23. A = 62°59'15"; B = 27°0'45"; c = 517.81.   **25.** 15,149, or

15,150 sq.units.   **27.** 94.598, or 94.60 sq.units   **29.** 20π radians

31. **a.** 142.2 mils.   **b.** 213.3 mils.   **c.** 711.1 mils.   **33.** 30°.

35. 3200; 6400.

Pages 295-297

1. AC; OC; FG; OD; OG.   **3.** sine and cosecant; tangent

and cotangent; cosine and secant.   **5.** sine and cosine.

7. tangent and cotangent.   **13.** period = 2π; amplitude = 2.

15. period = $\frac{\pi}{3}$; amplitude = ∞.   **25.** x = 270°.   **27.** x = 0°.

29. θ = 30°, 150°, 210°, 330°.   **37.** x = 90°, 270°.   **39.** θ =

0°, 30°, 90°, 150°, 180°, 210°, 270°, 330°, 360°

Pages 297-300

1-11. True: **1, 7, 9, 11,** False: **3, 5.**

13. a and **b.** A + B + C = 180° and $\dfrac{a}{\sin A} = \dfrac{b}{\sin B} = \dfrac{c}{\sin C}$

  c. $\dfrac{a - b}{a + b} = \dfrac{\frac{1}{2} \tan (A - B)}{\frac{1}{2} \tan (A + B)}$ and $\dfrac{a}{\sin A} = \dfrac{c}{\sin C}$

  d. s = $\dfrac{a + b + c}{2}$, r = $\sqrt{\dfrac{(s - a)(s - b)(s - c)}{s}}$, and tan $\frac{1}{2}$A = $\dfrac{r}{s - a}$.

15. a. See p. 220.   **b.** See p. 232.   **c.** See p. 235.

d. See p. 238.

17. 1377.6, or 1378.   **19.** 89.397, or 89.4 m.p.h.   **21.** 40,906,

or 40,910 sq.units   **23.** 111.32, or 111.3 sq.in.   **25.** r = 33.836,

or 34   **27.** A = 28°57'20", or 28°57'. C = 104°28'42", or 104°29'.

B = 46°34'6", or 46°34'.   **29.** A = 79°45'25"; C = 58°42'15";

a = 4776.7; A' = 17°9'55"; C' = 121°17'45"; a' = 1432.6

31. 138°6'18", or 138°; 296.9, or 297 m.p.h.   **33.** 218.48, or

218 m.p.h. north; 416.14, or 416 m.p.h. east.   **35.** AC = 1558.5,

or 1600 yd.; BC = 1097.1, or 1100 yd.   **37.** 49.8, or 50 yd.

Page 310

1. a = 28°56'; b = 57°10'; c = 61°40'

3. A = 67°12'; b = 8°1'; c = 19°59'

5. A = 78°38'   7. A = 114°54'   9. B = 60°25'30"
   B = 129°10'   B = 50°45'   a = 155°10'0"
   c = 99°26'   a = 122°57'   c = 136°50'37"

11. a. 111°10'22", or 111°10'20"
    b. 121°49'57", or 121°49'55"; c. 79°1'15".

13-1. a = 5.0499, or 5.05 ft.   13-5. a = 13.1366, or 13.14 ft.
      b = 9.9774, or 9.98 ft.   b = 22.7068, or 22.71 ft.
      c = 10.7629, or 10.8 ft.   c = 17.3545, or 17.35 ft.

13-3. a = 3.2056, or 3.206 ft.   13-7. a = 21.4589, or 21.46 ft.
      b = 1.3992, or 1.399 ft.   b = 7.9849, or 7.985 ft.
      c = 3.4877, or 3.487 ft.   c = 19.6001, or 19.60 ft.

14-1. 40.213, or 40.2 sq.ft.   14-5. 296.07, or 296.1 sq.ft.
14-3. 3.3489, or 3.349 sq.ft.   14-7. 190.13, or 190.1 sq.ft.

15. a. The first rule of species states that an angle and its opposite side are in the same quadrant. b. The sum of the angles of a spherical triangle are greater than 180°. c. Each side of a spherical triangle is less than the sum of the other two sides. d. The sum of the sides of a spherical triangle is less than 360°. e. The second rule of species states that if any two sides are in the same quadrant, the third side will be in the first quadrant. f. This violates the first rule of species.

Page 312 (top)

1. B = 72°47'; b = 52°38'; c = 56°18'.   B' = 107°13'; b' = 127°22'; c' = 123°42'.   3. A = 29°48'11"; a = 29°17'23"; c = 79°51'0".   A' = 150°11'49"; a' = 150°42'37"; c' = 100°9'0". 5. B = 45°22'; b = 36°46'; c = 56°38'.   B' = 134°38'; b' = 143°14'; c' = 123°22'.

Page 312 (foot)

1. AC = BC = 82°54'; AB = 108°46'.   3. A = 156°28'; AB = 82°12'; BC = 151°48'.   5. A = B = 87°21'16"; C = 42°43'. 7. A = B = 114°44'34"; AB = 79°11'44".

Page 314

1. B = 11°24'; C = 33°5'; a = 108°2'.   3. A = 47°15';

B = 57°23'; C = 111°27'. <u>5</u>. A = 31°59'8"; B = 121°54'49";
C = 63°21'24". <u>7-1</u>. 33.22 ft. <u>7-2</u>. 34.142, or 34.14 sq.ft.
<u>7-3</u>. 90.686, or 90.69 sq.ft. <u>7-4</u>. 338.92, or 338.9 sq.ft.

Page 320

<u>1</u>. A = 41°34'; B = 39°26'; C = 127°8'. <u>3</u>. A = 51°38';
B = 73°28'; C = 54°40'. <u>5</u>. A = 60°44'; B = 50°28'; C = 120°0'.

Page 321

<u>1</u>. a = 135°56'; b = 121°26'; c = 64°45'. <u>3</u>. a = 64°5';
b = 47°21'; c = 96°33'. <u>5</u>. a = 130°7'; b = 96°59'; c = 53°3'.

Page 323 (top)

<u>1</u>. A = 122°30'; B = 94°7'; c = 99°33'. <u>3</u>. A = 65°30';
C = 136°42'; b = 96°41'. <u>5</u>. A = 58°52'; B = 124°47'; c = 56°48'.

Page 323 (center)

<u>1</u>. C = 31°40'; a = 46°34'; b = 71°7'. <u>3</u>. A = 59°15';
b = 88°15'; c = 66°57'. <u>5</u>. B = 85°36'; a = 47°8'; c = 32°28'.

Page 326

<u>1</u>. B = 24°3'; C = 98°55'; c = 49°40'. <u>3</u>. No solution.
<u>5</u>. B = 7°42'; C = 33°31'; b = 8°52'. B' = 129°0'; C' = 146°29';
b' = 63°36'. <u>7</u>. A = 36°14'; a = 39°57'; c = 51°28'.

Page 327

<u>1</u>. 253.07, or 250 sq.ft. <u>3</u>. 1827.1, or 1830 sq.ft.
<u>5</u>. 1569.9, or 1570 sq.ft. <u>7</u>. 19,353, or 19,350 sq.ft.
<u>9</u>. 691.15, or 691.2 sq.ft.

Pages 332-333

<u>1</u>. 4676 nautical miles. <u>3</u>. 2756 nautical miles; 72°53' is
the bearing of Lisbon from Boston; 295°12' is the bearing of
Boston from Lisbon. <u>5</u>. 3003 nautical miles; 251°37'.
<u>7</u>. 3589 nautical miles. <u>9</u>. 7354 nautical miles; 194°19'.
<u>11</u>. 47°15'N; 65°23'W. <u>13</u>. 39°33'N: 98°32'W.

Printed in the United States of America